HIS MAJESTY'S SPANISH FLOCK

Plate I

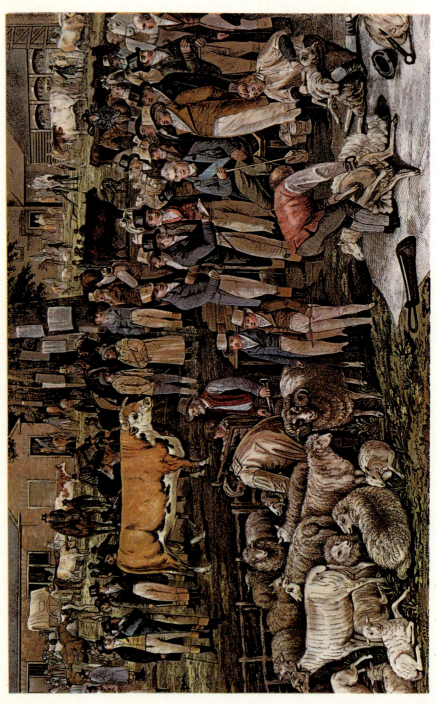

The Woburn Sheep Shearing, 1804. Sir Joseph Banks, P.R.S., and some of his contemporary agriculturists with specimens of the Spanish Merino in the left foreground.
From the engraving by George Garrard, A.R.A., 1811. By courtesy of His Grace the Duke of Bedford.

HIS MAJESTY'S
SPANISH FLOCK

Sir Joseph Banks and the Merinos
of
George III of England

By

H. B. CARTER

ANGUS & ROBERTSON

TO MY WIFE

First Published in 1964 by

ANGUS & ROBERTSON LTD

89 Castlereagh Street, Sydney
54 Bartholomew Close, London
107 Elizabeth Street, Melbourne
168 Willis Street, Wellington

© H. B. Carter 1964

Printed in Great Britain by Jarrold & Sons Ltd, Norwich

AUTHOR'S NOTE

In the course of this study I have been greatly privileged by the gracious permission of Her Majesty the Queen to make use of material in the Royal Archives and elsewhere. It is a pleasure also to link with this my appreciation of the approval by the California State Library accorded to my use of the documents in the Sutro Collection under its authority.

To His Grace the 13th Duke of Bedford I am much indebted for many courtesies in the search for relevant material and for permission to use the engraving of the Woburn Sheep Shearing of 1804 in his possession. To His Lordship the 8th Earl Bathurst I am most grateful for permission to use several papers from among the manuscripts at Cirencester Park. For a similar courtesy my thanks are also due to His Lordship the 7th Earl Spencer in reference to documents among the Althorp Papers.

The occasion cannot be allowed to pass without emphasizing my sense of obligation to Miss Phyllis Mander-Jones, formerly the Mitchell Librarian in Sydney, not only for the first real clues in my original search but for her sustained interest and active help in all my small inquiries—from distant library evenings in Port Jackson to the most recent days beside the Thames.

The whole task of deciphering and arranging the original key documents would have been greatly hampered but for the precision and uniform quality of the microfilms prepared under the supervision of Mr. William S. Hawken, formerly Director of the University of California Photographic Laboratory, to whom I am also grateful for later colour photography.

No work of this kind could be completed without the unfailing help of those devoted servants of learning, the staffs of The British Museum at Bloomsbury and of The British Museum (Natural History) at South Kensington. At all times I have enjoyed the benefit of the pleasant efficiency of Miss Maria Skramovsky of the General Library and of Miss Phyllis Edwards of the Botanical Library at South Kensington. At an early stage much was due to the help of Mr. M. G. Sawyers of the Photographic Laboratory of the same Museum. In the search for cartographic material at a later stage the generous assistance of Mr. R. A. Skelton, Deputy Keeper, and Dr. Helen Wallis, Assistant Keeper of the Map Room at Bloomsbury is recalled with appreciation.

This also is the moment to acknowledge many years of friendly help and advice received from Mr. William Park, Keeper of Manuscripts, and from Miss Irene Cairns (now Mrs. Athol Murray) of the same

Department in the National Library of Scotland at Edinburgh, particularly in relation to the recent acquisition of certain papers linked with this subject.

Over a long period also I owe much to Professor C. H. Waddington, Director of the Institute of Animal Genetics in the University of Edinburgh for scientific hospitality expressed in the ready assistance of his staff in so many ways, especially that of Mr. D. Pinkney and Mr. E. D. Roberts. To Mr. Roberts I am grateful for his patience and skill in sustaining my unexciting demands in the matter of maps and diagrams. So, too, within the same building I have enjoyed the enthusiastic help of the staff of the Commonwealth Bureau of Animal Breeding and Genetics under the stimulus of its Director, Mr. J. P. Maule.

To the Meteorological Office I am indebted for entrusting to me the original manuscript weather diaries of Thomas Hoy. For mediating this gesture my thanks are due to Dr. R. W. Gloyne of the Meteorological Office, Edinburgh, and to Mr. H. H. Lamb at Harrow.

Mr. John Bartholomew of The Geographical Institute, Edinburgh, generously made time for the preparation of the maps on the endpapers of this volume by the hand of Mr. John Dalgleish of his staff. For the base maps themselves I must acknowledge the courtesy of The British Museum and of the Ordance Survey in providing the working copies.

I am also in various ways under a debt for much assistance to the late Mr. Stephen Kay-Jones of Dr. Williams's Library, Gordon Square; to Mr. J. C. Torrington, Librarian at Australia House, Strand; to Mr. G. R. Clarke of the Crown Estates Office, Whitehall; to Mr. J. Norton of the Ordnance Survey, Chessington; and to Messrs. T. E. Pearson, J. Chapman, and T. G. Day, all past or present residents of Kew and Richmond living within or close to the boundaries of the former Marsh Gate Farm of His Majesty King George III. Mr. Pearson was generous in his hospitality and time in exploring afoot the scenes as they appear today where the sheep once grazed and earlier, as an officer of The Agricultural Research Council, in assisting my own smuggling operations. Miss Frances Redgrave (now Mrs. James Brand of East Fortune) has my gratitude for her speed and precision in producing order out of my tangled typescript.

In the book itself I have been mainly concerned to present a narrative as clear as I could deduce from the evidence available to me. The transcript quotations are deliberately generous and I accept full editorial responsibility for all errors and deviations from the original documents which are presented here as accurately as modern typography conveniently permits.

PREFACE

IT is occasionally the reward of research that the single-minded and narrow pursuit of a particular detail may in the end open a path to wider and even more intriguing vistas.

The scientific study of the Merino sheep from many biological points of view has achieved a prominent place in agricultural research within the past thirty years. Nowhere, for obvious reasons, has such work been carried further than in Australia. It requires, however, only a cursory interest in the origins and growth of that country's vast and expanding sheep population to uncover frequent allusions to stock said to have been derived in one way or another from the flocks of His Majesty King George III kept at Windsor, Richmond, and Kew. We have only to encounter a few such references to appreciate that probably no writers, even in contemporary reports, had any direct or extended knowledge of this Royal enterprise and that what we find in the available sources rests heavily on deduction and hearsay, distorted by much repetition. My own search began as a limited desire to establish a few undoubted facts about the actual numbers, sources, and kinds of animal composing the flocks for reasons associated with various genetic and kindred problems. This goal was elusive, but in the search many teasing mysteries became evident. The original scientific theme was invested gradually with shadows behind which it was clear lay the substance of something more than an interesting historical vignette—as well as the facts I sought.

In the end, after several years of desultory and profitless research on all the more accessible and likely sources of primary data, my attention finally settled on some unstudied papers of Sir Joseph Banks, P.R.S., stored in the Sutro Branch of the California State Library. For this important lead I am indebted to Miss Phyllis Mander-Jones who, during her tenure as Mitchell Librarian in Sydney, had in 1948 briefly noticed this material. Some time later from Great Britain I was able to arrange with Mr. Richard H. Dillon, the Sutro Librarian, that all the relevant documents should be recorded on microfilm and sent to me, after he had most generously spent much time in examining and reporting on their contents. The further problem of using these copies effectively was solved by the agreement of the Trustees of The British Museum to the printing and binding of near-facsimile enlargements from the microfilms. This step was made easy by the support of Sir Gavin de Beer, at that period Director of The British Museum (Natural History) and the collaboration of Mr. A. C. Townsend of its General Library. The print-ing and binding was executed by the Duplicating Division of H.M. Stationery Office and owes much at all stages to the careful supervision of Mr. W. S. Chilcraft and Miss Maud Rix. All these preparatory operations occupied much time, and it was not until November 1958 that an effective attack on the central problem was possible, that of sorting and arranging the pieces into some form of historical unity. In this process I have been aided immeasurably by the advice and interest of Mr. Warren R. Dawson, without whose scholarly calendar of 'The Banks Letters' the task would have been greatly impeded. It is a great pleasure also to record the friendly courtesy and help at many stages of Sir Owen Morshead, the former Queen's Librarian at Windsor Castle, and his successor Mr. Robert Mackworth Young and the Staff of the Royal Library and the Royal Archives.

The papers which are the key documents in this study are part of the great private collection of books and manuscripts amassed by Adolph Sutro of San Francisco which survived the earthquake of 1906 when half this library was destroyed. It would seem that these particular documents had also, in 1820, escaped possible destruction by the terms of Banks's will and its codicils, a fate intended for much of the bulky but orderly dossiers at 32 Soho Square and at Revesby Abbey. It is surprising, after a hundred and forty years, and the disturbance of their sale by Lord Brabourne at Sotheby's in 1886 and later, that these papers should remain apparently in much the same array as Banks himself knew them, though some sequences are broken and some obvious gaps occur. It must not be supposed, however, that the substance of this volume is bounded only by the contents of these old files. They are nevertheless the essential clues which link other widely scattered evi-dence and material into something resembling an intelligible whole.

In the present theme we are engaged with some of the first efforts at organized public research in agriculture in Great Britain and of animal breeding in particular. It is no argument against this viewpoint to say that the Royal flocks were merely the fancy of a monarch who amused himself with farming, who was always mentally insecure, and who finally became insane in his old age. The enterprise was in fact the well-reasoned and sustained effort of a man who, whatever his failings in other matters of State, had at heart the agricultural, scientific, and economic welfare of his kingdom. It was a venture in which, imitated later by many of his own illustrious subjects, he was prepared to risk his private purse in the public interest. Nor should we carp at the fact that possibly the first inspiration and certainly the main burden of daily execution belonged elsewhere. If the person and character of George III is perhaps somewhat dimly presented here it should not be forgotten that he remains withal a significant figure without whose opinion little or nothing of importance was done with the Spanish flock. To Sir Joseph Banks was delegated that authority directly from his Royal master which today is more deviously vested in Her Majesty's scientific civil servants of appropriate degree. That Banks was able to perform his quite honorary duties so effectively for so long depended greatly on the initial good sense with which the King selected him for his 'patriotic project' and the steadfastness with which on the whole, through so many personal and national trials and disasters, they both pursued the long course of their essentially happy association. The 'favorite hobby' of the distinguished biologist and President of the Royal Society and that of his King and friend must be accounted a symbiosis of no small value in the evolution of British agricultural research. In essence it followed an example in France at the Royal farm of Rambouillet, established two years earlier by another tragic King, Louis XVI. The Spanish Merino flock of George III of England, however, pursued its own star in its own way. Although, unlike the flock at Rambouillet, it has long since been dispersed, His Majesty's Spanish flock at Windsor, Richmond, and Kew was during its existence of some importance to Bakewell's successors in the art, if not the science, of animal breeding in the British Isles and the new British colonies of the South Seas.

For more than thirty years the enterprise of the King's Spanish Merinos maintained an active, if chequered, existence in the face of ignorance and misunderstanding, apathy and opposition in all parts of the realm. It suffered as much from the follies and inexperience of gullible supporters as from the calumny and criticisms of its more prejudiced opponents. Its history is closely entwined with one of the most turbulent, exciting, and productive periods in British affairs at home and abroad. In its growth and management it was a quaint hybrid: born of the Court and of the Royal Society; wet-nursed conjointly by the two Houses of Parliament. At all times, however, this odd creature is to be regarded as an experiment conducted in the public interest and judged as such against the standards of its own time, not ours. A strange quirk, indeed, but there have been stranger procreations of the British genius.

A series of unusual twists have for the past century and a half concealed its true character. In the end it would now seem that the same sequence of accidents has preserved for us a more complete record of one facet of Great Britain's agricultural history than of many other ventures whose mythology is woven more tightly into the folk-lore of this country. Less, perhaps, is now known or presumed of the precepts and practice of Robert Bakewell, George Culley, John Ellman, Francis 5th Duke of Bedford, John 15th Lord Somerville, or a dozen others of this great formative period in Britain's livestock breeding, than we have at last achieved in fact about the Merino flock of Farmer George, alias Mr. Ralph Robinson, of Windsor.

For the scientist, interested in the backgrounds of animal breeding, there may be some solace here in the few facts and figures it has been possible to isolate from the broken and scattered records of a small flock of sheep with a large influence on the thought and practice of its contemporary agriculturists in many countries. These were the men whose posterity carried its descendants to new lands and to new levels of productivity. These were the men who themselves, by various means, transformed the Spanish Merino from an envied monopoly of one nation into the essential foundation of the modern world trade in wool. Some may, perhaps, glow inwardly at the thought that we do these things so much better nowadays without the active engagement of the President of the Royal Society. Others may be inclined to fret at the absence of those neat and quantitative expressions with which modern animal science is now accustomed to work. Let us recall, however, that these twentieth-century concepts are still new and that we have not yet discarded from everyday practice, nor much improved upon, the terms and methods in breeding and general management here displayed by the men who exploited the Merinos of His Majesty's Spanish flock.

We may leave aside any special or technical concern and still find much of interest in the men and women themselves whose existence has been long forgotten, but who reappear in this story beside those whose names have found at least a place in *The Dictionary of National Biography*, if not also in the stones of Westminster Abbey and St. Paul's. As documents in the social history of Britain the written records clustered about His Majesty's Spanish flock have an intrinsic interest of their own. They present a small but neat section from top to bottom through eighteenth- and early-nineteenth-century society. These are not the conscious writings of the politician or ambitious man of affairs, oozing a 'sense of History'. The material is mainly the short note of complaint or reminder, the desk memorandum, the account of money owed or paid, the quick letter of some busy man concluding a practical arrangement. Such minutiae seldom appear in the *belles-lettres* or even the *obiter dicta* of the historical monographs but, collectively taken, transmit a vivid impression of the manners and modes of a period rarely found in this form so completely preserved.

Finally there is the ubiquitous figure of Sir Joseph Banks. Here I must add myself to the small but growing number of those who find in him a man whose importance to modern science and social history has been sadly underestimated and whose true place since his death has been almost totally ignored until recent years. My response has evolved almost unconsciously during the long process of studying the relics of his most ordinary correspondence and the surviving details of his every-day affairs not usually intended for the eye of posterity. Beginning with my attention more closely focused on Spanish sheep, I have ended with an enhanced respect for the man who, more than most others, in-fluenced their present distribution in the world—as he did that of so many other sources of natural wealth. With his own evident share of human weaknesses Banks emerges from this close scrutiny not as a scintillating brilliant of the eighteenth century but, within its context, as a man of superb honesty and generosity, devoted instinctively to that image of the truth which Science has since more self-consciously reared for itself. No single great scientific discovery stands in his name. His published contributions are few and slight. He must find his place, however, among the great as a scientific administrator, practitioner, and patron, whose judgement, wide vision, and fertilizing enthusiasm has not since been exceeded and whose directive influence is still perceptible in most corners of human civilization. His Majesty's Spanish flock may have been no more than his 'favorite hobby', but its brief history sheds much light on Banks as he lived and worked for the latter and most influential half of his life and on the society in which he moved.

From either the general scientific or historic point of view the un-covered story of His Majesty's Spanish flock may appear to some as an interesting but forgotten and unimportant detail in our agricultural progress. There are no Merinos in Great Britain now as economic sheep of any importance and probably little or no place for them. The Roman legions came and also disappeared from these islands, but our present society would no doubt show a very different pattern had they never penetrated here. The breeding of British sheep, perhaps, might also have taken a different path, at least in some regions, had not the 'outlandish' little Spanish sheep entered Britain when it did under the particular economic philosophy of its day. Almost certainly the early economic history of the British colonies in the southern hemisphere during the nineteenth century would have been diverted into other and perhaps less fruitful channels. Their growth may well have been retarded had not the Royal flock existed to show by its example at an important cross-roads in British commercial history the pitfalls and the possibilities for British livestock improvers with this unique breed. The growth and form of the present British wool manufacturing industries are intimately and inevitably connected with the rise and general character of the colonial wool supplies. From this has grown much of Britain's industrial strength and present standard of living. It is difficult to visualize the economic and social sequels had this country remained

longer as a dependant on purely European or other foreign sources of
fine wool of the higher qualities. For thirty years and more His
Majesty's Spanish Merino flock remained a focal-point of argument
and active interest to a considerable body of eminent industrialists,
agriculturists, Parliamentarians, and scientific Fellows of the Royal
Society. This must contain our final measure of its significance.

H. B. CARTER

Penicuik, Midlothian
Scotland
30 November 1962

CONTENTS

ILLUSTRATIONS

PLATES

FIGURES

Between pages 448 and 449

CHAPTER I

The Background, 1700–1800

I

ANY historical study is inevitably an arbitrary dissection on the living body of Time. However trivial the theme may be we cannot ignore the manner of its creation from the past nor the hints of its future. In this case, though the subject may be merely a small agricultural affair on a few Royal parks by the Thames, it still has its place in the wider context of European social and technological evolution. The problem is to set it in a reasonable perspective and to avoid elevating what may be an historical molehill into something larger than its due. It is difficult, however, to engage in the study of any topic, even the most modest, within the long and controversial reign of George III of England without being enticed far into the complex network of its activities and lost in their dynamic variety. But across the span of two centuries, in spite of these temptations, we can now see more clearly how the enterprises and ideas, scarcely thought of or begun in 1760, had by 1820 established themselves as the undoubted precursors of so much that is familiar in its adolescent or mature form now.

The backcloth against which the rise and decline of His Majesty's Spanish flock may be viewed has a rich pattern not easily restored even in outline. The clues to its original design lie deep in the commercial history of Europe. It may, however, be sufficient here to seek no further, for a point of orientation, than the technological rivalry which fed the imperial pretensions of England and France throughout the eighteenth century. In this contest the trade in wool and the woollen manufactures was a most conspicuous element. During the seventeenth century Holland had been England's most formidable mercantile rival, but by the early eighteenth century was one of her best customers and financially her most important creditor. Trade with Spain and Portugal had by this time declined, but the Peninsula still remained foremost as the prime source of imported fine wool and of gold bullion in payment for the manufactured woollen goods which Spain especially needed. As the century advanced the woollen trade with Holland grew less, but that with the Iberian Peninsula increased and at the end was more than matched by the exports to the American colonies. Manufactured woollen fabrics of many kinds throughout the century remained the source of seldom less than one-quarter of Great Britain's export income, and even in the last decade before 1800 was not much less than one-fifth. In an economic system wherein a favourable trade balance and the war-potential of the nation were so strongly linked the commerce in wool alone, therefore, was especially vital and exceeded in value that of cotton and iron combined. With France as the principal enemy and rival for the economic dominance of Europe and the expanding colonial world it followed that both the production and the manufacture of wool became the key to many of the mercantile and military problems besetting international politics in Europe at the latter end of the eighteenth century. No detail shows this more forcibly than the erratic and almost negligible figures for the export to France of British woollen manufactures throughout the long struggle which ended only at Waterloo.[1]

Behind the overt and more spectacular evidences of the conflict between the island kingdom and the continental power of France lay a devious strategy of trade laws and embargoes imposed by Westminster. In this spider's web some of the strongest strands were those of wool. With the ability of the nation to wage war so heavily governed by the state of trade and especially the overseas export of British woollen goods, the textile industries had clearly the most powerful of material incentives to advance their technology. If an additional spur were needed there was the knowledge that in France about the mid-century the Government was most active in its patronage of science and industry and the suspicion also that the rate of industrial growth was perhaps faster. Under the stimulus of this frequently real, but also sometimes imaginary, superiority in French national development, Britain gradually set about the full use of her storehouse of human skill and material resources. From the opposite side of the Channel France viewed the island beehive with similar feelings of envy and emulation. Englishmen visited France to study the sources of her strength. Frenchmen studied the English with the same intent and purpose whenever peace left a breathing-space in the long struggle but often, too, in the midst of war. Wool production and its manufacture remained a central theme in this duel of economies with important consequences both to the agriculture and the secondary industries of each of the two contending nations. In agriculture the relative merits of wool growing and food production in the national budget came under more critical scrutiny. In sheep breeding the different kinds of fleece by degrees encountered keener eyes as the manufacturer became more selective in his choice of raw wool for changing methods of production which steadily increased in the efficiency, perfection, and diversity with which the fabrics emerged. In secondary industry the accelerating intrusion of new mechanical and other inventions in all fields, especially from 1760 onwards, was changing the pattern of textile production, catalysed by the advent of cotton manufacture and its spectacular rise in the last quarter of the eighteenth century to its dominant position in the first quarter of the nineteenth. In textile manufacturing techniques the symbiosis of wool and cotton laid the solid foundations for the soaring advantage which England at last succeeded in establishing over France and the rest of Europe by the end of the century. The battle was one of quality in the fabric as much as in quantity and cheapness of manufacture. Whence it was that the strategic importance of Spanish fine wool became a factor of growing significance in European trade and politics.

II

For several centuries Spain had been the essential source of the finest wool available to the clothiers of Europe and latterly of England. Long and persistent had been the attempts of the Low Countries, of France, and of England, to obtain a trade monopoly of this coveted fibre, the demand for which increased with every small advance in manufacturing methods and organization.[2] A century before James Cook and Joseph Banks set out on that voyage of discovery in the South Seas which was eventually to revolutionize the world supply of fine wool, we gain some insight on its diplomatic status from the words of Sir William Godolphin to Lord Arlington in 1667:

As for the Woolls, because it was part of our Instructions to gain the best information we could, whether it were a practicable design to get for *England* the sole Merchandize of them; and that they might not be vended to any other nation, (in exchange whereof we were instructed to offer unto *Spain* the sole Merchandize of our Tin) I made the best Inquiry I could into the Nature and Traffick of this Commodity, both at *Madrid* and *Bilbao*, and to a journey express to *Segovia*, for my better information; and upon the whole matter, I judge it very difficult to enjoy them by way of Monopoly; for there requires so great a Stock to manage it, as may be estimated at two Millions of Pieces of 8;[3] and then the forbearance of the Money where they sell again will be considerable, and the dependance upon other Nations for leave to Vend them (there being but a small Quantity Vended in *England*) and at the present the *Spaniards* having liberty to sell their Wooll to whom they please, it will be hard to bring them into a Monopoly. . . .[4]

At this date Godolphin noted 'Holland, Hamburg, and the Adjacent Countries' as the pre-eminent users of Spanish fine wool, absorbing about 22,000 packs or 4·4 million pounds per annum. France was cited next as consuming 6000 to 7000 packs or 1·2 million to 1·4 million pounds per annum, with England in third place using 2000 to 7000 packs or 0·4 million to 1·4 million pounds. Venice and the ports of Italy took most of the remainder, estimated at 3000 packs or about 0·6 million pounds per annum. Altogether Godolphin estimated the fine-wool export of Spain, three hundred years ago, at 'about 36,000 to 40,000 Baggs' (i.e. packs or bales) per annum, of which no less than 20,000 were shipped through Bilbao. This represented a total annual export of about 7·2 million to 8·0 million pounds, figures which are not much different from those a century later. In a general way they are a fair measure of the textile argosy for which three vigorous mercantile nations contended, and, in various ways, partitioned for the next hundred and fifty years, modified only slightly by the entry of Spain herself again into the weaving of fine cloths at her Royal factories under the Bourbons. This export of fine wool probably represented the annual clip from no more than four million sheep, mainly the fleece wool of the better qualities for the lower grades tended to remain in Spain. Undoubtedly also this wool for export would have been drawn almost entirely from the produce of the finest and most superior of the travelling flocks—the best *cabanas* of the *transhumantes* or *ganadas merinas* —except for several whose fleeces were reserved for the Royal factories at some periods. On all the evidence it seems unlikely that 'the Spanish sheep' or 'the Spanish race', since more specifically identified under the name of 'the Spanish Merino', ever much exceeded four million during the eighteenth century on the pastures of its traditional home. This figure may be taken as a reasonable index of the level at which the Spanish fine-wool sheep lived out the eighteenth century in the some-what withdrawn pastoral economy of Bourbon Spain.

The pastoral isolation of the Peninsula, though slumbrous, could never be immune to the stirrings of international commerce especially those which touched its staple export. When Felipe V, the first Bourbon, secured his throne in 1700 the external trade of Spain was largely in the hands of the Dutch, French, and English. Through these channels, to her continued mortification, Spain was supplied with her luxury goods, among which the finer woollen cloths ranked high. For these alone the export of her own superlative raw fine wool to the looms of her mercantile masters was scarcely sufficient to pay. To break this humi-liating servitude and to drive Spain along the road to economic parity with the northern Powers became an early ambition of Bourbon commercial policy. One of the most important facets of this policy was the revival and expansion of manufacturing by the device, not un-common elsewhere in Europe, of establishing Royal factories, each endowed with its appropriate monopoly, to produce the luxury wares otherwise imported from abroad. The first of these was built at

Guadalajara in 1718 by Felipe V, significantly enough at this period, for the manufacture of fine woollens in the Dutch *mode*. From this soon grew a branch at San Fernando later moved to Brihuega in 1768. Guadalajara was the most famous and successful of the Royal factories in every technical sense, but, in common with other ventures of a similar kind in eighteenth-century Europe, it suffered from poor financial management and continued only under heavy subsidies from the Royal treasury. Until the advent of Carlos III it struggled to exist with difficulty except for a brief period after 1740 when a trained English weaver, Thomas Bevan of Melksham in Wiltshire, supervised it with other West Country craftsmen. In 1760 Carlos III placed its management under the Junta de Comercio, and for the rest of his reign it expanded to become the largest and most thriving of its kind in Europe. Guadalajara in 1786 was a prosperous and busy city with 4000 weavers and 800 looms at work producing the finest cloth, with 100 more looms in Brihuega. These 900 looms absorbed the yarn from about 40,000 spinners working steadily as far away as Madrid and La Mancha. This wide dispersal of the semi-manufactured wool, the distance of the town from the main shearing and washing centres such as those near Segovia, and from any large market except Madrid all added an excessive burden of transport costs to a management that was not in other respects financially efficient. The quality of the best cloths was at least equal to the French superfines at this late period, but all these efforts, subsidized heavily as they were, could not greatly reduce Spain's indebtedness to imported English woollens. In spite of an augmented production of fine cloth from the partially restored manufactory at Segovia, also revived by Carlos III, Spain still remained England's best customer in Europe for her finer woollens until this trade was finally disrupted by the onset of war with Revolutionary France.

Whatever may be said about Spanish efforts in textile manufacture they were at least following the same stream of industrial advance in this field as several of their northern customers for fine wool. Technically they were very little inferior. This aspect of Spanish economy certainly reflected clearly the early stirrings of the industrial revolution that was so soon to transform the rest of Europe. In her agrarian economy it was quite otherwise, although Spain in the eighteenth century produced several gifted thinkers and writers in this particular branch. There was no more firmly established and static segment of her agriculture than her sheep industry, its pattern broadly traceable far back into Roman antiquity. This is of less concern to us here than the appearance it presented to the merchant-adventurers who sought to understand its secrets as well as to rifle its storehouses of the unique Golden Fleece to feed the spinning-wheels and looms of northern

Europe beyond the Pyrenees and the Bay of Biscay. Here, again, we may turn to Godolphin for a concise introduction:

There is nothing of this Nature wherein the *Spaniards* are more curious, than in the manner of feeding their Sheep, which contributeth much to the well growth, and fineness of their Fleece: The Owners of them do therefore against the Winter Season send them to the warmer Climate of Estremadure; from whence in the Month of *May* they are brought to *Segovia*, and there Shorn; and from thence driven to the Cold Mountains of *Leon*, where they feed all the Summer long.

The Woolls of *Spain* are commonly known by the Names of *Segovia*, *Soria*, and *Andaluzia*; *Segovia* is the finest, and is sold (neither Sorted nor Washed) but just as it comes off the Sheeps Back) at 70 *Reales Vellon* the *Arroba*, an *Arroba* is 25 l. weight: *Soria* Woolls are next in fineness, and in like manner are sold at 50 *Reales Vellon* the *Arroba*. *Andalusia* Woolls are the worst and coarsest, and are in like manner sold at 20 *Reales* [*Vellon*] the *Arroba*.[5]

He that buys the *Segovia* and *Soria* Woolls at the first hand does wash them, and divides them into a first, second, and third sort: The first they call in *Spain* refined Woolls, which is of the part of the Fleece which is best grown: The second sort is of the part of the Fleece which falls towards the Belly and Flanks of the sheep: The third sort is the Wooll that grows upon the Legs, Tail, and towards the Head.

The Wooll being thus divided every sort is put up by it self in Canvas Bags that will hold from $7\frac{1}{2}$ *Arroba's* to 8, and from thence carried to the several Ports to be Shipped off.

Being in the Ports every Bag of 200 l. weight in Sortment, is sold from 1350, to 1400 *Reales Vellon*, being *Segovia* Cloth-Woolls in distinction from the *Segovia* Lambs Wooll, wherewith they make no Cloth but Hats.

The Sortment of *Segovia* is,

Of the Finest	3	⎫
Of the Second	2	⎬ Baggs
Of the Third	1	⎭

When the Buyer will have only the best of these Sorts, there is an encrease of 20 *per Cent* upon the weight, viz, for 100 l. weight of Wooll, he pays the price of 120 l. weights In regard the best sort being taken away, the second and third sort sell for so much less. . . .[6]

These are the essential facts on which an understanding of the nature of the Spanish fine-wool sheep industry depends as we see it during the last hundred and fifty years of its 'classic staple' under the declining sway of the Honourable Assembly of the Mesta of the Shepherds. No later writers have given a clearer picture or done more than embellish it with variable detail.

A century later there was no important change in the general character of the Spanish sheep industry nor of the Spanish wool export.

The sheep flocks producing the fine staple of international commerce, the *ganadas merinas*, still numbered in the order of four million. The unwashed fleece of the Spanish fine-wool sheep still averaged about five pounds. The total export was still not much more than thirty thousand bags. The price, however, had rather more than doubled. Holland no longer absorbed the greater part, having been displaced by the superior rivalries of France and England, though the latter seldom imported more than two million pounds or about ten thousand bags before the period of the American War of Independence. Thereafter the situation rapidly changed as the industrial machinery of Great Britain moved into a higher gear in pace with the new inventions and the rising population. Before the end of the century nearly two-thirds of the Spanish fine-wool exports or about twenty thousand bags were finding their way into the ports of Bristol and London from the Bay of Biscay, at an annual cost of less than three-quarters of a million pounds sterling or about three to four per cent of the total imports in value.

III

The eighteenth century, however, had witnessed more than a realignment of the mercantile positions of Holland, France, and England, and the partial dismemberment of the Spanish colonial empire. Spain no longer was the sole guardian of the Golden Fleece. After four centuries the jealous protection imposed by the edicts of the national Cortes, under pressure from the Mesta, over the Spanish fine-wool sheep had been broken. Sweden, Saxony, Austria, and France had all between 1723 and 1786 obtained and established significant numbers of the unique little animals whose escape from the Spanish embargo and the confines of the Peninsula was to herald the dawn of the modern world wool trade. It was, however, late in the century before Britain, whose premier industry relied so heavily on the infusion of Spanish fine wool for the choicer blends in its best broadcloths, took steps to secure herself against the uncertainties of its supply by seeking the animal itself from which the staple grew. This long period of delay is in part explained by the measure of self-sufficiency which Britain enjoyed in the supply of the finer short wools of high quality derived from its indigenous breeds of which the old Herefordshire stock are generally considered as pre-eminent examples. No other country among her competitors on the perpetually war-ravaged Continent could match her in the steady home production of superior wools for fine cloths. For at least three-quarters of the century the volume of trade was such that a comparatively modest introduction of the unexcelled Spanish fine wool was sufficient to sustain the broadcloth industry in the weaving of cloths more than adequate in quality to meet the export standards necessary. About seven pounds of Spanish wool added to thirty-one pounds of the finest English wool were sufficient to improve the quality of the cloth to an economic degree. For most countries in continental Europe the supplies of native wool could not be so easily blended for manufacture and nothing less than Spanish fine-wool breeding stock engrafted on the local sheep population was likely to make any significant change. After the War of the Spanish Succession and the Treaty of Utrecht had secured the first Bourbon monarch Felipe V on the throne, a new era of enlightened mercantilism began for Spain. This brought with it also a new series of family allegiances among the Royal Houses of Europe with the Spanish throne through which the fine-wool sheep filtered past the enmeshing toils of the Mesta embargo. On a wider landscape at a slower tempo a great agrarian change not unlike that occurring about the same time in England was transforming much of the Spanish rural economy. Against the waning resistance of the Mesta and the ancient pastoralism of the Peninsula, new forms of enclosure grew and field agriculture made steady advances into the grazing grounds of the fine-wool sheep. Slowly the well-kept monopoly of the noble and ecclesiastical flock-owners was eroded as much by the enlightened reforms of the first three Bourbon kings as by the insistent pressures increasing from beyond the Pyrenees. It was Carlos III and his most able Prime Minister, Campomanes, however, who after two exhaustive inquiries into the pastoral régime (1771 and 1779), so reduced the power of the Mesta that the prized migratory flocks lost much of their protection. If we except the earlier Swedish imports of 1723 of whose original nature and number little is yet generally known, all the important eighteenth-century explants of Spanish fine-wool sheep occurred in the reign of Carlos III—to Saxony in 1765 and 1778, to Austria in 1775, to France in 1786. From these basic stock the new fine-wool flocks of Europe stemmed and grew into viable populations that could have survived without any of the later additions which were in fact made. We cannot easily tell now whether this relaxation of the embargo of four centuries arose by default in the emergent new spirit of agriculture in which the sanctity of the fine-wool flocks had lost weight with the Royal autocrats. It is possible even that Spain still felt safe from undue foreign competition in fine wools influenced by the purblind notion that nowhere outside the Peninsula could such be grown. This is an embedded idea of cardinal importance in the history of the Spanish fine-wool sheep, especially in the eighteenth and early nineteenth centuries. It emerges so often in the sparse literature on the subject that it cannot be ignored. How far, on the other hand, these unique sheep were dispensed to allies and Royal kinsfolk as small but significant instruments of policy it is equally hard to see clearly. There is no doubt, however, that, whatever the proximate reasons, each exportation in the eighteenth century of the Spanish fine-wool sheep from its traditional homeland was a significant event in the commercial history of modern Europe as a step towards emancipation from the Spanish fine-wool monopoly.

It is therefore all the more noteworthy that, apart from an evident desire to monopolize Spain's fine-wool exports for herself as an article of trade, it was so late in the century before Great Britain showed any active interest in acquiring fine-wool sheep for herself. Certainly there were no associations with the House of Bourbon of sufficient note to elicit Royal dispensations of sheep. These no doubt may have been sought in any case had there been any grounds for supposing that the Spanish sheep were likely to thrive and produce their magic fibre in the British climate. Against this, however, there was the useful high quality of the native short wools almost in sufficient quantity to meet the needs of the fine broadcloth industry, especially of the West Country, for the greater part of the century. There was also the prevailing notion, well established among the English wool merchants and clothiers and uncritically accepted, that the special qualities of the imported Spanish staple were in fact due to the climate and the migratory pastoralism of Spain. In this they too shared the common European delusion but were in addition hedged out by political and geographic barriers from easily testing the reality by any form of experiment. Spain lay too much under the shadow of France for England to have anything other than the most tenuous and insecure relations of a kind favourable to a deeper penetration of the mystery of Spanish fine wool. It was not until the worsening financial crisis and industrial confusion attending the loss of the American colonies that Britain awoke to the full measure of her dependence on the fine wool of Spain and the importance of casting loose from her reliance in a critical article of trade on a country that had always been something less than a friend, and too often an enemy. It would be a mistake to suppose that this was at once or perhaps ever brilliantly clear to the mercantile interests of Britain, or to the political leaders of the country. There were no easily gathered, reliable, and neatly tabulated facts, accessible even to those most concerned, from which any suitable deductions on the national position could be made. The age of trade statistics was yet to come. Nor could the national budget be so well displayed as now. Too much rested on hearsay, on local rather than general knowledge, on private more than on public instances and experience. The eighteenth century was a long gestation of many technological changes whose definitive form was only apparent in the nineteenth. It is not therefore so surprising that the technical place of Spanish fine wool was not easily discerned even by the industries most concerned in its use. If its status was a matter of dispute even within the highly regionalized wool manufacturing industry of Britain, and further obscured by an inevitable measure of trade secrecy, it is not to be thought that the nation as a whole would appreciate its value to the economy. A brief but closer view of the British wool industry at home may make this clear.

IV

The eighteenth century opened with the woollen industry still the great staple trade of Britain, almost wholly English, and demanding little either in raw material or labour beyond that kingdom. Arthur Young, in 1767, could still with truth say: 'wool has been so long supposed the sacred staple and foundation of all our wealth, that it is somewhat dangerous to hazard an opinion not consonant to its single advancement'.[7] The pattern of the industry at the end of the century was still superficially the same as when Defoe had described it at the end of the first quarter. It was a most complete example of a balanced local economy in which an early system of manufacture drew its raw material from its surrounding agriculture and, with an indigenous labour force, created an export of international value. No more complete contrast with the Spanish domestic economy is possible.[8]

Although the fine ramifications of its influence spread through the entire country there were three definite regions in which the manufacture of wool were mainly concentrated for the greater part of the century. These were the West Country, East Anglia, and the West Riding of Yorkshire, with part of eastern Lancashire (until cotton claimed it for its own). By the end of the century the pattern was broadly the same, but the seeds of change had been sown. Yorkshire had inherited pre-eminence in the worsted manufacture from its birthplace in Norfolk. Cotton had established its priority in Lancashire. The West Country still managed to preserve its advantage in the finer woollen broadcloth manufacture. The new shape of the nineteenth century was beginning to appear, as steam power released important sectors of the industry from bondage to particular localities and the first steps in factory mechanization were tardily taken.

The wool manufacturing regions emerged on the whole as a nice balance between the volume and character of the raw material easily accessible and the features of the locality which favoured certain kinds of process. Thus the East Anglian region with its flat fenlands, and therefore its poverty in water power, specialized in worsted production which did not require fulling. At the same time the long-stapled fleeces of Lincolnshire and Leicestershire conveniently provided the combing wools needed for this form of manufacture. So too the West Riding of Yorkshire, rich in water power for the fulling mills by the Pennine streams, was able equally to tap the same large source of long-wool supplies. Production here thrived on the coarser woollens and in the end triumphed with its worsteds when steam favoured those industries close to the large coal-seams. Finally, in its day, the West Country was singularly favoured in the local combination of raw material and manufacturing facilities. In Gloucestershire, well placed to exploit surrounding supplies of some of the finest short wools in England, the manufacture of fine broadcloths and the twilled cassimeres or kerseymeres flourished along the base of the Cotswold escarpment and in the Stroud valley, where good heads of water could drive the fulling mills and meet the needs for dyeing and washing. Proximity to the port of Bristol permitted the enhancement of cloth quality by the introduction of the soft fine wools of Spain which were not matched in excellence even by the short Ryeland fleeces of Herefordshire. To the east a comparatively short wagon journey carried the finished cloths into the fantastic market of London and thence to the seaports of the world. In Devonshire, the clothing towns and mills at the foot of the Dartmoor plateau and along the rivers within flourished in the production of serges from the coarser longer wools. These were derived from the Cotswolds near by and the highlands of Devon, augmented by the long combing yarn imported from Ireland through Bristol, Minehead, and Barnstaple, and the shorter wools from the downs of Hampshire, Wiltshire, and Dorset.

For the greater part of the eighteenth century the west of England remained eminent as the great clothing district for the better fabrics, though it no longer produced the majority. It was in this region that the imported Spanish fine wool was almost solely consumed. Here, then, our attention may be most profitably directed for the particular industrial background of fine-wool manufacture. The region was not only favoured by excellent water supplies for power and washing and near-by supplies of some of the finest short wools in England, but there were also good deposits of fuller's earth near Bath, Cirencester, and Stroud, while the teasels used in the carding and finishing processes were grown in Somerset and the Vale of Gloucester. It was favourably placed between the two greatest ports of the period, London and Bristol. English wool provided most of the raw material, that from Herefordshire being most favoured as the finest available, though all the short wools, especially from the South Downs from Dorset to Sussex, were used and, as the century advanced, comparable wool was drawn from all parts of the country wherever it could be found.

The structure of the West Country industry was characterized by the capitalist clothier, though many small manufacturers existed. These entrepeneurs varied greatly in the number of processes which they managed. With the declining importance of the wool fairs in the region some increasingly bought direct from the farms before the wool came to market, controlling all the essential processes through to the finished cloth, except perhaps the special dyeing of some colours. Others increasingly depended on middlemen, such as the wool staplers and yarn agents of Cirencester especially, for their supplies of English wool. The supplies of Spanish wool were obtained mostly from the importing merchants in London or Bristol, who in turn either bought finished cloth—often for export—or took cloth in exchange for the imported wool. Almost all the wool so purchased required scouring, even the Spanish wool which had been washed in the large lavatories or wash-houses of its native country before export in a crudely sorted state. In England this washing was commonly done in the flowing streams, the wool suspended in baskets. But it was also more efficiently done in tanks with urine as the time-honoured if unsalubrious detergent. The most common practice then was to dye the loose wool. To this there was no alternative in the more popular cloths which were mixtures of white and coloured wool. Only in the case of the solid colours was there any choice possible between dyeing the loose wool or the woven cloth. For the twilled cassimere or kerseymere dyeing was reserved invariably until the cloth stage of manufacture.

The prominent basic colours used were blue and navy derived from indigo (which had replaced woad), red from madder, yellow from fustic, and brown from different redwoods, all variously mordaunted with compounds of chromium, iron, aluminium, and copper. The excellence of the colours was one of the outstanding qualities of eighteenth-century broadcloth on which it is said it would even now be difficult to improve.

After dyeing and drying, the conversion of the wool into yarn began. The first process, under the general term of 'carding', was usually done at the clothier's own premises. This consisted of three operations— willeying, scribbling, and carding—all designed essentially for opening and mixing the loose wool into a mass of randomly arranged fibres ready for the spinner. It was in this respect that the woollen yarn differed from the worsted. For the latter process the fibres were combed into a parallel arrangement in preparation for the spinning-wheel or the spindle. The preliminary mixing of the dyed wools in the right proportions for a particular colour shade was usually done in the first willeying stage. At the same time the loose wool was treated with some lubricant to ease the process of mixing and to reduce the fibre breakage as the mass was opened on the cards. For this purpose either imported olive oil or, more commonly, the native butter was used. The rotary card derived from the early Arkwright invention for the cotton trade, and which revolutionized this process in the woollen industry, was slow in reaching the West Country. It was used in the latter half of the eighteenth century for scribbling, though the final process was apparently still a form of hand carding. Willeying and scribbling by the rotary process were both easily adapted to the application of a power-drive, notably by water, though the horse-wheel was sometimes used. The final results of these mixing and opening processes were of a high quality. Eighteenth-century cloths were excellent in the uniformity of the mixing, of which the most stringent test is in the mixing of a white and a coloured wool. Any unevenness in the mixture is here revealed by small specks of white wool or 'neps' and from these defects West Country cloths were extraordinarily free.

Until about the last decade of the century most spinning was done by hand with the simple one-thread spinning-wheel, though much was still done by the more primitive spindle. The spinner received the carded mass of opened wool fibres. From this the wool was drawn out as one process, the twist applied, and the spun yarn then wound on to the spindle. The continuous drafting and twisting of the faster Saxony wheel used for the long combing wools in the spinning of the worsted yarn was never suitable for the woollen yarns derived from the shorter and finer carding wools. Spinning was the great limiting factor and the production of yarn, even for the simple hand-loom, had for centuries been the clothier's constant worry. To close this gap carded wool was distributed through the villages for a radius as wide as thirty miles from the clothing towns of the south-west. The introduction even of the simple hand-driven spinning-jenny, the earliest mechanization of this process in the last quarter of the century, did much to restore a balance, though at the cost of some unrest and appreciable distress in the scattered villages. While it remained simple the jenny could still be adapted to a cottage industry, but its impact on village economics was considerable.

With the exception of Kay's flying shuttle which was the one advance in weaving by the simple hand-loom, coming very late in the century to the West Country, this process remained static. The broad-cloths were a plain weave in which the attractiveness of the finished material depended mainly on the colour and the quality of the finish. They were, as their name suggests, woven on a loom ninety to one hundred inches wide. A more complicated loom was developed for the narrow twilled cassimeres (or kerseymeres) derived from Francis Yerbury's patent of 1766, and which were a new type of cloth for the

West Country made in Trowbridge and Bradford-on-Avon. The looms were only thirty-six inches wide and the cloth was at most only lightly fulled as the twilled design was an important part of the finished appearance.

For broadcloth, the first stage of the finishing processes was the fulling which included the scouring of the piece as it came off the loom by the same unsalubrious methods applied to the raw wool. Fulling was a wet shrinking process and was an extreme form of the modern milling whereby the original cloth woven at ninety inches or more was reduced to a width of about sixty inches in a series of power-driven operations that extended over several days. The cloths were then stretched and dried on large tenter-racks which were a prominent decoration round the clothing towns and villages.

The final important stage of the finishing processes was the dressing of the cloth. This consisted first in 'raising' the surface of the cloth with teasels and then in shearing the nap with the ponderous and peculiar hand-shears that were so long a feature of the industry. Mechanical raising with the teasels fitted on the surface of a cylinder was done by the gig mill mainly in Gloucestershire and was one of the few mechanical advances readily adopted by the West Country clothiers. Everything suggests that machine-raised cloth was preferred by the buyers to that done by the hand-frame. No attempt was made to mechanize the cumbersome hand-shears until the nineteenth century when the first rotary machine was patented in 1815. Until then this important process of shearing depended on the strength and skill of the shearmen in operating a device that had not changed much for more than two thousand years. The last touch of all was pressing—usually a simple matter of applying weights or by the use of some form of hand-press operated by a screw.

The special quality of the broadcloth made in the western counties was not equalled anywhere else in England. This much even the Yorkshire clothiers admitted. Its superiority rested mainly on the perfection of the finishing processes in which all the important subsequent advances were made by West Country skill.

The new cassimeres were finished in a different fashion to the traditional broadcloths. As the pattern of the weave was intended to show in the finished cloth the mending was done more carefully. The fulling was only light and done for a few hours rather than for days. Little or no dressing was needed. Cutting, as far as it was needed, had to be careful and thorough to bring out the full appearance of the twilled pattern. No hot pressing was necessary.

It is probable that by far the greatest market for the best cloths of the west of England was at home, and this mainly through the 'Great Wen' which was now London of the eighteenth century. Clearly the rising standard of living in every way and the accelerating growth of the population in the Home Counties alone were almost sufficient to skim the cream off the cloth production from the western counties. The demand, however, was not by any means for the higher qualities, and the competition from Yorkshire which had specialized in the cheaper fabrics was a powerful obstacle. Thus a considerable quantity of the superior West Country broadcloths could be exported and thereby did much to enhance the reputation and trading strength of the whole country. Apart from the European channels where French competition was strong, the Turkish market absorbed the lightest and finest of cloths and the East India Company provided a further important export route. A more variable but considerable branch of the trade which mainly passed through London was that for the Army, the Marines, and the Militia. Towards the end of the century this became a large and more steady market as the French wars established themselves as an almost endemic threat. Some cloth was sold at the local markets and fairs and some directly to wholesale or retail dealers or foreign customers. But there was always a heavy reliance on the factors of Blackwell Hall, the great clearing house in London and a selling agency which the clothiers could not lightly set aside though they frequently complained. The Blackwell Hall factors were an undoubtedly powerful element in the trading operations, often controlling the final outlet of the finished cloth as well as the supply of the imported Spanish raw material, and, moreover, giving credit to the clothiers. Any disadvantage arising from these middlemen was to some extent meliorated by the economic services they rendered and the influence of competition among them in maintaining price levels. At all events the clothiers were content to use this method as a major device in their marketing and did not attempt to set up their own selling agencies.

This, then, was the general character of the West Country woollen trade in the eighteenth century and into which the Spanish fine wool found its way on the small ships of the Peninsula sea routes. It was a region of 'gentlemen clothiers', middle-class capitalists who bought and owned the wool but thereafter, as entrepreneurs, had all the processing, except fulling, done at the workers' homes in the scattered villages and towns of the countryside. In all this they were in broad contrast to the small clothiers of Yorkshire, who tended both to own the wool and to make the cloth themselves with limited assistance perhaps from labour outside their own families. They were two different forms of a domestic system bridging the period between the old guilds and the nineteenth-century factories. Both were essentially rural, but the differences in organization emerged from the original preoccupation of the West

Country with cloths for export and of a kind which called for capital investment in the fulling mill. In contrast Yorkshire at first served the home trade with cloths that were seldom fulled to the same extent, or, as in the case of the worsteds, not fulled at all. After 1780 much more than half England's total woollen export came from Yorkshire in the form of the cheaper and coarser cloths to meet the expanded demands of the outside world, not least in the former colonies in America. But the West Country production of fine fabrics maintained itself far into the nineteenth century, threatened and stimulated only by the success of Benjamin Gott with his new steam-powered mills and his pioneering use in Yorkshire of Spanish and later of German fine wool for the classic superfine broadcloths so long the special hall-mark of the west.

V

The turning-point in the character of the woollen exports most certainly came after the American War of Independence had launched an incipient new economic force into world trade. This is clearly stated by Lord Sheffield in 1783 as he took stock of Pitt's first Bill 'for the provisional establishment and regulation of trade and intercourse between the subjects of Great Britain and those of the United States of America':

In this great and capital item [woollens] Great Britain will have little competition, except in superfine cloths made in France, to appearance of equal quality to those made in England; they fail in firmness and durability but are afforded cheaper; they have a superior lustre. France excels in single colours; but the demand of the superfine cloths from America will be very inconsiderable; the consumption of that country is chiefly under fourteen shillings per yard; the quantity of those of higher price bears no proportion to that of any one of the inferior qualities, down to the coarsest and cheapest. . . .[9]

Here is a convenient clue to the trade pattern unfolding in the last decades of the eighteenth century into which was woven the destiny of the Spanish fine-wool sheep—competition from France in the superfine cloths; coarse cloths for the new American States; the foreshadowed triumph of the combing-wool interests of Yorkshire. There is, however, more to be noted. Behind and around the cottages of the workers in the wool industries of England, north, east, or west is the landscape of a fast-changing agriculture not easily dissociated from the manufacturing pattern. Among all the varied aspects of the rural economy to which volumes have been devoted none is so relevant and none so hard to trace and clarify than the course of sheep breeding and the factors which guided it through the century. The tightly knit association between the sheep population and the eighteenth-century woollen manufacture in Britain evidently seemed so obvious and permanent as to have been taken for granted, its intricacies accepted, its nature left very largely unexamined. There is a dearth of exact writing on the whole wide field of animal breeding in Great Britain in this formative century. We know little more about our own indigenous breeds in all their variety than we do about the more obscure affairs of the sheep of the Spanish countryside at the same period. One thing only can be said with reasonable conviction. While there was much regional variation the usual list of recognized breeds or types of sheep in the eighteenth century was commendably short—less than twenty in fact. Even these could, without straining any definitions, be further reduced to little more than a dozen. Most of these could be fairly readily grouped by regions or localities. All the important breeds from which the woollen industries drew their essential materials lay within what had once been the civil zone of the Roman occupation.

As a broad statement the region of the long-wool breeds was a triangle with its base extending from The Wash to the Tees and its apex in the Cotswolds neatly bisected by the old Fosse Way, a nearly perfect median, running from Lincoln to Exeter roughly along the Jurassic Ridge. To the north from the moors of Derbyshire into southern and western Scotland the various heath breeds were dominant. Through the Highlands and Western Isles, the Shetlands and the Orkneys, the scattered remnants of the little short-tailed sheep of the north had still not been displaced and were still relatively unknown except as the producers of a fibre of legendary fineness. To the south and east of the long-wool region was the main area of the finest short wools to which the classic exception was the pocket lying north-west of the Cotswolds in Herefordshire, the country of the old Ryeland, the 'Leominster ore'. From Kent (the sole long-wool pocket outside the main triangle) to Devon all through the southern counties was a broad region of short wools, including the old form of the Wiltshire breed. In East Anglia, but mainly in Norfolk and Suffolk, the native wool supply was characterized by the short fine wool of the black-faced Norfolk, the old horned type, its fleece unwanted by the near-by worsted industries. In the same fashion the Cotswold long wool was an anomaly in relation to the neighbouring woollen manufactures of Gloucestershire. But the distribution of the raw material was not ordained according to the rational needs of the wool manufactures but rather according to the pattern of agriculture and the philosophy of the farmer.

Thus, between the clothier and the agriculturist lay the business territory of the wool stapler, a middleman who took it upon himself to collect the miscellany of fleece types from many districts and to sort and

classify them for their appropriate form of manufacture. The eighteenth-
century occupation of the stapler was changed from the old medieval
function in which he was the gatherer and exporter of the country's
wool almost, if not entirely, without sorting. He had now become
virtually the agent of the manufacturer. In his hands the raw material
passed through the first preparatory stages rendering it fit for its most
suitable form of processing. In the seventeenth century the sorting of
wool was scarcely known in any degree. It was only during the
eighteenth century that it became the elaborate art which it still remains.
It was a further step in the division of labour which is a feature of every
evolving industry. In time the English wool stapler viewed with scorn
the early simple *triage* of the fleece which remained the basis of the
Spanish mode of sorting wool, denouncing it 'a lazy and artless operation'—without, it may be noted, quite appreciating that no more
elaborate method was then much justified due to the intrinsic but
relative uniformity of the fine Spanish fleeces as a whole. The number
of sorts established by the stapler or his modern counterpart is always
arbitrary. Eighteenth-century practice recognized three broad classes of
manufacture—hosiery, worsted, and woollen—for which the number
of sorts made varied widely. For the hosiery section about six or seven
sorts were made. The worsted and woollen sections of the stapling
trade made as many as sixteen or seventeen sorts and even with the
most inferior types of fleeces seldom less than nine. However, it is
important to note that some manufacturers were still able to content
themselves often enough with but three or four distinctions. A catalogue of the sorts commonly recognized in the clothing or carding
wools may be set out briefly in order from the coarsest to the finest,
noting that from the earliest days of sorting as a distinct occupation
there was always presumed to be an association of the closest kind with
the fineness of the fibre:

1. Short-Coarse:	a self-evident description.	
2. Livery:	} old sorts in to which the fleece was divided.	
3. Abb:		
4. Second:	probably a second or better abb.	
5. Downrights:	perhaps intended to convey the idea of superlative perfection.	
6. Head:	or chief.	
7. Super-Head:	an advance upon the preceding sort.	
8. Picked-Lock:	probably at first the small quantity of the very finest.	
9. Choice-Lock:	still better than the former.	
10. Prime-Lock:	the most recent addition in the scale of fineness, in one instance called Pic-Nic after the fashionable society of that name.[10]	

Other sorts were derived from these especially in those sections of the scale broad enough to admit them. Thus there were such descriptions as Better Livery, Small Abb, Best Second, and so on. These were all adapted to those portions of the fleece which were whitest and therefore best suited to the lighter colours. For the kinds which were marred by naturally coloured fibres a parallel list of sorts denominated Greys existed, and these were used in fabrics dyed by the deeper or stronger colours. Many of the terms evolved in the eighteenth century have survived to the present day, while the essential details of the practice of sorting are certainly very similar as far as the domestic English wools are concerned.

It was the object of the wool stapler in his purchases from the farmer to obtain as high a proportion as possible of the superior sorts (down-rights, head, super-head, etc.) for the agreed price. Fineness was with him always the first consideration to meet the perpetual urging of the manufacturers, especially in the woollen section of the trade, for raw material suitable for cloths of increasingly delicate texture. The demand for Spanish fine wool was the ultimate expression of this pressure after the resources of the domestic production in fineness of fibre had been exhausted.

The next quality of importance was the length of the staple as this determined the general class of manufacture—whether woollen or worsted—for which the fleeces were suitable. The carding process, which was the first step after scouring in preparing the wool for the woollen manufacture, required two chief qualities—a short staple rather less than four inches, and a high degree of crimping along its length. For the combing process which was the first stage in preparing the wool for worsted manufacture, a staple longer than four inches was needed with a lesser degree of crimping. The hosiery industry absorbed a proportion of the wool between the lengths of four and eight inches. For both main sections of the manufacture soundness and uniformity of length and fineness throughout the fibres of the material purchased was an understood and universal goal of the wool stapler then as now.

There was a continual bickering between the farmers and the wool staplers, born of a misunderstanding that was in some measure inevitable from the high degree of specialization that stapling developed, simple though it would seem to have been as an occupation. Thus the farmer was confused by a babel of conflicting preferences and recommendations which seemed to him capricious or cunning—as in fact some of them certainly were. Much of the trouble arose from an over-specialization in which different staplers reflected the genuine needs sought by particular sections of the manufacture. Few if any staplers or manufacturers, however, could speak with authority beyond the relatively narrow limits of their own speciality, a point which was by no means easily apparent to the farmers who seldom had the means of judging by more than they heard at their own barn door.

Even among staplers in markets where every kind of wool was sought there would be some who bought only in the north, others only in the south, some in the east, and others only in the west. Many took a middle course. Some specialized in long and others in short wools. Many understood only the requirements in the lower sorts and yet others only in the finer, more expensive types. Others specialized in the foreign wools alone. Some staplers confined their operations simply to buying and sorting for sale to the particular type of manufacturer with whom they had chosen to work. Others carried their manipulations of the raw material to the process of scouring and beyond. Conversely, many manufacturers incorporated the functions of wool stapler within the range of their own operations working directly with the farmer who supplied his special material and not using the assistance of any form of middleman in these transactions.

Such a pattern merely reflected the growing versatility of the English wool manufacture, its improving standards and expertise. This one might expect within any industry in a state of active technical advance. The farmer perhaps understood little of the technicalities which dictated the operations of the wool staplers beyond what he could see in the neighbouring villages—if he was fortunate enough to be near some manufacturing area. On the other hand, the wool stapler, a travelled man, in varying degree had a fairly shrewd idea of the limits within which the farmer had to work in breeding his sheep and producing the raw fleece. However, if evolving techniques of manufacture were introducing more stringent standards and more specialities in the use of the fleece, it is equally true that the agriculture of the eighteenth century was drastically changing the farming pattern and the conditions under which the sheep were reared and the purposes for which they were bred. If there was a confusion of tongues among the clothiers and wool staplers on the requirements of their industry and trade, this was matched by the endless contentions of the farmers and the breeders of livestock on the ways and means whereby the new spirit of improvement might best find its expression, especially in the latter half of the century.

VI

If a symbol be needed to epitomize all that this meant to English agriculture and its relations with the woollen manufacture 'the Dishley breed' will serve us very well. In the centre of the long-wool triangle a minor revolution was forming from about the mid-century onwards.

This inner turbulence was slowly transforming its medieval tranquillity until the innocent shape of the old region might almost be said to have assumed the menace of a dagger directed at the heart of the West Country and its fine broadcloth industry. A few miles north of the old Fosse Way in the valley of the River Soar on the road to Derby lay the tenant-farm of Dishley Grange. Here Robert Bakewell was shrewdly distilling the ingredients of the sheep that was to enter the nineteenth century as the New Leicester, and for the last thirty years of the eighteenth century as the Dishley breed was to spread its genes into every county where sheep were bred—bedevilling the ancient heredity of many an old breed, but heralding the day of the new fat-stock farming that was rising within the security of the spreading enclosures. Whatever the final assessment of Bakewell's contribution to modern farm animal breeding may be, there can be no doubt that he was a vital and symbolic figure in agricultural society among his contemporaries, an important catalyst in the new synthesis that was preparing almost fortuitously in British farming to meet the emergencies of a protracted war and the more sustained pressure of an urban population fast increasing in number and in the standard of its demands. The Dishley breed, however, posed an old problem in a concise form with a new and acute emphasis.

How well could a sheep serve two competing markets—that of the butcher seeking a fat carcass for the discriminating table, and that of the wool manufacturer seeking the perfect staple for his cloth? Even the instinctive wit of Robert Bakewell never solved this dilemma, for it never greatly worried him or many of his adherents in the controversies that revolved for so long about the small farm at Dishley. Except to the extent that the fleece may at times have receded from the best attributes of a combing wool, neither the worsted interests of the West Riding and East Anglia nor the hosiery interests of the Midlands had much cause to contest the spread of the Dishley breed. Preoccupation with the niceties of the table joint, the distribution of the fat, the recovery of the tallow, the efficiency of food conversion, certainly distracted the eye of the farmer from the subtle qualities of the fleece. But a relaxation of selection standards affecting the quality of wool in a breed that was still patently a long wool rather than of the short clothing type did not greatly mar its utility. The contemporary standards at least of the Yorkshire trade were such that they could absorb any sort of combing wool to sustain the fast-growing output of worsted and the coarser cloths on which its early strength was founded. For the West Country cloth trade the consequences were more serious. The grounds of a vigorous but ineffectual controversy were early established, contesting the slow but inexorable spread of the New Leicester and all that it

implied to the home supplies of the carding wools. This finally
effervesced into the windy clamour of argument when, for a few years,
the Spanish Merino was set in the lists as the antagonist of the New
Leicester, a combat which, in one sense, neither survived intact. The
ending of the Napoleonic Wars effectually destroyed the basis of the
arguments of both sides. The English scene was exchanged within a
generation by both breeds as an arena for the distant pastures of
Australia and New Zealand.

CHAPTER II

The Foreground, 1782–1788

I

In the very week that Yorktown fell and the surrender of Cornwallis brought the American War of Independence to an effective end, Henry Butler Pacey, F.R.S., Recorder of Boston, wrote a letter. It was addressed to the young President of the Royal Society and new baronet Sir Joseph Banks, well settled in Soho Square among the scientific distractions of London.

May I presume to trespass upon you in ye present situation of our County, & to hope y^t ye distresses of ye same may plead for ye indulgence.

I presume you are not entirely unacquainted wth ye low state of our wool trade, & ye distress consequent thereon, & of ye meeting of ye County intended to be holden for considering ye same, & whether any means & what can be devised for relieving ye s^d distress.

How happy sh^d I esteem myself could I be made acquainted wth yr sentimst thereon, but how much more happy if yr other avocations w^d permit you to visit Lincolns[hire], where upon ye spot—seeing ye facts you might with more readiness bend yr mind towards finding some relief.

As ye present quantity of wool upon hand seems to me to arise in great measure from ye fashion & alteration in ye dress of ye lower ranks of life, by wch means ye home trade for coarser woollens is greatly lessened, more than from ye situation of our public affairs, I sh^d conceive it was capable of some relief from ye legislature.

I have likewise some reasons to apprehend y^t there may be a combination amongst ye wool-buyers to keep down ye price of wool in ye present plenty of ye s^d commodity, if such there sh^d be, no method appears to me so likely to counteract ye same as some vigorous resolutions adopted at ye Co. meeting by ye most respectable persons of ye s^d County, As I trebly apprehend, tho much will be to be done after ye s^d meeting any future success will in a great measure depend upon ye respectability of that meeting, & ye vigour & resolution which shall appear thereat. With such conceptions, need I add how much as an individual, as well as I think ye County in general, w^d think themselves obliged to yr talents & station in life if yr presence w^d sanction that meeting.

I do not presume to suggest a remedy, c^d only wish a fair investigation of facts, & a removal of antient prejudices, & then I flatter myself some relief might be obtained not inconsistent wth ye good of ye state.

M^{rs}· Pacey takes ye liberty of desiring her respects to Lady Banks & of suggesting y^t if Sr Joseph sh^d deign to attend ye meeting, & if failure of his house at Revesby being sufficiently aired w^{d} accept a well aired bed and homely fair in ye Friary, it w^{d} be esteemed an honor & confer a happiness upon . . .[1]

Neither the persuasiveness of Mr. Pacey nor 'the well aired bed and homely fair' offered by his wife could tempt Sir Joseph away from his new responsibilities in London. The meeting of 31 October in Lincoln Castle passed without his presence, though not without his expressed support of its intentions. So from a distance gradually the landowner of Revesby and the evolving savant of Soho Square began his association with a controversy that was to engage him actively for some years and to seal his interest finally in all things concerning the sheep industry and the woollen manufactures of the kingdom.

The young man of action, the former companion of the late Captain Cook, the biological explorer of the coasts of Newfoundland and Labrador, of the continents and islands of the South Seas, of the Scottish Hebrides and of Iceland, had come to rest at last in London. The roving bachelor and man of wealth was now transformed into the young married man, wedded no less to Science and the growing herbarium and collections of 32 Soho Square than to his compliant and charming wife. Surrounded by the accretions of his journeys and the learned companions of his botanical explorations his preoccupations with natural history in all its forms heavily outweighed his agricultural activities at this stage. Especially was this so in the autumn of the year when the business of the Royal Society was in the ascendant. It is not surprising then that even the cry from his native Lincolnshire could not draw him out in person from the capital. The days had not yet come when the late summer and early autumn would regularly find Sir Joseph immersed in the affairs of the county, his private estate, and all forms of agricultural improvement. The great office and orderly files of Revesby Abbey had yet to assume something of the intellectual authority in such matters as was already in other fields to be found in the study and collections of Soho Square. It was, however, the exigencies of Time only, not in any way a poverty of interest, that kept him in London when the distresses of the landowners and small farmers of Lincolnshire pleaded for his intervention. The Royal Society demanded his presence in London. But there was still much that he could do there as a Lincolnshire landowner, close by the entrenched citadels of Westminster and Whitehall, in what was soon to become a very wordy fracas of pamphlets and letters to the Press, combined with active lobbying.

Mr. Charles Chaplin of Tathwell very soon added his pleas to those of Henry Pacey. Before the end of November 1781, Sir Joseph had been firmly committed to the cause of the Lincolnshire gentlemen in their abortive contest with the merchants of Yorkshire, Norfolk, and Essex. The meeting in the White Hart Inn at Lincoln on 3 October had done little more than confirm that the distress of the county was very great.[2] For this the only remedy proposed was that existing laws should be revised to permit a limited exportation of wool. The price for the local long combing wool had fallen in five years from 8d. to 9d. per pound to a point somewhere between $3\frac{1}{2}$d. to 4d. This clearly reflected the general state of the country's finance. Another measure of disaster was the deficit in the balance of trade for the first time that century and probably for the past one hundred years or more. The low price of long wool itself mirrored the influence of the war—depression in the manufacture and export of the coarser woollens, particularly from Yorkshire; the inevitable loss of this particular trade with the American colonies; and the general disturbance arising from the temporarily insecure command of the Atlantic sea routes. The crisis also serves to demonstrate effectively the crucial position in which the woollen manufactures stood in relation both to the solvency and the security of the nation at this period. It is perhaps also a measure of the desperation of the Lincolnshire graziers that they should contemplate a solution so radical as even a qualified exportation of their staple product, a material which they well knew from more than a century of experience, was as much a jealously guarded monopoly of the English manufacturers as was the Spanish fine-wool sheep of its own country. Moreover, to raise such an issue when Yorkshire in particular had but recently secured its own future as the woollen Titan of the north was certain to evoke the powerful resistance of a shrewd industrial group well versed in all the arts of pressure politics. The signs of this were soon displayed.

II

On 1 December at Leeds in an inaugural meeting of merchants it was resolved to hold a special meeting in the Moot Hall on 19 December

. . . to take into consideration the proceedings of the wool growers in the county of Lincoln, and other parts, for the purpose of obtaining powers to export the wool of this kingdom, and to prohibit the importation of Irish yarn.[3]

With this step, it may be said, began a seven years' civil war which arrayed the merchants in woollens with the woollen manufacturers of Yorkshire against the noblemen, gentlemen, yeomanry, landowners, and landholders of Lincolnshire. Issues were raised of the widest significance to the country as a whole. But no measure of finality was achieved until the Wool Bill of 1788 became law as the Act, 28 Geo. III,

c. 38. Equally it may be said that here began the seven years' apprentice-ship of Sir Joseph Banks to the sheep and wool affairs of the kingdom. This would establish him as an international authority of great weight and substance in this field and as the natural choice of his King when, in the course of time, a colleague and confidant was needed to establish an experimental sheep flock in the national interest.

The meeting at Lincoln Castle on 31 October, under the Chairman-ship of the 5th Duke of Ancaster and Kesteven as Lord-Lieutenant of the County, had unanimously resolved that a Committee be appointed

. . . to consist of the Peers of the Realm, owners of land in this county, the members of the county, the members representing the city and boroughs of the county, together with such other gentlemen as choose to attend, to meet and consult what immediate relief can be given to the present distress, and what remedy it may be proper to seek, to amend the general state of our wool trade for the future.[4]

To this body Banks was appointed as a landowner and gentleman of the county. Perhaps for the first time in his life he found himself drawn into an arena that he preferred consistently to avoid. However, as a member of what was for some years known as the Lincolnshire Wool Committee he bore himself conscientiously, pursuing his duty to the county, his attention close to the practical issues rather than the political, his eyes probing the situation as an agriculturist. His mind gradually assembled the facts about the animal and the material under dispute. Eventually the local problem was turned into a forcing house of ideas of national consequence leading far beyond his own first intentions.

The Committee was charged first,

. . . to consider how far an immediate relief can be given to the present distress, by having permission, under the regulations of a temporary law, to export to the foreign market that surplus of our wool which is now unsold and un-saleable at the home market, and how far it may be expedient to pursue the same.

They were further instructed to

. . . consider how far it may be expedient or otherwise to apply to Parliament for a repeal or amendment of the Act of Parliament, which permits the importation of Irish woollen yarn, and how far it may be expedient or other-wise, to apply to Parliament for leave to export, — months after clipping, that surplus of wool which remains on hand, and can not be sold at the home market at higher prices than — shillings per tod.

In all this they were

. . . to consult, correspond, and cooperate with such other committees or bodies of men as may be appointed in other counties, upon the same matters, as also with such manufacturers, and others, who can give them information touching this business.

On this basis the Lincolnshire Wool Committee met briefly and adjourned to the second Wednesday after the Christmas recess, appointing the St. Alban's Tavern in London as the place of meeting.

From the Moot Hall in Leeds on 19 December came the counterblast of resolutions by the merchants and manufacturers of Yorkshire:

1. That the exportation of any sort of wool, the produce of this kingdom, would be injurious to the trade and manufacturers thereof, and any steps towards obtaining a law for that purpose ought to be strenuously opposed.
2. That any application for a repeal of the Act of Parliament which permits the importation of Irish woollen yarn into this kingdom, ought also to be opposed.
3. That the merchants in woollens unite in one body, and the manufacturers of woollens in another, to oppose every attempt to procure laws for that purpose.
4. That it is the opinion of this meeting that the landed interest of the kingdom would be materially prejudiced by a law being passed, giving leave to export wool, and prohibiting the importation of Irish yarn.
5. That on the adjournment of this meeting, a committee of merchants be appointed who, in conjunction with the committee of woollen manufacturers, are requested to open a correspondence with the other merchants and manufacturers of this kingdom, requesting their concurrence and assistance in opposing any attempt to obtain a law for leave to export wool, or prohibiting the importation of Irish woollen yarn into this kingdom.
6. That the landed interest be applied to for their assistance and support, in such manner as to the committee may seem most advisable.[5]

The rallying-point for the merchants and manufacturers in London was established at the King's Arms Tavern in Old Palace Yard, Westminster. There, on 28 January 1782, gathered delegates of the trade from all parts of the kingdom.

III

Before the opposing groups settled in the taverns of Westminster and St. James's, Banks found himself involved in many preliminary tasks that quickly followed his membership of the Lincolnshire Wool Committee. His reputation as a man of affairs was too well known for the county to neglect him as an instrument of effective action. At the end of November Charles Chaplin of Tathwell wrote to him voicing the opinions of the most influential landholders and farmers:

Since the Meeting at Lincoln several Gentlemen in the Country, have been dissatisfied at the long Adjournment of the Committee, as they apprehend it will be very late in the Sessions before they can be sufficiently inform'd to make any progress in the Business. It is also supposed that a business of such consequence must be attended with an Expence wch it would be un-reasonable to lay upon the Committee. It appears absolutely necessary to know the price of every sort of Long Wool at Ostend, Amsterdam, & Embden the wch unless it can be procured by correspondence shou'd be had by sending over some intelligent Person. Your Sentiments on this subject & if you cou'd assist us in procuring the Information or recommend a proper person, acquainted with the language to send over to obtain it, will oblige this Neighbourhood, & we shall readily adopt any mode you may recommend of Subscription, or inquiry into ye state of the Foreign Markets. Sir John Dalrymple (a Baron of the Exchequer in Scotland) is now in Town in his way to Bath for his health he had taken much pains to inform himself of the present State of Wool & has wrote an excellent Pamphlet, wch he means soon to publish on that Subject, If it is not too much trouble I wish you wou'd permit Mr Wrigglesworth the bearer to bring about an interview between you, & him, as I am certain you wou'd find him very intelligent in this business, & you might settle something with him that wou'd tend to promote it. It is of too much consequence to this Country to neglect any opportunity of obtaining relief for the present distress, occasiond by the low price of Wool, & I fear little will be done unless Men of Business will exert themselves, & for this reason we are anxious to prevail upon you to take it up seriously. You will excuse me in taking the liberty of requesting your assistance wch may be attended with a good deal of trouble, but the opinion of the Country of your Abilities & inclination to be of service to them, have induced me to communicate it to you. . . .[6]

This plain letter from the Wolds of Lindsey set in motion a sequence of actions by Banks that not only fulfilled the purposes of the Lincoln-shire gentlemen but initiated a course of inquiry that led him very far indeed into the intricacies of sheep breeding and the wool manufacture. The meeting with Sir John Dalrymple precipitated into circulation one of the first pamphlets of the controversy—*The Question considered, whether Wool should be allowed to be exported, when the Price is low at home, on paying a Duty to the Public*—which the Scottish baronet generously released as the working basis of the Lincolnshire case.[7] Within a week specimens of the new pamphlet were on their way to Pacey, Chaplin, and Banks's own Steward, Benjamin Stephenson.[8] All accepted it as a good general work but not beyond criticism. All agreed that it was bound to elicit an answer from the manufacturers, for there were indeed some arguments that could be easily contraverted. How-ever, no such reaction was immediately apparent. Instead Mr. Henry Pacey could note that 'there seems a mighty storm brewing in ye north, wch being joined from the East & ye West will make a formidable junction in ye metropolis'.[9] The merchants and woollen manufacturers were acting vigorously to organize their own interests by meetings at Halifax and Rochdale, Norwich and Colchester, with one at Exeter representing the tardy response of the West Country whose interests were less immediately assailed by the gentlemen of Lincolnshire. They were collectively a tightly organized phalanx which had defended the wool monopoly successfully for more than a hundred and twenty years against many such desultory attacks. Now their instincts told them that this was a threat that could not be easily turned aside. So the users of wool conserved their fire and focused their energies precisely on the point where the issue was bound to be settled—within the precincts of Westminster. Here, in its very heart, the Yorkshire barricades were set up at the King's Arms Tavern in Old Palace Yard.

On the other hand the Lincolnshire Wool Committee had an enormous inertia to overcome in the ignorance and individualism of the wool growers of every degree. Any such issues as those now put forward in Sir John Dalrymple's first probing pamphlet were strange intrusions on their normally sequestered calm. Hence it was important that a campaign of education in some form should be directed not only to Lincolnshire but to all the counties where long wool in any form was grown—Leicestershire, Warwickshire, Northamptonshire, Staffordshire, Huntingdonshire, Nottinghamshire, Yorkshire itself. Pamphlets in the hands of the men most concerned was then the only sure way of breaching the sessile remoteness of the country gentlemen of England with any faint hope of success. Support and correction to the first pamphlet came in the second admonitory essay which appeared early in the New Year of 1782 as *Considerations on the Present State of the Wool Trade . . . by A Gentleman Resident on His Estate in Lincolnshire*.[10] This sounded the authentic note of free trade against protection and possibly more than matched the case made by the Scottish baronet. It was an encouraging example from within the ranks of the wool growers themselves. Another shaft of light followed from the same quarter on *The Propriety of Allowing a Qualified Exportation of Wool, Discussed Historically . . .*,[11] printed anonymously and circulated before the end of January to anticipate the important meetings at the St. Alban's and King's Arms Taverns for which handbills and newspaper notices had been circulated by the two opposing groups. This third paper was written by Sir Joseph Banks himself and, in a valuable appendix, it introduced facts and figures on the woollen exports and wool prices for the previous century. On these three documents the wool growers' case for the time being had to rest. But neither Sir Joseph, nor Henry Pacey, nor Charles Chaplin were content.

It was all too evident that hearsay and dogma, tradition and doubtful authorities, exceeded exact knowledge and clear thinking on the issues

involved. The lethargy of the landed interest was aggravated by the
seeming ineptness of the county's representation in the Houses at
Westminster. Where were the facts? How much wool in truth did lie
unsold about the farms and estates of the long-wool counties? What
was the price of long wool in the markets of Europe? How much was
it used in the continental manufactures? What were the costs of manufacture in the various branches of the home industry and what was the
profit on the finished goods? Was it true that the Lincolnshire farmers
and graziers had by their steady agricultural improvements and selective
sheep breeding increased the weight at the expense of the quality of the
fleece and established something in the nature of a glut of inferior wool,
as the manufacturers so cunningly hinted to explain the low price of
longer types? The answers to such wide-ranging questions were not to
be found in a few short weeks. Again it may be taken as a measure of
the Lincolnshire crisis that, with no machinery and no liaisons available
to help in the search for this knowledge, some practical attempts were
actually made. Their nature is an interesting clue, both to the urgency
of the situation as it appeared to the most afflicted county and to the
level of mutual ignorance under which the Lincolnshire Wool Committee laboured. In this there was no more cogent example than Sir
Joseph himself. At this stage in his career, it may be noted, he does not
move with a sure step in his search for enlightenment on the questions
raised. Nor is he yet the shrewd initiator of inquiry in this particular
field. It was at the suggestion of Chaplin that he met and collaborated
with Sir John Dalrymple. It was Chaplin, Pacey, and Wrigglesworth
who shouldered the burden of organizing a census of the unsold wool
in the various divisions of the County of Lincoln. So also it was from
the urgings of Chaplin and the gentlemen of Lindsey that Sir Joseph
was induced to seek out a person to venture on to the Continent and
reconnoitre the status of long wool on the very doorstep of the
country's foreign competitors. From the same source was urged the
need to inquire 'into yᵉ state of the Foreign Markets' by correspondence.
But whoever urged and whoever obeyed it was clear that neither
Chaplin nor Banks had any certain knowledge of the most direct path
to be followed. All the county knew was that Banks was a sound and
sensible man of business in whom trust could be safely reposed. All
Banks knew was that the county expected much of him as a gentleman
of property and as one close to the seats of influence in the capital. It is
doubtful how far he was looked to in this contingency as President of
the Royal Society. It is probable that he was highly regarded mainly as
a man of wide knowledge already in agriculture and natural science,
with an intellectual detachment from which much could be expected in
achieving a solution in this very complex business.

By the middle of December 1781, Charles Chaplin had found in Sir Joseph Banks a source of great comfort and satisfaction and was convinced that in him the county had an able advocate for the redress of their grievances against 'an infamous combination and Monopoly, wch will be found to be the chief cause . . .', and a happy exception to those 'people of property so idle & dissipated that they will not think of, or attend to any business . . .'. Chaplin was constrained therefore to enlarge his own views of the situation to a man who was already adept at inviting such confidences, apparently without effort, in the simple directness of his own letters:

. . . Your Country will be greatly indebted to you for your exertions, & I have no doubt that this part of it [Lindsey] will very readily enter into a Subscription to defray any expences you may find necessary, for wch purpose we shall soon call a Meeting; the only thing we shall have to lament, is, that we cannot have your assistance where it may be most wanted; this misfortune should have been thought of at a proper time, wch nothing but a hasty application from a quarter that laid me under restraint, would have prevented me from signifying my sentiments about it to the Country. We are certainly in an awkward situation for a Leader in the House. I fear our County Members will not be willing to undertake it, & more that they would not conduct it ably; Lincolnshire must take the Lead, & therefore if the above supposition is right, the Lead must devolve to some other Member, perhaps the Member for Lincoln, who tho' a Man of Business, is not well attended to in the House. I cannot help (in confidence) signifying my Apprehension of our failure in Management & wishing that some very able Member cou'd be prevaild on to take an Active part, when the Application comes before Parliament. Any Pamphlets sent down to me shall be distributed without delay. Some Arguments are necessary to stimulate those whose Interest it is to obtain relief, but the greatest use of them will be to remove prejudices in disinterested people. The inclosed was at one time given to Mr. Pacey, but I have since heard it was not his; it treats the Subject in a proper light, & as you may not have seen it, I have sent it to you. I have collected Samples of almost all kinds of long wool, & marked their Sorts, & present values by wch the person you send will be able to distinguish not only the difference in the wools, but the comparative value. Must not some care be taken, or some application be made for leave to carry out even this small quantity? I shall at all times be happy to give you all the assistance in my power, by making enquiries that may be necessary, or obtaining information within my reach, & shall esteem it an honor to act under you, in the service of my Country. May it not also be proper to enquire into ye price of Labour thro' the whole process of Manufacture abroad? We have every reason to believe we are grossly injured and imposed upon, but without we can give a good account of price of Labour, & ye value of the goods both at home & abroad, we shall not be able to point out where or how we are injured. I understand our wool goes thro' so many hands before the manufactured goods are exported, that it is difficult at present to say where we are most abused. The Woolstaplers combine to fix ye price of wool, the Manufacturers oppress the spinners, & the great Merchants (that have large sums at command) take advantage of the time, to beat down the value of Manufactur'd goods in England, & buy them so as to afford an enormous profit abroad. It may be said that the last has always been, & will be the case, but when we know the price & value of our wool abroad, we shall endeavour to come as near it as possible, & when the Manufacturers know the value of goods abroad, they will do the same, & perhaps many more of them engaged in Foreign Trade so as to render a Middle Man unnecessary; nor must we forget the proportion of our goods consumed at home of wch the Manufacturers are well informed of ye selling price. Unluckily I was from home when yours arrived, & cou'd not get the Samples sooner, as I had not the different sorts by me, but hope this will arrive as soon as your Emissary can be ready. As ye Fly will go to Town as early as the Post, I shall put this Packet into ye Box with the Samples of Wool. . . . N.B. I have sent some Skin Wools wch is what is pulld from Skins that were not shorn. The Skinners Company I hear are heartily with us. . . .[12]

IV

When Sir Joseph returned home from a dinner abroad on the evening of 18 December, Chaplin's letter and the box of samples were waiting for him in Soho Square.[13] The samples particularly were everything he had required of them—for this practical touch was his. He had not, however, yet found a person suitable to send abroad on the mission which would enable these samples to be used with good effect. It was not in fact until 5 January that Banks was able to secure a passport from the Secretary of State, David Murray 7th Viscount Stormont, for one Charles Hellstedt,[14] a Swede with a command of several European languages and apparently sufficient knowledge of the wool trade and business to pass convincingly as a merchant in search of orders. So in the depth of winter Hellstedt set out on his uncomfortable excursion in mercantile espionage which, over a period of six weeks, carried him more than a thousand miles via Dover, Calais, Dunkirk, through Ostend, Bruges, Ghent, Brussels, Antwerp, Breda, Gorcum, Amsterdam, Harlingen, Gröningen, Delfziel, to Emden, and thence back again to London. For this his travelling expenses were in all £54, or a little more than one shilling a mile, a sum which Banks willingly paid out of his own resources.[15] The journey was not wholly profitable in its returns of exact information and it was certainly unpleasant for Hellstedt, whose homing letters were interspersed with sad comments on his experiences. The low point of his journey was reached in Amsterdam from whence came this *cri de cœur*, written on 25 January 1782:

. . . I didn'te expect in the Centre of a commercial nation to find the hatred
of the inhabitants against all that is English, grown to a perfect enthusiasm.
I have always gloried, when upon my travels, to pass for an Englishman. but
here I am glad to shelter myself under the much lower tho' true appellation
of a Swede, nor would they believe me to be one, did I not speak high Dutch,
which they say the English people never learn. Some good natured persons
have advised me to assume the character of an English American, which
people are much carressed here.[16]

His spirit clearly shaken by the horror of this discovery, it was almost
as an afterthought that he added the values he had been able to elicit
from the suspicious Dutchmen for the samples he had to show them.
His method of getting information was to apply to the merchants in
the various cities for the prices of their wool as if he wished to buy and
to show the samples of the English long wool as though he had some
to sell. He found a general tendency to rate the samples as though they
had been picked for the French market. At Calais as he passed through
he was told that even his coarsest sample was worth there no less than
2s. 6d. sterling per pound. At Brussels the values ranged from 1s. 8d.
to 2s. 2d. sterling per pound; in Amsterdam from 10d. to 1s. 4d.; at
Emden a value of 2s. 6d. for the best.[17] In general also he found an
ignorance of English wool, or so he thought. At Ghent he found a
certain Mr. Robert Barclay, an English merchant living and operating
in the Low Countries, who determined for him that the average quality
of the samples he carried would fetch the equivalent of nearly 4s.
sterling per pound if sold in the Louvain market. Barclay displayed a
smouldering interest in the wool business of Mr. Charles Hellstedt and
gathered many opinions for him favourable to the idea of a supply of
English long wool if such were ever possible. These points were all in
due time passed on to Banks. How well Hellstedt had dissembled may
perhaps be judged from Robert Barclay's letter of 15 February:

I had the Honor of addressing you of [on] 22^{d} Ultimo to Amsterdam & in
consequence of the wool Business confided to my Care I have now the Satisfaction of inclosing you extracts of the Answers to my several Letters in the
Limbourg County which I am persuaded you will find quite Satisfactory in
[if] the Permit is allowed for the Exportation of Wool—
   In short I have so much the Interest of my native Country at Heart that
did I think even a temporary Bill of this kind to pass our House of Commons
I should feel myself greatly concerned at such an Event. but for my own part
on the Contrary if a certain priced wool be considerable on Hand & too
weak in price for the Landed People I see no Danger in a temporary Export
subject to *Strict Regulations*—I have not nevertheless the smallest opinion that
such Bill will be permitted to pass merely from the Credulity & Hasty
Judgement of an enraged Minority & now *violent People*—

At all Events in this & every other Matter that may merit your Speculation in this Country I beg leave to reitterate to you my very best Services particularly in the Expedition & charging of Vessels with our Growth under our *Neutrality*—which I believe I observed to You when here was the principle part of my Business here as well as in the Exchange Bills &c—
I shall be happy & impatient to hear from you in the wool Business.[18]

For all his protestations the letters of Barclay were suitably vague as befits one merchant in the opening manœuvres with another. Hellstedt therefore wrote one more letter drawing attention to the absence of any prices other than the one general figure he already had. He pressed for more details. These never did emerge though Barclay certainly replied a month later promising more information. Hellstedt retired from his temporary occupation as a wool merchant with a very bad toothache, a difficult task on the whole well done, expenses paid, but no pecuniary reward. He rested content with a comparatively gentle plea for patronage from Banks in some public office, should one become vacant, which might require his proficiency in 'European Languages, Book-keeping and Calculations'.[19]

V

Meanwhile Banks had instituted the first stages of what became an extensive foreign correspondence on matters concerning sheep and wool. It extended in this emergency to 'all the merchants of Europe where the woolen manufactury is at all Flourishing'.[20] The questionnaires were widely cast—to Hamburg, Hanover, Göttingen, Leipzig, to Amsterdam, even into France to Abbeville. To these centres answers were gathered by a subsidiary correspondence which, in a relatively short time considering the state of war existing, covered the wool centres of Western Europe fairly well. Few if any of the replies, however, had reached Banks before the crucial meeting at the end of January. Neither had Hellstedt's letters been able to add anything of much use by that date. But, though the foreign intelligence may have failed in its immediate purpose, the neat letter files of Sir Joseph were primed with first-hand reports which laid a good foundation for later years. They served also to clarify many things before the winter was out, and before spring and the quick changes of Ministry which followed the fall of Lord North's long and fateful government had set an end to Parliamentary petitions about Lincolnshire affairs. Gradually many fascinating intricacies of the wool trade of Europe and his own country were brought home to Banks, uncovering for him a new field of inquiry very much to his taste. The variations in a natural product, its uses to Man, the economics of this relationship, were all attractive features of the long-wool dilemma of his home county viewed simply as a challenge to the natural sciences as he was coming to know them. The foreign correspondence only added grist and put the matter as a problem in animal economy on the same wide base as his more familiar botanical inquiries. One point soon emerged from the mass of detail and opinions. The long wool of England was not as universally known or as highly regarded in all quarters as perhaps the Lincolnshire graziers, or even the self-satisfied wool merchants of Yorkshire, might have cared to see. There were evidently local pockets of long wool in Europe sufficient for the demand and in many cases regarded as superior in quality to any English long wool that leaked out of the port of Hull or elsewhere in neutral vessels—for this suspicious notion was always apparent. It was certainly clear also that however the price may have varied in different European centres the general level was three or four times the current disastrously low price for long wool in England. All this was encouraging to the idea that with a free market the distresses of Lincolnshire and other affected counties might well have been relieved. There was also one significant fact interpolated time and again. Europe seemed much more interested in the Spanish fine wool and the difficulties which the war had caused in its supply to the looms of Europe than with the English long wool. Moreover, there was the curious silence and tardiness of the clothiers of the West Country in rising to the call of Yorkshire against the long-wool gentlemen of Lincoln. Their concern was more with the fine wools of England whose price had not fallen but rather increased and with the imported Spanish fine wool which, after three years of acute scarcity, was at last appearing to restore itself in spite of the war. The regionalism of the English woollen industries had still not yet broken down under the weight of a common national emergency. Meetings in Somerset and Wiltshire soon added their support against the exportation of long wool, however qualified, on the thesis that 'if the exportation of combing Wool be permitted, it will discourage the growth of fine wool (which is already inadequate to the demand) and will eventually prove very prejudicial to the clothing trade of this kingdom'.[21] It was by degrees becoming very clear that the subject of long wool could not be dissociated from that of short and fine wool. It was perhaps significant, therefore, that on the day after the meeting of the Lincolnshire Wool Committee at the St. Alban's Tavern Banks should receive his first leading clue to the possible economic significance of the Spanish fine-wool sheep in the years ahead. His correspondent from Hanover, whose name we do not know, wrote:

Saxony produces the best wool of the whole [of] Germany. A Present of some Hundred Spanish Rams which the Elector receivd directly from Spain about 13 years ago have much improvd the breed & the amelioration now extends over almost the whole of that District I have myself on two of my Estates in Saxony this improvd breed their wool sells by the heavy stone of 22 lb. at 6 Rixdaler Those Estates who still possess the first generation of these sheep sell the same weight from 12 to 14 Rixdaler This Wool is chiefly sold at Leipsig fair very little if any is sent out of the country none I believe by sea but neither English or Spanish wool is now imported[22]

Here was an instance that would not be forgotten, though its relevance in the present contest was apparently slight. It remained for some years with Banks—the 'still small voice' insistent but remote.

VI

The meeting of the Lincolnshire Wool Committee on 30 January with the manufacturers, so long expected, was a disappointment to Banks, who then seems to have realized the true weakness of his country group:

... such a meeting I never saw, Lincolnshire stood alone no other county or Body of men of any description Even Huntingdonshire who had signed a petition joined them & they were represented by a small part indeed of the men of property in the County most of whom literaly came up on Tuesday [the day before] & came into the meeting declaring before hand that they came for information
    The Manufacturers on the other hand attended in a well arrang'd body of members of the house of Commons headed by several good Business men who well [k]new how to arrange the Ideas of the whole proceeding

At the end of the meeting he thought the Lincolnshire case so ill-prepared and ineffectual against the arguments of the manufacturers and merchants that

... it will be in vain to attempt to talk away the advantages of a set of people who have had possession for 140 years & who in all probability even at that distant period got possession by attending diligently to the business of conciliating votes in the house while the country gentlemen were battening at home in Idleness & apathy nothing can I am convinced assist us but a further diminution of Price the Country gentlemen must outnumber the manufacturers in the house whenever they are sufficiently pinch'd but like Lions they want a great proportion of Hunger to excite them. . . .[23]

To this catalogue of disillusionment his correspondent and counsellor in Edinburgh, Sir John Dalrymple, replied out of the fullness of a long life in political controversy:

You must all ways [know] by your account that at General Meetings Merchants will beat country Gentlemen in Argument & plausibility, because men in the world must have great knowledge & the power of using it than men in Solitude.

But the house of commons which contains all the good sense of England when Industry does not chuse to change its course cannot be missled in that manner; & therefore I allways told Mᵣ [Charles] Chaplin to throw himself upon the good sense of *all England in parliament*.

Meeting with men who come not to be convinced is perfect triffling. How in the name of wonder could you submit to meet such a meeting! . . .²⁴

Sage advice from the north of this kind was too late to steer the 'country Gentlemen' from a further meeting in a sort of neutral ground at the Thatched House Tavern in St. James's Street on 2 February. Under the Chairmanship of the Duke of Ancaster they found themselves face to face not only with the 'Merchants' but with a very large sample of 'all the good sense of England', Members of the House of Commons. But in this throng Banks could detect 'among them all not one who was not somehow interested in the manufacture'. With great dexterity the 'Merchants' and their well-briefed supporters quickly introduced an all-obliterating resolution:

That it is the opinion of this meeting that the Exportation of British raw Wool will be prejudicial to the landed and commercial interests of this kingdom.²⁵

This the Duke of Ancaster refused to put to the meeting and retired with all the gentlemen from Lincolnshire, leaving the field to the Yorkshiremen, who immediately carried the resolution unanimously, and so published it in the Press that day. The Lincolnshire Wool Committee, from St. Alban's Tavern, promptly published a disclaimer, saying that the resolution

. . . does not appear to this Committee to apply to the question, on the Expediency or Inexpediency of exporting long or coarse British raw Wool, under certain restrictions, and for a limited time, as this resolution speaks of a general Exportation only.²⁶

Thereafter the Committee concentrated its efforts on the petition to Parliament, duly drafted by Joshua Peart of Lincoln's Inn Fields. This was agreed to by the Committee at St. Alban's Tavern on 12 February 1782.²⁷ Intended to be the rallying-point, it was sent not only to the High Sheriff of Lincolnshire to arrange its public ratification but to all those of the other counties considered to be most affected. The petition, however, seems to have remained in a state of suspended animation, lingering on as a contentious theme during the spring and summer of 1782, thwarted by the downfall of Lord North in March and the quick sequence of changes to the Rockingham and, in July, to the Shelburne administrations. Peace with the United States in November removed one of the worst of the limiting influences of the long war on the wool trade. Finally the Treaty of Versailles in February 1783 appeared to open a new lease of prosperity for the merchants of England. It is evident, however, that from the abortive meeting of 2 February onwards the Lincolnshire Wool Committee was the parent of a lost cause, an infant premature and virtually stillborn, unlikely to survive in a world of hard political reality. *The Morning Herald* had this unkind but not unreal comment to make:

In the present ticklish situation of public affairs, we may lay it down as a maxim, that administration will hear of no measure like that of the export of wool, which can raise in the most distant manner, discontents among the manufacturers; if such a law was to pass, and the price of wheat was accidentally to be high, and the poor in the woollen towns distressed, the master manufacturers would persuade them all their distresses arose from that measure, and the mob might then assemble. This is terror to government. There is combustion among these manufacturers—a spark might light it. But as to graziers and shepherds scattered about the country, they carry no similar terrors with them.[28]

It was very true that on one ground or another the political tide was set against any ideas of free trade in wool for many years to come, but the issue was to remain an uncomfortable spectre at the bedside of many a clothier, manufacturer, and wool merchant, at least until the Lincolnshire men were silenced.

VII

The events which followed the first meeting of 3 October 1781 had showed that the contest was to be a hard one. Peace or no peace, the problem continued to simmer from year to year, and to extend the range of interests and the list of persons to whom the matter seemed of importance. Banks, Pacey, and Chaplin, the trio on whom the burden of the original petition and its case had fallen, were determined but not hopeful of success, and continued to foster anything which seemed likely to ventilate the question from any angle and so keep the problem open to study—the legal, the economic, the agricultural, the technological, or the scientific points of view—at all times directing a wary eye on the political scene in which lay the final hope of decision. Lincolnshire had started a fire of controversy that was to run far beyond the boundaries of the county and eventually to illuminate the whole of the woollen industry. The movement of the problem into wider territory was already apparent to Charles Chaplin in February. This he expressed in his letter to Banks not long after the draft petition had been framed:

. . . It occurs to me that the Counties wch produce the short clothing Wool, are in very great error, if they either mean to oppose us or do not wish to be included in our Bill. It has rarely happened that their wool has bore a better price than ours, on an Average of a Number of years not so good a one, if they know anything of their own produce they must be sensible that the Spanish Wool is *far superior* to the *best* that is grown in England, that the finest wool of this Country is very triffling in Quantity, & that the inferior sorts when Spanish Wool can be had, are of little value. Can they see no farther than the present time? or do they suppose the Spanish War to be a perpetual one? They cannot expect a prohibition of ye Importation of Spanish Wool, as that wou'd be giving away a great balance in Trade wch in time of peace is always in our Favour for Stuffs &c made of Long Wool. That the War cannot continue long is too evident, that on a Free Importation of Spanish Wool the Clothing Wool of this Country must fall to the usual price or under, & that then the Growers of Short Wool will repent that they are not included in the Bill for a limited exportation is very clear to me, & I think by a Sensible address to the Growers of short wool on this Subject, they might also be convinced of it. . . .[29]

There was much good sense in Chaplin's appraisal of the case in the West Country. But it is not in the nature of Man easily to give much thought for the morrow when today he is well provided. Hunger and ruin were not pinching the growers of short wool nor the makers of fine broadcloth. Until the awful realities of peace appeared they were content to suffer the blessings of war and were not easily to be stirred into a closer inspection of the crystal ball.

In April, Chaplin saw clearly that there was no hope for any help from Parliament:

The present [Rockingham] administration having long since declared against our Wool bill, their Connections, the irresolute, pitiful, & weak conduct of many of our Countrymen, whose Interest ought to have made them active in it, are not favourable to our attempts. With reason & Justice so strongly on our side, I cannot however despair; & hope by persevering in a good cause, we may still prevail. . . .

He could, however, already see a glimmer of economic if not legislative change for the better and was not slow to note it:

. . . What has been done already has alarmed the Manufacturers so that I believe they will never venture to beat down wool so low again, & they begin now on the change of Administration & prospect of peace with America to advance it, & if there should be a truce or peace, I am of opinion (between ourselves) that it will advance rapidly, but let that be as it may we have suffer'd greatly already by the very low price & shoud proceed with just the same zeal to prevent the like again. . . .[30]

Chaplin at this point had also reached the conclusion that without powerful support it would be better to postpone the application to Parliament and, without dissolving the Committee, to adjourn further meetings to the country. It is fairly clear that Banks was in harmony with these views and that in time they were shared by the majority of the more active agriculturists. The Lincolnshire Wool Committee, or at least the group which had rallied about this creation with active support, gradually changed its role from that of attack to one of defence with a self-assumed watching brief over the price of long wool. On this score they had the general satisfaction of witnessing the rise of prices which Chaplin had already forecast. With a gradual recovery of economic stability in the county, Yorkshire fell silent as the exports of all forms of woollen goods climbed steadily again from their lowest point for half a century. National industry, gauged in the volume of its exports, began that fantastic climb which for the next twenty years was to be the envy of Europe. The merchants and manufacturers of wool were no less ardent protectionists because they were now less vocal than formerly. They had been badly frightened by the Lincolnshire uproar. Now it was more evident than ever, with trade expanding again, that every pack of home-grown wool of whatever kind, long or short, was critically needed. Having averted successfully the major threat of a qualified export of long wool they quietly turned their attention to sealing off those leakages which everyone knew occurred in the maritime wool-growing counties, particularly of the south and east coasts, in some degree. No one was sure just how much wool left the kingdom through clandestine channels, but it was an intriguing theme and an excellent pretext for further restrictive legislation.[31]

VIII

This opportunity was seized with ardour by the manufacturing interests and from the first meeting at Bristol in September 1784 a series of meetings were held at the Crown and Anchor in the Strand by the merchants, manufacturers, and dealers in wool under the Chairmanship of Mr. John Anstie, of Devizes in Wiltshire, one of the most eminent of the West Country clothiers.[32] At the second meeting in December 1784 a memorial was agreed on to be presented to the Lords of the Treasury, stating the grievances of the manufacturers and asking that the existing laws should be enforced. During 1785 abstracts of these laws were prepared and published by John Anstie and distributed throughout the kingdom. Rewards were also held out to any persons discovering offences against the existing laws. The meetings continued until early in 1786, when at a general meeting in London of the manufacturers and related interests it was unanimously determined to apply to Parliament for relief by obtaining a repeal of all the existing laws—a long and confusing list—and their synthesis into one new and more effectual enactment. For this purpose a Committee of Manufacturers under the Chairmanship of John Anstie was formed in April 1786 and the first form of the so-called Wool Bill of 1788 was drafted. The spark lit by the Lincolnshire graziers in October 1781 and doused by the Yorkshire worsted interests in October 1782 was now being blown upon by a strong anticyclone from the broadcloth men of the West Country. The embers of resistance now glowed again in the heart of Charles Chaplin, who wrote to Banks on 31 May:

The Bill you mention to be brought into Parliament by M.r [John] Anstie will be very troublesome & injurious to this Country, therefore shou'd have the strongest opposition made to it.

As this is a General attack upon all wool, the Landowners & Growers shou'd unite to repel it, & if possible obtain the only Security against Smuggling (so hurtful to y.e Grower & Manufacturer) by a limited Exportation. A general Meeting shou'd I think be called without delay to prevent the apprision of the Excise Laws being extended to private Families, already too much oppress'd in their Property. A Registry of all Wool Shorn within 15 Miles of y.e Sea must be attended with Expence & trouble, will occasion innumerable litigations about Tythe, as well as frequent Penalties & Perjuries. The whole Plan seems calculated to keep down the Price of Wool, w.ch now the old Stock is done, requires some Artful Pretence. . . .[33]

Swift action followed and the first meeting of the Lincoln growers of long wool in the new campaign took place at the Peacock Inn in Boston on 14 June 1786, under the Chairmanship of Robert Vyner, the Member for Lincoln. Others followed elsewhere in the county, culminating in a plenary meeting

of Noblemen, Gentlemen, Graziers, Farmers and others, Owners and Occupiers of Lands in the County of Lincoln; convened by the High-Sheriff at the Request of the Most Noble his Grace the Duke of Ancaster, the Lord Lieutenant, and other Noblemen and Gentlemen of the County, and holden at the County Hall on Thursday the 19th Day of October, 1786 to take into Consideration a Bill entitled 'A Bill for Explaining, Amending, and Reducing into One Act of Parliament, the several Laws now in being, for preventing the Exportation of Live Sheep, Rams and Lambs; Wool, Woolfels, &c. And for preventing Frauds and Deceits in the winding of Fleece Wool'.[34]

With His Grace the Lord-Lieutenant in the Chair appropriate resolutions were taken—a petition was signed and a subscription immediately entered into; a Committee of seven was appointed with the High Sheriff and Sir Joseph Banks, Baronet, named as two with powers to nominate the other five and empowered to correspond and act in conjunction with other counties and persons inclined to oppose the Bill, their expenses to be defrayed out of the subscription money; Joshua

Peart of Lincoln's Inn Fields to be Treasurer; Robert Lely of Lincoln and Benjamin Handley of Sleaford to be Clerks to the meeting. The petition was signed before the end of the year by two hundred and seventy-two Lincolnshire men of varying degree and the sum subscribed for the expenses of the tussle ahead was £1383.[35]

IX

Almost exactly five years had now passed since Banks had first been drawn into the interminable and involved wrangles with the wool trade. Again he was called upon to assume a leading part in a political gamble that was against his inclinations, and which in his inner thoughts it was clear he knew was lost from the first throw. This did not deflect him from a loyal obedience to the wishes of the county, and he laboured industriously against the Bill in all its forms and through all its stages. What he could do nothing to prevent *in toto* he did much to modify *in parte*. Whenever it was at all possible he contested the evidence adduced by the manufacturers (which largely turned on the extent and significance of smuggling) and rationalized many of the more burdensome restrictions on the growers. With Arthur Young who was, characteristically, the voluble publicist especially for the wool growers of Suffolk, Banks tried to find the facts both at home and abroad, in agriculture and in the woollen industries, which might shed light on what, he believed, were too many unsupported statements designed to dupe the Legislature and the nation.[36] They could find no evidence to support the old and stale notion that the French could not make merchantable cloths of their wools without an admixture of what the English manufacturers and growers together were fond of imagining was the superior English staple. They could not swallow the extraordinary estimate of John Anstie that no less then ten thousand packs, mainly of combing wool were lost annually by the home manufactures to France, an amount which at the time would roughly have equalled the import of Spanish fine wool. They found it strange that a West Country clothier who worked only the fine short clothing wools should presume to speak so authoritatively for the combing wools and prefer to be questioned only on these. Their qualified views of Mr. Anstie's competence to ventilate the protectionist policies of the wool trade of England were shared on other grounds by West Riding manufacturers, who saw in the new Bill a subtle device of the West Country to impede their own trade by making it difficult for the northerners to collect their raw material. Pemberton Milnes, in his dual capacity of Lincolnshire landowner and Yorkshire wool merchant was emphatic about this:

This infamous Bill hath other Objects in View than to prevent Smuggling of Wool when the Secret comes to be unravelled it will be found, that the principle and real cause is, to strike at the very existence and stab our Yorkshire & Lancashire Trade to the Heart at one Blow, by depriving us coming at the raw Materials in the way we do at present. . . .

Then, speaking with the awful authority of the Chairman of the West Riding Committee of Merchants, Manufacturers, and Dealers in Wool, he thundered anathema:

. . . my own Opinion is and I believe it [is of] every Merchant & Manufacturer in Yorkshire and Lancashire, that this Bill ought to be rejected in toto by the Meeting, its principles are founded in Iniquity, will tend to the Ruin of many Trading Towns and Manufactory's, will Harass and plague the Growers of Wool and ought to be Burnt at the Market Cross in every Town in the Kingdom. . . .[37]

Anstie's first Bill could hardly withstand this onslaught when it was translated into action by the Yorkshire deputies in London. It did not pass its Second Reading in the House. A new Bill no less inimical to the growers of wool but more in tune with the collective views of the manufacturers appeared from the ashes of the first. It pushed its inexorable way through in slowly modified form to its final appearance in the House of Lords. In April 1788 Arthur Young and Sir Joseph Banks on successive days stood before the Bar of the House of Commons as the principal spokesmen of the wool growers. Again, in early June, they appeared before the Bar of the House of Lords. Their testimony at this stage could do nothing more than form a record in the minutes of evidence of honest opinions honestly formed. The passage of the Bill was already certain. There was little that Banks could do beyond achieving a last-minute easement in section 14 ('my clause').[38] In this the fleeces shorn from sheep for the sole purpose of sending them to market between March and 1 July each year did not have to be certified till after the general shearing—the last of many small details which he managed in this case to modify with the aid of Lord Hawkesbury in the few days of the final reading.[39] Then on 18 June 1788, by a majority of twenty-four to nine at the Third Reading, the Bill passed on to become the Act 28 Geo. III, c. 38.[40] With this the protectionist curtain fell firmly into place round the wool clip and the woollen manufactures of Great Britain until it was lifted thirty-six years later—four years after the deaths of both Young and Banks. Their struggle for a free trade in sheep and wool had failed before the entrenched mercantilism of the English manufacturers. But they had spoken clearly, as reforming agriculturists, in the authentic language of 'the new Science of Political Economy'. It was in the the same spirit of enlightened inquiry that

Banks, even as the protectionist door of his own house was being locked more firmly, was seeking the means of entry through another, no less traditionally barred and bolted—but with a difference.

England had for upwards of one hundred and forty years set a legal wall about her sheep and their wool under the illusion that there was no wool like English wool and that, denied the blessings of this magic staple, foreign cloth manufacture was condemned to permanent inferiority. There was one qualifying thought. The fine staple of Spain, in some quarters at least, was reluctantly conceded to be the exception. Spain, however, for over four hundred years had also kept a similar guard on her principal staple but with a qualified export under a duty. The fine-wool sheep that grew it was as rigidly protected as the long-wool sheep of England—and as hedged about with myths. The tedious controversy from 1781 to 1788 over the status of English wool and English sheep had raised comparative issues of the most intriguing kind to a man who was beginning to think clearly as a scientific biologist in his view of agriculture and the natural products with which it was concerned. It was a natural extension of all his earlier and more specific interests in the plant kingdom. But, where plants might in general be so easily collected and transferred from place to place, as seeds, seedlings, or cuttings, few animals were so amenable. All domestic farm animals were conspicuously large and troublesome both to feed and to transport especially over long distances by sea in the relatively small ships of the period. Moreover, they had a disquietingly high mortality rate in transit from strange and unforeseeable maladies. To obtain a new animal from abroad for first-hand study was at best a chancy project. When to the natural hindrances were added political and legal barriers imposed by sovereign States, even without the modern refinements of quarantine, the difficulties were daunting. So many questions for which there seemed no ready answers other than those to be got by first-hand observation and experiment had been raised concerning the different kinds of sheep and their fleeces in the course of the wool disputes that Banks could not long resist their challenge.

Finally there is the odd reflection that out of this conflict between the rising manufacturers of Yorkshire and the long-wool growers of Lincolnshire there should have emerged into agricultural history a fine-wool flock by the Thames through which, in a sense, the dispute would be resolved in the South Seas. In the end the long wool of Lincolnshire would blend with the fine wool of Spain and the prosperity of Yorkshire would be assured. But this consummation would only be attained by that very exportation of long-wool sheep against which the manufacturing interests organized so successfully. Lincolnshire would gain its point at last but Yorkshire would profit—as always.

COMPARATIVE STATE OF WOOLS

Cloathing

Spain, Mountains of Portugal, higher
parts of Rousillon, in France   Hereford and Shropshires
The adjoining part of Gascony

Languedoc, and other parts   South Downs, Norfolk, Sherwood
of the South of France   Forest, part of Devon and Dorset-
Italy, some part of   shires, part of Wales and Scotland,
Barbary,   &c.
Levant, some parts of

Spain, lowlands of   Wiltsh., Middlesex, Hants, &c.
Portugal, ditto   Scotland, ⎫
Italy, most of   Wales,   ⎬ parts of
France, most of
Levant, part of
Germany, some part of
Flanders, ⎫
Holland, ⎬ most of

Germany, ⎫
Denmark, ⎪   Northumberland, ⎫
Sweden,   ⎬ most of   Scotland,   ⎬ part of
Russia,   ⎪   Wales   ⎭

Combing

Flanders, between Lisle & Ipres   Western isles of Scotland
                                      Romney marsh
Eiderstadt, in Holstein   Lincolnshire, Northamptonshire,
Marshes, in the north of France   Cambridgeshire, Norfolk, part of
and Holland   Bedfordshire and Derbyshire, part
                                      of Gloucestershire, part of Durham,
                                      &c.

[Banks, Sir Joseph, 'Instruction given to Council against the Wool Bill',
    Ann. Agric., IX (1788), 479–506; above pp. 480–1.]

CHAPTER III

The Savants, 1782–1794

I

WHILE the American War dragged on and Lincolnshire suffered in the economic toils of a depression in long-wool prices, the house in Soho Square was something much more than an intelligence centre for the gentlemen of the Wool Committee. Secure under the catholic mantle of Science, its rooms and collections were the haunt of a brilliant young Frenchman, not yet twenty-one, a botanist from Montpellier engaged in the unlikely study of fish. Under the tutelage and inspiration of Banks, Pierre-Marie-Auguste Broussonet was embarking more deeply on those zoological and botanical inquiries which were soon to carry the system and nomenclature of Linnaeus across the Channel into the opposing academic camp of Buffon. With them travelled the seeds of a collaboration that would bear many strange and unforeseeable fruit. After two years' close research in England Broussonet returned to France, a Fellow of the Royal Society and author of an excellent study in systematic zoology based on Linnaean principles.[1] In this he described many rare fish, some entirely new to Science. He carried with him also a talisman in the assured friendship of Sir Joseph Banks, whose true value would emerge in the troubled wanderings of his later life. Meanwhile in Paris he was equally fortunate in finding an academic haven under the protection of Louis-Jean-Marie Daubenton, then beginning his brief tenure of the Chair of Rural Economy at the École Royale Vétérinaire at Alfort. Here, in January 1784, Broussonet became an Associate Professor in a small galaxy of clever young men gathered for a fleeting year or two around Daubenton before they scattered into wider spheres —Flandrin, Vicq D'Azyr, Fourcroy. Among them, Pierre Flandrin, Professor of Anatomy, was soon to add his own contributions to rural economy in his direct studies of fine-wool sheep in Spain itself and of long-wool sheep in England. This he achieved within the next few years before the Revolution which, unlike so many savants, he and his companions were to survive. In this short interlude of peace between the Treaty of Versailles and the storming of the Bastille the subject of rural economy flourished greatly in the 'généralité de Paris' under the patronage and inspiration of the Controller-General of Finance, Bertier de Sauvigny, with whom, as a fellow-traveller in Great Britain,

Broussonet had been to some extent acquainted in his years abroad. It was Bertier's vision that reorganized the École Royale Vétérinaire at Alfort to incorporate the theme of rural economy under Daubenton. it was Bertier also who had rejuvenated the Société Royale d'Agriculture, and who, mindful of the ardent young Frenchman whom he had met in London, persuaded Broussonet in 1785 to become its Secretary. The botanist from Montpellier was now deeply committed to animal science and, having served an apprenticeship in fish at Soho Square, was at last introduced to the larger mammals by the savant from Montbard. Daubenton, as an old associate of Buffon, was by no means ready to accept the Linnaean doctrines of Broussonet fresh from a course of Banksian breakfasts in London. But he was not in any way prevented by such heterodoxy from accepting the young man as a valued colleague nor from extending to him all the help of his generous nature. It was not long therefore before Broussonet found himself the willing channel of communication between Paris and London on the subject of sheep and wool. In him Banks found the means of advancing the rural economy of the world in one small but very significant step—the introduction from France to England of the first undoubted Spanish fine-woolled sheep.

After his return from London Broussonet spent a year botanizing through the South of France and in the Pyrenees with John Sibthorp, Radcliffe Professor of Botany at Oxford.[2] During the expedition he sent full and frequent accounts to Banks in London. It is clear, however, that when he joined Daubenton at Alfort in January 1784 he had not forgotten the former distractions of his English host with the problems of the Lincolnshire gentlemen and the price of long wool during the last months of his stay in 1782. At last installed under the immediate eye of the man who was the acknowledged authority, after twenty years of experiment at Montbard, in all matters relating to the husbandry and breeding of sheep for improved wool production, Broussonet had many reasons for reporting all he saw and heard in this branch of rural economy to his eminent friend across the Channel. Much of it was the gratitude of a young man to a scientific patron of singular generosity. Much was certainly the instinctive communication from one enthusiastic and observant investigator to another, recalling past discussions on the problems and curiosities of fine-wool growing. Some at least evolved from the innocent hopes that Broussonet briefly expressed not merely for some specimens of English wool but for some English sheep to improve the specimens from that source in the flocks at Alfort. Recalling no doubt that this, after all, was one of the main points at issue between the manufacturers and the wool growers of England, he troubled Banks no further on this point. Instead he sent full information about the Spanish sheep bred by Daubenton at Montbard, and in April 1784 followed this with samples of fleece wool and an actual offer of some sheep from the Montbard flock itself. He further titillated the burgeoning interest of the English savant with news of a paper on wool read by Daubenton before the Académie Royale des Sciences on 21 April.[3] This was the same evening that Lavoisier with Meurnier first demonstrated the extraction of 'inflammable air' from water. From Daubenton himself we have no sign that he ever wrote directly to Banks on this or any other point. Indeed a mild and somewhat diffident inquiry through Broussonet in August 1784 for duplicates of some 'zoophytes', if Banks had some to spare, is the only hint of such a scientific contact at this time.[4] No doubt the ebullient and artless garrulity of the younger scientist left both the elder savants breathless and slightly embarrassed. It is even possible that Broussonet, leaping on impetuously, had committed Daubenton to sending sheep without exploring the niceties of the situation. There is a fine dispassionateness about scientists in the exchange of knowledge and material—in theory. When it comes to the point of making the gesture itself strange difficulties often arise with clutching hands to impede it. We need not think the worse of Daubenton if perhaps he required a year to assess his own feelings in the matter. Buffon had for many years battened on his compliant good nature and even the best of men under this form of assault in time grow wary. Thus either for this reason or from other difficulties in the case it was a full year before Broussonet could tell Banks that two Spanish fine-wool sheep, a ram and a ewe, each with an iron collar stamped with Banks's address had been sent off from Paris to Rouen on their way to England.[5] So in the late summer of 1785 there arrived at Spring Grove near Hounslow in Middlesex the first 'real' Spanish fine-wool sheep to be seen in England, as a gift from the French scientists at Alfort to the President of the Royal Society for his own small private experimental flock.

II

It is now nearly two hundred years since Daubenton began his experiments and observations on the breeding and management of sheep and established his small flock at Montbard on the Côte d'Or in Burgundy.[6] Begun in 1766 at the instance of Daniel-Charles Trudaine, Controller-General of Finance under Louis XV, his work on the improvement of wool in particular is an early modern example of the harnessing of science to a problem of agricultural and industrial importance in the national interest. It has a very good claim to consideration as the first such attempt in Europe of any real significance to us now within the wide scope of rural economy. In the special field of animal production, the Montbard establishment became perhaps the first effective experimental farm in the world. The modesty and self-abnegation of Daubenton, which enabled him to withstand for so long the tiresome occlusive vanities of Buffon at the Jardin des Plantes cannot now deny him a very strong claim as the first modern scientific breeder of livestock whose work has any present-day relevance. In this sense he was indubitably the first experimental breeder of sheep for the improvement of wool at a period when this raw material ranked high in the industrial economy of Europe. Daubenton himself would trace the origin of this work as far back as the reforming days of Jean-Baptiste Colbert the great Minister and Secretary of State and Controller-General of Finance under Louis XIV. Colbert certainly saw clearly how important it was to France that her native wool supply should be improved to meet the growing international competition in fine textiles. Later Ministers made various attempts to put the concept into practice, and it was scarcely ten years before the establishment of the Montbard experiments that the young Abbé Claude Carlier had been asked by another Controller-General of Finance, Bertin, to report on the means of developing improved breeds of fine-wool-growing sheep in France.[7] But valuable as the deductions of an archaeologist and a historian may be, the problem and the spirit of the age demanded something more. Thus Daubenton, the retiring but patient and exact scientist, at the age of fifty was called at last from beneath the shadow of the egocentric Buffon 'to investigate by a series of well-conceived and carefully executed experiments the most favorable natural conditions for the improvement of wool'. Behind this demand the reasoning was simple. Again it was the absolute necessity in the manufacture of fine cloths to import the best wool of Spain to attain the highest quality in this branch of manufacture. Again there was the fear that Spain might refuse to supply this critical material or that war might disrupt the trade. All this Trudaine the elder, as Intendant-General of the nation's finance, could clearly see. Also, perhaps, as a member of the Académie Royale des Sciences he could as clearly see where lay the nation's best insurance, and incidentally its ultimate freedom from an annual tribute of more than twenty-five million livres tournois (about £1·1 million in Georgian sterling). At this period such a sum would have been about twice the value of the English imports of fine wool from Spain. Trudaine the financier proposed, therefore, no less than the transformation of the French fleece into wool as fine as that of Spain. He asked his friend Daubenton the biologist if he thought this could be done. Recalling the experiences of twenty years' research in the field of zoology and comparative anatomy, Daubenton thought that if selection under domestication could change the hair of the wild moufflon into the fine wool of Spain or the rough coat of the mastiff of the old Gauls into the fine fluff of a Court lap-dog then perhaps this feat could be accomplished. He postulated, however, that only by a careful series of breeding experiments with different breeds of rams and ewes could the right path be chosen and selection towards improvement made certain and not merely a matter of chance. This alone would still not satisfy Daubenton, who considered that studies should at the same time be made on all matters affecting the health, feeding, and management of sheep for he knew that in the numberless confusion of breeds not only did 'one breed differ from another in characters almost imperceptible' but that 'different factors caused them to vary at different places and at different times in the same environment'. All this complexity Trudaine was content to accept. He offered Daubenton his full support with financial assistance from the State in whatever experiments he considered necessary. Thus, in a spirit of mutual trust, the small farm at Montbard came into being towards the end of 1766. In 1767 the flock was formed with sheep from Roussillon, Flanders, England, Morocco, and Tibet. A ten-year course of complex cross-breeding between these representative 'races' was begun with every sort of precaution to ensure their genetic accuracy. For ten years the sire and dam of every lamb born was carefully noted, an objective demanding the closest attention, above all 'during the season of their *amours*', so that in the end three generations could be attained wherein the pedigree was exactly known. A flock of several hundred sheep came into being on which observations were made on every animal at all ages and in all states, supplemented with an assessment by autopsy of the cause of death.

Recognizing the vague and uncertain basis of the manufacturer's visual judgement of the fineness and quality of wool, Daubenton for his own experiments introduced objective standards, using the microscope to determine the fibre thickness of the seven grades from coarse to fine which he distinguished. By this means he also recognized the infinity of grades among the fibres within each staple and how this could vary from sheep to sheep. His experiments showed him two important effects. According to the choice of parent stock he could eliminate the coarse hairy fibres from the fleece. By the same means he could render the fleece finer. He also discovered that in many of these crosses the fleece weights of the progeny could be twice, even three, times the weights of their dam's fleece. Most important he found that all these forms of improvement were much modified by the state of health and the nutrition of the parents as well as of the lambs themselves. He found, moreover, that after ten years of selection in his own flock at Montbard his finest fleeces were superior to those of the rams

of Roussillon from which source they had originated. Even more significant, he found by a close and exacting comparison, including micro-
metric measurement, that his best wool was but one grade less fine than
that from the Escorial flock, one of the best in all Spain. Reporting these
results in 1777 in a memoir to the Académie Royale des Sciences he
concluded, with due caution, that it was possible, inexpensively, by the
direct choice of the finest and most uniform rams, such as were to be
found among the best of Roussillon, to improve the wools of France to
the second degree of superfineness. To achieve the highest degree of all
he acknowledged that rams for this purpose could only be found in
Spain. The force of this demonstration had not been missed by the
liberal intelligence of Turgot. During his brief tenure as Controller-
General of Finance, he authorized the addition to Daubenton's flock in
1776 of a small flock of sheep from Spain itself, acquired by some means
not disclosed. With these Daubenton was able at last to satisfy himself
that he could indeed so breed the sheep of his experimental flock as to
match the superfine wool of Spain without drawing further on outside
sources. No buyer or seller or manufacturer of wool, he was convinced,
could distinguish the best of the Montbard fleeces from those of Spain
itself. So after a further nine years he reported the substance of his
selective breeding experiments with the Spanish importations in a final
memoir to the Académie on this subject in November 1785. He had
carried his investigations through to a comparison of the finished cloths
made from the sheep of his own flock with those made from the best
Leonese wools of Spain. The ultimate judgement was sought from the
firm of Julienne, Oger et Cie, clothiers and dyers of the Gobelins, in the
manufacture of fine scarlet cloth. M. Oger averred that only the most
expert could distinguish the two and that in the brilliance of the scarlet
dyeing, the wool from Montbard exceeded that from Spain. With
other wool from the same sources M. Decretot, a manufacturer at
Louviers, confirmed that Daubenton's fleeces could not be rated less
than equal to Spanish wool of the first quality. This addendum was duly
presented to the Académie in March 1786 and both were later published as one pamphlet the same year at the Royal printing-house, from
whence, by the help of William Eden, Sir Joseph Banks eventually
secured a copy in May 1787.[8] From that time forward, in the view of
Daubenton, the way was open to France if she wished to attain independence in the growing of fine wool and the problem had finally become
one of public instruction in general not so much of research in principle
as on points of detail.

He had already in 1782 published the fruits of his experience at Montbard in the form of his *Instructions pour Les Bergers et pour Les Propriétaires des Troupeaux*... as a sort of catechism, illustrated and rounded out

with extracts from some of the earlier memoirs. In 1783 he had been inducted into the École Royale Vétérinaire at Alfort by Bertier de Sauvigny to occupy the first Chair of Rural Economy. Bertier had also persuaded him to establish a small flock at the École Royale Vétérinaire that same year, for which four rams and nine ewes were drafted from Montbard, and had set aside sufficient land for this purpose to form a small demonstration farm under the Société Royale d'Agriculture. Here, near Charenton, Daubenton built a small replica of his *bergérie* at Montbard, and on 19 October 1787 it was visited by Arthur Young during the first of his three visits to France. At the École Royale Vétérinaire itself Young met Chabert the Director-General and his son-in-law Flandrin, the anatomist whom he had already entertained in Suffolk. Of Daubenton he saw nothing and of the farm he said little, and that both acidulous and bleak:

... As to the farm, it is under the conduct of a great naturalist, high in royal academies of science, and whose name is celebrated through Europe for merit in superior branches of knowledge. It would argue in me a want of judgement in human nature, to expect good practice from such men. They would probably think it beneath their pursuits and situation in life to be good ploughmen, turnip-hoers, and shepherds; I should therefore betray my own ignorance of life, if I was to express any surprise at finding this farm in a situation that—I had rather forget then describe. In the evening to a field much more successfully cultivated, Mademoiselle St. Huberti, in the Penelope of Picini.[9]

Arthur Young may well have been right in what he recorded of this first impression in these terms in his own journal. But there is a hasty touch about it that displays that 'want of judgement in human nature' of which he did not wish to be accused. He was pleased enough to meet Broussonet for the second time two days later.[10] With him he spent a couple of hours very agreeably. On this short acquaintance he was prepared to deliver this judgement of the young man who, both as the Associate Professor of Rural Economy and as Secretary of the Société Royale de l'Agriculture, had much more, in fact, to do with the demonstration farm and its present state than the elder savant Daubenton:

... He [Broussonet] is a man of uncommon activity, and possessed of a great variety of useful knowledge in every branch of natural history; and he speaks English perfectly well. It is very rare that a gentleman is seen better qualified for a post than Mons. de Broussonet for that which he occupies, of secretary to a Royal Society [of Agriculture].[11]

Broussonet continued to rank high in the esteem of Arthur Young to whom he extended endless courtesies and easements in the next two years of Young's travels in France. The high point of their relations seems to have been reached when, on 18 June 1789, less than a month before the Bastille fell, Broussonet proposed General George Washington, on Young's recommendation, as a member of the Société Royale d'Agriculture on the grounds 'that the general was an excellent farmer, and had corresponded with me [Young] on the subject'. Dining and wining frequently with Broussonet in the growing uproar of Paris, he added his own to the unanimous votes of the Société that night, admitting the President of the United States.[12] For Daubenton, however, Young maintained a low opinion, at least in respect of the published *Instructions pour Les Bergers* . . ., the reading of which he rated as of less value than the verbal instruction of a few minutes from an old shepherd to an apprentice. This insular arrogance invited from Christian Auguste Wichmann, Daubenton's German translator, the shattering comment that this opinion was of a piece with the nonsense to be found on almost every page of the voluminous writings of that 'demi-savant' on the subject of political economy, and that it was no more difficult to refute Mr. Young on this point than on many others[13]—an opinion which in principle had many echoing voices on the other side of the Channel, much nearer Bury St. Edmunds and Bradfield, Suffolk.

The European reputation of Daubenton survived the petty carping of Arthur Young. If any refutation had been needed this clearly lay in the sequence of translations into all the important languages of the Continent within the next twenty years and the numerous editions in which the *Instructions pour Les Bergers* . . . was published—except in England. This neglect and the scornful dismissal of the work by Young the 'demi-savant' was not shared at Soho Square. Banks gathered everything pertaining to 'the Flock managd in Burgundy at the Royal expence by M. Daubenton', and studied it closely.

III

It is now very clear that the zeal for experiment by breeding for the improvement of wool was directly transferred from the savant of Montbard and the Jardin des Plantes across the Channel to the savant of Revesby Abbey, Spring Grove, and 32 Soho Square. The vector of this infecting enthusiasm was Pierre Broussonet. By the same medium there had been also at the same time a small but pleasing exchange from Banks, the staunch companion of Captain James Cook, to another great seaman and explorer, Count Jean-François de la Pérouse, then about to leave Brest on his last voyage. As he set sail on 5 August 1785, La Pérouse took with him two magnetic needles formerly used by Cook and some pistols among many other things which Banks had sent to the expedition through the hands of Broussonet[14]—valued symbols of the good-fellowship of both science and the sea, which were to disappear for ever three years later in a Pacific storm on the island of Vanikoro. No less valued were the two small Spanish sheep which arrived at Spring Grove, the same week in which the French expedition sailed. These were symbols too, in their own mute way, of the comity of science and the heralds of a new advance in the commerce of nations.

From the vine-clad hills of Burgundy to the edge of Hounslow Heath was a sharp change for the sheep from Spain. Their journey was no greater nor more arduous than that of the Scotch ewes which they were to meet from Caithness and the windy flats near Thurso Bay, travelling by sea to Dunbar and thence transhipped to London in the winter of the same year.[15] The questing desire for the improvement of wool was spreading fast for here, at a stroke, a new force of great energy was enlisted in the young Mr. John Sinclair of Thurso Castle. He had responded with great enthusiasm to Banks's call for sheep to mate with 'Monsieur Ram' from Montbard, as Pierre Broussonet termed him. In December 1785 Sinclair with an introduction from Banks had met Broussonet in Paris, and the foundations were well laid for the Scotch laird's own unique contributions to the new science of rural economy and the cause of British agriculture in particular. From the Downs of Sussex near Lewes came the Southdown ewes from Lord Sheffield to join two small Herefordshire ewes sent by Robert Bakewell of Dishley from his entrenchment among the rolling Midland hills. There were also the two fat Lincolnshires from Mr. Fowler of Retsby. Finally with two of the old horned Wiltshire breed, with long legs, Roman nose, and naked belly, from among those grazing Hounslow Heath near by, the experimental flock of Spring Grove in Middlesex was born in the spring of 1786.[16] Twenty years had passed since Daubenton himself had taken the same small and groping steps towards a distant vision, but at the 'Royal expence'. Here now, though the goal was the same, the theme was varied. Instead of stony hill-sides on land carved from among the competing vines to effect the well-conceived idea of a Royal Minister at public expense, the scene now was the small grassed field near an English country-house; the idea that of a wealthy landowner and scientist who read widely and well; the funds from his own deep pocket. Here, too, was the same kind of material for the breeding experiments ahead—the fine and the coarse, the long and the short and the tall, the rough and the smooth—all the important ingredients of the British sheep population and the British fleece reduced into one small compass for this first enlightening study, opening the way to British emancipation from the restrictions of the Spanish fine-wool trade—in the footsteps of France.

For nearly ten years the Spring Grove flock of Sir Joseph Banks was the centre of a web whose strands spread into many corners of the kingdom. As a scientific experiment it was not to be too closely compared with the work of Daubenton. As a scientific demonstration of technological value it was a stimulating success even if we measure it only by the one important consequence of Sir John Sinclair's enlistment to the cause of the improvement of British wool, for this effect it certainly achieved. Its essential value, however, was as a confirmatory demonstration to Banks himself of the truth of what he had read in the memoirs of the French savant and as a source of direct experience with the living material about which so much had been heard and written, and about which so little was really known in England. It was a very small essay but it was a beginning. And it was an actual trial not a wordy speculation at many removes from the reality. Moreover, it was close enough to the rides and bypaths of Royalty in its progress from Windsor to St. James's and to the Royal parks and gardens of Richmond and Kew for it to receive some comment in Court circles, even without the entry of Robert Fulke Greville as the King's Equerry so early in 1787 and so soon after the establishment of the flock at Smallbury Green. If this were not enough there was the business of Mr. William Herschel's new telescope and the Georgian Planet[17] and its satellites and all the frequent consultations with His Majesty about this time from whose liberal pocket were so largely financed these new explorations of outer space.[18] Banks had ample need to travel often along the pretty hedge-lined road from Smallbury Green to the edge of Windsor Forest and to Windsor Castle, mediating the causes of astral science while at the same time groping among terrestrial mysteries of sheep and wool. How often in this pursuit at this time did the President of the Royal Society in the summer of the year pass that way, witnessing the scenes which another French savant at the time so explicitly described?

The house in which Mr. Herschel makes his observations stands at one end of the forest of Windsor, and is about twenty miles distant from the house of Sir Joseph Banks; but with good horses, and in an English chaise, the journey may be performed in three hours.

This was about the time [between seven and ten in the evening] when highwaymen usually come upon the road, to prey upon the imprudent traveller. They are numerous, and perform their dangerous business on horseback; some of them are even mounted on hunters; but we were informed that though our danger would have been great on the evening before, we were safe that night, which was Sunday, as the road was covered with people of all ranks, who, having passed the day in the country, were returning to London, to be ready to resume their usual occupations on Monday morning.

The evening was most beautiful, the air was calm and mild and the sky sparkled with stars; the road was carefully made, and as smooth as the avenue of a public walk. It was bordered with quickset hedges, almost all in flower, serving to inclose charming gardens and parks, ornamented with beautiful trees, in the midst of which were scattered so many simple but elegant houses, that they seemed to dispute the ground with each other.

The road was, at this time, covered with a multitude of men and women, on horse-back and in coaches. Carriages of every kind, most of them very elegant, but all of them substantial and commodious, and many of them with superb equipages, succeeded each other without interruption, and with such rapidity, that the whole seemed the work of magic: it certainly announced an opulence and population, of which we can have no idea in France. All was life, motion, and activity: and, by a contrast only to be seen in this country, all was calm, silence and order. A tacit and inviolable respect for each other seemed to regulate the individuals composing this impetuous mass of population, which was directed to one point. A scene so extra-ordinary, faintly illuminated by the stars, transports one, who sees it for the first time, into the fields of Elysium.

But the story of Elysium is fabulous, and that which I have related is real; for it is what I have seen, and what all Englishmen, and those who know their country will acknowledge to be a just description. How then does it happen, that so much tranquillity and order is preserved among an immense multi-tude of persons in motion? It has its origin in the state of the public mind, which is well formed; the education which is good; and even the forms of worship, which are stripped of much of that vain superstition they have in Roman Catholic countries, and which permit the day consecrated to repose to be passed in innocent relaxation.[19]

On some such summer evening Banks might well have travelled home from Windsor clad in one of the two blue coats from the Spanish fleeces grown at Smallbury Green in the years 1786 and 1787 by 'Monsieur Ram' from Montbard and 'Madam Ewe'.[20]

During that spring of 1787 Banks had been deeply engaged in the burdensome problems of preparing the arguments for the 'torpid landed interest' against the Wool Bill. The essence of these he had drafted into the form of a pamphlet which was now in the hands of Lord Sheffield at Sheffield Place, twelve miles north of Lewes in Sussex.[21] As summer spread over the South Downs this literary cross-fertilization was finished. In June it had returned to Soho Square, fecundated with copious notes in pencil from one of the leading authorities of his period on all things pertaining to trade and agricul-ture.[22] Another force of great potential had been grappled more closely to the cause of wool growing in the man whose voice in the years to come would annually be heard from the dining-room of the Star or the Bear in Lewes after each Wool Fair in a summer price review of that commodity for the kingdom. For Banks this onerous event had not yet laid demanding hands upon his time and energies. Out of Sussex this summer there came only Sheffield's enticement to a social visit with 'The Ladies', and the added bait that 'If you do not migrate into Lincolnshire before Augst you will find [Edward] Gibbon here.' In August, then, Sir Joseph was to be found that year not only enjoying with the Sheffields the erudite company of their mutual friend from Lausanne, but himself charming the daughters of the house with his own love of plants and plant collecting. These glimpses of Banks at his ease, and yet never idle, convey much of the spirit of these early days:

... How I wish it had been possible to have had you this summer [1788]. I would have made a Botanist of you. Sir Joseph Banks Company was the greatest Treat that I could possibly have in that way, and with his assistance I have made a tolerable proficiency in the Study. My collection is a pretty considerable one; I have above 250 plants all gathered by my own hands within five miles of this place. . . .[23]

Seven years later for Maria Josepha Holroyd the spell still remained as she describes again to her correspondent Aunt 'Serena'[24] another summer idyll and a visit from the new Knight of the Bath:

... The Banks family came on Sunday.[25] The Ladies, as usual, visited Mrs Newton, and Sir Joseph and Papa the Wool Fair at Lewes on Monday. . . . The Red Ribbon has made no alteration in Sir Jo. in any other respect than that there is a red ribbon across his waistcoat. He sprawls upon the Grass, kisses Toads, and is just as good humoured a nondescript of an Otaheitan as ever. . . .[26]

The year 1787, though perhaps distinguished as the year in which Maria and Louisa Holroyd 'turned Botanists',[27] was no less to be remembered as the year in which the Lewes Wool Fair was established by their Papa and Sir Joseph. Less obvious to the community but of great importance to it was the purchase by Banks of twenty Southdown ewes. He 'received keep for them at Sheffield Place', and to them that autumn 'he sent a Spanish Ram for the use of Ld Sheffield & himself'. This was the tup hog, the son of 'Monsieur Ram' from Montbard and the first English-born 'real Spanish' sheep, who died prematurely in the following spring, having left sixteen Southdown ewes 'in blossom' at Sheffield Place. Sir Joseph also left with Lord Sheffield the 'French Memoir relative to Wool' which William Eden had sent him—*Observations sur la comparaison de la nouvelle laine superfine de France, avec la plus belle laine d'Espagne, dans la fabrication de drap*—a seed which there found fertile ground and yielded a demand for more the following year. Daubenton had gained another disciple, and one of wide influence in the years to come.

The following year in 1788 Banks purchased twenty Sherwood

Forest ewes and established keep for them with Major Cartwright at Marnham near the eastern border of Nottinghamshire. To them he sent the second son of the old French ram. In 1789 he established a similar flock to these others with the local sheep of the Downs east of Epsom on the North Weald at Woodmansterne near Banstead 'in the hopes of improving the down sheep of that County [Surrey] & introducing the Cross'.[28] At Revesby Abbey in his own park in Lincolnshire were more Nottinghamshire ewes and two black-faced Norfolk ewes given to him by Thomas William Coke for crossing with the third son of Daubenton's ram,[29] soon to be sent to Sheffield Place to replace the first among the Southdown flock. His meagre stock of fine-wool Spanish blood was augmented the same year at Spring Grove by the addition of four *métis* ewes as a gift from His Majesty from among those which had by then been imported from France to Windsor and Kew.[30] These *métis* ewes (of which one very soon died) were of mixed blood in the sense that they were by Daubenton's 'real Spanish' rams from Roussillonnais ewes. These latter, as we have seen, were almost as fine as the Spanish sheep, but came from the French slopes of the Pyrenees near Perpignan. In 1791 His Majesty was also pleased to give him 'a Tup of the True Merino Breed'.[31] This now meant a ram which had come direct from Spain by one devious means or another. But in this particular case it was one of the sheep attained by Banks's own direct negotiations in France on the King's behalf and was of Daubenton's breeding. Thus by 1794 with these and the increments of their natural increase he found it possible from Spring Grove to send 'Merino Sheep' into Nottinghamshire to the extent of two rams and four ewes.[32] These were distributed by Sir Robert Milne of Edwinstowe in the hope of introducing the cross among the native sheep flocks of Sherwood Forest. Sir Robert himself kept a ram and two ewes; to a Major Boothby he gave one ewe; to a farmer named Denton one ram and one ewe.

In 1792 Sir Joseph determined to part with all his sheep at Spring Grove and at Revesby except those of the 'pure Spanish blood'.[33] The flock at Spring Grove by this time had become essentially a small group of three significant crosses, apart from 'the thoroughbred Spanish'. There were specimens of half-bred Southdown × Spanish, Herefordshire × Spanish, and Lincolnshire × Spanish, both ewes and wethers, with back-crosses to the Spanish in each case giving a small number of three-quarter-breds. The Scotch ewes from Caithness and the Wiltshire ewes from Hounslow Heath and their offspring had in the main disappeared, although one three-quarter-bred Spanish and Wiltshire ewe still remained.[34] In addition, as tangible evidence in the disputation in which he was then engaged with Sir John Sinclair over the virtues and failings of the Shetland fleece, there were four 'kindly' specimens of this breed in his fields belonging to Sir Thomas Dundas, who had brought them down from his Scotch estates to try the effect of the Spanish cross—in this case made with 'the Tup of the True Merino Breed' from His Majesty. All told there were probably not more than twenty-five sheep of all kinds at Spring Grove that year. At no time were there ever many more than thirty. The numbers were continually checked by the killing of the wethers and the unwanted ewes for the family table and by the disposal of rams and ewes to interested collaborators such as Lord Sheffield. In any case, one original ram from Daubenton in 1785, even though he lived long and performed valiantly until August 1792, and one original ewe, which died in 1788, were very tenuous beginnings. Premature losses of young rams at Sheffield Place and the gift of a Spanish ram to John Hunter as a classic specimen of *Ovis hispanica* Linn.[35] for dissection all whittled down the possibilities of natural increase. The gifts from His Majesty served to sustain the flock but, in any case, the pastures of the Spring Grove villa were small, and no large number could be kept there without difficulties and other risks of loss from starvation and disease. More than anything the favourable turn of events, when the King caught something of Banks's own enthusiasm for 'the Spanish breed' and saw it in its right economic perspective, set a logical term to the private efforts of the President of the Royal Society. The wider vision and also some measure of his own form of self-effacement in this, as in so many other imaginative and important creations of the time, led him to present the small remnant of the pure Spanish flock, which by this time was all derived from His Majesty's stock, to Arthur Young at Bradfield Hall in Suffolk, in 1795. Thus, after ten years, the small breeding experiment at the villa in Middlesex gave place to the larger and more significant Royal venture not far distant across the Thames in Surrey. The English savant then continued solely as the unpaid scientific civil servant of his King in this field. His decision not to continue his own flock he explained to himself and to an unknown private correspondent by saying:

. . . were I to do so it would look like a competition between my breed & the Kings, but in truth, in order to do away all idea of Rivalship as also to secure to the right owner every degree of credit, which could accrue from his truely patriotic exertions, I long ago parted with my whole Spanish Flock so that there now remain in the country but his Majesties.[36]

IV

This was true of England and of England only. Banks was certainly aware of 'the Scotch Society' at Edinburgh about whose methods he had a critical view, but whose aims he generally approved. He was also aware of the existence of a small flock in Ireland which, established in 1784, in date was the first known introduction of the true Spanish sheep to the British Isles, and one year earlier than the Spring Grove experiment. There is no evidence that the Irish flock was anything other than the in-dependent affair of the Right Honourable William Burton Conyngham of Slane Castle in County Meath, Teller of the Exchequer and a Privy Councillor of Ireland. As William Burton he had in 1781 inherited estates from his uncle Henry, Earl Conyngham, in County Donegal as well as in County Meath. Soon after he had undertaken a journey during 1783 in Spain, where he had taken a very practical interest at least in the possibility of importing from thence two Spanish horses. On this matter from Madrid he corresponded with Mr. Robert Liston, the British Minister-Plenipotentiary then at the Escorial, but without succeeding in his aim.[37] Nothing appears about a similar interest in Spanish sheep, but it is very certain that he explored this subject at the time with more discretion, though with no greater success in any official way.

In time it was through Lord Sheffield who, as the Irish peer Baron Sheffield of Dunamore, County Meath, had direct contact with William Conyngham the Irish Member of Parliament, that Banks heard of this intriguing enterprise. From its originator he obtained directly the essence of its story and its progress in a letter which he received in the summer of 1788, not long after he had attained some success himself in extracting Spanish sheep by illicit means.

. . . In answer to what Evidence I have relative to the success of my Cross from the Spanish sheep I have the Pleasure to tell you I have the greatest Reason to believe that the Breed may be greatly improved. I imported one Ram and two Ewes which were procured for me by the Governor of Almeida on the Borders of Old Castile and the same Number from the Borders of the Province of Alentrejo [sic] which were procured by a Portuguese gentleman very curious in his Breed. I have now above two hundred Rams from the Spanish Rams & have crossed with the Ewes of Connaught, most esteemed for their Wool & I had the Strongest Proof of the Benefit of the Cross as my fleeces of the two Years old last year weighed four pounds at an average & sold for twenty five shillings the Stone of 16[lb]— which is very near Eighteen Pence per Pound of your Money. I have ordered my agent in the County of Meath to send you a more particular account of the Progress of the Breed as likewise a Specimen of the Wool. we compared it with samples I brought from Lord Sheffield & it was judged to be much finer. I had told Lord Sheffield that I would send you a Ram in the Course of this Summer but I shall add some Ewes. If you will commission some Person at Liverpool or Whitehaven to receive them. I should have mentioned that Wool was remarkably high last year and that my fleece Wool sold for 19[s] 6[d]—Wools are undoubtedly dearer in Ireland than in England but the

Quality is in General finer & the Breeders find that they have hurt our Irish sheep by the General cross from England but the principal Reason of the high Price of Wool here is the demand in Munster & Connaught for the Spinners the Women being universally employed in it though they some-times do not earn above Tenpence for the week the Factors buying up the Yarn for England and the Price being determined by that Market.

Since my coming here [Rutland, County Donegal] I have made the discovery of a Plant which I believe is a Wild Beet it grows in some of the Islands which are remarkable for fattening Sheep I have it transplanted & will send you a more particular account of it. . . .[P.S.] My Stock of real Spanish Breed is increased to twenty & the Cloth I had made from it is Superfine.

The Discovery of the White Beet which in Irish is called Machin Bin or the Rock Parsnip was made by the Master Builder of my Dockyard who seeing a Plant resembling the Mangel Wurzel transplanted it to his Garden—I will take care to send you the Seed.[38]

The report from Conyngham's agent confirmed this in general and stated the number of real Spanish sheep as twenty-seven (thirteen rams and fourteen ewes) at that date, with a hundred half-bred and a hundred and nine three-quarter-bred Spanish and Irish sheep.[39] This was a very satisfactory outcome in little more than four years for the small numbers originally imported. There is no evidence available, however, to suggest that any Spanish sheep did come to Spring Grove as Conyngham had offered to Banks, though it is not impossible that Lord Sheffield might have been a willing recipient. The correspondence was kept alive, as we may be sure Banks would make certain with an experiment of such relevance to his own thinking, and it is not surprising therefore to find it still active in 1791 as a prelude to a notable step in the affairs of 'the Scotch Society':

. . . I hope my Speculations in Sheep will be of more use than those in Botany. I have written to Sir J[ohn] Sinclair and sent him Specimens of my different Fleeces—I have not a Doubt of the advantage of the Cross of [the] Spanish Breed—though I apprehend those that I imported are not the finest, the Clothiers in Bodburgh sending me word that it is not within one Shilling per Pound so fine as the finest Herefordshire, the Wool of the mixed Breed is nearly as fine—I have not yet found a conveyance for the Sheep to Glasgow —Sir J. Sinclair mentions the advantage that he has proved by Experiment of Shearing twice a year this is a practice [from] Time immemorial in Ireland, and on my Estate in Donegal They say the Wool is too coarse for Yarn Stockings when not shorn twice in the year.

The Bodburgh Clothiers send me word that my Wool is too Long in the Staple—I have an Inclination to make an Experiment this year at Norwich If I knew to whom I could trust it to have a fair Experiment made—perhaps you could assist me.[40]

As the Conyngham sheep prepared to join the growing flocks of the
Society for the Improvement of British Wool in Scotland as this letter
denotes, Banks recorded his unqualified opinion that their wool was
undervalued by the Bodburgh clothiers, a matter he was by then in a
position to judge with some accuracy out of his own experience from
the samples which had come to him from Ireland. It was more than
a little encouraging also to have from Thomas Sibbert, William
Conyngham's manager at Slane Castle, some further report on the
performance of the Spanish sheep in the damp Irish climate and in their
sedentary state contrasting so strongly with the circumstances of their
native Iberian home:

. . . I have found the Spanish Sheep to endure the Winter of this Country
equal to any other Sheep; and less inclined to degenerate, either in Wool or
Form: The half-bred the same, which are very good. The Whethers [sic]
at 3 Years old, have produced $6\frac{1}{2}$ lb. Wool; the Ewes $5\frac{1}{4}$ the Younger in
proportion: their Mutton weighs from 18 to 20 lb. p^r Quarter. I have seen
the great Fairs of Ballinasloe and by examining the Flocks from the different
Quarters found that the halfbred Sheep exceeded in bone half the Sheep in
the Fair of their Age. Low Grounds with long grass do not agree with them
so well as higher ground and shorter grass. They are subject to the Footrot
rather more than Irish Sheep, having a softer hoof than either sheep. I find
that blue vitriol powder put to them is very good and some Tar the next day.
From the closeness of the Fleeces of the halfbred Sheep, they are inclined
sometimes to a Yellowness in the Wool and Skin. But if the Wool is divided
in [lines] on the Back and a little Sheep Water rubbed, will prevent the
encreasing the Symptoms of Scab.[41]

V

The advent of the Spanish sheep from Castle Slane in Ireland was
foreshadowed as far back as December 1785. When Broussonet
returned from Montpellier to Paris he there dined with Mr. John
Sinclair from Castle Thurso in Caithness, a meeting of 'true minds'
made possible by their mutual friend in Soho Square.[42] When Sinclair
returned to Scotland early in the New Year of 1786 to become Sir John,
the 1st Baronet of Ulbster, his communings with the French savants
had established a relationship that was soon to yield a dividend of fine-
woolled sheep. These were destined eventually to travel farther north
than any of the same breed in the British Isles derived from France or
Spain. But this would not be their prime claim to distinction. They
would in fact more appropriately symbolize by their presence in
Scotland a classic advance towards the new spirit in agricultural science
which was to owe so much to the driving energy if not always the

clear-headed thinking of the new baronet. Before this could happen Sir John set out on that extensive journey of seventy-five hundred miles through northern Europe which with characteristic comprehensiveness was

. . . to obtain political knowledge, to ascertain the state of other countries, and to discover every means, which had been sanctioned by the experience of other nations, that could be successfully introduced for the improvement of Great Britain.

The journey, if not the purpose, he accomplished between May and December 1786 and from which he returned not only gratified with 'the extent of the tour and the rapidity of its execution' but

. . . full of ardour, to establish, in my own country, all the beneficial institutions which were scattered over others; and to make this island, the centre of the various improvements, of which political society was capable, more especially those of an agricultural nature, to which a person of landed property is naturally partial.[43]

His disagreement with William Pitt soon after his return blighted his expectations of much progress towards this exalted goal through Parliamentary channels. However, he had found during his tour 'that much might be effected by the exertions of one man, if uninterruptedly devoted to one object . . .'. Therefore having gestated the second volume of the *History of the Public Revenue of the British Empire*, which he launched upon the public in 1790, he found himself and the general public so distressingly ignorant of the political and other circumstances of the country that nothing less than an institution for collecting this information seemed to be required. Inspired in 1790 by the spectacle of the General Assembly of the Clergy of Scotland, of which he was a lay member, he decided to release its potential energy. In this way began that extensive undertaking, the first *Statistical Account of Scotland*. To complete the twenty volumes of this work the Caithness laird mobilized and goaded the efforts of no less than 'nine hundred individuals of intelligence and ability', both clergy and laity. Early in the onset of this labour he heard much of the presumptive fine wool of the Shetland Islands and of an infectious disorder which threatened the flocks. Finding the resources of the Highland Society 'too confined, for carrying on any measure on a great scale, for the safety of that sort of sheep, or the improvement of the other breeds in the kingdom . . .' inevitably he saw 'the necessity of erecting a new institution, for the special purpose of improving British wool . . .'. From this it was for him clearly but a small step further towards an institution for the improvement of all British agriculture.[44] Long before the logic of this struck him, however, we find Sinclair in October 1790 troubling his French friend Broussonet with the subject of Shetland wool.[45] The following year, having been founded on 31 January 1791, the Society for the Improvement of British Wool or 'the Scotch Society' as Banks would term it, was in full cry under the lash of the single-minded laird from the far north. Hunting back along his tracks of just five years earlier, Sinclair was soon in touch with Broussonet again concerning the fine-woolled Spanish sheep, and in the summer of 1791 the young Scottish Lord Daer was in Paris negotiating the matter successfully with Daubenton and Broussonet.[46] From them both he had much information to impart to Sinclair. Broussonet, with whom Lord Daer had a long and instructive conversation on 4 June 1791, had already executed the commission from Sinclair to obtain sheep 'of the Spanish breed' from Daubenton. Fifteen head (ten rams and five ewes) had been selected for 'the Scotch Society'. It appeared that, had more been asked for, more might have been got, even though the demand and the price for them were rising. From a butcher's price of about twelve livres for the rams before the Revolution their value had risen to forty-five livres a head, and Broussonet, who was himself at that time floating on a high tide in the new régime, foresaw that

... from the rapid progress agriculture promises under the new free constitution, and the great number of speculative gentlemen and farmers which the Revolution has already produced, that in a few years these sheep may sell for six or eight louis.[47]

Lord Daer, therefore, suggested that a contract with Daubenton for some years at a fixed price of two or even three guineas a head at Montbard or, better still, delivered at Rouen or Dieppe would be worth the consideration of the Society if Sinclair could authorize it. If not, then he was prepared to enter it as a private concern if others would join him, but there is no evidence to hand that this was ever taken any further. The fifteen sheep for Edinburgh seem to have been the only other fine-woolled sheep from France to reach the British Isles, apart from those more than three years before for His Majesty.

The 'Daubenton flock' of the Society for the Improvement of British Wool had a long and troublesome journey from Burgundy.[48] Travelling most probably by way of Paris and Rouen, they reached Brighthelmstone,[49] where His Majesty's Customs impounded them under threat of slaughter invoking one of the old laws for this purpose. An application to the Lords of the Treasury and the Commissioners of His Majesty's Customs in London ensured their release, and they journeyed on to await a ship at Hawley's Wharf on the Thames.[50] Sinclair was anxious that Banks should inspect them as they passed through the capital at the end of July, but the message miscarried and Sir Joseph was disappointed to learn of their transit a week after they had reached Leith.[51] Sir John, however, reported their arrival with jubilation and matched them in his opinion with some other Spanish sheep which he had seen in the spring in Soho Square.[52] Sir Joseph was inclined to bridle almost peevishly on this point and to admonish his uncomfortably enthusiastic inquisitor from the north:

. . . I am sorry you call your Rams Spanish being of opinion that every deviation from accuracy is liable to throw discredit upon the Society [for the Improvement of British Wool].[53]

The French sheep were joined at the same time by four rams and six ewes, obligingly sent by Lord Sheffield from Sussex and together they were settled in the parks belonging to the Society at Bowbridge near Morton, four miles from Edinburgh on the Linton road.[54] Here where the west winds blow round Caerkitton and over the snug village of Swanston the flock was to be seen on Saturdays by any who could show to the shepherd an order from the Society for that purpose.[55] And here later in the year they were to be joined by a ram from His Majesty's Spanish flock at Windsor, so that by the end of 1791 'the Scotch Society' had gathered under one authority the blood of the Spanish fine-woolled sheep bred at Montbard, at Spring Grove, and at Slane Castle. Much indeed had been effected by the exertions of one man uninterruptedly devoted to one object! That object, however, would not have been achieved had there not been in two countries, lately enemies and soon to fight again, two savants sharing a devotion to Science as they knew it and with a single-mindedness no less unswerving than that of the Scotch laird.

VI

The pace of the scientific communications between the French and British savants had not flagged since the Treaty of Versailles. Information and material of the utmost scientific and commercial interest to both sides of the Channel passed between London and Paris with an artless, even innocent, enthusiasm pleasant to recall in a later more disillusioned generation. Few realized how often poisoned was the flow and how many unseen death-warrants were written between the lines in letters and papers that had no other intent than to serve the growth of human knowledge.[56] Nor, of course, was it all disinterested. The undertone of national rivalry waxed and waned from letter to letter, but on the whole there was a pretty free trade in ideas among the savants, whatever the protectionist attitudes of the merchants may have been. The active revival of the Lincolnshire Wool Committee in 1786 brought about by the appearance of John Anstie's Bill was for Sir Joseph Banks a rededication to a task which five years before had been shouldered by him on behalf of the county, but which he now assumed as a responsibility in the interests of the nation. To inject into his correspondence with the learned men of Europe various systematic inquiries about the sheep of their countries and of their wool production and manufacture was now a natural step in his normal procedure of winning knowledge. Five years had produced a good harvest of intelligent correspondents willing and able to collaborate on a wide range of subjects. Apart from his own broad interests the business of the Royal Society opened leads in many profitable quarters, and now that the 'dissensions' of the past few years therein had subsided Banks was mentally free to explore these fruitful fields.

Among the savants of the day one such correspondent of some years standing was the Yorkshire-born Abbé Theodore-Augustin Mann, the natural philosopher and Perpetual Secretary of the Imperial Academy of Brussels. Typical of the complexity of this form of communication concerning sheep and wool are the letters from Mann in which excellent information on the sheep industry of the Austrian Netherlands is entangled with his own candidature for foreign membership of the Royal Society, inquiries about Dr. William Herschel's 'Observations with his great Telescope', and comments on his own short treatise, *On Sea Currents & their Effects, applied to the Seas & Coasts of Europe, more especially to those which surround the British Islands.*[57] But where Mann's information was of the greatest value to Banks in establishing the realities of Europe's long-wool resources, there is no doubt that Pierre Broussonet excelled most others in the gossipy variety and unstinted flow of useful titbits from the Continent. After a brief visit to London in the early spring of 1786[58] Broussonet became even more active than before in the development of the École Royale Vétérinaire at Alfort, especially its economic garden and menagerie, and in meetings with farmers leading up to the official opening of the new college in September 1786. To this commendable advance in agricultural education Banks was making various contributions with seeds and plants of species economically useful in various ways—tea, Chinese hemp, Lincolnshire potatoes, even pigs—and many papers and publications on a great range of topics—to which there was a steady counterflow to Soho Square. Among the good things sent or offered by Broussonet were specimens of the newly acquired Angora goats and further supplies of sheep from the flock now rapidly increasing at Alfort about the nucleus of Daubenton's sheep. Thus in the early New Year of 1787 when Sir Joseph received the first explicit commands of His Majesty to gather fine-woolled sheep for the greater economic glory and security of the kingdom the channel of communication opened by the Spring Grove flock was not only still open but flowing fast with the means of fulfilment. The French source was thus inevitably the first practicable one to be explored and to succeed. A precedent had merely to be followed.

In early April, therefore, the business of sheep for His Majesty was promising well as Sir Joseph Banks skilfully carried it forward in an apparently ordinary extension of his own private and established interest at Spring Grove and as one savant to another exchanging material of mutual scientific concern. The subtle negotiation matured quietly through the maze of other matters on which letters travelled almost weekly, and often with even greater frequency between London and Paris. The overtones of the correspondence were certainly those of Banks's inquiries concerning the wool production of France as he gathered material for the final battle with the manufacturers over the Wool Bill of 1788. Samples of wool, with prices and details of manufacturing use were sent freely by Broussonet,[59] and Banks replied as far as he was able with specimens of English wool, notably the long wool of Lincolnshire, in which the Frenchman was interested as any professor of rural economy well might be. The spirit and the practice of this communication among the savants may be contrasted with the situation in another quarter. The vexed question of trade in wool and the woollen manufactures and the legislative scene appeared differently to the commercial mind. This was well expressed in the summer of 1787 by William Davy, a manufacturer of Crediton in Devon to Lord Sheffield:

The Wool Business has taken the exact Course I expected it would take & however firmly I am persuaded Something is necessary to prevent the Increase of an Evil really existing, [i.e. smuggling] yet I am as fully convinced that the Plan lately proposed was not founded on right or just Principles. The Calculations & publick Declarations of the Quantity of Wool smuggled into France are extravagantly erroneous. This probably some people were at last convinced of & in Consequence slid off the Business to an uncertain Hereafter. The Cause appears to lose its Zeal in the West & M^r [John] Anstie seems also tired of his Hobby Horse. It would be prudent were he so anxious to prevent the French Gentlemen who visit him from prying into the Secrets of his Business with Effect—He has I know been so much off his Guard as to expose his curious Manufactory to the Inspection of two very capital French Fabriquants who there collected the most essential Information on the best Method of Manufacturing his Superfine Casimere, & this these Gentlemen in my Presence boasted of & this has caused me to resolve that no Frenchman shall inspect my Manufactory though not so interesting to them as that of Mr Anstie's & others in the Superfine Articles & I wish

sincerely that through some proper Channel a striking Caution were conveyed to all the Manufacturers in the Kingdom as such immense Crouds of
Frenchmen will now be visiting them— . . .[60]

From which it is clear once again that the exchange of human knowledge runs like quicksilver, defying all forms of statutory limitation on
its spread and ignoring national, geographic, or any form of ideological
confinement.

VII

On 2 April 1787 Broussonet assured Banks that he had just succeeded
in securing a promise of sheep 'as fine as those you have already' and
that he could send to England eight or ten as soon as Banks was ready
to receive them.[61] These he thought would be no finer than the second
back-cross progeny of the ram already at Spring Grove mated with the
fine-wool ewes of England—presumably meaning those from Herefordshire. Broussonet also thought that the cross of the fine-woolled ram
with the long-woolled ewes of Lincolnshire would be most interesting,
but in this he was no more prescient than Banks, who had already
covered this point. Six weeks later in May the available number of
sheep was still uncertain, though Daubenton had now promised fifteen
to twenty with a prospect of a hundred from Spain itself.[62] It was now
time, in Broussonet's estimation, to consider the question of shepherds
and how the sheep were to be transported. In June he sent samples of
wool from the Spanish sheep then in Provence, but reported that
Daubenton now seemed unwilling to send those he had formerly
promised.[63] In this way the year passed without any firm advance until
the autumn when, what Banks very rightly referred to collectively as
'Dr Broussonet's Flock',[64] at this time was at last gathered and *en route*
for Calais, although later the file on the subject was no less appropriately
labelled 'Daubenton's Flock'.

Early in December 1787 Sir Joseph heard that the sheep under the care
of the French shepherd Villard were approaching Calais, and on the
18th he wrote to Monsieur L.-D. Mouron, a prominent French
merchant and owner of packet-boats, concerning them.[65] At the same
time through Mr. Daniel Braithwaite[66] he told Mr. John Walcot, agent
for H.M. Packet-boats at Dover, to make arrangements for their transport and reception, proposing himself to send two men and a cart to
aid in their escort from thence after the voyage. On 26 December, John
Walcot was able to repeat to Banks his former assurances and to report
that 'Captn Sutton, of the *Union* Packet Boat, late Master of M^r
Shuttleworth's vessell, is particularly charged with this commission—'
and that 'a more steady, attentive, & able person could not have the

execution of it'.[67] A barn had been bespoken for their shelter in Dover with a supply of turnips, coleseed, corn, and hay, while a tilted cart was also ready if it were needed. He had written to Mouron that night by the mail which went with Captain Sutton, and was proposing to return to London the following day, leaving the further transaction of the business in the hands of Mr. R. Thompson as his representative in Dover. On 29 December, Mouron himself wrote to Banks for confirmation of Walcot's letter and for instruction to send them over by the packet-boat with a shepherd to go with them as far as London.[68] The following day he reported the arrival of forty-three sheep at Calais with Villard's intention to rest them there for three or four days and willingness to travel to England with them. While the flock was resting in Calais John Walcot, from Whitehall on New Year's Day 1788, was able to report further to Soho Square on the progress of arrangements.[69] Thompson had in fact now got 'a very good roomy stable for the sheep on their arrival, a field to air them in & everything proper, as turnips, corn, &c. &c.'. Moreover, if Sir Joseph approved there was also 'a sober steady Romney Marsh Drover' to be had 'who is acquainted on the road and can have accomodation at all places used by the drovers'. Captain Sutton was also prepared if the weather should make it in the least necessary to 'part off the packet's hold and take every other necessary precaution to prevent the sheep being thrown from side to side'.

At last on 4 January 1788 Mouron was able to write to Thompson at Dover:

According the honnour of your Letter I have Ship'd the Little flock of 42 Sheep and 4 Lambs on Board of the union Cap.[n] Sutton under the Direction of the Shepherd [Villard] who as took the necessary food and will follow your orders for is voyage to London.

the Said Shepherd as lost one of the Ewe in is Road and one other at is arrival here but I hope the rest being in a good State of Health and well rested will come very safe to London with the 4 Lambs newly born which makes 46 in all.

I hope, Sir, youll be so good as to do all What is necessary for the Said flock and the Shepherd in the absence of M.[r] Walcot to whom I present my best respect.

I have the honour to write to Sir Jos. Banks and Should be very happy to Serve you this Side of the wotter and to show you how much I am with sincerity . . .[70]

This letter Thompson sent to Sir Joseph on 6 January, reporting the safe arrival of Villard and his flock about nine o'clock at night on 5 January in Dover harbour 'in very good condition after their voyage, one of the Ewes having yean'd upon the passage;—another hath since dropt her

Lamb, the Flock therefore consists of 42 sheep & six lambs'.[71] They were landed and attended by four men from the quay to the stable of Matthew Kennett, where they rested for three days, sustained with turnips, oats, bran, and hay. On 7 January they were cleared inwards 'for private use Duty Free, graciously to the Honble Comm[rs] order of the 19th ulto' by James Gunman, Collector, and S. Colebrand, Controller, of His Majesty's Customs at the port of Dover.[72]

On or about 9 January they set out from Dover under the expert care of Thomas Winstone, the 'sober steady Romney Marsh Drover', and with the tilted 'Invalid cart'. The roads being bad and some of the ewes heavy in lamb, though none were lame, Winstone did not think he would be able to travel more than twelve miles a day and if there were heavy rain he intended to rest them altogether. However, he had completed his task and was home again in Dover after nine days, having taken the sheep by a route through Canterbury, Sittingbourne, Chatham, Northfleet, Welling, and Clapham to Kew Green, where the flock probably arrived on or about 15 January 1788.[73] This was almost exactly one year after His Majesty and his Equerry Colonel Robert Fulke Greville had set out on the winter ride to Richmond when the subject of fine-woolled sheep had been broached between them and the assistance of Sir Joseph Banks enlisted so soon after.

Meanwhile, relieved by Thomas Winstone of his charges so well shepherded to their destination across France and the Channel, and having spent one night in Dover under the roof of John Tilley, with board and lodging for 2s. 6d., Villard went to London. Here, it would seem, he was the first shepherd from the Continent with direct experience of fine-woolled sheep to be seen and questioned by Banks, who now heard something of the origin of the flock even then travelling through Kent to its new home by the Thames.[74] Villard had apparently started in Provence where he had gathered first two rams and twelve ewes from the flock of the Baron de la Tour d'Aigue, some twenty miles north of Aix beyond the River Durance. From thence he had travelled north again along the Rhône valley to Daubenton's farm at Montbard, where he had added three rams and twenty-two more ewes. Finally he had passed through Paris on his way to Calais and had taken up five ewes from the École Royale Vétérinaire at Alfort. Thus the original flock consisted of five rams and thirty-nine ewes. Of these two ewes died on the road or at Calais. With six lambs added, to our knowledge, the flock to reach Kew Green was thus at least forty-eight. Of these three rams and twelve ewes were of the Spanish flock at Montbard; ten were young métis ewes from the same place; two rams and twelve ewes were of the presumptive 'Spanish' flock at Tour d'Aigue; five were of the métis flock at Alfort. In the end, two of the ewes from

'Daubenton's Flock' and one of the ewes from Alfort were recorded as dead on the journey, a very small loss in a protracted journey of about seven hundred miles by road and sea with at least some of the ewes well forward in pregnancy. In the future not all the additions to this French foundation of His Majesty's Spanish flock would travel as far with as little loss by the way.

After some days in London Villard, the good shepherd, returned to Dover. After boarding one night with a John Harvey, he disappeared across the Channel into a France that was restless and stirring in the premonitory pains of the Revolution. Sir Joseph himself was perhaps more concerned after this brief encounter to turn again to the problems of the Wool Bill and to complete his inquiries into the state of the smuggling traffic in wool which the manufacturers alleged was such a drain upon the industry in England. His French correspondence on the subject thrived as he extracted figures not only from Broussonet but also from the Controller-General Bertier de Sauvigny himself on the state of trade with France.[75] All this information he was busy synthesizing into a long paper reviewing the whole position—'Instruction given to the Council against the Wool Bill'—which Arthur Young duly published in his *Annals of Agriculture*.[76] Young himself was hard at work supplementing the research of Banks by his own correspondence with M. Mouron at Calais in the interim between his first and second journeys to France against the day when they would both be called to the Bars of both Houses of Parliament for their evidence against the Bill.

In addition to these public burdens Sir Joseph was afflicted with his own private handicap in his first real attack of gout which, perhaps more than anything at this stage, frustrated him in gaining a full measure of enjoyment from the arrival of the French flock. It is, therefore, not surprising that in the interim Mr. Daniel Braithwaite settled the immediately urgent accounts submitted by Mr. John Walcot for the last stages of the enterprise from the landing at Dover to the arrival of the sheep at Kew Green. This was a sum of £16 11s. 5d. which with the cost of the sheep, the journey across France and the Channel (£54 19s. 0d.), and Villard's expenses in London and return to Dover (£2 3s. 4d.) made a total of £73 13s. 9d. for the recorded outlay on this by-product of Banks's correspondence with the French savants.[77]

VIII

This happy piece of Anglo-French collaboration, conducted in a normal spirit of scientific communication and exchange, effectively established His Majesty's Spanish flock at Windsor in January 1788. It was quietly done, but nevertheless openly, though with no hint to the participants in the transaction that the sheep were destined for the Royal parks not for the small fields of Spring Grove. Almost that same week, in a very distant part of the globe, another small enterprise was being established in the colony at Port Jackson whose destiny would in time cross with that of the Royal flock. Meanwhile, the remote colony had its own small contribution to make to the last phases of the exchanges between Banks and Broussonet before the French Revolution changed the whole course of their relations. Mindful of his many debts to Broussonet, none greater than those for Spanish sheep, Banks had promised him a specimen of the new zoological curiosity, the kangaroo from New Holland, as soon as the first consignment from Port Jackson should arrive. In April 1789, seeking news of the lost La Pérouse, Broussonet pressed for more information about both subjects.[78] In May, Banks renewed his promise, though he could give no news about the ship expected,[79] but by 1 July the first kangaroo to be seen in France had arrived at Dieppe. At the end of that grim month Broussonet acknowledged receiving the kangaroo in Paris and introduced to Banks a German who, he said, could give him news of the Revolution which had taken place during the past fortnight.[80] How much was crowded into that short time for Broussonet! The Bastille had fallen on 14 July. Soon after, on 18 July, his old friend and patron, Bertier de Sauvigny, was arrested by the Revolutionary mob. On 22 July before the Hôtel de Ville to which Broussonet as an elected member of the States-General had been called that day, Bertier was struck down before the eyes of his young protégé and his terribly mutilated body dragged through the streets of Paris. Thereafter Broussonet himself was in frequent peril of his own life, even while serving as an elected member of the people and as one charged with responsibility for the provisioning of Paris itself. After the National Convention was established in September 1792 he retired to Montpellier and later, in 1794, as a Girondin he fled across the Pyrenees into Spain and for nearly ten years was an exile.

CHAPTER IV

The British Factories, 1787-1792

I

EARLY in the first week of January 1787 Colonel Robert Fulke Greville of the 10th Dragoons joined the King at Windsor as his Equerry again,[1] resuming a duty that had been his intermittent but arduous task for nearly six years and would remain so for another ten. That same day he stepped into the pages of Fanny Burney's diary as 'Colonel Wellbred', and through her eyes we may capture passing glimpses of this tall, elegant, and urbane godfather of His Majesty's Spanish flock. On 16 January the Royal family removed to the Queen's Lodge and the society clustering about St. James's Palace.[2] From thence soon after one brisk winter day the King and his favourite Equerry together rode across the Thames to Richmond and Kew. There they walked through Richmond Gardens to view His Majesty's flock of Wiltshire sheep. With a common interest in rural affairs their conversation soon turned to the important topical question of wool. Greville, by his own account written many years later, then told the King about the progress of the Spanish fine-wool sheep introduced more than twenty years earlier by the Elector of Saxony in whose realm they had prospered as a pure breed and had also wrought great improvement among the native sheep of the Electorate.[3] These details were almost certainly derived by Greville from many former conversations with Sir Joseph Banks with whom he had been long acquainted.[4] The casual conversation now became more serious as the King pondered this story which, so Greville assures us, was new to him. His Majesty then asked whether it might not be possible to procure some Spanish sheep for England. Greville was sure this could be done if due secrecy were observed in the operation. He was forthwith commanded to pursue the matter and report to the King when next they rode together. The topic of a passing hour had now become, almost by accident, the first sure step to the growth of an idea that would spread its influence further in time and space than either the King or Greville could ever realize.

Greville was probably in little doubt about his next step. As soon as possible he saw his friend Sir Joseph Banks and, in strict confidence, related the conversation about the Spanish sheep and the command he had received. To the sheep breeder of Middlesex, the experimentalist

of Spring Grove, the ardent patron of the wool manufactures of the
kingdom, Greville's words were the sparks to a tinder long prepared
for such a moment. His interest was vehement and strong. His humble
services, if they could be thought useful, were His Majesty's to command to the utmost of his exertion. When this response was reported
by Greville to the King some few days later we have small cause to
doubt that in fact the King instantly replied, 'Sir Joseph Banks is just
the Man. Tell Him from Me that I thank Him, and that his assistance
will be most welcome.' From this moment no further spur was needed.
Greville soon conveyed the warm enthusiasm of the King's acceptance
in terms that would certainly have melted a far less committed enthusiast than Banks. There could have been no happier nor a more suitable
flux in sealing the union between the King and his scientific commoner
than Fanny Burney's 'Colonel Wellbred'.[5]

The three conspirators met together soon after in suitable privacy,
either at Windsor or St. James's. The subject was fully explored in all
its aspects and thorough plans laid and set in motion.[6] So far the only
Spanish fine-wool sheep brought direct from Spain to the British Isles
were those obtained in 1784 by William Conyngham and now being
bred at Slane Castle in County Meath in Ireland.[7] Apart from these, as
we have seen, Banks himself had succeeded in 1785 through the agency
of Broussonet in securing a Spanish ram and a ewe from Daubenton's
flock at Montbard in Burgundy. As far as we know these were the first
true specimens of the fine Merino in England itself, but they were
secured from a French source and therefore did not wear, for the purist,
the full authenticity of stock direct from Spain. In the prevailing spirit
of the day the French channel was still open as one means of finding
Spanish sheep for His Majesty's farms. This was not to be neglected.
The main objective, however, was to get sheep from the Spanish flocks
themselves, and there was no sure or truly legitimate way of doing this.
George III of England had clearly no part in the Bourbon Family
Compact or any other tie of blood sufficiently strong or close to elicit
a Royal gift of Spanish sheep from the Spanish throne. Nothing less
than this seemed likely to bring the Spanish fine-wool sheep into
Britain in sufficient strength to set a good foundation for the breed.
Conyngham, however, had shown that there was another but slower
way in which the storehouse could be broached. The contraband routes
over the Portuguese border from Spain were always open to a traffic
in mules and horses. Sheep were merely a slower and more troublesome
form of cattle, but not much was known about the problems of getting
them by these means in spite of Conyngham's small success. The committee of ways and means at Windsor (or St. James's) was fully determined to explore what was clearly the only way then open to them in

which Spanish sheep of the right kind might be got from authentic sources. As His Majesty's name could in no suitable way be associated with the speculation openly, the campaign was for many good reasons left where it had really begun—in the capable hands of the President of the Royal Society.

II

The first delicate steps were soon taken by a succinct inquiry sent through Mr. Under-Secretary Evan Nepean to Horace Walpole's cousin His Excellency Mr. Robert Walpole, the British Ambassador at Lisbon. The long-drawn-out game of hide-and-seek with the migrating Spanish flocks was now begun.

Sir Jos. Banks who has for some time speculated on the subject of Sheep has conceived an opinion that if he could procure the Famous Merino breed to be brought over he will be able to manage them so as to retain the Fineness of their wool here as this is a matter of great importance to the woolen manufacture this office has undertaken to assist him as far as they are able & will be obliged to you [if you] will do your part.

The intelligence we wish you to obtain is whether there would be any difficulty in having some scores of them purchased during the time they are in Estremadura which is the whole winter & driven down to Lisbon from whence they might be shipd home Sir Jos: would send a shepherd to take care of them on board who might if necessary accompany the person employd to buy the sheep to see that the Finest only are procurd.[8]

Evidently Mr. Walpole on receiving this brief but explicit demand conceived that no better course offered than to establish direct contact between Banks and a reputable and well-informed member of the British merchant community in Lisbon. Without delay a correspondence began with the senior partner in the firm of Thomas March and Company. Banks opened the negotiation by drawing attention to the old-established practice by which the Spanish shepherds received besides their wages a proportion of the sheep as a perquisite which they were allowed to shear and sell for their own profit. He was doubtful whether or not they were permitted to sell the sheep out of Spain, but if it were so then it seemed probable that little difficulty would attend the acquisition of a small number. Banks thought eight ewes and two rams of the very finest sort would be a very good beginning to be brought to England in one trip by Captain Michael Firth, a sea-salt already known to him and to his correspondent. At this early stage optimism ran high with Banks, but it was tinctured with preparedness for many lets and hindrances, including the general probability of high prices and heavy costs.

There is every reason to believe that among themselves they give Large prices for the very Finest Rams consequently large prices must be given if the very best breed is expected & to this Sir J B could have no objection if only care was taken to purchase the very Finest, for sheep whose wool is coarse are found even among the best Flocks . . . if in order to preclude the danger of such an accident it is thought expedient to employ a person skilled in wools as the purchaser S^r J B. could not have any objection to make a competent acknowledgement besides all other expences and indeed for all expences which in the judgement of the gentleman who is so good as to undertake the commission may be thought necessary.

Lest if this undertaking should become a matter of Conversation difficulties might be thrown in the way of its execution by the Governments either of Spain or Portugal S^r J B. wishes it may be kept as secret as it conveniently can be.[9]

Thus, with expense no object, Banks opened the Portuguese campaign as an outflanking manœuvre in his first attempt on the Spanish fine-wool citadel itself. Its ultimate operation was to rest heavily on the mercantile acumen of the British colony in Lisbon. The valley of the Tagus was to be the southern portal of entry for the commercial raiders during the winter season while the great *cabanas* were basking in the Estremaduran sun. This, with the more open French negotiations, was to be the personal concern of Sir Joseph himself. There still remained the northern approach to Spain itself while the elusive quarry, shorn of its burdening fleece, roamed the *dehesas* of Old Castile to the borders of the Basque provinces behind Bilbao. This plan was left entirely to Evan Nepean to organize in the same clandestine manner, but more directly through the trading liaisons of some of the big London merchants in that quarter. Thus at an early date in 1787 Mr. Collier of New Broad Street was prevailed on to write to his partner Mr. Henry Hinckley in Madrid, seeking the means of getting two rams of 'the Spanish breed' for a 'Friend' in England. Some interesting and mildly discouraging views were the first fruits of this gambit but no immediate prospect of sheep, although it seemed that no impossible obstacle at the time existed to prevent their export. On the other hand, the seeds of doubt and despondency were astutely sown by some practised hand among the few grains of hope deferred. Mr. Henry Hinckley was willing to press on with the matter if, after all, Mr. Collier's 'Friend' was still inclined to try the experiment and to incur 'so great & apparently so unsatisfactory an expense'. He naturally supposed that the sheep wished for to be of the kind which produces 'the fine Spanish wool' and wrote on that assumption, for here as so often at this early period we seem to be dealing with a breed without a name. Hinckley said:

... I made particular enquiries respecting them while I was at Bilboa from whence all that Fine wool is shipped for England. I found that there would not be any difficulty in obtaining permission to ship off two or as many of these animals as you please but the expence of purchasing them in New Castile [sic] & bringing them over the Biscayan mountains to Bilboa would be considerable & no good end be afterwards obtained. These animals immediately degenerate or at least their wool does on their being prevented from going through two long journeys they annually undertake from Castile to Estremadura to pass the winter & Feed on fine rich pasturage & back to Castile in the summer to be shorn—the Quality of the Wool certainly proceeds from the two cooperating causes of the exercise of the journey & the excellence of the Pasture the wool of the sheep that are bred & remain in either of these provinces is ordinary and indifferent—the King of Spain is so perfectly satisfied of this that he has permitted Flocks of these sheep to be sent to Berlin and Paris whose wool in a couple of years has turned precisely the same as that of other sheep of the same country.[10]

Evan Nepean passed this equivocal news quickly on to Banks who, with the letter thrust in his pocket, set out for Kew on Tuesday, 7 August 1787. As he strolled through the Botanic Garden, hoping for an opportunity to deliver it to the King and at last to take swift action after months of waiting, his eyes perhaps smiled his unspoken thoughts. Here again was the Great Spanish Illusion in a last effort to bemuse and defeat those who sought the ultimate source of Europe's finest wool. Banks, who had always doubted the Spanish fine-wool legend, was certainly not now to be deceived into thinking his plan worthless. He had studied the problem too long and had framed his hypothesis for the experiment on an impressive weight of evidence. He had his own small experiences at Spring Grove to rely on for some visual proof that fine wool could be grown and remain fine even in Middlesex. He had much more than this. He had for several years studied with the aid of his friend Broussonet the progress of Daubenton's small flock at Montbard, and even now had quite recently armed himself with the latest memoirs written by the French savant sent to him from Paris several weeks before by William Eden at his request. These left no doubt in his mind that the Royal project was eminently worth while.

His inspection of the Botanic Garden at Kew ended without meeting the King that day, and hence without any Royal commands. His impatience and his confidence, however, were such that he sent by that night's post a request that two rams and four ewes of the finest Spanish breed should be secured by Hinckley's agent Mr. Rexford at Bilbao and sent home without delay.[11] On Friday, 10 August 1787, he explained the matter to His Majesty:

... Knowing that the migrating Flocks leave Old Castile, which is in the neighbourhood of Bilboa, in Autumn on their journey to the confines of

Portugal where they spend the winter, he conceived the utmost despatch necessary lest they should have begun their journey before the order could be executed; fearing also that whenever M^r D'aubenton's pamphlets, which your Majesty has perused, fell into the hands of any well informed Spaniard, the prejudice of Spanish wool being subject to degeneration which may have been raised by the French for the purpose of obtaining the Sheep would be done away, he is not sure but that he should have ordered a larger number; but he can by this night's post either countermand those already ordered if his Majesties pleasure which he will be ever solicitous to obey with the most punctilious exactness is signified to him.[12]

There came an immediate, cordial, and interested reply from St. James's which effectively demonstrates the close attention with which the whole project was watched at its birth by the Royal patron.

The King is much hurt that he was not apprised on Tuesday that Sir Joseph Banks was at Kew; (indeed he never heard of it till he received his note this day) or he would have found time to have seen him.

The King is much pleased that two Rams and four Ewes are sent for and should wish the Commission could be extended to twenty Ewes and ten Rams; as from the judicious remark of Sir Joseph Banks that Spain may soon find the evil of granting such Exportations, it may not be possible long to continue acquiring those useful Animals.

The King trusts this number from Bilboa will not stop the attempts of getting some through France as well as others through Portugal.[13]

The extract of the letter from Madrid is not returned, as it is supposed Sir Joseph Banks does not want it.[14]

The year 1787, however, passed without any finite achievement to mark it in the form of imported sheep. It was a year of correspondence and preparation, of high hopes and disappointments. Progress seemed slow, but it was definite, as the web of contacts spread and information grew. The optimism of Banks was at all times supported by a probing determination that made no doubts of final success but did not carry any illusions on the difficulties to be overcome. By the autumn there seemed some prospect of sheep from France and a faint hope that some might come from the Tagus. The imminent birth of His Majesty's Spanish flock was, however, heralded by a portent and a sign that lingered on to haunt its rise and progress and to preside over its decline. Sir Joseph suffered his first attack of the gout in the prime of his middle age as the autumn leaves of November whirled about Soho Square. The year closed with the sheep business in good heart, but with Sir Joseph writhing in the agonizing restraint which never left him long in peace thereafter. From his King came some of the first words of sympathy which as the years passed were to become, from all quarters in his correspondence, something of a formal ritual:

The King is sorry to find Sir Joseph is still confined; and though it is the common mode to congratulate persons on the first fit of the Gout, He cannot join in so cruel an etiquette.

He is glad to find that a small flock of Sheep are near arriving; as he thinks it may be a means of improving the Wool of this Country, which he thinks a most national object.

The hopes that, through Portugal, Spanish Sheep will also be attained, seems now to bear a good appearance.[15]

III

The winter was to pass and the spring of 1788 to come before the hopes of His Majesty were to fulfil their good appearance. After more than a year of correspondence and planning punctuated by months of waiting and rumours a letter arrived at Soho Square in the crabbed penmanship of Captain Michael Firth from the *Betsy* off Dover on 4 March.

I Have got for you 2 Yews & one Ram of the Best Spanesh Breed & if you Like them you May Have More of the same sorte the next season as the Spanish Contrabandays Can get me any quantity I want. . . .[16]

Thus baldly and bluntly was announced the impending arrival of the first Spanish fine-wool sheep from Spain itself to enter England and to make their humble contribution to the King's 'most national object'. Two of them, the ram and one ewe, branded on the face with something like an H were very fine and judged as excellent by Banks. The second ewe he rated as excellent also, but probably inferior to the others, though he confessed himself not 'Fully master of their Comparative merit' until he had seen their fleeces shorn, washed, and thoroughly examined in that state.[17]

The three sheep were soon sent down to enjoy their first English spring at Kew. Here on 4 April 1788 the King saw them for the first time on a day cold and cloudy with a high wind and showers of snow.[18] This date in after years Sir Joseph regarded as the true beginning of the Spanish Merino in England and in effect the birthday of His Majesty's Spanish flock. In the delight of the moment the King ordered Banks to pay Captain Firth, the good seaman but 'bad Penman', a gratuity of twenty guineas which was done and no receipt taken or asked.[19]

Banks now took up the theme again with Thomas March, acknowledging the receipt of these sheep by the hands of Firth, 'which I do not know that I could by any means but by your Friendship have procurd at all . . .'. He professed himself more than ever convinced that wool could be grown in England to a much greater degree of fineness than had hitherto been done and told March that if he could rely on his assistance he proposed to set it on foot on a large scale. To try it on a proper scale and to execute the plan he had formulated for dispersing them into different districts and to ensure a quick increase he estimated that 'near two hundred sheep' would be required. With the Spanish flocks already on their way north, Banks saw no prospect of more sheep from Lisbon until the following summer and, in the interim, hoped March would aid him with advice and criticism on his plan before he formed it with any distinctness.

. . . What occurs to me is that as the sheep are in Andalusia only in Winter & cannot be commodiously transported but in summer it will be necessary to hire land & shepherds somewhere within a reasonable distance of Lisbon that they may be ready to be sent when the season arrives.

That & the selection out of various Flocks as some are known to grow a more valuable wool than others is all that at present strikes me as necessary to be settled but many more things will probably occur to you who live on the spot.[20]

In August, Thomas March replied at some length expressing himself willing to give every assistance in the plan and proffering some very practical advice and information, which found Banks in Lincolnshire busy about the affairs of his Revesby estate. They set out the Peninsula background admirably and clarified the issues to be faced:

Ganado marino [sic] may be got from Spain across the frontiers by means of natives of that country who make a trade of running mules and horses into Portugal. As no other sort of men will be enduced to undertake a business so full of danger in Spain we must be satisfied to take the chance of their bringing the very best kind, rejecting however, such as are not realy marinos [sic].

To be on the prudent side it will be advisable to engage only 40 or 50 each season till your plan is filled up—it will be difficult to find masters of vessels to take proper care of more than 6 or 8 a voyage—and there will be danger of the officers of the customs outwards from this city refusing to receive a duty and give permit for a small number which might be refused on entry of a larger; or enquiries made that might possibly hinder the business. Without a permit and proper license I should deem it imprudent to export sheep altho foreign out of this country. You will also by the adoption of this slower means have time to make such remarks and observations from year to year as may cause the plan to be completed more conformable to your view.

The first parcel may be bought in March or April next—the shepherds will have better roads and dryer weather to conduct them thro' Portugal than

Plate II

Fleece samples from the first Spanish Merino ram lamb received through Evan Nepean's 'Bilbao Plan', received 28 June 1788.

Fleece samples from the three surviving ewes of the shipment from Lisbon on the *Juno*, Captain George Kennedy, received 6 May 1790.

in the depth of Winter and as they will get to Lisbon at the fit time to ship off as vessels offer, there will be less expense for feeding.

The poor man who brought the 3 that Capt Firth carried has sent word that he made a mistake in the original cost of them, about 80 rials, which I have ordered my friend to pay him; a trifle I would not mention only it may affect your opinion with regard to others.

As to the justness of your opinion that Wool may be improved in England by introduction of finer sheep, I hope you will excuse my observing that there are flocks of Gado muyrinho [sic] which retain their fine wool in this country although they never enter Spain or travel northwards, but have remained on the same farms separate from other sheep ever since the Castilians brought large flocks to pasture here. This practice noticed by some authors must have been very common formerly as it is mentioned in a Portuguese Law dated 1462—It seems to have been checked in 1499 when restraints were put upon the introduction of Spanish woollen cloths with which they were accustomed to pay for the grass.[21]

This illuminating document Banks promptly sent to the King, then in residence at Kew. He applauded the zeal and caution which March had displayed and though he felt pained at the delay in meeting His Majesty's commands could see no means of obviating it.[22] At the end of September, having evidently received some form of agreement from the King, he felt able to reply to March and not only approve his plan, but to press him to draw upon him promptly for any money disbursed on account of the sheep as he was 'much convinced of the adage that short accounts make long Friends'. While being reconciled to the situation which left them very little choice of the flocks from which the sheep were to be got, he emphasized that if by accident those of Patrimonio (Escorial), Perales, or Lasteri were encountered they would be very acceptable as the British wool merchants had a great respect for the fineness of their fleeces. He ended with a typical Banksian peroration:

Your Friendship on this occasion to a person unknown to you I shall never forget & hope the Country will never forget that you are the man to whom they are obligd if we succeed of which I have no kind of doubt it will be a national advantage of a magnitude such as the nation has rarely received from individuals.

This persuasive appeal to his distant collaborator he followed to a conclusion which set down clearly and finally the seldom spoken but essential motive which permeated the unresting labours of the President of the Royal Society towards the establishment of the Spanish fine-wool breed in Great Britain.

To depend upon a Country naturally unkindly to you for the Raw material of the finest branch of your Principal manufacture & to be in hourly danger

of the privilege of Obtaining it being resumd is a humiliating consideration
to a great nation to put her in possession of that Raw material then is an act
deserving the best kind of Gratitude.[23]

Upon this simple creed was fostered and reared the 'most national
object' of the King and 'the favorite hobby' of the President of the
Royal Society.

IV

While Sir Joseph and his ladies were on their way south in the great
family coach from Lincolnshire the premonitory events of the 'melancholy situation of affairs' that was to bring 'all business to a standstill'
were shaping in the Queen's Lodge at Kew.[24] In an ill-defined fashion
the King had not been well for some time, but on Friday, 17 October
1788, he was sufficiently unwell for the return to Windsor to be postponed. The uncertainty of his complaint continued from day to day,
and it was not until Saturday, 25 October, that the Royal Household
returned to the Queen's Lodge at Windsor.[25] Here the unpleasant
symptoms reappeared attended by new changes in the King's manner:
he became more peevish to those about him; he talked incessantly and
on a strange array of subjects; he slept only fitfully; he rambled in his
speech to the point of incoherence and wildness. With exacerbations
and remissions his condition steadily became worse until by the middle
of November there was no secret that the King was gravely ill and
public prayers for his recovery were duly ordained. Before the end of
November the awkward word 'Regency' was being whispered and the
Prince of Wales was in command of the Household affairs. On the
advice of the physicians the King was to be secluded at Kew with a
reduced body of attendants until his health was restored. A meeting of
the Privy Council at which the Prince of Wales presided was held at
Windsor Castle on Friday, 28 November, to authorize this removal
and confirm with the physicians on oath that this step was necessary to
the King's well-being.[26] The next day with great difficulty His Majesty
was persuaded to follow the Queen and her small retinue away from
the place he liked 'best in the world' to residence at Kew in the White
House, a place to which he had always maintained an aversion.[27] Here
the month of December passed as the King's state approached its lowest
ebb and most distressful and violent phase. About the middle of
January 1789 there were signs, increasingly hopeful, of improvement.
The daily bulletins, however, maintained their note of caution, which
Greville as the sole Equerry in attendance on the King had never
departed from in his accounts to Banks from time to time. Banks himself had during December taken a most pessimistic view even to

doubting the possibility of the King's recovery at all. He was now to swing to a premature optimism, scattering a few cheerful indiscretions abroad and earning Greville's gentle but firm reproof. On Saturday, 17 January, Banks came to Kew Gardens to look over the King's flock of sheep and there met another Lincolnshire man, the Senior Doctor, John Willis, under whose particular care the patient now was. In answer to Sir Joseph's inquiry how the King was that day Dr. Willis answered without preamble, 'He is charmingly, and is now as Mild as Milk', adding that one of the King's pages had just reported that he had never been 'so sensible'. Banks, as Greville noted, 'went away rejoiced at this good news, & it spread rapidly on the road—'. This unwarranted indiscretion was not pleasing to Greville, who noted in reference to the incident:

Throughout this long & severe illness the suddenness of opposite changes have been frequent & most remarkable, & much disappointment has followed from the over-impatience of spreading these transient reports of confirmed Amendment, when in fact all trembled on an aweful balance. Comparing the King's situation during the last night, & the earlier part of this Morning, with what it was reported in the Evening, a more sudden contrast has not appeared—[28]

And yet in fact, as Greville conceded, that day had seen the King more nearly normal than at any time formerly.

Then on 6 February the King was so far improved, during one of his walks in the Botanic Garden in conversation with William Aiton, as to recall Sir Joseph and to express a wish to see him. Dr. Willis then arranged for such a meeting to take place as if by chance next day at the King's Marsh Gate Farm near Richmond. From then on Banks and the King met frequently, either in the Exotic Garden or among the sheep as often as seemed wise from day to day. Greville describes one such walk on 21 February when with Dr. Willis's permission Banks joined the King:

The King seeing Him coming stopped for Him, & after a gracious reception They walked on. The Weather was uncertain, & the day at times interrupted by heavy showers—The King however continued his Walk with Sir Joseph Banks about three hours. They first visited the Exotic Garden, thence walked through Richmond Gardens where The Sheep were looked at, Thence they proceeded across The London Road to March Gate where H. My. has lately made a Farm yard & erected Farm Offices. While there it rained, & was late. A Gentleman's carriage was borrowed in the neighbourhood, & it had begun to proceed when the Weather cleared. The King expressed a Wish to get out & continue his Walk. He did so & giving the Coachman a Guinea, He dismissed The Carriage[29]

Greville and Banks had a long conversation after this walk from which Banks had drawn the impression that the King 'was very near right'. This was both a surprise and a pleasure to Greville, but he pressed Banks further and elicited a few qualifying comments. The convalescence was evidently developing well, but Greville, remembering Banks's former gossiping indiscretion, administered a fatherly warning about any statements he might possibly be inclined to give, especially to Ministers of the Government to whom it would doubtless be important.

I observed to Him that this was a moment of anxiety & of difficulty, that He must be on his guard not to let Himself be quoted, as reporting The King quite well, for tho' to The Doctor Willis's & Myself, He had expressed Himself much pleased & satisfied with what He had seen and heard, still some chequering shades had been observed by Him. He must not therefore (I told Him) risk the imputation of blame, in bringing Him too forward & which might be eventually laid, to his Intelligence by those who might be willing now to risk an experiment, but afraid to stand Themselves, the hazard of a reverse.[30]

Greville found Sir Joseph now well aware of such possibilities and was happy to find him fully persuaded that every prudence was necessary at this critical period in the King's convalescence. No further miscalculations escaped from Banks to worry or distress Greville, who by now after nearly four months' attendance on his ailing master was an exhausted man. Almost daily now the King and Banks took their rejuvenating walks together by the river and through the gardens and farm. By early March it was clear that the King was a sane man again and able shortly to take up at least some of his Royal duties. On 1 March a prayer of thanksgiving for the King's recovery was read in all the churches. On 4 March, Greville was relieved from his long waiting so well performed when Colonel Robert Manners succeeded him as Equerry. Normality seemed to be fully restored when the reunited Royal family returned to Windsor on 14 March, the King himself riding back with a large company of gentlemen to be received by the whole town with almost ecstatic demonstrations, supplemented by the explosion of forty guineas worth of fireworks that night.[31]

For Banks the winter that had just passed had been a sadly distracting one in which, as he had earlier written to Lord Hawkesbury, business had been almost at a standstill. Latterly he had found himself much involved with the distressing problem of the King's illness very directly and had played his own useful part in speeding and smoothing the period of convalescence. He had in the course of these experiences been drawn more closely into the Royal family circle and had at the same time learned a few lessons in courtly discretion from 'Colonel Wellbred'. Held back by the dark events of the winter from any hopeful vision of a future Spanish flock, the returning spring now found him unable to wait longer for the next positive step forward. On 10 April he wrote to Thomas March:

> I trust to your good nature to excuse the anxiety which makes me impatient to hear from you at this period which if I am not mistaken is exactly the time when my wishd for Sheep are to be brought down from the mountains
>
> A Line from you when you have got them specifying the number you intend for this years supply & the means which appear to you the most proper for sending them will be a great Favor
>
> The Ewes you were so good as to send last year have brought a Lamb each & tho the weather was intensely cold & the ground covered with snow they Lambd perfectly well as well to all appearance as our English sheep[32]

For more than three months there was no answer from Thomas March. Then, late in July, came a brief note with the unwelcome news that,

> By the negligence of the men in Spain the Business in which I wish to serve you has miscarried this season. . . .[33]

He was assured that more effectual measures had now been taken to secure sheep when they appeared on the frontiers of Portugal again, and that if nothing occurred to prevent it a few animals of the right breed could be expected in four or five months. This was a sad strain on any man's patience. Banks, on 31 July, could only reply with sorrowful but obvious restraint:

> I greive over the negligence of your Spanish undertakers or the accident whatever it may have been that has prevented your Obliging undertaking in my Favor from being Carried into Execution as by that circumstance a year more of my life wastes away without making progress in a plan which is near my heart I verily beleive from the conviction I feel that it promises real utility to my country. . . .[34]

None of Banks's eloquent pleadings was to produce any sheep from Lisbon in 1789, which in every way was to prove a most unfruitful year. At the end he found himself 'repeatedly mortified by the Failure of his Lisbon plan when he had every reason to believe it at the point of being successful . . .'.[35] This was due, he had by then discovered, to the ill-health of Thomas March, who by the end of the year was dangerously sick, after being for many months in a decline which left him 'inactive in business'. The frailty of the human body from the beginning was a burden to the rise as well as to the progress of the Spanish flock.

V

Meanwhile in other quarters a thriving correspondence with the Iberian Peninsula had developed under the guiding hand of Mr. Evan Nepean. On the one hand Mr. Collier and his partner Mr. Henry Hinckley were probing the Spanish defences at Bilbao, meeting at close quarters the subtle evasions of the Spanish fine-wool myth. On the other hand some interesting exchanges were passing from Mr. John Lodge at 14 Seething Lane to Mr. William Warre in Oporto by whose assistance William Conyngham had in 1784 secured some of his small flock of 'real' Spanish sheep. He was willing again to engage in the business and set about securing sheep by the same means that he had employed for Conyngham four years earlier. Brigadier-General Calder, Governor of the frontier town of Almeida, accepted the commission from Warre as he had done before. Again the difficulties and uncertainties of the contraband trade were emphasized, the length of the day making the enterprise troublesome and expensive. William Warre also shared the general belief that the excellence of the Spanish wools depended on the migrations of the sheep, the pasture, and the climate. He did not think Conyngham's sheep had answered very well in Ireland from what he had been told. However, he was not on that account inclined to put obstacles in the way of an experiment in England.[36]

At last in March 1789 Lodge received a letter with word that Brigadier-General Calder at Almeida 'was not unmindful of the Commission' and was waiting for the moment for completing it when the flocks passed north near his town on the border. Warre also conveyed the feelings of the British Factory in Oporto on the King's illness:

We all rejoice here like loyal subjects in ye happy event of the King's recovery and are willing to flatter ourselves that the publick accounts may be true tho I think that perfect permanent health of mind is more to be desired than expected after so great a derangement & after all a doubt must ever remain. I hope however that matters will be so settled as to go on prosperously which at this distance is what may only interest me tho perhaps some of my friends may be disappointed at least in a suspension of their expectations.[37]

William Warre probably never knew for some years afterwards that the sheep which he was arranging to acquire by contraband means at Almeida were to become the property and interest of the King in whose restored health of mind he was so pleased to rejoice. At last nearly three months later he was able to tell John Lodge that a Spanish ram and three ewes had been got 'thro the influence of General Calder' and that they were now shipped on board the *Hope* under the command of

Captain Hopkins. It was not possible to get more but they would provide at least a sample of the breed. As the weather had till then been remarkably cool he had thought it better not to shear them. The first cost of the sheep and the cost of fodder for the voyage was £5 10s., and they were in good health at the time of sailing. His valedictory remarks to John Lodge confirmed his view once more about the over-riding influence of the environment on the fleece:

I am very much inclined to believe that soil & climate has a proportionate influence upon animal as well as vegetable productions & am persuaded that it is as difficult to obtain the fine wool of Spain in England as [it] would be to get the long wool of Lincolnshire in Spain. The experiment however is laudable & I wish it may succeed & should be equally glad to hear that you had got some of the Sheep from Thibet thro the influence of the grand Lama to whose holy protection I comit you. Adios.[38]

With this parting whimsy William Warre sent his contribution to the King's flock on its way and retired from its further history. Seven days from Oporto and on 24 June 1789 the ship *Hope* was at anchor in the Thames with the four sheep in fine health and condition. Evan Nepean secured their easy passage through the Custom House and sent them by water to Kew Bridge, where Banks noted their arrival as being on 26 June.[39] With this small shipment the British Factory at Oporto began and ended its operations in contraband sheep for the King.

VI

This cheerful break in the long gloom of the past year occurred just as the King set out for an extended period of relaxation at Weymouth, in future to become his favourite watering-place. Banks, however, judged it prudent to defer troubling the King even with this innocuous titbit of business so early in his convalescence. The brooding sense of disappointment at the endless delays and the paucity of the results no doubt also added their restraint to his natural caution at this time. It was not, therefore, until the autumn was well advanced that a letter from Evan Nepean, taking the waters at Bath, stirred Banks with its news and prompted him to acquaint the King with the small but hopeful progress of the year 1789.

After more than two years of waiting Nepean was able on 22 November 1789 to report the first-fruits of 'the Bilbao plan' in the arrival of one ram and two ewes, safely lodged at his stables in Cleveland Row, and the daily expectation of more from the same quarter.[40] Without delay Banks wrote a short report on this encouraging turn of events to the King at Windsor, tinctured with his feelings of mortification at the failure of his 'Lisbon plan', but laced with new glimmers of hope in the fleece samples and the news from Lord Auckland recently home from Spain itself.[41] The note of mild pessimism from Soho Square was diluted with a cheering note from Greville which in itself carried Banks forward into a new relationship to the whole enterprise and at a stroke removed much of his early diffidence in the affair.

> I have time only by two lines to thank you for your letters and to answer them.
> His M. is very glad to hear of the arrival of the Ram and two Ewes, which he desires may be sent to Richmond as usual. He asked me how your Sheep were going on; I said well, and that you was as anxious about them as ever —I added you had made enquiries of me also of his Majesty's Flock, but that I could give you but little information, as I had not seen them for some time, and that you would have gone yourself to have visited his flock, had you not been afraid of intruding. His M. said he was in hopes you had always continued your visits there; and added that he thought he had expressed himself so from the first. . . .[42]

The year which had opened with such unrelieved depression was now closing in the brightness of the Royal smile, and illumined further by the successful ending of 'the Bilbao plan' in the arrival of a further consignment of one ram and two ewes on 30 December. The old year passed with ten sheep of the 'true Spanish breed' added to the foundations of 'his Majesties patriotic plan'.

The failing health of Thomas March to which Banks had alluded in his report to the King of 25 November 1789 did not prevent entirely that faithful spirit from pursuing to the end his promise to the man he scarcely knew even by reputation. On 22 February 1790 the dying merchant of the Lisbon Factory penned a few optimistic lines:

> I had determined not to answer your last letter till I could at [the] same time acquaint you that the Marino [sic] sheep I am so desirous to find could be actually put on board ship—but Cap[n] Firth departing at this season of the year without them will make you think I have neglected that object intirely. They have been expected in Lisbon for this month past, and I am assured that now a part of what are brought are on this side [of] the frontier. My next I hope will acquaint you they are safe at last in Lisbon. Cap[n] Firth carries the Viridarium Grisler. . . .[43]

Nothing came of this immediately, but in the spring of the year, on 24 April, Thomas March had the final happiness to write that 'Cap[n] Kennedy of the brig *Juno* on departure for London will deliver you Five ewes & three lambs of the true Marino breed. . . .'[44] Of this small consignment only three ewes survived to reach Kew on 6 May. Within a short time thereafter Thomas March was dead, but 'the Lisbon plan' which owed so much to his persistence had at last begun to yield dividends of 'the true Marino breed', and, in small lots of up to as many as thirty sheep, these continued to find their illicit way down the Tagus. The business now flowed fairly smoothly under the guiding hand of Thomas March's cousin, John, who carried the plan through to a satisfactory end.

The three ewes which survived the voyage by the brig *Juno* arrived in so emaciated a condition that Banks for a time doubted whether they would live. He had no doubts, however, that they were of the true Merino breed and recorded them as 'especially very Fine'. He therefore paid Captain Kennedy five guineas instead of the three guineas agreed upon at embarkation should only three sheep survive. This may be compared with the six and a half guineas which would have been paid to the Captain had all the consignment been delivered. He also paid one guinea to the seamen who had the care of them on board in spite of the stark failure of their ministrations. He wrote now to the man in Lisbon who was already dead:

as Expence to me in procuring these sheep is no Object I beg the Favor of you if in future you are so good as to Continue to Favor me with your assistance to make whatever bargain you please on my account with the People who procure or those who bring over the Sheep I have full reliance on the justice & honour of your character to defend me from absurd over-charges but I wish all Employd may have in the Price given an interest to make them active in carrying the business into execution

You will do me a Favor Sir whenever you are pleased to draw upon me for expences incurrd on this subject I shall thankfully honor your bills if you can put me in the way of rendering you similar service here you will confer an additional obligation on me

If you send any by Firth I have no doubt he will bring them safe he talks of making me pay 5 pounds a head for Freight in which case he is to carry out hay from England & I have paid for the erecting of Pens I mention this only to shew you that I am not Contrary about Price[45]

Scarcely had this letter been sent than Captain Michael Firth entered the Thames with the *Betsy*, having on board one of the largest parcels of contraband sheep to emerge from the Tagus under 'the Lisbon plan'. On or about 24 July 1790 there were received at Kew eight rams and sixteen ewes, the survivors of thirty sheep embarked in fulfilment of the last order placed by Thomas March before his death.[46] For these Banks willingly paid the purchase price of £30 15s. 8d. sterling to Mr. John McGowan of 11 Charterhouse Square, the London agent of Thomas March and Company. He also readily paid the demand of that hard bargainer, Captain Michael Firth, for three guineas a head for freight. Though he thought this an exorbitant charge he considered it of no consequence in comparison with that of 'getting the animals safely conveyd which I think a matter of national importance'. Firth volunteered the advice that no more than ten sheep ought to be sent on one ship and that at three guineas a head for freight any sea-captain would take such a consignment.[47] No one in fact gave much thought to the first point for it was of paramount importance to carry whatever number of sheep were available in this chancy business. On the other hand, the grapevine of the mercantile marine, then as now, saw to it that the rates of freight kept in line with each other at the level set by the hardest bargainer on the whole. In this field Captain Firth forced the issue and set the pattern. Throughout all these operations from the Tagus the freight and general costs per head of obtaining the sheep remained about two to three times the initial price per head of the sheep themselves as paid to the Spanish *contrabandista*.

The year 1790, which closed with no less than twenty-seven Spanish sheep added to the Royal experimental flock, had shown the most satisfactory progress so far especially in its increase of the breeding ewes. The total number in the flock was, however, still far from the two hundred which Banks had earlier mentioned as a useful goal. But 'the Lisbon plan' was not exhausted. John March did not relax his efforts to procure sheep of the right kind nor to seek 'such Captains as can be most depended on, which is the more necessary seeing the freight is so exhorbitant'.[48] Here he thought himself particularly happy in meeting with Captain Anderson of the *Jemima* as a man 'who understands the proper treatment of sheep, and I have no doubt will deliver them all safe'.[49] Captain Anderson delivered three of the remaining four consignments of sheep from the Tagus, losing only six out of sixty-seven sheep embarked. He was much to be commended also for his modesty in charging two guineas per head against the three guineas demanded (and got) by the other captains. In the summer of 1791 on 20 August, Banks felt constrained to write to John March in terms of some satisfaction:

I have from time to time delayed an answer to your Last Favour in hopes of being able to send you over something manufactured from the wool I have grown here with your assistance so long that I am really ashamed of myself and the more so as I am at last disappointed I shall however before long effect my purpose of obtaining some cloth & shall then trouble you again.

The experiments succeed to the utmost of my wishes as hitherto I do not observe any degeneration in the wool so I am now very sanguine indeed in the hope of producing an extensive advantage to the country at Large of which however you sir not me must have the credit of being the principal promoter.

The six ewes by the *Speedy* arrivd safe and in tolerable condition The *Jemima* brought me only 13 ewes & one Ram 6 ewes having died in the course of the voyage they were however much reduced, in better condition than those I receivd last year.

The Ram proves a very fine woold Sheep as do all the Ewes one only excepted so that I must have general reason to be highly satisfied with your goodness to me in procuring the right sort & consider the obligation you confer on me in assisting my views as one of real importance.

The Price of Freight is certainly high but as I have resolvd to surmount all obstacles to the carrying a point from whence I now think considerable advantage will with certainty accrue I make no kind of objection to paying it & the less so as the Reasonableness of the Prime Cost makes the expence at which they are obtained in the whole a matter of no great consideration.

Let me beg of you sir to proceed in your goodness to me by Procuring me another importation next Spring Some of the Rams have been already distributed so that I hope in two years from the present time a feeling of the benefit to be expected will eventually take place by the improvements they will produce in the wools of the sheep they beget.

I have taken the liberty to consign to you a hogshead of Porter not under any Idea of Retribution for the Favors you have done me but merely to show that I am sensible of your Kindness I should be happy if it proves in my power to obey any commands of yours here . . . The Porter is on the *St George* Capt Williams & has your address upon it.[50]

Stimulated by these appreciative favours, John March sent in November 1791 for what was the last shipment of contraband sheep to His Majesty's Spanish flock, and the last but one to leave the Tagus under 'the Lisbon plan'. They were expected to reach the coast by February 1792.[51] Months passed[52] and the summer was well advanced, however, before John March was able to assure Banks on 9 June 1792 that the sheep were then hourly expected on the opposite bank of the Tagus, and that the unusual delay arose from the death of the 'person formerly employed and the difficulty of meeting with a proper one to manage the business'.[53] Eventually in August the last twenty-six ewes of clandestine origin arrived in the Thames in the *Jemima* under the efficient care of Captain Anderson. With one more voyage by the *Jemima* in October that year, carrying sheep from Lisbon via London for His Majesty's estates in Hanover, the contraband sheep trade from Spain under the astute direction of the President of the Royal Society came to an end. Through this channel the Royal flock received fourteen 'real' Spanish rams and seventy-three ewes in the four years from 1788 to 1792, or about two-thirds of all the true Merino rams imported and one-half of all the ewes. And for all these illicit treasures it would seem that the cost to His Majesty was exactly £218 3s. 6d. over all.

CHAPTER V

The Diplomats, 1787–1792

I

In the steady search for Spanish fine-wool sheep for the Royal experiments by the President of the Royal Society no paths led to more success than those pursued among the quiet backwaters of diplomacy. In October 1791, quite suddenly to the surprise of no one more than Banks himself, His Majesty acquired the sheep that became the effective foundation of his Spanish flock as it developed during the next twenty years. No incident among the small array traditionally associated with the Merino flock of George III has been more frequently proclaimed than this. Few historic anecdotes can have suffered quite so much in the assaults made on the few known facts. Briefly these were that a small flock of sheep from the Negretti *cabana* reached England in 1791 as a present to the King from the Count and Countess del Campo di Alange; that the flock was established on the Royal farms at Windsor and Kew; that in return 'a set of English carriage horses' from the Royal stables was eventually sent to Spain. Little more than this has ever been known for sure. Gossip and invention abhor an apparent vacuum and the very simplicity of the story was a challenge. Many odd twists have been given to the incident, but few versions quite match this oddity from Sydney in 1834 as an example of the strange garbling that can beset the oft-told tale. Let fiction here, for once, appear stranger than the truth:

The wish of his Majesty [for Spanish sheep] was to be gratified at any cost, or by any means, and his 'aids' set their wits to work accordingly. The Spanish ambassador was applied to, but he was too much of a patriot to enter into any project prejudicial to the interests of his own country—further hinted, that both his appointment and his head would be endangered by his undertaking to bring Merino sheep from Spain, and that the flocks were exclusively the property of the clergy and the Church, which would render any endeavour to obtain them still more uncertain and hazardous.

But his Majesty's employees were not to be deterred by this repulse. The lady Ambassadress was closely beset and watched—to find if any vulnerable point could be discovered whereby she might be taken, and induced to enter the conspiracy against the Merinos.

Shortly after this the Ambassadress went to see the King go in State to the House of Lords, on which occasion she expressed great admiration of the state coach cream coloured horses.

'Would her Excellency accept of a pair?' 'Oh! they were above all others the most beautiful, and to be desired!' A pair was ordered from Hanover, where they were bred, and at a cost of nearly £8,000 brought to England, and presented to her. Her vanity was now gratified, as she possessed what no other Lord or Lady could boast of.

The donors would accept a few Spanish sheep in the way of a complimentary return.

To make any direct application it was well known would be useless—but a class of men who abound in Spain, contrabandista, (i.e. smugglers) were applied to; they took a favourable opportunity by night to select (steal) from the flocks what number and gender they required; and their prey were driven northward, through Spain, France, and part of Germany, and shipped at Hamburg, for London. Many were lost on the journey, but a sufficient number were obtained.

The sheep, upon landing, were first placed to graze in the Royal Gardens and Parks about London, and the writer of this has seen the Spaniards who had them in charge, playing at chuck and toss with dollars and doubloons, the reward of their enterprising speculation.[1]

Clearly this is the work of a film script writer of genius, born a century before his time on the wrong side of the Pacific, flirting with facts as though they were starlets. It is almost with regret that we return to cooler latitudes and more frigid truths.

If the story has any definitive origin we may perhaps find it in the letter of one Etonian to another, more than four years earlier, in March 1787. Glowing from 'the obliging remembrance' of his old schoolfellow, William Eden, which had brought him a much-sought pamphlet from Paris, Banks felt authorized to trouble him further:

I have sometime turned my Thoughts towards the subject of wool & lamenting that we in England [who] are so Famous for that article were under the necessity of drawing our supplies For the finer Manufactures from Spain I have attended much to the Flock managd in Burgundy at the Royal expence by M. Daubenton & have hitherto procurd all that has been publishd on the subject with any appearance of authenticity till I was Foild by a book Publishd *à l'imprimerie Royale* at the end of the last year under the tittle [sic] of '*Observations sur le comparaison de la nouvelle Laine superfine de France avec la belle Laine d'espagne*'. tho I applied the instant I saw the work advertisd I was told that it was *épuisée*. now knowing as I do that in matters publishd at the Royal printing office a little interest is sometimes necessary I have taken the liberty of requesting yours a word I trust will get it indeed I should be sorry it gave you much trouble.[2]

On this muted note began a small piece of 'business in a Philosophical way' between Banks and Eden that was to weave its way unbroken during the next four years through a concert of events whose historic overtones would quite obscure it.[3] On 11 May 1787 Banks was able to write to Eden a short letter of acknowledgement:

a Thousand thanks for the pamphlet which you have procurd me it has satisfied a curiosity which I conceive to be of some importance I am not quite so great an infidel on the subject of French wool as you are for reasons which I will with pleasure explain when we meet . . .[4]

As this letter crossed the Channel to France by the Dover packet, Captain Arthur Phillip in the *Sirius* was making his last preparations to rendezvous at the Mother Bank near Portsmouth with the rest of the First Fleet to sail from thence to Botany Bay on 13 May 1787. The germinating curiosity of Sir Joseph Banks on the subject of French wool and the sea-borne nucleus of the remote Colony so soon to be established had a mutual importance to each other that no one could perceive that spring. Banks himself was much more concerned at the happy outcome of Eden's diplomatic labours to consolidate the Thirteenth Article of the Treaty of Peace with France of 1783:[5]

This day the blessings of a mutual commerce between two nations who have been enemies these thousand years began & from hence forwards we may I think hope that they will remain Friends at all events however it cannot be but that all parties will be benefited & if gratitude is not shown to heaven after . . . some of it will Fall to the Share of the great promoter of the happiness & concord of two rival nations excuse this Flighty effusion of an old school fellow . . .

Before Eden reached Madrid as Ambassador in May 1788 the new colony at Port Jackson had been established and Banks had fully explained to him his concern with the growing of fine wool, a theme which by now was flowering vigorously under the expressed patronage of the King. During his one year at the Spanish Court, Eden was able to draw Anthony Merry, the Consul at Madrid, into the circle of conspirators and charged him with the task of obtaining samples of Spanish fine wool. Eden himself, in the touchy diplomatic atmosphere of that time, discreetly laid some plans for obtaining sheep eventually from his friend Don Gaspar de Montijo. However, the best he achieved in any official way was a licence for the export of a Spanish male ass. This he refused—presumably on the grounds that it was irrelevant and perhaps a trifle flippant.

Another year passed. In May 1789 it became necessary for Eden to leave Spain for Paris to defend against the new Revolutionary Ministry of the National Assembly the commercial convention which he had negotiated and signed at Versailles on 31 August 1787 with the French monarchy.[6] Even for a diplomat during the portentous summer of 1789 France was certainly uncomfortable as the Revolutionary cauldron simmered to the point of boiling.[7] William Eden seems to have conducted his business, therefore, from various places south of Paris as he observed the crumbling of what had been Banks's hopes of 'happiness & concord' culminate in the destruction of the Bastille on 14 July.

South of the Pyrenees Carlos IV, as yet uncrowned and scarcely six months on the throne of Spain, was already in dispute with England over the trading station at Nootka Sound in Vancouver.[8] The days of the Family Compact with France were ending as the National Assembly grandiloquently renounced wars of conquest and refused him aid. At the Escorial his Queen, Maria Luisa of Parma, was expecting a child, and the diplomatic corps was now agog to transmit the glad tidings of its birth.

II

Anthony Merry, by now Consul-General and chargé d'affaires in Eden's absence, unperturbed by the Royal accouchement or the distant rumble of war and revolution, had dutifully discharged his task. Unaware that it was for Banks or the King, so discreet had Eden been in the matter, he informed his absent senior:

... I have at length in my possession the samples of the finest Spanish wool, in its natural state. As I do not recollect the name of the person for whom you wished to procure it, I propose to send the packet to Mr Fraser to be held at your disposal by the courier which will be dispatched from hence when the Queen is brought to bed. . . .[9]

On 16 July 1789, two days after the fall of the Bastille, Merry wrote to Eden that the samples of Spanish wool had at last been sent by the Courier after the Queen's recent delivery.[10] In September, Eden was raised to the Irish peerage as Baron Auckland, and from this point forward Banks epitomized this 'philosophical negociacion' as 'Lord Auckland's undertaking', in his private notes. Some time before November, Auckland and Banks met in conference at Lambeth Palace, and the prized samples of Spanish fine wool were seen by the one man in England who could most appreciate their significance. These specimens were all the more valuable to the informed observer, which Banks by this time certainly was, as they were in their natural state. This meant that they had not been washed after shearing according to the Spanish practice and which was the state in which all the fine wool from Spain entered the English wool trade. Banks was, therefore, able to compare the natural fleece growth of Merry's samples directly with what he now knew so well, the natural state of that grown by the few imported stock at Spring Grove and at Windsor. Accordingly he reported to the King:

> . . . Ld Auckland who has brought with him from Spain some samples of the finest wool Sir Jos: has ever seen speaks of the procuring Spanish sheep as a matter of little difficulty if his Majesty would lay Commands on his Lordship or honor Sr Jos: with directions to confer with him on the subject it is probable that the completion of his Majesties patriotic Plan might be materially accelerated. . . .[11]

Merry, as he later disclosed, had in fact procured these specimens from the flock of the Marquis de Perales not from that of Don Gaspar de Montijo as Auckland supposed at the time.[12] Thus they had come from one of the most famous of all the Spanish piles and one which in fact at that period John Maitland rated as the very first. As samples they were of sufficient merit in themselves not only to fire the imagination of Banks but also to spur the interest of the King. Soon afterwards, 'early in the year 1790', Sir Joseph was honoured with the Royal command[13] 'to converse with his Lordship on the subject of wool, and to procure by his means, if possible, some of the sheep that produced it, which his Lordship believed to be the Flock of Don Gaspar de Montijo . . .'. This must have been before March 1790 when Auckland presented his credentials as Ambassador to the States-General and to the Prince of Orange at The Hague.

From Holland, then, almost immediately Auckland wrote very fully and particularly to Anthony Merry at Madrid, 'respecting the cargo of Rams & Sheep to be procured from Don Gaspar de Montijo's Flock for the purpose of *ornamenting* His Majesty's Farms . . .'.[14] This letter to Merry was sent as more than one copy by private hands and also as an extract in cipher by the post, thereby setting the standard of secrecy which Auckland hoped would be observed.[15] He had great confidence in Merry as a capable and zealous agent, he told Banks, and expected that in the course of that summer the commission would be done; 'Unless (which is not impossible) some sudden and great jealousy should impede it . . .'.[16]

Every discretion was to be observed as Banks had been careful to impress upon Auckland. His Majesty's name was at no time to be mentioned in the transaction. On this point both these old school-fellows were fully agreed, and all suitable precautions were taken in the matter of codes and couriers. In this employment Auckland was a practised exponent with a high reputation for discretion, but the times were hazardous and unsettling. It is questionable how far this secrecy was kept in fact, even though most of the important letters travelled by the safe hand of King's Messengers or by post in code. If the Spanish Court perhaps remained ignorant of the progress of these plans it was because its attention was directed to events abroad. Anthony Merry himself, a relatively young man of thirty-five and a novice yet in diplomatic as distinct from consular affairs, was an agent who was already showing those qualities of tact and industry in negotiation which were the foundations of his later distinguished career in the steps of men like Auckland. He was not able, however, during the summer of 1790 in 'the inauspicious period of the Paper War and Naval Preparations' arising from the dispute over the trading station at Nootka Sound to find either Floridablanca or Carlos IV in that parti-cular brand of good humour necessary for an application so full of subtle complications. Many months passed before Merry could find and recognize the enchanted moment, the *mollia tempora* for which all good diplomats pray.

The substance of all these hindrances was conveyed to Banks by Auckland, anxious as ever that 'my zeal and punctuality may continue to stand fair in your opinion'. Autumn came and the summer flurry over trading rights in Canada was resolved by the convention signed in October 1790, but the travelling flocks had by then migrated south. The season for exportation in the opinion of Merry was over for that year. Banks had to remain contented with his Portuguese contraband shipments of 'ganado Merino' which his merchant confederates had been able to move by 'gradual means' down the Tagus in the spring and early summer. He could not resign himself to this delay without further word from Auckland to confirm his fears and to give weight to his report at Windsor on 'how all Foreign correspondence goes on'.[17] The whole theme was now somewhat muted by the competing claims of his correspondence with Auckland about the second expedition to bring the Bread-fruit from the South Seas to the West Indies. But in December the diplomats were still in doubt 'whether the returning cordiality and good humour are yet such as to ensure all the com-plaisance that we wish'.[18] With this the anxious shepherd had to console the Royal patriot and in patience endure the ensuing silence of a whole year, conceding that diplomacy here knew best when the time would be ripe to begin these operations again.

III

Then in October 1791 the thin powder-train of these diplomatic niceties exploded into a running fire of correspondence. At Revesby Abbey, Banks's autumn preoccupation with Lincolnshire affairs, and in particular this year also, no doubt, Mr. Arthur Young and the iniquities of the Leicestershire Tup Society, was suddenly diverted on 22 October by a letter from the master of a merchantman, written a week before from Southampton:

I here acquaint you that I have on board forty-one sheep ship^t at Santander by order of Anthony Merry Esqr consignd to you I arriv^d last evening at a 11 o'clock this Morning went to the Custom house & reported my Cargo according to my Manifest, the Collector informd me the sheep with the vessell was both confiscated according to Law. informd him I thought the sheep belongd to a power that would not permit any such thing as that to happen, the Collector hath given leave for them to be taken proper care of untill he may have an order from the Commissioners of the Customs to release them I beg S^r you will wait on the Commissioners for leave for their enlargement as they are in good order though I have had a rough passage I beg S^r that you will despatch this business as quick as possible pray let me hear by Mondays post. . . . Please to direct to John Burnell Master of the *King George* at Southampton.[19]

His Majesty's diplomatic corps had indeed moved in a mysterious way, but the wonder had been performed. Here at last was the consummation of another 'philosophical negociacion'. Here also was a pretty pass! Captain Burnell's letter, written on 15 October, had not been put into Sir Joseph's hands until late on the night of the 22nd, 'owing to a variety of ill-luck' as well as his own absence from London whence, no doubt, the assiduous Jonas Dryander had sent it north post-haste. Joy was tinged with annoyance at the tangle, but neither sentiment checked the smooth efficiency with which Banks next morning set the machinery of his influence in motion to resolve it. A reassuring letter of congratulation and inquiry went immediately to Southampton. Another to David Maclean at the Custom House, London, with a petition to His Majesty's Commissioners for an order of release for ship and sheep was in the pattern of other past indulgences sought by Banks for similar cargoes. These would attend for the moment to the apprehensions of Captain John Burnell. There was time now for an exultant letter to Auckland, relaxing with his family at Beckenham in Kent:

Merry has at last done his business very well . . . [The moment for mutual congratulations, it seemed, had come.]
I hope in about a fortnight to have the pleasure of thanking you in person & if H. M. does not do it before I come to town I am sure I shall have a special commission to signify to your Lordship H. M. gracious acceptance of the service you have done him which I consider as very important & have every reason to believe is considered in that Light at Windsor.[20]

From Beckenham and that other Eden a week later came the counterflow of warm felicitation:

I must heartily congratulate you on the safe arrival of our Spanish cargo of Ewes & Rams:—The number goes beyond my highest speculations, & if they are of Don Gaspar's flock, or of any other genuine Spanish breed, I am of opinion that not only His Majesty but his people may have cause to thank you for a very important service:—You are too generous in allowing to me so large a share of your merit on this occasion; I claim none beyond that of listening to your instructions with that attention which is so peculiarly due to you. My dutch mission obliged me to consign the execution of this enterprise to our friend Merry who seems to have acquitted himself not only with zeal but with success—I shall not have an opportunity of paying my duty to his Majesty before the 4th Nov; I shall then have the honour of congratulating him on the satisfactory result of your unwearied perseverance in this Business.[21]

In this brief exchange of compliments we have nothing that strains our credulity. The King and Banks, Auckland and Merry, all seem here to stand in the right perspective. His Majesty was indeed fortunate in the dedicated service which, over a period of four such portentous years, could achieve this end from the unforced collaboration of three busy men, each of them harried by daily pressures far removed from Spanish sheep. Each of these three busy men also was fortunate in his confederates in the scheme. Without their collective good sense and mutual trust we may doubt whether the enterprise would have succeeded. Auckland's letter seems in the hindsight of a hundred and seventy years to assign the credit titles fairly. But in the immediate present of October 1791 the situation viewed from Revesby Abbey did not bear quite the same aspect. The high tide of emotion ebbed and small hard doubts appeared through the congratulatory froth. What, in fact, had Merry done? There had been no timely letter in advance of the cargo on which Banks could act to make straight the way and smooth the path through the Custom House in the discreet fashion appropriate to this Royal secret. Sheep there were at Southampton, undoubtedly, for his literary friend William Seward had seen them and had lost no time in confirming the sad straits of Captain John Burnell, even to the point of noting the 'foolish Statute' of Charles II which was used to justify the seizure.[22] But what sheep were they? Were they in fact of a kind suitable 'for the purpose of *ornamenting* His Majesty's Farms'? The bare phrase 'forty-one sheep ship^t at Santander by order of Anthony Merry Esqr', left much to the imagination.

Two more days of doubt and speculation and on 25 October a month-old letter from Merry cleared the mystery but only to rouse a flickering anger:

The application which I made some little time since through Count Floridablanca for the License in question expressed that the Sheep were intended for the King, and the permission for their exportation was instantly granted by His Catholick Majesty. The number which Lord Auckland specified in his Letter was two Rams and eighteen sheep or four Rams and Thirty six sheep. I have preferred sending the larger quantity lest it should otherwise be too much reduced by accident in the transportation; and I trust that the sheep are of the finest quality as I have procured them from the Count del Campo di Alange, the Minister for the War Department, whose Flock has the first reputation, and who has obligingly allowed them to be picked from it.[23]

The sea-road had proved a faster route for news than the safe hand, but at what a cost to the subtle intent of the whole clandestine transaction! The well-kept secret of four years, protected by complex ciphers and dauntless Couriers to and from the Escorial had vanished at a stroke in 'the disagreeable circumstance of the King's name having been made use of in procuring the Sheep'. Merry had in the end, perhaps, not done his business so very well. The thought rankled in Banks's mind as he saw an end to further plans. These irritations were for the moment thrust behind the more urgent consequences of Merry's tardy letter of advice, the public seizure of the ship and its cargo, and all the unwonted process of petitions for their release. Moreover, as Banks was to find later, there were 'consequently the silly paragraphs which appeared in some of the newspapers of that period'. The first sweet savours of heady success had become acrid in some degree. Of this there were the almost daily letters from an impatient and justly incensed sea-captain to remind him.

Let it be said, however, that the steps which Banks had taken towards the release of the schooner *King George* and the sequestered sheep for His Majesty King George III were as effective as the times allowed and as speedy. His letter from Revesby Abbey on 23 October was in the hands of David Maclean, Assistant Inspector of Customs at the Honourable East India Company, on 25 October but, alas, 'it being a holiday at the Custom house, there was no Board sitting . . .'.[24] Another day passed before Banks's concise and clear petition could be presented to the Commissioners of His Majesty's Customs:

as these sheep are imported solely with a view to the improvement of the Quality of British Wool and as by experiments which I have been permitted to try under Favor of your indulgence in the article of importation I have great reason to believe that an amelioration in that article of considerable material importance is likely to be effected I humbly request to be indulgd with a permit to land these sheep on paying the usual duties

as from the circumstance of my being absent in the country these sheep have been some time arrivd I humbly request that all convenient despatch may be given to this petition[25]

The formalities were observed as Banks was always careful that they should be. His petition was granted as Banks always knew it would, and Maclean ensured that an order was sent by the night's post to Southampton on 26 October to comply with the request. Then Maclean turned dutifully to another matter on Banks's behalf that same day. Having heard that the transport *Neptune* was arrived in the Downs he also made application to the Board for certain plants to be brought up from the ship and sent to William Aiton the elder, the Royal Gardener at Kew, where in due time the offspring of the sheep from Santander would also find their home.[26]

All this expedition and dispatch, civil service holidays notwithstanding, could be of small comfort to Captain John Burnell treading the docks at Southampton and wondering what the deuce to do. Cargoes of wool from Spain were one thing, but the strange little beasts that grew it seemed to conjure problems into existence that no honest sea-captain could be expected to foresee. Pleasantly assured by Banks's first and only letter to him[27] which he received on 26 October, Burnell had importuned the Collector of Customs, William Smith, 'to enquire of any News from the Board but not a scylable since our first Arrival'.[28]

Three weeks had now passed since the sheep had been embarked at Santander under the particular care of Santiago Blanco, the English Vice-Consul at that port. The small flock had arrived after a journey of more than one hundred miles from their mountain pasture near Cervera in Old Castile, entirely at the expense of the young Countess del Campo di Alange under the care of one of her shepherds.[29] To the original number of four rams and thirty-six ewes a tame wether or *manso* had been added to lead the flock in the accustomed Spanish manner. Blanco had shipped them in good health with a sufficient quantity of fodder, largely a dry oatmeal, but (so it was reported) too little water. Burnell had accepted full responsibility for them at an agreed freight of £20. He seems to have been at all times concerned for his charges on the voyage and after landing them at Southampton, where he shared with the Collector a personal interest in their well-being. Originally their destination was to have been London, but at the last moment this was changed to Southampton. On the bill of lading they were consigned to 'Sir Joseph Banks, President of the Royal Society or His Brittanic Majesty', and on 7 October 1791 their voyage began.[30]

Seven stormy days followed, but the *King George* was 'as fine a vessell as swims about 160 tons Burthen', and at the end Burnell could 'safely swear that neither one of them had a foot wet with Fresh or salt water during the Passage'. His normal trade was between Santander and Bristol with occasional voyages to London, presumably carrying

Spanish wool for the owner, Mr. John Newland of Salt Hill, Chichester, one of the largest importers of that vital commodity.

The voyage ended safely in Southampton Water on the evening of 14 October, and Captain John Burnell had thoroughly discharged his task and his cargo, to find that the reward of virtue was 'an arrest on acct of the sheep'. This was bad enough, but Burnell felt aggrieved at the manner in which the Collector had acted, 'which do not much redound to his Honour'. Burnell had gone to Portsmouth to buy an anchor and in his absence an officer was put on board so that when he returned and thought to put to sea he was prevented. It was of no avail to explain, with every documentary proof, that the sheep were 'a present from his Catholick Majesty to his Brittanic Majesty only'. It was of no avail to ask the Collector 'if he would permit me to sail if I gave sufficient security to be answerable for the value of the vessell which is Eight Hundred pounds'. William Smith, Collector of His Majesty's Customs, 'an extremely liberal and sensible man', upheld the dignity and honour of his post and was not to be moved from the due process of the law.[31]

So on 27 October, John Burnell found himself under the disagreeable necessity of acquainting Banks that he was still detained and that he would continue so to do by every post until an order came with leave for him to sail. He had noted a protest as he was under demurrage with a cargo waiting and added that 'in order to Augment this unlucky affair there is two Ladys from Bristol come here to take their passage to Spain in the *King George*, and Southampton is a very expensive place. . . . I Ly here at a very great dayly expence. . . .'[32]

The exasperation of Captain Burnell was now soon to be relieved by the arrival that same day of the order from the Commissioners ensuring the release of the sheep and, by inference, his own 'enlargement'. Banks received but one letter more from this active and conscientious merchant-captain and that written with obvious relief 'seven miles from Southampton on My Passage to Spain', dated 29 October, setting out the freight and charges to the total sum of £34 5s. od. which he had drawn a bill on Banks payable in thirty days, and promising 'when plese God I arrive in Spain shall Acquaint Mr Merry what hath happend'.[33] This news was confirmed by William Seward, who had returned to Southampton and to whom Burnell had confided the position and the reasons for drawing the bill. 'The Captain assures me that he is orderd to do this as he has a Cargo for Spain which he has been obligd to detain here till the Custom house order comes down to this Port.' Seward left for Bath after writing on 29 October also, but not before arranging matters with the Collector of the port 'who is a very sensible and worthy man' and who 'will give you any assistance he can in this business. Two only of the Sheep are dead. The others are healthy & well.'[34] John Newland's clerk in Southampton, probably on the advice of Captain Burnell, applied to the Collector for the sheep, but was very properly refused until an order came from Banks himself.

IV

Meanwhile in Revesby Abbey four days had elapsed without news. Banks felt constrained, therefore, to write to David Maclean on 3 November, expressing himself 'in some degree uneasy being uncertain whether all is right or not at Southampton'.

I must therefore request that you will on the Rec^t of this send some trusty person to Southampton whose charges I will willingly pay to see how the Sheep are circumstanced, hire a proper person to look after them till they are ready to travel & pay the Freight & such reasonable charges as may be thought justifiable excluding any disputable ones for my determination

he should also take account of the Sheep specifying the Sex of each & whether any pregnant Ewes or Lambs among them and make an agreement with some person for their pasture & the care of them during the time they are to remain & judge as far as he is able whether they will travel or whether they must be brought in a carriage & if so whether one wagon will contain them

Enclosd is a bill of lading by which it appears that the freight is 20—there will be charges on them for Provisions &c &c about 6—Expenses of the Person sent—Present to the officers if it is found as I believe it will be that they have behaved with propriety and civility—Expence of noting the vessel & demurage if a reasonable sum only is chargd—

in order to cover these Expences which must be left to the Prudence of the Person you send I enclose a draught for £50 if they exceed [this] I dare say the Persons concernd will give me credit till my Return if not you will be so good as to Acct with me for the surplus when we meet

I shall be in London on the 9th of this month by which time I conclude the person will be returned if he will call in Soho Square any time on the 10th and before 11 in the morn I shall be ready to receive his report on the business.[35]

These commands David Maclean was 'honoured to receive' on 5 November and promised to send 'My Son Henry (that is in the Servitory office) to Southampton to Execute your Orders to the utmost of his power not being able to procure any other person that will pay so much attention to them—'.[36] Henry Maclean duly set out on 6 November attended to the matter faithfully according to Banks's orders, and returned in good time to present his report in person at Soho Square, wherein it appeared that the Collector of Customs, William Smith, had bestowed 'obliging care' on His Majesty's sheep for which he was thanked in a letter from Banks on Friday, 11 November.[37] This was received in Southampton on Saturday, 12 November, and replied to that same day by the Collector and the Controller, W. Pintott, jointly setting out the arrangements for the journey to Windsor, starting on Monday, 14 November.[38]

During their enforced stay in Southampton of exactly four weeks the sheep had been well provided in the Collector's arrangements for them. At night they were accommodated 'in a dry Coach House and Stable' owned by William Rogers with access to hay and water. When the weather permitted they were turned into a field to graze for three or four hours in the middle of the day. Two men attended to them daily over the whole period, during which they consumed a ton and a quarter of hay or about two and a half pounds per head per day. According to Henry Maclean all the ewes were in lamb except two; two apparently died soon after they were landed under circumstances not easily deduced, but which may have been associated with the manner of their feeding and handling during the passage from Spain. Of these two casualties Banks noted later:

The people who brought them up inform me that the sheep which died sufferd for want of water on board they having been fed with dry oat meal and other such matter & that when opend their stomachs were full of the water they had drunk on shore most likely had the passage which was only a week been very little longer all or most of them would have died also.[39]

The sheep set off from Southampton travelling afoot for Windsor on Monday, 14 November, under the care of William Whiteway and Thomas Zurd, two Extra Officers of the port, 'who formerly have been Butchers and who understand the business'. The journey of sixty miles was arranged in stages of an average twelve miles a day and it was completed as scheduled by noon on Friday, 18 November, when they were delivered into the custody of John Robinson at the Queen's Lodge, in the Little Park.

The droving route led in stages to Winchester (14th) then Poping Lane (15th), Basingstoke (16th), Harford Bridge (17th), then via Bagshot Heath and Blackwater to Hatchet Lane (18th), and so to Windsor by noon on the same day. The total charges of £2 13s. 6½d. for the sustenance of men and sheep and turnpike fees were settled by John Robinson with Whiteway and Zurd before Banks could deal with the matter. In consequence they gained this sum over and above the £6 that Henry Maclean had allowed them already. Banks noted them down as 'very Shabby Fellows'. Apparently only the additional charges for the sheep themselves; that is, their hay and the turnpike fees for their journey were to be refunded.[40]

Meanwhile Banks in correspondence with Ramsay Robinson, the Clerk of the Royal farms and gardens, had duly warned him of the expected arrival of the thirty-nine Spanish sheep and inquired after the King's intentions for the morning of Saturday, 19 November, in case His Majesty should choose to see the sheep while Banks was there himself.[41] Robinson called at Soho Square on Wednesday, 16 November, without seeing Banks to convey the news that the King 'in all probability will leave the Lodge to go a Hunting about 1/4 Past nine (as it is called [a] long hunting day)'.[42] In the end it seems that Banks took his first view of the little flock that was to be his constant care and preoccupation for the next fifteen years without his Royal master.

His impressions were immediately recorded at Windsor and the more urgent problems of their future discussed with Ramsay Robinson on the spot.

. . . they are very similar to those that have been procurd before & have extremely fine Fleeces Whether however they are finer than those already in H. M. possession can only be determind by experiment I think myself there are some among the old ewes quite as Fine

the Rams have their horns broken off very short & the Ewes have their Right ears slit & most of them the upper edge of their Left ears cut out there are some few variations in the ear marks besides these both sexes have their tails cut off close to the Rump.

in the year [1789] a Ram & 3 Ewes were brought from Bilboa by means of M[r] Nepean docked and broken horned exactly like these I have directed M[r] R [obinson] to examine [these] & write me word whether the ear marks are the same

Six of the Ewes have horns all but one seemd to be one year old sheep the Rams also are young but the wether is an old sheep it seems he was cut when young he certainly has not been twitchd in our manner

Here in a few words is a first-hand picture of the thirty-nine survivors of the forty-one sheep from Santander, the port they had left six weeks before. These are the thirty-nine sheep among whose descendants would be numbered those eight which, thirteen years later, on 29 November 1804 from Portsmouth, would set sail in the *Argo* for that same coast which Banks as a young man had explored with Captain James Cook. These are the thirty-nine sheep which became the essential nucleus of His Majesty's Spanish flock as it would eventually be known to British farmers for the next twenty years, and to the new colonists in the South Seas. These are no 'contraband lot' but an open gift from the former Spanish Ambassador at the Court of St. James's, and now the Minister of the War Department in his own country, and from his lovely young wife in some measure as a gesture of appreciation for His Majesty King George III. So also was that fête at Ranelagh over three years before. For the moment, however, this background of diplomacy and courtly niceties was far from Banks's mind. The important thing was to instruct Mr. Ramsay Robinson on the management and security of this precious new importation. He was therefore desired,

to cover the shed & make it Rain tight
to cover the bottom of it with sand that the sheeps feet may be kept dry
to Fodder them always in the enclosure & shut them in it of nights
to make a smaller fold for the Ewes when they Lamb & Fence it round with Rye straw as is done at Kew leaving however a part of the shed at one side of it
to give the sheep bran & oats with a little salt twice this week and about once a fortnight afterwards
to keep them wholly confind if the weather is very wett[43]

V

Having left these explicit commands at Windsor, Banks returned to Soho Square, perhaps not entirely free from concern for the husbandry of his new charges but with a gathering anger again for the consequences of this elaborate exercise in diplomacy. That evening the full importance of these things seemed to loom large again now that the practical issues of settling the sheep at Windsor were done.

Mr Merry has put a Final stop to what I always intended as [a] Finish by his impudent and unauthorisd application to the Court of Spain I meant if the Experiment had been Provd really valuable to this Country to have suggested to H. M. the Propriety of asking his Spanish Majesty for a supply of sheep but should never have been contented under 50 or 100 Rams at least the late Emperor who askd a similar favour took 2000 at one time
Possibly it may be worth H. M. while yet to ask for a Spanish Shepherd much information might be gaind from him it is Probable that for a[n] annuity of £50 a year for Life such a person could engage to stay here 6 or 7 years during which time the whole of his knowledge would be easily got from him[44]

So ran his thoughts on that Sunday morning of 20 November 1791 as he cast his mind over the situation in general. New troubles seemed to have burgeoned from that letter which he had found waiting for him from Lord Auckland ten days before on his return from Revesby Abbey.

I understand that Lord St. Helens has also written to Lord Grenville on the subject of the inclos'd Letter. The Transaction on the Part of the Alange's Family is certainly handsome in the extreme; & I think it possible that our Flock may prove a Treasure of infinite value to His Majesty's good old Island of Great Britain.[45]

The 'inclos'd Letter' from Merry was the real source of his present dilemma, but the reference by Auckland to this 'Treasure of infinite value' seemed to add salt to the rub. Value! It was this matter of value that somehow had become magnified and out of all proportion, certainly not to infinity, but beyond all reason in the estimation of a very sapient President of the Royal Society who had by no means overlooked the point. Small wonder Merry had written to Auckland,

. . . to crave your Lordships interference both as to the explaining [of] it fully to Sir Jos: to whom as being both an entire stranger I could not take the liberty of writing so confidentially on the subject, & as to the using any other means you may think proper of informing H. M. of the nature of the case.

As to the nature of the case,

. . . unfortunately the most embarrassing part of it remains to be settled, & lays me under the necessity of intreating your Lordship's assistance to get it compleated in a becoming handsom manner:[46]

Merry's explanation of how the sheep came to be presented as a gift to the King was all very reasonable, granted that it was unavoidable that it should be known that the sheep were intended for His Majesty King George III of Great Britain if a licence for their exportation was to be procured at all. Lord Auckland's friend Don Gaspar de Montijo, on whom all hopes in the business had been placed from the beginning, had by some form of indolence and neglect deprived Merry of the means of completing his commission. In the sunny atmosphere of returning favour at the Court of Spain there could be no more natural response than 'M. & Mad. del Campo di Alange's gallantry on the occasion' in offering their sheep as a present in the easy generosity so 'conformable to the usage of their own Country, which your Lordship is acquainted with'. Moreover, there was, it must be remembered, in the minds of the Alanges some recollection of former hospitality and friendship at the Court of St. James's and at Windsor.[47] We can well believe that Count Bernardo and the Countess del Campo di Alange had no thoughts whatever of any return from the King at Windsor when the sheep were made available in response to Merry's request. Equally we can believe Merry that he 'had no idea when the sheep were embarked but that he would have allowed me to pay for them'. It is easy to see how a difference in perspective could lead to this confusion. To the Spanish Count and his wife what, after all, were thirty-six ewes and four rams from their vast flock of many thousands? To the English diplomats there was no question but that protocol should be observed, however small the gift, in a negotiation that now had openly involved the King. It was unfortunate, perhaps, but, said Merry,

. . . Lord St. Helens and I imagining that the King might possibly think proper to make some return, we suggested what we considered might be an acceptable one to the Spanish Minister or his Lady.[48]

Clearly, as this return was to be made by Royalty in a 'becoming handsom manner' the ordinary canons of *quid pro quo* should not be expected to apply entirely. Merry in his dilemma naturally turned to his senior diplomatic partner through whom the whole commission had been transmitted in the first place. He trusted that Auckland would see the necessity of the King's making some kind of acknowledgement and would use some means of having it conveyed to the King's knowledge 'in order that H. M., & indeed myself also, may not appear in a bad light in the eyes of the Spanish Minister & his Lady'. In this manner, then, was born the payment in kind that so outraged the exacting conscientiousness of Banks:

It occurs, my Lord, that, as it may be agreeable to your Lordship & to Sir Jos: that I should mention what may be a proper and an acceptable return from H. M. to Madam del C[ampo] as [a] present (as the Sheep, but particularly the Rams, of the fine breed of this Country bear a great value) I cannot suggest a nearer equivalent for them, considering it as a present from the King, than a Set of English carriage horses, which (the Countess being very sick & overstock'd with diamonds) I conceive may be more acceptable to her than anything else.[49]

There can have been few occasions in Banks's long life of meticulous business transactions when his careful estimates were so rudely upset, and we may surely excuse his private fulminations on the 'impudent and unauthorisd' activity of Anthony Merry at this worrisome stage in the whole protracted affair. His own calculations had disposed him to think in very different terms and he was shocked at the disparity in values which the comparison revealed. This estimate he had noted down:

Valuation of the Santander Sheep at the Rate Paid
in Estramadura[50]

3 Rams [sic] at 17^{s}/	2 : 11 : 0
1 wether at Do	0 : 17 : 0
36 Ewes at 12/4	22 : 4 : 0
	£25 : 12 : 0

With values in this order of magnitude, which Banks knew from many past transactions and inquiries were reasonable and likely, the 'Set of

English carriage horses' wore the aspect of a mad extravagance. Somehow, in his single-minded devotion to the utilitarian and scientific objects of the 'Patriotic National project', he was not to be wooed into diplomatic gestures or graceful gallantries to Spanish countesses, however 'sick & overstock'd with diamonds'. On the other hand, if this were to be the inevitable finale to this diplomatic gambit in which he had trusted to the judgement of his old friend Auckland, then he was ready enough to let nature take its political course with a good grace, but not without some protest:

Ld. Auckland having communicated to me your Letter on the subject of the Present expected in Return I took the earliest opportunity of mentioning to H. M. the manner in which the sheep had been presented to him but understanding during the conversation that Ld. St. Helens had written a Letter on the subject & that his Lordships Letter had been already forwarded to Windsor I judgd it not Prudent to enter into further explanation, as his Lordship has no doubt in that Letter stated the Political reasons which justify the propriety of accepting a present in the King's name & incurring thereby the necessity of a Return of all of which being totally ignorant I had it not in my power to enter upon any kind of explanation[51]

If Anthony Merry, quite humanly, desired not to appear in a bad light in the eyes of the Spanish Court neither perhaps did Banks wish to endanger his own reputation for care and accuracy in the information he was continually laying before the King. If his assessment differed from that of Merry then 'because H. M. has received different information from me the contradiction will be expected to be authenticated' and,

Unluckily for this business H. M. has long ago receivd information concerning the value of the Merino Sheep in Spain collected from the best Authorities I was able to obtain; among others made use of I find Lord Auckland who in answer to some queries of mine writes that the common price of a Ram of the Travelling breed is 60 Reals [vellons] when his wool is off & opposite to the question of what is the highest price that has of late years been given for a Ram of the Superfine sort leaves it a blank whence I concluded that no Price much if at all above the common one is ever given. to Fill up this blank will Sir be a matter of no small importance to the business in hand & I shall be much obligd if you will furnish me with authenticated Facts of Large Prices being Paid for such sheep as the Countess has sent which you may be assurd I will make the proper use of without the least delay[52]

In writing thus to Merry the sun had set often enough on Banks's first wrathful feelings to remove the sting from any reproofs that he may have felt tempted to administer, though he makes it very clear that in his opinion the matter was somehow out of hand. This letter was given

to Mr. James Bland Burgess, Under-Secretary at the Foreign Office on
2 December 1791, and Banks hoped Merry would 'consider H. M.
business contained in this Letter as a sufficient apology for its being
wrote confidentially & markd Private'. Here the correspondence with
Spain rested until the spring of 1792, while Banks in the meantime
addressed himself to seeking confirmation about the prices of Spanish
sheep in other quarters. He had been informed that the late Emperor
of Austria about 1785–6 had asked permission from the Spanish Crown
to export Merino sheep from Spain. This had been granted and two
thousand were instantly shipped off. Such a liberal interpretation
being regarded as excessive, the business was stopped. Banks submitted
this also to Mr. Burgess at the Foreign Office for the attention of Sir
Robert Murray Keith, the Ambassador in Vienna, on 2 December:

> if the Prices at which these sheep were purchasd could be obtaind it would
> throw much light on the value of the Present of Sheep sent to his Majesty
> by the Countess del Campo de Alanges & lead toward fixing the value of a
> proper return as the Emperor is said to have spard no expense in obtaining
> these sheep from the Flocks most esteemd for the value of their Wool[53]

He had embodied the same query in his letter to Merry saying that
'any anecdote relative to the business will be highly acceptable'.
    On Christmas Eve 1791, Burgess received a brief letter in cipher from
Sir Robert Murray Keith which was decoded and sent under cover of
a letter of 7 January 1792[54] to Banks:

> I am glad to seize an opportunity of executing a Commission of yours
> and of rendering even the slightest service to Sir Joseph Banks.
>   The following is an Extract from the Books of the Late Emperor's Private
> Treasury and the precision of it may be relied on.
>   The Spanish Sheep, Male and Female, cost on the spot from Fifteen
> Shillings and Fourpence to Seventeen Shillings and Sixpence per Head.
> They were brought by sea to Leghorn, and from thence to Trieste at the
> Emperor's Expence; yet when they reached there they could not be sold
> for less than Two Pounds Sixteen Shillings each, as during the Journey, and
> in the first Two Months after their arrival in Germany, Two Thirds of the
> Sheep died[55]

This information, as Burgess remarked, was all very much 'as we
had conceived it to be and I do not know why it should be imagined
that more ought to be given for that Commodity now than when His
Imperial Majesty made His purchase'. Viewed as a matter of business
this was undoubtedly true. As a matter of diplomacy it was doubtful.
As a matter of common sense and tact it left much to be desired. As a
point in international amity and *politesse*, when we recall the full

circumstances, this pinch-penny attitude seems to have been wholly blind. There was no strict comparison possible between the two affairs.

His Imperial Majesty had made a direct application for leave to purchase sheep as an ordinary business procedure to the limits within which there is ever an ordinary commercial undertaking between two crowned heads of State.

Sir Joseph Banks and Lord Auckland had connived in a diplomatic raid on a vital Spanish commodity in a manner designed to conceal its true purpose, that of ultimate independence from the need to buy Spanish fine wool. Morally it was an abuse of hospitality. But then so is much that passes under the guise of diplomacy in practice. Against the background of eighteenth-century ethics it was certainly less flagrant than we may flatter ourselves it would be now. Against any social standards, however, we must feel that something is lacking when the putative thief being caught in the act and then presented with the loot complains because the coals of fire are too hot. When the secret was out the sheep seem to have been given with a simple generosity that is still an attractive mode in any pastoral community. We may reasonably accept the Alanges' disclaimer of any interest in payment as genuine, and that they certainly did not spread hints about carriage horses. This 'acceptable return' seems to have had no origin other than in the awakened consciences of the English diplomats who were close enough to the actual events to appreciate the true spirit in which the gift was made. Lord St. Helens and Anthony Merry could sense the importance of an *amende honorable*, the more important perhaps because Spanish courtesy brushed aside the need. As the episode drew to its close in the spring and early summer of 1792 these issues seem eventually to have weighed with Banks now that he had established the basic valuation of these livestock to his own satisfaction. Merry's last letter to him on the subject dated 1 May 1792[56] had apparently set the issues more plainly in his mind as he finally conceded the field to a diplomatic conclusion of the affair:

as I conjectured in my last the business of the Present from the King to the Count del Campo di Alange has been transacted wholly by the Minister without any degree of interference of mine [I] should readily have done my utmost had any misunderstanding taken place to explain the true state of facts with which you have favoured me to the King but as matters appeard to go on smoothly without my interference I have judgd it prudent hitherto to remain Quiet should however the slightest hint be dropt relative to your conduct which renders it necessary I shall not fail to state fully the Facts communicatd by your last letter which amounts in my opinion to the compleat justification in your Part

The high feelings of the previous autumn about Merry's 'impudent and unauthorisd application' had subsided under his rising sensations of success achieved and his new understanding of the critical part which His Majesty's Consul-General and chargé d'affaires at Madrid had really played. So far in fact had these old annoyances receded into limbo that Banks was ready again to enlist Merry in active service pursuing the same quarry:

The King has now got together a Flock of about 100 individuals of the true Spanish breed among which yours are certainly the best he is fond of them & wishes for more especially for the purpose of sending to his Hanoverian dominions if you sir could procure a licence for the sending of any number not less than 20 or more than 100 without running any risk of another lot of Horses becoming the necessary political return you certainly would do a thing very grateful to H. M.[57]

Of this last direct attempt by Banks and Merry to wrest the Golden Fleece from Spain we know little or nothing in detail. The jocular warning about avoiding the risk of 'another lot of Horses' seems to have been well taken for we encounter no more flutterings among the diplomats on this score. All we find that could possibly reflect the success of this final scheme is a brief note by Banks made ten years later:

by Cost of 21 Merino Sheep imported
from Lisbon & sent by H. M. Command
to Hanover. Mr. Best paid the
Freight & all other charges—£27. 12. 6.[58]

Business in the Banksian manner was back to normal and thenceforward his problems were those of guarding and developing this 'Treasure of infinite value' within the finite limits of the Royal farms. There were no more foreign adventures in the sheep trade for many years as the shadows lengthened over Europe and Britain once again was slowly driven to adopt her defensive role of island fortress.

As the affair of the Countess and the carriage horses lapsed into its obscure historic niche the Revolutionary mob in France was tearing down the old Monarchy at the Tuileries. In Spain the star of Floridablanca had set, and that of the shallow adventurer Godoy was appearing in the chaos that was rapidly spreading over the Peninsula as war with the new French Republic drew closer. On 11 August 1792, the day after the storming of the Tuileries, the massacre of the Swiss Guard, and the imprisonment of the King of France, Banks wrote his 'Statement relative to the Sheep received from Madrid in consequence of Lord Auckland's undertaking' for the King of England, as though nothing could, or would, disturb the future he had determined for the flock. He could close his report on the undertaking with satisfaction that all had come right at last in everything but the settlement of the account:

They are of the Negretti Flock, the second in estimation of all those whose wool is imported into England: the Perales is the first: and the difference between these two is scarce perceivable to the best Judges, so that in point of utility for carrying on your Majesty's experiment, they must be considered as a most valuable acquisition; and it is no more than Justice to Mr Merry to state from a Letter of his, dated May [1, 17]92, that he had no idea, even when the sheep were embarked, but that he would have been allowed to pay for them.[59]

In the final estimation of the President of the Royal Society this should have been exactly £33 15s. 6d., not 'a Set of English carriage horses'. In the estimation of His Majesty's diplomats carriage horses there must be, and before the month of August was out the incident had been closed 'in a becoming handsom manner'. Diplomatic honour was at last satisfied, and the conclusion suitably and succinctly noted by the Press on 27 August 1792:

The whole of the ROYAL FAMILY are in perfect health and spirits.
HIS MAJESTY lately received a present from the Duchess CONDESA DE CAMPO ALANGE, consisting of some of the finest SPANISH sheep her country could afford. As some return of kindness to the fair Spaniard, his MAJESTY has sent eight fine bay horses of uncommon beauty, which were shipped off from the Tower on Wednesday last [22 August 1792] for Bilboa, and are to be conveyed with all due care to their intended mistress.[60]

The lapse of a further year seemed so far to have smoothed the first asperities of Sir Joseph's outraged sense of business over the carriage horses that he was prepared, on 6 August 1793, to prosecute the idea spontaneously in his report to the King. He appeared now even to grapple the notion to himself with some enthusiasm. There is every sign that, having pondered the whole affair quietly for some months, it had developed attractions of whose charm he had been formerly unaware. The prospects of further success, however, were now remote. The outbreak of war with France had changed everything. But even the prodigal excess of the gift of carriage horses seems to have acquired in his mind the virtue of an expedient and well-justified expense as he ruefully covered the matter in his final reference on the point to the King:

in Consequence of the war which compels merchant men to fit their Ships in such a way as to be able to resist a small Privateer or to order them to wait for Convoy both which measures render the Carriage of Live stock much [more] precarious than it is in times of peace Sr Jos: Banks has not made any attempts to import sheep this season as soon as peace returns he means to avail himself of the Kings Gracious Permission to renew his attack upon the Negretti Flock & he has no doubt that the Generous Present his majesty made to the Countess del Campo de Alange will render her completely propitious to his request.[61]

The Count, as Spanish Ambassador, and his young Countess spent a brief period again in England before hostilities drew them for ever away from the Court of St. James's. The war extended in 1796 to bring Spain into enmity with Great Britain. Old age intervened in all the parties to this small diplomatic incident before peace returned. The fortune of war added its own hindrance. Count Bernardo found it in the end more expedient to foster the French interest and finally to adopt its cause. Sir Joseph was never able to discover how far the carriage horses had rendered the Countess 'propitious' to his or His Majesty's further request for sheep. Fifteen years later military force supplanted the need for diplomatic nicety.[62]

CHAPTER VI

The Faithful Shepherd, 1788–1811

I

THE President of the Royal Society assumed the additional burdens of scientific shepherd to His Majesty's Spanish flock slowly and by no means certainly. No Royal letter of appointment set a seal on his position or defined his sphere of authority. No form of emolument was offered or even suggested, nor, it seems, was any formal plan of management conceived which in itself we might dignify as an experimental design for the study of Spanish sheep. All that we can discern is a groping by trial and error towards a better practical understanding of what the Spanish fine-woolled sheep was in fact, and towards a working relationship within and without the Court and the Royal estates under which the breeding of this highly important little animal could be fostered to a stage when it could indeed serve the national interest. There were trials for everybody concerned and errors in plenty.

Sir Joseph Banks, as we have seen, had been drawn into the forum of the controversies which arose in Lincolnshire and Yorkshire over the crises of wool production and trade at the end of the American War of Independence. He found no great relief from this tedium until the final passage of the Wool Bill in July 1788. The affairs of the county, of the Royal Society and its 'Dissensions', of the wool trade and its fears of French competition, and finally his own initiative in establishing the Spanish fine-woolled breed at Spring Grove had all in their various ways conspired to thrust him forward in public notice as something more than the savant of Soho Square. He had become established as a man of probity and perceptiveness in a national way and as one of singular knowledge in most things concerning the sheep industry and the wool trade of Great Britain and Europe. The King himself had been relieved perforce, by the dissolution of the North administration and all that followed the loss of the American colonies, from a large measure of personal intervention in the nation's affairs. He had, therefore, since 1783 turned increasingly to an active interest in agriculture. This took the very practical form of converting many of the Royal parks into places where various farming 'experiments' in the eighteenth-century sense could take shape and grow. His genuine concern for the economic well-being of his kingdom and for its scientific advance in all fields of knowledge had over the same period engaged his personal interest in the various wool controversies. This inevitably had drawn him by degrees closer to a common interest on many things with Sir Joseph Banks. Ever since Mr. Banks, the young biological explorer, had returned with Captain Cook after the first Pacific voyage there had, of course, been ample contact between the King and his scientific commoner.[1] But it was not perhaps until the agricultural distresses of Lincolnshire and its conflict with Yorkshire on the Parliamentary battle-field of Westminster that their relationship found a true common purpose of the kind from which a ripe friendship could grow. More-over, it was not until Robert Fulke Greville entered the inner Court circle as the King's Equerry in 1782 that the last important link in the chain of human relations necessary to its mature growth was forged. The mutual friend who could with ease and suitable authority pass from Soho Square to St. James's or Windsor was the vehicle of communica-tion by which immediately mere interest was translated into effective action. With the advent of Greville the course for the next fifteen years was clearly set and His Majesty acquired the dedicated service of the man who in time he jovially dubbed on occasions 'His Farming Secretary'.[2] Whatever else the duties of an Equerry may have been there is no doubt that Greville certainly performed this secretarial function in some measure for the King. As such in the earliest stages for several years he did much to supervise the Spanish flock at Windsor and to mediate in this way between Banks and the King. It is also clear that Banks did not force himself actively into the business of the King's Spanish flock, however much the subject in general may have been close to his own heart and interest. Of this we have more than a hint when in late November 1789 Banks had told the King, through Greville, of the impending arrival of the second lot of sheep from Bilbao organized by Evan Nepean. To this welcome news Greville had replied for His Majesty in those soothing terms in which he was so fluent.[3] He neatly conveyed to Banks the impression of recovering interest by the King in his little flock. Conversely, he had evidently warmed the Royal heart with subtle glimpses of Sir Joseph's own bursting anxiety for the same theme, struggling against the chains of commendable diffidence and a dutiful fear of intruding on regal privacy. The upshot was all that Banks could have wished as Greville concluded:

Therefore, my Dr Sir Joseph, go when you chuse, and get *exact* lists which the King will be glad always to receive from you.

    The state at Kew this day is
        3 Old Spanish Rams
        1 Young one

18 True Spanish Ewes
  2 True Spanish Lambs and one Ram Lamb
    Others expected to lamb in a month
I thank you for your last letter; this is all my present hurry allows me to
say—I will resume in another letter, at present, Adieu.

Before the end of the year Banks had checked these figures and noted
the additions from Bilbao. Beyond this nothing could be done until the
following summer. Greville's letter was the beginning of Banks's
effective stewardship of the Spanish flock and as close to a real directive
as he ever seems to have received. It is true that earlier, on 4 June 1789,
he had 'washed his Majesties sheep' with '7 people in the River opposite
Mr Keen's house at Richmond'.[4] Also the year before on 26 June 1788
he had 'Weighed his Majesties wool', learning much in the process.[5]
But between these events there had been the very distressing period of
the King's illness and the long convalescence of 1789 spent at Weymouth. Banks noted that the King 'had not regarded them much since
his recovery' and therefore 'did not think it right to trouble him on the
subject'.[6] Thus it was not until 15 August 1790, when Banks visited
'H. M. Flock at Windsor to see the sort of sheep kept there & their
respective conditions' that he really turned shepherd for his King. It
was auspicious, perhaps, that as he returned home along the road to
Spring Grove he met the King himself that day and had the 'honor of
Speaking to him on the Road near [Dr.] Herschel's when His Majesty
readily agreed that the Ram may not be put to the Spanish Ewes till
St Luke tide [1 October] as they are certainly a more tender stock than
the native sheep'.[7] Forthwith Mr. Ramsay Robinson, Clerk or Superintendent of the King's farms and gardens, was ordered by Banks to
attend to this and much else, for there were many things to be set
straight. 'Goddard [the shepherd at Windsor] neglected the whole
business of the Sheep during H. M. illness', had not made any distinction 'between the Lambs of the Metis Flock & the Real Spanish ones or
indeed [had] any marks put on any Lambs', and had been so careless 'in
dividing the sheep that I found an imported Spanish Ewe among the
Metis which the Shepherd did not miss till I shewd it to him'. Moreover, there were strong grounds for suspecting that some of the true
Spanish ewes had been crossed by a Wiltshire ram as had also the
Gloucester Notts and that this arose from the same careless supervision.
Whence Banks was constrained 'to submit whether it is not necessary
to have some one Person answerable that the Different Sorts are kept
distinct'. The wool clips of 1788 and 1789 had been confused and even
the recent one of 1790 'Left in the Care of Goddard the Shepherd' and
which Banks had 'many times desird might be kept separate' was 'mixd
in bringing it from Windsor to Marsh Gate where it now is as well as

I could pick out the Fleeces'.[8] Slowly and as tactfully as possible Banks straightened this tangle delegating the practical responsibilities for the future conduct of the flock to Ramsay Robinson, not to the uninformed vagaries of Goddard.

II

The summer of the year 1790 may reasonably be set as the beginning of a pattern of operations which was to continue with few important deviations for nearly fifteen years. Sir Joseph began his diary notes concerning the flock when on 15 August that year he took stock of the sheep at Windsor and found so much amiss. The following summer in June 1791 he attended his first clipping of the sheep and on 5 August he

Visited the Sheep and examind each separately, made a list of the whole experimental Flock and another of those part[s] of it which appears proper to be kept of which the copy is in the wool book.[9]

This was the first of the comprehensive annual inspections of all the sheep in the flock, but especially of the rams, on which so much thereafter depended. On these occasions he attached much importance to his view of the sheep recently shorn and without which he would not presume to pass a final judgement on an animal, however beautiful the wool it may have grown. The August 'classing' of the flock determined the rams and ewes that were to be mated in the autumn, those that were fit to be presented or sold to an increasingly clamorous array of nobles and commoners as the years passed, and those that were to be sold for mutton. On this occasion in 1791 Banks, having attended to the sheep, then packed the clip of that year which had been laid out in the Lodge since the shearing in

. . . three Baggs the Large one Containing the Fleeces of the imported & true bred Spanish one of the small ones N° 1 those of Daubentons metis the other N° 2 those of the Herefordshire and Spanish cross & orderd M^r [Ramsay] Robinson to forward them by the Stroud waggon to M^r [John] Hawker of Dudbridge[10]

He then saw the King on the terrace at Windsor Castle, 'who was graciously pleasd again to approve of what I had done & to command my attendance at the Lodge at 9 the next morn'.

Thus early on the morning of 6 August 1791, His Majesty King George III of England and the President of the Royal Society conferred together in the Lodge as appointed to take the first of many joint and practical decisions for the well-being of the flock and the future of the Spanish breed in the United Kingdom. The King was 'graciously pleasd again to approve' Sir Joseph's measures respecting the sheep, to inspect his wool book, and to accept from him a debtor and creditor account with His Majesty made up to 5 August that year. At this point in their association the King was indebted to his scientific shepherd for the disbursement of no less than £299 17s. 11d. on account of the various importations of Spanish sheep since January 1788.[11] This sum was by no means a small one in the currency of the day, and it was no doubt with some pleasure that the King received the next document which recorded the account of the true Spanish sheep received for this outlay. This stood at sixteen rams and fifty-eight ewes for the past three and a half years of far-flung and devious negotiations. Though this was certainly progress, neither the King nor Banks was satisfied for many reasons. They were certain that better sheep could be got in time, for neither had very high expectations of the quality to be gleaned from the contraband routes. The King, however, was sufficiently encouraged to say that as soon as he was satisfied that the wool was of the best sort he would order some for Hanover. Therefore, he instructed Banks that day to continue to import sheep from Lisbon or any other place whence the Merino breed could be got. Meanwhile the state of the flock was sufficiently secure in breeding stock for the King to agree readily to the list which Banks presented of persons who might be considered worthy to receive those rams not wanted for his own flock and to add Sir Joseph's name to the six submitted for his approval. Next day John Robinson was ordered 'to deliver them according to this List to the Persons whom the noblemen & Gentlemen for whom they are intended shall send for them'.[12] Who, then, were the honoured recipients of this first Royal dispensation from the Spanish flock? It was intended that they should be the 2nd Earl Bathurst (Ram No. 2); Mr. Arthur Young (Ram No. 3); Sir Joseph Banks (Ram No. 4); the Right Honourable Henry Dundas, Principal Secretary of State, on behalf of the new Society for the Improvement of British Wool in Edinburgh (Rams Nos. 5 and 6); the 4th Duke of Grafton (Ram No. 9); the Secretary for War, the Right Honourable Sir George Yonge (Ram No. 10); and the 2nd Duke of Newcastle (Ram No. 12). All reached their destinations that year except No. 6 for 'the Scotch Society'. By a misreading of Banks's list sent to Windsor only No. 5 was delivered to the Steward of the Principal Secretary of State. So No. 6 served in His Majesty's flock for three more years and as far as we know never reached Scotland.

On such a foundation of close personal relations was built the joint interest of the King and the President of the Royal Society in the flock that was to grow into a 'most National project'. It was a collaboration in these early years in which the King was to share in more ways than that of a Royal director. He was to suffer in the cause and to be tied as firmly to the wheel of Science as Sir Joseph could with decency contrive. Even as the orders for the distribution of the rams were being transmitted to John Robinson in the same letter Banks was preparing an ordeal that would test the devotion of his master to the search for truth and understanding:

as it is Probable that H. M. will be curious to tast the Spanish mutton I beg I may be acquainted when any of the 5 Ewes that were separated for the purpose of feeding are Fat & that none of them be sold to the butcher without my being acquainted with it[13]

And so fattened they were upon turnips until Wednesday, 28 March 1792, when they were killed and soon after, probably to His Majesty's surprise, appeared in the relatively Spartan fare at the Royal table. The following week Ramsay Robinson, by the King's command, sent some of the Spanish mutton to Soho Square which he thought 'from appearance will turn out exceeding good'.[14] But this was no novelty to the experimental biologist of Spring Grove who with his family for five years past had explored the culinary delights of Spanish mutton in all its forms and in many crosses from his own flock. The gustatory discernment of the King was put to the test for three years until in March 1795 he prayed for quarter. He sent Ramsay Robinson personally to Soho Square on this mission to tell Banks 'that T. K. had desired to have no more Spanish mutton at his Table'. Thus, as all the wethers of that year were fat, Banks told Robinson he desired 'that those now fit for the Butcher may be Fairly Sold to an honest man & the Price Reported to me'.[15]

Meanwhile the King had acquired from Spain in the autumn of 1791 the small flock from the Countess del Campo di Alange, that 'Treasure of infinite value' whose sudden advent had so transformed the vision of the future for the experimental Merinos under his patronage. The shearing of the 'Santanders' or the 'Old Negretti' flock in the early summer of 1792 was therefore an event of some moment. The King, Banks, the interested equerries, and all within the small circle at Windsor concerned with the sheep were curious to see the fleeces, part Spanish, part English grown, from the best and certainly the most authentic of all the fine-woolled stock from Spain. On 28 May, Ramsay Robinson called on Banks at Soho Square 'to Acquaint him that the Flock at Windsor will be ready to Clip on Saturday June 9ᵗ Where R will be by 8 o'Clock in the Morning'.[16] Promptly at eight o'clock on that Saturday morning Sir Joseph arrived to find five shearers under orders from Ramsay Robinson not to proceed as the rain on Friday had made the sheep so wet. Robinson had sent a letter to Spring Grove deferring the clipping until the following Monday, but Banks not being there this news had escaped him. After some discussion with the shepherd and the shearers who agreed that the sheep were dry enough Banks ordered them to proceed, taking the lambs first. It was the beginning of a long day. The fifty-five lambs required more than two hours at an average of eleven minutes and forty seconds each for one shearer. At ten o'clock His Majesty attended by his Equerry Major William Price was pleased to visit the scene and to order a ram for Lady Stormont, who came to Windsor the next morning and chose No. 7, one of the original contraband lot. He allotted another to Major Price who, then and there, chose the polled ram, No. 27, Windsor-bred out of the original Spanish. At ten minutes past eleven the shearers began upon the thirty-four ewes of the San-tanders. Then came the four rams and the bell-wether or *manso*. These were followed by the Windsor-bred ewes and rams until, by five o'clock, some sixty sheep had been shorn at an average rate of twenty-five minutes a sheep for each shearer. This year Banks was careful to see that the wool was kept carefully separated in three lots:

Santanders those presented to H M from Madrid
Original Spanish those imported before the last arrival
Windsor bred

Each of these was piled separately in a room at the Lodge except that from the original Spanish ewes which was put with the original rams' fleeces. Because the sheep were not very dry at the shearing Banks thought these piles might heat spontaneously. For this reason he wrote to Ramsay Robinson on Sunday morning directing him 'in case he found any heat among them to spread them out on the floor carefully keeping each parcel separate'.

Soon after five o'clock Sir Joseph was obliged to go away leaving the original Spanish ewes to be clipped after his departure. As he took his leave he gave the shepherd and the shearers a guinea—an annual gesture out of his own pocket, not the King's. He carried away with him some recollections of groaning shearers who had unanimously assured him that the Spanish sheep were shorn 'with much greater difficulty than English ones on account of their extreme greasiness which cannot be washd out by cold water'. On this note ended the second shearing of His Majesty's Spanish flock attended by Banks and the first attended by the King in person.[17] For another ten years or more this was to be a regular summer festival for Banks at Windsor where the rams continued to be shorn, and also at Kew where from 1793 the ewe flock of the 'Old Negrettis' were established, and shorn mostly 'in the Barn opposite the Pagoda' across Kew Lane and in a field of the King's Marsh Gate Farm. It is perhaps more correct to say that these shearings were attended by Banks as often as he could manage, although there were very few such occasions at which he did not spend some time, and these only when by sheer force of circumstances he was prevented. At length his own physical infirmity set a limit to practical activities of this kind with the flock, but never to his inclinations or his interest in them.

In August 1792 it had been determined that there would be no less than twelve spare rams out of the nineteen in the flock that year. On 11 August therefore the 'Destinations Proposed by Sr Jos: Banks, for his Majesties Spare Rams' was presented to the King for his approval and with it the first tentative notes from which in later years more ample reports were to grow:

The whole number of Rams in his Majesties Flock this year being 19 Seven will remain for use if no others are applied for which is more than sufficient, it is to be observed however that one of the Negretti Rams appears to have been partially castrated [the *manso*] by cutting off half the Testes and scrotum transversely a custom of which we are wholly ignorant, it is therefore impossible for us to Judge what proportion of work he will be able under this circumstance to do.

Sir Joseph Banks has some pleasure in stating that three of those candidates for his Majesties Gracious Bounty who are Farmers [Messrs. Farman and Knight of Kent; Mr. Slater of Surrey] have been advised to apply by his wool stapler [Bell of Bermondsey Street] who sorted & examind the wool of the different breeds of sheep that he has crossd with the Spanish

Sir Jos: Banks will be happy if he is permitted to state in future the progress of His Majesties Experiment on Spanish Wool in the same manner as M^r [Nathaniel] Kent reports the progress of the improvements in Windsor Park & he has reason to hope they will in a short time become interesting.

he has not yet receivd the account of the Merino wool of 1791 which he sent to be manufacturd by M^r [John] Hawker of Dudbridge in Gloucestshire but he has been informd from time to time that it is likely to answer very well

Till the Last year when Sir Joseph attended the Shearing in Person the wool had never been kept separate he has therefore sold the wool of the former years in its mixd state to his wool stapler who is highly delighted with the Samples of the Finest & Sr Jos: hopes to Encourage him to wash the whole & sell it as Spanish wool having no doubt that the greatest part of it is Equal in all good Qualities to such Spanish wool as is usually imported[18]

In this short paper is the formal style and germinating idea of five later and more elaborate reports on the affairs of the flock ending with that last document dated 17 August 1803 and published in July 1804 to usher into existence the first of the public sales of the King's Merinos.[19] There was nothing very regular or exactly annual about these papers. However, from this first small note in 1792 they form a sequence and a convenient short history of the early formative years of the experimental flock.

III

Behind the reports to his King on the subject of Spanish sheep and behind the extensive and growing passage of letters and notes on their management and disposal, all couched in terms of uniform courtesy and almost unvarying good humour, there lay a scattered series of notes forming a loose sort of journal over the years from 1790 to 1803. Here in Banks's private repository the same level temper appears, the same factual and patient recording of the details necessary for his advice to the King and the fulfilment of the Royal experiment. There are here, however, little flashes of annoyance, occasionally of real anger, but seldom any that would not appear to have been well justified by the event, whatever excuse the human error involved may have deserved. Sometimes we cannot now discern where the fault lay in many of the incidents that caused Banks's distress. It is very sure, however, that the whole situation was one to test the saintliness of an archangel. The sheep were His Majesty's. The parks and gardens where they were kept were His Majesty's. The servants who tended them as shepherds and who ordered their estate from day to day were His Majesty's. The gentlemen whose honest but dilettante interest in the sheep influenced so many of the King's decisions were the equerries and the grooms of the bedchamber. The whole enterprise had its being in a secluded world of its own to which a commoner, however distinguished his position as President of the Royal Society, had only a limited access. Once within the Royal gates there was still a host of unseen and unwritten restraints to the free exercise of an authority which, had the flock been on his own estates, Banks would certainly have used to solve innumerable practical problems and to discipline ineffective servants with incisive speed. Instead he found it necessary to delegate and direct at one or more removes with all the tact at his disposal the tasks that had to be accomplished and often enough withal to keep his own counsel. Seldom did his frustration break out into public view, but it is not surprising to find some evidence of it in his desultory notes from time to time on the course of events.

More than anything else these annoyances were associated with the form of management at Windsor where the rams were most commonly pastured. This difficulty was recognized in other quarters and certainly shared by Robert Fulke Greville, who wrote in the autumn of 1794:

. . . I am quite sorry that this Windsor *Robinson* & the Shepherd here are so little to be depended on as to their skill, or *zeal*. I shall watch the Flock now & then, & endeavour to help out a little at proper opportunities.[20]

Indeed, had it not been for Greville's timely and generally sensible mediation on many occasions the situation of the Spanish rams at Windsor might have been much worse than they mostly were. But Greville was not always on duty as Equerry, nor by any means always at Windsor when he was. There was much, therefore, in that year of 1794 to pain Sir Joseph and to give substance to Greville's autumnal strictures on the régime. The ram shearing of 18 June had been a sorry spectacle, and Banks noted that:

The washing has been abominable ill done. I never saw anything so worthy of blame in that way
The sheep have been neglected in a very great degree they are abominably full of Ticks & much struck with the Fly T[he] K[ing] orderd them to be washd sensible I hope of the necessity of ordering it sooner than was intended by the Shepherd

But in spite of the King's intervention on this occasion,

The Shearers say the sheep were washd too late the sweat had got into the wool so that it could not be washd out tho much pains was taken[21]

And yet, although his review of the rams that day and his individual notes thereon make sad reading as he lists them—'Lean very full of Ticks Peeld on the Rump'; 'Abominable dirty & shamefully full of Ticks The Picture of Famine'; or 'Tolerable case shockingly full of Ticks'[22]—Banks could yet note that 'The Sheep in General at Windsor are in better Condition than usual I think the Spring which has been remarkably mild & early with little East wind has agreed with them'. It was, therefore, surely a merciful Providence that also made it possible for him to record: 'The Feet of these Sheep are in much better order than those at Kew they have had little Foot rot this season'.

This year also the Santander ewes and their offspring at Kew were not in much better case. In addition to the rampant foot-rot which had infected the Wiltshire flock as well and was not improved by the shepherd neglecting to pare their feet, some of the old ewes were 'miserably Lean & the greater part in moderate store condition'.[23]

Finally, 'The days Fixd upon by Mr Robinson this year were so particularly inconvenient to me that it will be necessary another year to specify the Part of the week when I am least engaged'. From all of this we may deduce much about the recurrent tribulations of Sir Joseph and the vicissitudes of the Spanish flock, especially in the first years of its existence.

For about ten years Banks managed the affairs of the flock almost entirely through the agency of Alexander Ramsay Robinson, the Scot, who from Kensington supervised the practical details of the King's farms and gardens. His cousin John was 'the Windsor Robinson' whose skill and zeal were so deficient in the eyes of Greville and who was in charge of the gardens at Windsor Castle and, therefore, of the rams or of any sheep grazing in the Little Park. It was from John Robinson that the servants or agents of those who received the King's bounty in Spanish rams took delivery of their masters' stock. In later years it was Thomas Peasey, the King's Cowman at Frogmore, to whom the notes of authorization were delivered for sheep from the Little Park. All these however, were, until 1802, under the immediate authority of Ramsay Robinson, and it was with him that Banks maintained the necessary correspondence on day-to-day affairs. With Colonel Robert Greville the relationship was naturally different, even though at times it operated at the most ordinary level of daily practice. Greville was in the role of a liaison officer between the King and the outside world beyond the Castle gates. In the matter of agricultural affairs and those of the sheep flocks in particular, Spanish and otherwise, Greville was very truly the King's 'Farming Secretary'. As such, and as an old friend of Banks on many past botanical rambles and expeditions of other sorts together, Greville conveyed the King's thoughts and translated their motives and meanings to the President of the Royal Society for whom 'H. M. Mind' was by no means always transparently clear. There is a glimpse of Banks's dependence on the courtly sagacity of Greville when, in August 1796, he submitted the draft of a letter to be sent with the printed plan of a report which he hoped to elicit from the noblemen and gentlemen who had received Spanish rams from Windsor in the previous five years:

immediately on the Rec^t of yours I orderd M^r [William] Bulmer [of St. James's Street] to Print off 250 of the papers & Shall distribute them by degrees Enclosd you have a draught of a Letter to accompany them I do not think it necessary the King's approbation of it Should be askd but I fain would have your opinion as I am always in Terror when I use the King's name lest it should be done in such manner as would leave any kind of possibility of supposing me to do it in any other than the most respectable & considerate manner[24]

The following year this source of comfort was removed when Greville married his first cousin, Louisa Countess of Mansfield, and the former Lady Stormont, the young widow of the late Lord President of the Council, the 2nd Earl Mansfield. 'Colonel Wellbred', the married man, was lost for some time to Court circles and the friends of his bachelor years. Adorned now by the red ribbon of the Order of the Bath, Banks was perhaps by this time less in need of the moral support which Greville had provided for so many years. Much more to the point was it to find some worthy shoulder on which to lean, figuratively at least, as the years of gout took their toll and made the physical tasks of the summer with its shearings and sheep selections an increasing and, at times, an almost intolerable burden. 'His Majesty's Clip at Kew' on 18 June 1796 in the barn opposite the Pagoda was notable for the first appearance of the man who was now to give that form of support to Sir Joseph humbly and with great devotion. Moreover, a new form of occupation was created that day whose influence was to stretch down the next century and a half wherever the Spanish sheep were scattered when

Lacock[e] M[r] [John] Buxton's Foreman was employd to pick out the finest woold Sheep to mark them on the Right Shoulder & to mark those with less fine wool on the left Shoulder he watchd each sheep during the time it was shearing & examined the Fleece when cut off.[25]

In such a manner Henry Lacocke unobtrusively became the prototype of the sheep classer of the future and from that day forward was Sir Joseph Banks's man. The association of the Knight of the Bath and the elderly foreman wool stapler of Messrs. J. and J. Buxton of 62 Bermondsey Street, Southwark, grew slowly into a mutual dependence and an artless friendship of more than fourteen years' standing. It is one of the happier episodes in the very mixed personal relations which the Spanish flock called into being. Brought into the business originally for his special knowledge as a stapler of the finer wools and for his working experience as a foreman under John Buxton, Henry Lacocke remained to become one of the first practical experts with Spanish sheep in England under Sir Joseph's patronage.

IV

The year 1796-7 was disastrous for the Royal flock, marked by the heavy mortality during the winter and early spring. Nearly one-quarter of the ewes had been lost already in the winter of 1795-6. Now, at the shearing tally of 1797, it was found that the general loss for the flock was about twenty-eight per cent. At Windsor no less than fifteen of the thirty-seven rams had died. At Kew thirty-one out of a hundred and twenty-one ewes and ewe tegs were dead. The position was aggravated by a diminishing number of lambs born and surviving. There is no doubt that this year was the nadir of the Spanish flock. If ever Sir Joseph's private fulminations were justified it was during this period. At Kew no less than at Windsor total mismanagement was totally evident. Some great change was needed if the flock was not merely to do credit to the King's intentions but even to survive.[26]

It had long been clear to Banks that if the Spanish sheep were to be kept in a reasonable state some separate arrangement must be made for them. To have some one person answerable for their well-being, at least until their special peculiarities were better understood by the English shepherds, was an early point he had made with the King. If His Majesty had perceived its good sense the force of it had certainly not as yet penetrated the ranks of his servants. The Spanish sheep had remained the daily task of no one in particular. They had suffered under this diffuse system as unpopular intruders. Most evidently determined to break through this situation Banks seized his chance, in the desperate condition of the flock, to argue the need for some complete change. There were good reasons perhaps for keeping the rams at Windsor. This was in fact the King's own desire. But the grazing grounds and the husbandry of the ewes could certainly receive attention. With the King's consent Banks reconnoitred the situation in the Duke of York's park at Oatlands near Weybridge.[27] Armed with a long list of no less than twenty-six questions he found the answers he was seeking. All of them led to the conclusion that a total removal of the ewe flock to Oatlands Park was both feasible and certainly much nearer the standard of supervision he sought. Here were two to three hundred acres of sheep-walk, totally enclosed, on which the Duke of York kept only a wether flock of about three hundred for fattening and sale at Guildford market. Although the whole area was open no breeding was done there. Hence the ewe flock could here be safely mated, free from risk of accidental crossing with other breeds—the continual problem of the past at Windsor and at Kew. In any case it was arranged that the flock should be separated from any other sheep on a good tract of grassland by a hurdle fence which the Duke was to find and erect. Room was available in which to keep hay during the winter and in which to shelter the sheep if necessary during exceptionally inclement weather. A barn was available in which to shear and, if necessary, shelter the whole flock for a day or two after shearing 'in Case of Cold Rainy weather'. There was board and lodging in a cottage near at hand where the King's Shepherd could live when such a man was appointed from the neighbourhood. An old man who was 'not a writer' could indeed be hired for twelve shillings a week. For one guinea a quarter Woodruff, the Duke of York's Shepherd, would undertake the general care of the flock under the supervision of Robert Dickson, who was the Duke's Steward at Oatlands Park. With a final agreement that 'a fair Price for Joist' would be 'about –/3ᵈ a week [per head] this to be considerd of after a years tryal' the arrangement was satisfactorily concluded.

At last, after ten years' struggle against a disordered and neglectful husbandry, Sir Joseph had achieved a system for the breeding flock more suitable to his peace of mind and more particularly under his own control. The new régime began for the King's Spanish flock 'from May 29 1798 when it was Removed by his Majesties Commands from Kew Gardens to the Park of H.R.H. the Duke of York at Oatlands'.[28] They were conducted to their new pastures by Woodruff whom Robert Dickson, confined to his house by gout, had sent to Kew on 28 May, 'thinking him a more proper person to attend the Sheep in Travel[l]ing than the New Shepherd' and to take Banks's 'directions for the management of His Majesty's Sheep when at Oatlands'.[29] Significant of the new system and setting the final seal on its inauguration was Banks's brief note to Dickson of 1 June:

I enclose to you a Bank note of £25 also forms for Monthly accounts [of the sheep] to be filld up by the Shepherd the sooner I have one the better as it is the first of this month under the word Remarks anything respecting the Flock may be inserted particularly when the money is exhausted I beg to have notice that I may make further remittance[30]

The seven fruitful years from 1798 to 1804 had now begun. They were the apotheosis of His Majesty's Spanish flock under the general direction of the President of the Royal Society as 'his favorite hobby'.

A regular system of monthly stock returns from the shepherd to Sir Joseph had been established that was to continue unbroken for the next fourteen years. A financial accountancy with the stewards of the Royal parks and gardens for the expenses of the flock and Sir Joseph's disbursements thereon was made regular and clear. In the same fashion the financial transactions with Henry Lacocke and his employment as wool stapler to Sir Joseph and sheep classer to the flock was put on a proper foundation. Banks had at last found the shoulder on which he could lean for assistance at critical periods in the annual round of the flock's affairs. He had also found the eyes and ears by which he could keep himself informed not only about the well-being of the sheep and the execution of his commands but also about much else in the world of the wool trade in practice. This was a relationship that had developed slowly from the first occasion of Lacocke's employment to class out the ewes at the shearing of 1796. Each year produced a further step in the intimacy of the association, and the removal of the sheep to Oatlands made its practical confirmation possible in a host of different services which the old wool stapler of Magdalen Circus could offer to the sage of Soho Square. Banks accepted this aid with gratitude. But he found himself amused sometimes at the occasional expressions of self-importance by Lacocke 'who wishes to make himself of consequence' —a tendency which Banks did nothing to dissuade and which he fostered to the general advantage of the flock.[31] At the same time he remained not so much the benevolent patron as the true friend of Henry Lacocke who always so regarded Banks and served him accordingly.

V

The debilitated condition of the flock was not immediately improved by the change to Oatlands Park, though by the shearing on 18 June 1798, three weeks after their arrival, Banks could detect sufficient advance to note that they looked 'better than usual'.[32] However, one ewe teg 'died under the Shears she had been unable to walk for some days & had a bottle under the chin & all appearances of Rot opend her & found her liver quite clean & good and without a single Fluke'. The shepherd told him that there were six more ill of a similar disease, and before the year was out ten sheep had died.[33] Another wether was 'so goggly that I ordered him to be killd', a circumstance which perhaps records the existence of scrapie among the sheep at this time.[34] For the main condition Banks prescribed 'Fleat's Medecine' and sent a bottle of it to Robert Dickson a few days later. On 24 August he visited Oatlands again '& found the Flock in better condition than I have ever seen it yet', though several sheep were lame from foot-rot. Two of the ewes who had received 'Fleat's Medecine' were still weak and unlikely to recover but the rest were now well.

With the November 'Monthly Return of His Majesty's Sheep at Oatlands' Robert Dickson reported the whole flock as very well and that the shepherd had drawn ten wethers as fat and tolerably good mutton.[35] For these, however, the butcher had offered him only eighteen shillings a head, which was low, and on this point he sought Banks's opinion. He also suggested that it was time to prepare some temporary shelter for the sheep during the coming winter as had been discussed earlier. Banks replied from his bed in Soho Square:

I agree with you in thinking 18/- a head too Low a price for the wethers but if a better cannot be obtaind profitably it will be wiser to Close with it Those that were fatted at Windsor were sold for 25/- a head but mutton was then dearer than it now is. They provd so remarkably good mutton that the gentlemen of the neighbourhood were very desirous of buying them possibly if the butcher finds the same good Quality in these he may give a better price for the next we have to sell I confess I am a friend to timely Price whatever it may be

I have been more than 2 months confind chiefly to my bed which is the Reason I have not been at Oatlands I am yet very feeble as soon as ever I am able I will come over in the mean time as I am wholly incapable of travelling I must Trespass on your goodness to superintend the Shed that is to be made for the winter The great Object is to provide a dry Layer where their feet may grow dry while they chew the Cud[36]

This wise provision of winter shelter and a 'dry Layer' was a comfort which the flock had seemingly not always enjoyed at Kew in spite of early injunctions on the subject. It was, therefore, some satisfaction to Banks, in his own crippled state, to learn from Dickson by the next monthly return that, for once, his worrisome charges were reasonably secure against the chills and risks of the coming winter:

Agreeable to your request, I have got a Shed Erected for the Spanish Flock, 40 feet in length, & 15 feet wide, have thatched It with Straw which I hope will meet with your approbation, I have sold Ten Wethers to the Butcher for Nine Pounds for which I promise to be accountable to Sir Joseph Banks. . . .[37]

Well provided with hay the flock emerged from the winter of 1798–9 in extremely good order. It was found, however, that twelve of the ewes had become pregnant by the ram lambs of the previous year before they had been separated from their dams, and that in January six of these ewes had already lambed though the main breeding flock was not due to do so until March. Banks also noticed by this return, what his ill-heath had prevented him from noticing before, that the three rams, Nos. 120, 122, and 132, which had served the flock at the last tupping were in fact still at Oatlands contrary to what he had understood.[38] He prompted Ramsay Robinson about this on 10 February, but received no immediate answer. He wrote again on 12 April, again without result, although the rams were finally removed that month.[39] The Robinsons were not the most punctilious of Sir Joseph's collaborators. One suspects, at times, that they suffered a chronic state of mild umbrage to receive something less than Royal commands.

The situation of the rams was obscured by a brief threat to the continued agistment of the flock at Oatlands when Robert Dickson called at Soho Square on 9 April and informed Banks that the Duke of York wished the King's flock to be removed to make room for some 'new Kind of Sheep which H.R.H. meant to try'. Banks expressed his regret and asked Dickson if he thought the Duke would relent in this most untimely decision in which case he would ask leave to see His Royal Highness. Dickson thought it most likely that the Duke would concede the point and accordingly Banks attended at York House where the Prince was graciously pleased to allow him to continue the flock at Oatlands, but warned that next year the park would be enclosed when the sheep of course must be sent away. This amnesty, however, remained and the sheep were not further disturbed for another three years—that is, until they were finally removed back to the King's farm and parks at Kew and Richmond in October 1802.

The second shearing of the flock at Oatlands attended by Banks and

Henry Lacocke was apparently an occasion for much satisfaction. Setting out at 7 a.m. on 14 June and arriving at Oatlands through the Walton Gate by 8.40 a.m., Banks found five shearers ready and also Henry Lacocke who had come to Weybridge by the evening coach the day before. He 'found the sheep in excellent condition The footrot almost intirely curd. the shepherds in good spirits saying they had no doubt of the Flock succeeding'.[40] Delighted, he paid Dickson his first year's account for the keep of the sheep—£124 5s. 6d.[41]—and noted that

The Flock have fard much better & had fewer losses than ever before the King's Goodness in allowing a shepherd to watch them constantly is the Reason[42]

A fortnight later, with Henry Lacocke, he attended at Windsor to see the rams shorn on 28 June. This was a more happy sight than usual but still a great contrast to the state of the ewe flock. He recorded that:

They were in better condition than usual but some of their Horns maggotty from carelessness in not clipping round them when the sheep are daggd ...[43]

Better, indeed, but still not quite good enough.

VI

Exhilarated by the prospect of an improved future and breeding security for the ewe flock after so many years of chastening and frustrating mishaps, Sir Joseph found occasion after the June shearing at Oatlands to ponder an old question. He had never been satisfied from the first year of his active association with the Royal experiment with the methods used by the shepherds for identifying individual animals. This had been no special problem among most of the adult rams with their convenient horns suitable for the fire-branding of numerals.[44] It was quite otherwise with the ewes, of which some only were horned, and with the lambs. It was true that an elaborate system of three colours (black, red, and blue), body sites (poll, neck, back, loin, rump, side, etc.), and marks (dots or lines) had been used as a shepherd's code for identifying the ewes with their lambs of both sexes.[45] But these had to be renewed at shearing and by their very complexity, especially with semi-literate shepherds, had many risks of error. Now that the elements of reasonable husbandry had been at last achieved, with the heart-warming support of the Oatlands shepherds, he was tempted to try a new system.

Engaged as he had been for several years on the Coin Committee of the Privy Council and as the friend of Matthew Boulton for more than twenty years, it now occurred to Banks that the ingenious Birmingham engineer, who had been so successful with his minting machines, could find a solution to the problem of marking sheep. Just before the ram shearing at Windsor Banks set out the problem and his own suggestions in a letter to Matthew Boulton from Soho Square, dated 26 June 1799.[46] He pointed out that sheep breeders generally needed a means of marking individual animals permanently; that it had occurred to him that Boulton could easily manufacture what was required in the form of small split-rings of pewter (which would not rust or oxidize); that these, engraved with a date or number, could then be fixed in the ears of the sheep; that he was sure that many breeders would adopt the device if it were put on the market. Boulton thought the idea excellent and was prepared to make and submit samples forthwith. He thought, however, that the rings should be made of a cheap metal, not worth stealing but strong enough to resist damage by thorns and bushes, and that a tool should be devised and sold with them by which to stamp distinguishing marks or numbers thereon.[47] By 4 July, Boulton had produced specimens of the 'pastoral ear-ring' with two alternative pendants for the number or mark, one of tinned iron and the other of block tin. The ring itself could be opened for insertion into the ear and would close by its own springiness. He estimated that the price would not exceed a penny each, but could not fix it more closely without making a number.[48]

Banks thought the samples were excellent but suggested that their size could be reduced. The block-tin label was the better and could be stamped on one side with the owner's initials or mark and on the other with the date. The price itself was of no importance if kept about the figure that Boulton had tentatively estimated. He proposed to go to Lincolnshire about the middle of August, but before this there was the important Lewes Sheep Show and Wool Fair which he proposed to attend on 26–30 July, although he was at present suffering from gout. If by then Boulton could provide him with a gross of the rings this would be an occasion to make them widely known.[49] While Boulton was digesting these points Sir Joseph, in spite of his gout, set out with Henry Lacocke for Oatlands to choose the ram lambs of that year, to look over the ewes, to try the new 'pastoral ear-rings' with the shepherd, and to find a way to bore the ears.[50] This succeeded well enough, but the shepherd criticized the circular shape of the ring and suggested that a design more like the link in a chain would be less likely to be caught in bushes. Banks transmitted his shepherd's suggestion for the improvement of the ring on 10 July with another from no less an authority than Sir Benjamin Thompson, the Count von Rumford, with a drawing of the shape in section. He added that he was most anxious for a supply of the rings and pendants in any shape to take to Lewes Fair.[51]

Boulton, who had meanwhile been much engaged that week by a

visit from Lord Hawkesbury to view his new coin minting press, replied on 14 July:

. . . My attention has been too much taken up last week wth my Lord to allow me to attend to your Earrings but I will send you by tomorrows Coach a specimen with such tools as I think every shepherd should have viz a pair of plyers to open and shut them, a hammer a small anvil to mark the pendants upon, a set of figures, and I refer to your own consideration whether there should be an alphabet or whether each person should have his own name engraved on one punch

I am now satisfied that the Farmer cannot strike his numbers upon a pendant of Tin'd Iron without endangering his puncheons & therefore I have made tools to cut the Pendants out of hardend Block tin which may be marked with very little trouble & the intrinsick Value is too small to be worth catching a Sheep & taking the ring from the Ear as they are not worth one Shilling p^r hundred to Melt—As to the form of the Wire Earring I am not yet certain which will be best—That of Count Rumford ○—Ə— is a good form but not too conveniently made nor easily opend & shut to put into the Ear of ye Animal or quite so Cheap as those of this form ∽—I wish you to see a few of them tried & hung to the Sheeps Ear, & then fav^r me with your remarks & directions which I shall instantly conform to. The parcel will be delivered to you in Soho Square on Tuesday I suppose by noon. . . .[52]

This first batch of ear-rings seemed too heavy and on 17 July Banks asked Boulton for some of a lighter weight to demonstrate at Lewes, proposing in the meantime to have some of the heavier kind fixed as an experiment to the ears of the King's sheep.[53] Thus by the night coach from Birmingham on 22 July Matthew Boulton sent a second small but weighty parcel to Soho Square containing three gross of thick and one gross of thin wire ear-rings, four gross of block-tin pendants, an anvil and spacing device, a set of figure puncheons and, in addition, one dozen copper pendants tinned as specimens for trial—'for Experience must decide what is the best size & most proper metal'. He himself was sure the thicker wire would answer better than the thin which was more likely to cut the ear of the animal and to be opened and pulled out by bushes and brambles. He was prepared when Banks had decided on the best design and metal to make 'Millions at [a] few days notice'.[54] Unfortunately this comprehensive array of impedimenta did not reach Soho Square before Banks had set out for his annual rendezvous and stay at Sheffield Place. He thus had only pendants but no suitable rings to display. A short report of the occasion marks the event and suggests that even these few pastoral trinkets may have carried a point:

Lewes Wool Fair, on Friday last, was very numerously and respectably attended. Upwards of a hundred persons dined in the different rooms at the

Bear Inn, amongst whom were Lord Sheffield, Sir Joseph Banks, Sir Geoffrey Webster, T. Kemp, Esq., and many opulent buyers. Little if any business was done on that day, but several contracts have been since made, and at advanced prices. The best samples fetched from 60s. to 64s. the tod. Sir Joseph Banks, after dinner, presented the company with pieces of metal, which he had invented for the better marking of sheep, and to prevent the use of tar and tiver, by which a considerable portion of wool is annually spoiled. Some trifling objections were made to them, but they were easily obviated by Sir Joseph. Lord Sheffield appeared in a coat of cloth made wholly of English wool of his own growth, which might have puzzled the best judges to have distinguished from superfine cloth, manufactured of a mixture of Spanish and English wools.[55]

Immediately after his return his letter to Boulton of 2 August set out various criticisms of the rings which had come too late. The lighter forms were made half the size of the heavy ones and were too small; he wanted rings light in weight but the same size as the heavy ones; the anvil for stamping was too heavy; the slot for the pendants was too small and the disks spread out when struck and could not be removed. In any case this particular tool was too heavy. However, the Duchess of Gordon had written to him for specimens of the 'pastoral ear-ring' and he had referred her to Boulton for supplies.[56]

    Then on 10 August he arranged to meet Henry Lacocke at Oatlands at eight o'clock in the morning to put the ear-rings into the ears of the ewe tegs and the ewe lambs for which the holes had been bored during their previous visit on 10 July. Here a small contretemps with the shepherd occurred, for he declared that these holes had healed in most of the sheep '& in others that their Ears were still very sore which he attributed to the Flies'. Banks doubted the whole account for he was of the opinion that in the case of the sheep he was shown as an example of this healing, the ear seemed never to have been bored at all.

He seemed very desirous of boring the ears himself & said as he does in cutting Lambs that a proper season for doing it would arrive of which he alone is the judge Concluding from this that he meant to practice a kind of scarce dishonest deceipt in order to render himself of more consequence I agreed to his proposition & left the instrument & rings with him to manage as he pleasd[57]

With this Sir Joseph retired from the practical business of boring the ears of sheep and left it to the shepherd and to Henry Lacocke, who was daily becoming busier in the affairs of the flock as a sort of unpaid overseer. This delegation of the tasks seems to have succeeded as far as the 'pastoral ear-rings' were ever destined to succeed. At the next shearing in 1800 it was found that only one ewe had lost her ear-ring, which was immediately replaced. Another year passed and in 1801 the shearing revealed that most of the rings were in place but that in some of the ewes the ear had festered, even in those that had worn them for two years, while in the lambs many had outgrown the size of the ring. It was noticed also that the sheep had tended to nibble the pendants, in some cases obliterating the numbers, so that Banks

Offerd the Dukes Shepherd 6^d a sheep for every sheep we shall hereafter shear on condition that he takes care to Look after the Rings & change them as often as they are in danger of dropping out or of being defacd by the gnawing[58]

In spite of these defects the system of using metal labels was evidently sufficiently encouraging, and the interest general enough, to warrant production on a large scale. In May 1800 Sir Joseph paid Matthew Boulton £29 for ten thousand labels and rings (at 25s. per thousand for each component), six sets of figure puncheons at 4s. 6d. a set, twelve pairs of pliers at 9d. each, and six 'steadiers' at 7s. each—a formidable supply far beyond the needs of the Royal flock alone for many years to come.[59]

VII

While the ewes prospered on the sandy rises in Oatlands Park the rams suffered and struggled to survive on the low grounds of the Home Park beneath the Castle walls at Windsor. The contrast, always evident, was thrust home again to the attention of Sir Joseph during the summer of 1801, and he taxed Ramsay Robinson once more with a call for better supervision:

When I visited H. M. Rams at Windsor on the 10th of June I found them in very good condition & was much pleasd with the care that had evidently been taken of them during the winter

When I visited them again yesterday I was seriously mystified to Find them all Lame & much fallen away. Their Feet appeared to have been wholly neglected & the Sheep themselves most Certainly in a Condition very disgraceful to the King's Farming & I was the more hurt because I came immediately from Oatlands where out of 160 Ewes & Lambs not even one was Lame.

as I have the King's orders to sell these Sheep & all of that can be Spard are bespoken I must request you to give any orders & to take the best measures as are most likely to get them curd & into some kind of Condition as quickly as possible as at all Events they must be sent away in the Beginning of September & I should be grievously sorry if they were not in much better Condition than they now are when sent into different parts of the Kingdom . . .[60]

The reply, sent by Ramsay Robinson to this on the following day 23 July, presaged the final turn in the affairs and particularly the management of the Spanish flock. It appeared that a long illness had kept him from visiting Windsor for some time. Even then he could do no more than write 'to regulate this misfortune and do every endeavour to get them into proper condition without loss of them'.[61] He had recovered sufficiently by 13 August to take in hand what proved to be his last harvest for the King, only to find that Banks himself had succumbed briefly to his habitual complaint and was immobilized. However, in spite of the precarious harvest weather, the pulmonary disease of Ramsay Robinson, and the gout of Sir Joseph Banks, the rams were somehow attended to, and, before the end of August, their allotment for the year had been completed. Henry Lacocke was deputed 'to weigh up the Kings Fleece' at Marsh Gate[62] and Banks retired north into Lincolnshire as soon as he was able to travel.[63]

The health of Ramsay Robinson steadily failed as the year progressed into autumn. Henry Lacocke, worried at the reports indirectly received of the continued lameness and poor condition of the King's rams at Windsor, pleaded with Banks for orders to go there and set matters straight. This was more than Banks could or would do at this stage. Any intrusion at Windsor Castle, however sad the condition of the sheep there, was to infringe the domestic privacy of the King. This he never at any time had ventured except through the equerries or the Royal staff. It was plain that the long years of Ramsay Robinson's service were about to end. But Henry Lacocke, loyal and willing though he may have been, was not one whom Banks was prepared to send as his deputy into the Home Park even in the emergency of this difficult pause in an always difficult situation. Frustrated and remote, as Banks was at Revesby that October in the matter of the rams, it was perhaps some solace to learn by letter from Henry Lacocke of the great rise in the price of Spanish wools and to be 'acquainted with the Blessed ring of peace that we Rec[d] last week and hope it will be Confirmed this week or Soon to the great Joy of this Nation . . .'. [64] But the winter was to pass and the spring of 1802 almost to appear before the Peace of Amiens became a reality, though even at the first hint of 'the wellcome News of peace people begins to look more lively than before hoping Trade will ever more flourish amongst us and food be more Reasonable than what it has been in time past . . .'. Thus Lacocke could record a passing gleam after nine long years of war. Among these national jubilations the retirement of Ramsay Robinson from the affairs of the Royal parks and gardens near London was scarcely noted. Nor perhaps was his departure abroad observed in the peaceful, though brief, invasion of the Continent by the pent-up British bursting with curiosity about Revolutionary France. Neither can it be said that the appointment of Richard Snart in the summer of 1802 to this vacancy in the Royal staff produced much stir in the national scene. For the Spanish flock, however, Richard Snart was the harbinger of important changes and ultimately the arbiter of their daily life in the strange and stormy years ahead. It was, therefore, on a significantly high and formal note that on 21 September Snart wrote to Banks:

I am commanded by His Majesty to request you will take the Trouble to inform me at what Time you propose to remove The Spanish Sheep to Kew—With Regard to the Attendance upon them His Majesty has been told by the Duke of York that no constant Shepherd has been attached to them, but that they have been attended by an Labourer or Boy who could be most spared under the Direction of His Royal Highness's first Shepherd. If it should be your Pleasure to continue the same Plan at Kew the Expense would not be so heavy upon the Spanish Sheep as by employing a Man continually about them—and equal Justice would be done by them; more particularly as it would prevent any Jealousy among the Shepherds.[65]

Written with graceful flourishes in a fair and clerkly hand there was rather more than a touch of oblique patronage in this opening communication. Here was the first sign of a different régime to mark the passing of Ramsay Robinson who, for all his minor lapses, had been tractable and suitably humble in his daily relations with the President of the Royal Society. Certainly, he had not been tempted to fling Royal commands at Sir Joseph in quite such ringing tones. Wherefore Sir Joseph replied with an authoritative punctilio he had seldom before employed with the King's servants:

I beg you to acquaint his Majesty with my Hble duty that I have not Receivd the Slightest intimation from H.R.H. the D[uke] of Y[ork] of any intention to have the Spanish Flock Removd from Oatlands. When I had the honor of speaking to his Majesty at Weymouth on the subject I stated that as H.R.H. had purchasd more sheep than I thought Oatlands could maintain in the winter it seemd Probable to me that as soon as the hay & Potatoes /that are/ provided for winter Pasture /were become/ are nearly exhausted I shall be Calld upon to Remove the Spanish Flock because there will not be sufficient maintenance for more than the Dukes own stock.
Respecting the Shepherd you may Recollect that I proposd to you when I saw you at London to try at Kew the same mode of proceeding as I have usd with success at Oatlands which is to have a Laborer to attend the Spanish Flock under the orders of the King's Shepherd & to allow the King's Shepherd as I did the Duke of York's a guinea a quarter for superintendence if this succeeds and the Sheep are kept sound and in Good Condition as they have always been at Oatlands there can be no occasion for any other management.[66]

Clearly and firmly it was made apparent to Richard Snart that Sir Joseph was in the confidence of the King and that Sir Joseph had now no need of instruction in the state of His Majesty's mind on the ordering of the Spanish flock and its affairs from day to day. Snart was also to learn that there was an important shadow cast by the evident substance of Sir Joseph and that this, in the person of Henry Lacocke, was more important than at first sight would appear. Nor was Henry Lacocke himself disposed to allow Sir Joseph to forget that he was this shadow and a very faithful shadow withal. Lacocke had written to Banks almost at the same time as Richard Snart, conveying to the baronet of Revesby Abbey his own evident feelings of insecurity as well as of doubt in the changing régime at Windsor:

. . . I think of going to Oatlands after Michaelmas to See how they go on with the Spanish flock which I Shou'd be Sorry to See them do any otherwise than well as we have got them So far on as they are now, if the duke of York Shou'd turn them out, I hope Sir Joseph you'l get the King to take them to Windsor and there I will Turn Shepeard my Self Sooner than let them be Spoiled and Come to Nothing, you [k]no[w] Sir if the King wou'd be Gracious Enough to give me one of the old Knights places at Windsor if a Vacancy Shou'd take place by death I could live in one of those Houses and then properly turn Shepeard my Self and be useful in many things about the King's Bisiness and Likewise yours in managing the Spanish flock and other things Belonging to the King, I have been informed Sir Joseph that if you wou'd be so good as to Speak to his Majesty and Say that old Laycocke who have been and now is the Kings woolstapler and Sir Joseph Banks's man, his Majesty wou'd give me the place, I hope Sir Joseph if I've made too free as above you will pardon and forgive me in Troubling your generous mind I desire to acknowledge all the favours I've Rec.^{d} from you with thankfulness and Gratitude and Ever Bound to pray and thank God I ever Saw and Knew you as my friend and helper when none Ells wou'd—[67]

Banks replied to this letter on 26 September the same day that he sent his mild corrective to Richard Snart.[68] On 30 September the old man inspected the Spanish flock at Oatlands for the last time on those pastures. He found to his horror, as Robert Dickson confirmed in his monthly report to Sir Joseph,[69] that His Majesty had arranged with the Duke of York for the flock to be removed to Richmond Park. This wrung from Lacocke a despairing protest, sent immediately to Lincolnshire:

. . . now Sir this is the worst Step that has been taken to Secure or keep the Spanish flock pure from Cross as I understand they are to [be] kept in Richmond park amongst other Sheep that are in the park, if So, then you may be sure that other Rams Besides the Spanish Rams will Spoil all the Breed by mixing together which will prove very hurtful for any further Experiment in the Spanish Sheep this unhappy Cross will frustrate yours and my purpose to have Brought the Spanish Carcase into a good mould without any Cross with other Sheep, but now my hopes is over. . . .[70]

Again there came a letter of support from Revesby written on 8 October, but by the time Lacocke received it the sheep had been sent from Oatlands. By arrangement with Woodruff, the Duke's Shepherd, Lacocke was told of their departure on or about 10 October in good time for him to intercept them the same day at Marsh Gate. Here also he was fortunate enough to meet Richard Snart. This was the first meeting of the two men who, between them, were to manage the practical details of the flock for the next ten years more or less on the pattern which the previous ten had established with so much difficulty. Of Snart, Henry Lacocke reported to Banks:

. . . he Seems like a good kind of a man by saying he wou'd pay all the Attention possible he Cou'd to See they were well Look'd after and that they Shou'd be keept from any Rams that was in the King's other flocks, which I was pleas'd to find so kind a friend to the Spanyards as he promis'd me to be. . . .[71]

So the breeding ewes, eighty in number with twenty-six ewe lambs, returned to Kew, led by the two sires of that season—Old Snags (No. 133) and Young Snags (No. 148) with whom they were still being mated. Henry Lacocke, primed with Banks's written authority, prevailed on Richard Snart to remove all other sheep from Kew Gardens and to keep only the Spanish flock there, suitably folded under the constant attendance 'of a strong Boy who has been accustomed to Sheep & who will be superintended by the head Shepherd'.[72]

VIII

So, then, in the autumn of 1802 the breeding flock came home again to Kew and to the supervision of the man who would remain their immediate guardian until they ceased to be the King's sheep.

The small neat script of Robert Dickson on the 'Monthly Return of his Majesty's Spanish Flock at Oatlands' changed to the bold schoolboy hand of Richard Stanford on the 'Monthly Return of his Majesty's Spanish Flock at Kew'. But between October 1802 and May 1803 there was a brief interregnum—the period of Stanford's initiation by Henry Lacocke into the mysteries of keeping exact records for Sir Joseph. Diligent and watchful, the old man was not prevented by the bitter weather of the New Year of 1803 from pursuing his self-assumed task of liaison officer and instructor in the affairs of the flock:

Yesterday was at Kew and Saw the Shepherd and the Sheep. I think the Shepherd has made a Complete place for their Lodging at Night, to Shelter them from the Severity of the weather and a good place for them to Lamb in they have plenty of Good Hay and Turnips to feed upon, very little grass, the Shepherd has promis'd me to take all possible Care of them he Can in Lambing, Some of them Looks very forward. Shou'd Suppose will have Lambs in, a fortnight or 3 weeks Because they Begin to Spring very much Some of them I desired the She[p]herd to give them a few potatoes to increase the Ew[e]'s milk just before they Lamb, he Say, he will and do all thats needfull for them, I Likewise left him Blank papers to fill up Every month and give you a Return of the Stock, Either Sick, Lame or dead——However Sir I Shall give my Attendance at Kew once a month if not Offner as I See needful by your Leave. . . .[73]

This was the message to Soho Square written on the first 'Return' from Kew, filled in by Lacocke and also signed by him 'Richard Stanford' as an example to the newcomer to the select circle. It was not until May 1803 that the King's Shepherd first appended his own carefully contrived signature to one of these small papers. By the end of that year the name 'Richard Stanford' had achieved the large and business-like abandon which for the next ten years was to be a regular monthly decoration at the foot of this summary of the healthy, the sick, and the dead with the varied catalogue of strange disorders to which they succumbed.

Stanford was soon deeply involved in the affairs of the small Spanish flock. By the end of April 1803 the lambing was over without mishap, and he could record an increment of twenty-six ewe and thirty-three ram lambs in his 'Return' of 1 May that year. But by the end of July he had noted the loss of eight from among the eighty breeding ewes received from Oatlands the previous autumn and six from among the twenty-six ewe tegs—over thirteen per cent of the effective ewe flock within three spring and summer months. By his diagnosis this was due to the 'scours'. From this circumstance therefore the ewes available for mating in October 1803 were ninety-two only.[74]

In June 1803 these ninety-two ewes, young and old, had been washed in the Thames at Richmond and shorn in the barn opposite the Pagoda at Kew for 5s. 6d. per score with an additional 6s. for beer to sustain the washers and shearers on these occasions.[75] The clip so gathered weighed 305 pounds or 3·32 pounds per head. Sorted by Henry Lacocke at the rate of one guinea per pack of 240 pounds and scoured by his men at 3d. per pound—again with 2s. 6d. worth of beer to lubricate the process—the clip that year yielded seventy-three per cent of clean wool or 223 pounds. Of this total, 202 pounds were rated as prime at 6s. 9d. per pound; 20 pounds were choice at 4s. 6d. per pound; and 1 pound was noted as fribbs at 1s. 9d. per pound.[76] This was equivalent to an average price of 6s. 6d. per pound clean or somewhat more than 4s. 9d. per pound as washed on the sheep's back in the

English manner. The gross return per sheep was therefore 15s. 9d. from the fleece alone.

The first financial year of the new régime ended at Michaelmas 1803 with a total charge for shepherding of £24 9s. 3d. to be set against the returns from the clip and the private sales of the sheep. Of this by far the greater part was for the wages of Richard Winslow—the 'strong Boy who has been accustomed to Sheep' under the eye of Richard Stanford —at 7s. per week or £18 4s. for the whole year. The gratuity to Richard Stanford himself for his supervision of the Spanish flock above and beyond the call of his normal duties was 4 guineas. The washing and shearing charges were £1 11s. 3d. in all. The balance that year was accounted for by such small items as: 2s. 6d. for the 'mixture to cure the Foot Rot'; 2s. 6d. for the 'Medecine to cure the Sick Ewes in Winter'; 3s. 6d. for a 'Peck of Salt'; and 1s. 6d. for a 'Mixture to dress the Heads' —almost certainly those of the rams and ram lambs with their fly-struck patches near the base of the horns.

As the King's Shepherd Richard Stanford had been comfortably settled for at least seven years in The Orange Tree Cottage or The Shepherd's Cot in Kew Foot Lane, not many yards south of Clarence Street.[77] Through the farmyard and meadow at the rear Stanford had convenient access directly into the Royal gardens and the Old Deer Park where the flock so often grazed, especially the young rams. But this address was noted by Banks at the time as 'near the Blue Anchor in Kew House Road', and thereafter this was the general form of the direction given for finding the King's Shepherd on matters of business. But 1803 was apparently Stanford's first year of direct responsibility for the Spanish flock. It was also, perhaps, his least worrisome year with these highly problematical strangers to the British way of sheep-farming.

For the next ten years Richard Stanford served a hard apprenticeship in the husbandry of the Spanish fine-wool sheep. His 'Monthly Returns', faithfully lodged for a whole decade with the President of the Royal Society, were to form a statistical record of great value in the annals of the flock—embellished and made lively by its catalogue of strange maladies among the Royal sheep. The syndromes involved may perhaps remain too often obscure even to the intuitive percipience of the latter-day clinician. But these mysteries were recorded at the time in terms direct and colourful, tracing out the bill of mortality over the years in losses from the 'red water', the 'white waters', the 'black scour', the 'broken belly', the 'mad staggers', the 'worms in the lights', the 'flounder in the liver', the 'murrin', the 'dropsy', the 'gripes', and the 'goggles', to say nothing of the faggs, the foot-rot, the maggots, and the scab.

In all this long list of pathological incident and disaster there is one
episode which has the first glimmer of a message for the twentieth
century. This was the mortality among the ram lambs during the
winter of 1804–5. The onset of the trouble was insidious, but there was
no doubt whatever of its existence in the sharp reminder of the figures
in Stanford's 'Return' dated 2 February 1805. Six of the thirty-three
young rams at pasture near Richmond had died during the past month,
one of the most severe Januaries for several years. This sudden blot on a
formerly good record demanded some comment and Stanford expressed
his perplexity to Sir Joseph:

It is out of my power to say what they Die with I think it is a Distemper
among them and I am afraid that we shall loose a great many more I have
done everything that is in my power to save them they have oats and bran
and salt good Hay and Turnips and I have made them a good many Aleburrys
and other dronks and I get them plenty of ivy—Mr Laycock was with me
to day and he cannot se[e] as I can do any better by them.[78]

With this first letter from the King's Head Shepherd to Banks and its
short tale of the heavy casualties at Richmond came the end of the seven
fruitful years of the small Spanish flock. Seven lean years of struggle
against a loosening system of control in its management now lay ahead
for Banks—with its ensuing episodes of disease among the sheep. But
in the present instance this disaster to the young rams was perhaps
beyond the capacity of anyone then either to foresee or to explain.
What was a stain on his professional record and a blow to his pride with
Richard Stanford was high tragedy to Henry Lacocke as he quickly
sketched the scene for Banks:

on Satuarday I went to Kew on purpose to See the Ram Lambs, but When I
came there I was much disappointed to find they were not so well as M^r
Snart Represented to me in his Letter Six of them were dead and by the
appearance of Seven more I Should Suppose by this time they are in the
Same State, I never was more struck when I came to See them, there have
been everything administered to them to keep them alive but all in vain at
present, the Shepherd inform'd me they began to droop the Beginning of
January and have continued until now, and is afraid most of them will dye
Except a great alteration in them, I'm Really vexed to See the disorder they
have on them Rage so fatal as it does—my Two favourites poll'd Rams one is
dead and the other I think cannot live, it appears the disorder to me comes
first into their Head & Eyes, there's Several of [them] now alive almost
Blind—and Some of them wastes away to a Skliton Before they dye, the
Rams [according] to what I See have been well attended unto, they have had
Everything that you purposed and more, the Shepherd is wore away almost
as bad as the Rams, in vexing himself of this unfortunate disorder come
amongst the Sheep, he say he's had no Sleep at night on their acc^t, I ask'd

him whether he found anything amiss in their liver or lights when he opened them, he Said they were as Sound in every part as any Sheep can be, he attributes the disorder to the Easterly wind which have been so long in that Quarter, but However I look higher than the winds for this Calamity amongst the Sheep, if a Sparrow don't fall to the ground without God's notice, I'm Sure these Rams don't dye without his pleasure, then we must Sir Joseph [say] thy will be done, I had [been] not So much vexed if he [had] been pleas'd to have Spared my 2 Idols the polld Rams I intend please God to Spare my health to go down to Kew next week or the week after to See how they Stand . . .[79]

Whereas Henry Lacocke was prepared to take issue with the Almighty over the disorder and to contest it as a personal affront—even at the risk of Divine displeasure—Sir Joseph was more plainly concerned to seek a cause more earthly and even lower than the east wind. He was inclined immediately to wonder

how Can it happen that the young Rams only are sick while the Ewes & the old Rams are Quite well unless something unwholesome has been accidentally mixd in the Food they have had which the other sorts of Sheep have not Partaken of I have orderd Enquiry to be made.[80]

The investigation and the fatalities proceeded together. With the first two which had died in December 1804 the whole loss before the spring came was fourteen from the original thirty-three ram lambs that had been first placed in the river bend near Richmond the previous August. This was a shattering loss among the potential sires for the King's flock and for the sales to the British public so recently and with such difficulty established.

Stanford was able to dispose of the notion that there was something strange about the diet, of which the substance was the same as that given to the ewes which were unaffected. But by the middle of February he had at last come to suspect that the lungs were a likely seat of the trouble. He appealed then to Banks specifically on the point:

. . . I think the Disorder is in the Lights and I have thoroughly examined them I can find nothing but the Lights failing and I should be very happy to se[e] you as you may se[e] what a state they be in . . .[81]

With this invitation the mystery seemed to turn towards hope of a solution, as Banks set about tracing out the history of the affair in a manner that foreshadowed the course of so many such field investigations in the history of veterinary medicine since. By the end of July 1805 he had established a clear picture of the occurrence with a shrewd estimate of the likely causes though not necessarily of a likely cure. This he summarized as 'Some Account of a Disease which affected the Ram Lambs of His Majesties Merino Flock in the Winter 1804–5 in Consequence of their being Pasturd in Autumn on land that had been overflown in the Spring'. It is a neat example of its kind and worth citation in full:

in that part of Richmond Gardens nearest to the Town of Richmond is a small piece of Land that lies below the level of the high water mark of the River Thames & is defended from Floods by a Bank on which the Towing Path passes

in February 1804 this Bank gave way & about 15 acres of Land was laid open to the River & overflown by every Spring tide & [the] Land flood[ed] in some places to the Depth of Six feet for near 3 months

in Spring the Breach was Repaird soon after which the Land that had been flooded was Hurdled off from the Rest with 3 or 4 acres of dry land & a few sheep & lambs nearly fit for the Butcher put into it, after they were sold the land was kept without Stock till August when it became very excellent Pasture & for that Reason was appropriated to the Ram Flock which consisted of

> 5 Spanish Rams
> 33   D°   Ram Lambs
> 8   D° × Ryeland Ram Lambs
> 7 Wiltshire Rams

About old Michaelmas the young sheep were observd to fall off & the whole were immediately removed into clover [near the Pagoda] where at first they appeard to do well but soon began to cough & to fall away in Flesh

in October one Spanish Ram Lamb died but as its Carcase was not examind it is not certain what was the disease The deaths of the Spanish Rams were afterwards as follows

December	2
January	6
February	4
March	1
April	1
Total	14

during the whole time of this mortality among the young Rams the Old ones Both Spanish & Wiltshire appeard healthy & thriving Tho kept in the same Pasture except one Spanish Ram [Revesby No. 15, Sale Lot No. 2] that was so ill in August 1804 as to be deemd unfit for Sale & never Recoverd from that disease but died in November. Tho none of the 8 mixd Rams died the whole were very ill & are in worse condition now than/*the average of*/the Spanish ones that have survivd

The disease first Shewd itself by a husky cough immediately after which sy[m]ptom the Sheep affected by it fell away in Flesh sometimes scowering and at others being costive, as no one could ascertain the nature of the disease no medecine was administerd except that Laudanum pills were

Plate III

Ram No. 15

Ram No. 83

Ram No. 98

Ram No. 120

Ram No. 133
'Old Snags'

Ram No. 148
'Young Snags'

Fleece samples of some sires of His Majesty's Spanish flock, 1791–1803.

occasionally given to those that scowered much Great attention however was given to the food of the sick Sheep & bran with oats & some Salt were given to them

Notwithstanding all the attention that was paid to their Food the Sick Sheep grew daily worse but continued to Eat both grass & dry meat, They breathd hard & coughd much & by degrees grew so weak as to be unable to stand.

in this Stage of the disease some few Continued to Eat but in general they Refusd food & apparently were unable to Ease their lungs by coughing, in one two or three days they died without a Struggle

During the time that this/*mortality*/disease was prevalent among the young Rams The King's Shepherd had under his care in the Gardens of Kew & Richmond & in Richmond Park near 1500 Sheep of different kinds 135 of which were Spanish Ewes & Ewe Lambs all of which did well & it is Remarkable that not one of these Spanish Ewes & Lambs died or was Sick

M[r] [Everard] Home whose skill in Comparative anatomy the Public are well acquainted with Obligingly undertook to Examine the Seat of the disease & to Superintend a drawing made by M[r] Cliff Keeper of the Hunterian Collection of which an Engraving is annexd Exhibiting the State in which the Lungs of these Sheep were found after death[82]

In this account of the circumstances in which the young rams succumbed to a massive infestation of the lung-worm (*Dictyocaulus filaria*) we gain something more than insight on the disease itself. Much may be deduced about the general management of the flock at Kew and Richmond and of the relations between its several custodians during the latter phase of its existence.

Scarcely a year now passed without some crisis associated with the health of the flock. The moderately care-free days of the régime at Oatlands Park were not continued after the return to Kew—for just what reasons it is hard to tell. In part it may have been the natural condition of the grazing grounds available. The river bend at Richmond was but one kind of hazard. It may also have been due in some measure to Richard Stanford himself to whom the Spanish flock was a new experience and—at least in the beginning—but a small part of his total charge in the parks and gardens about Richmond and Kew. Much more likely was it, however, that the flock was the victim of a form of management from day to day that for many reasons had developed weaknesses due to the increasing distractions in other ways among all who were associated with it. 'We are famous for being infamous Shepherds' was the bitter comment wrung from Banks at one point as he accepted responsibility for what he knew well should have been avoidable trouble under a proper system. But apart from the growing infirmities of the King, of Banks, and of Henry Lacocke, impeding their relations with Richard Snart and Richard Stanford, there was above all the whole background of a war that was moving into a new phase of dire threat and general confusion. The rising figure of Napoleon cast a spreading shadow that had at last found even these quiet reaches of the Thames.

The outbreak of lung-worm infestation among the young rams had scarcely cured itself than the sale of 1805 was concluded, to bring in its train a flood of complaints from aggrieved buyers who had found their sheep, both rams and ewes, infested only too obviously with the scab mite.[83] For this outbreak Banks was inclined to lay the blame squarely on Stanford who, he said, had concealed the matter from him.[84] The persistent breeding habits of the Spanish Merino was another source of confusion and trouble to an English shepherd accustomed to the decent and well-regulated continence of his native breeds. For at the same time as the outbreak of scab there came the news that the females purchased privately by Thomas William Coke had lambed before the end of 1805 and had therefore been supposed to have taken the ram before the sale in August.[85] This was confirmed for Banks by Stanford's 'Return' for 2 January 1806 to which was appended a humble plea:

I hope you will not be angry at what happened for before the lambs was weaned 20 of the young Ewes took the Ram and they have lamb'd and they have 22 fine lambs 14 Ewe lambs & 8 Ram Lambs[86]

All these mishaps were the events belonging to Richard Snart's strange year of silence on the subject of the Spanish flock, a state of *incommunicado* which was resolved only a short while before the public sale in August 1806.

But before the autumn was far advanced there was an obvious recrudescence of lung-worm among the young rams. On this occasion Banks lost no time. He called on the advice and experience of William Moorcroft, then in practice at 222 Oxford Street as a prosperous veterinary surgeon. Together they consulted over the rams on the spot at Kew. Moorcroft formed the opinion that he could do much for the sick sheep and Stanford was instructed to send two of the worst cases to the premises at Oxford Street.[87] Here they survived and convalesced under Moorcroft's eye until January 1807 when Richard Snart visited Oxford Street on behalf of the rams that had remained at Kew—of whom six had died that month. The result of this consultation was transmitted to Banks:

I take the liberty to acquaint you that I found M.ᵣ Moorcroft at home yesterday & had with him a long Conversation on the subject of the Spanish Ram Lambs—One great Difficulty at present is the getting the Sheep now under his Care to eat such Food as he is desirous they should have, & which is attributed to their confined Situation and want of Air—

Mr̤ Moorcroft has found it impossible to procure a Pasture with the requisite Conveniences of Contiguity, Dryness &c. and I therefore proposed to remove the Whole of the Ram Lambs to the Queen's Garden, to which Place that Gentleman may have access when he thinks proper, & where the Sheep will have every advantage of Shelter, Dryness of Soil, &c.—I will be careful to select the most intelligent of the Under Shepherds to attend them, and the Ram Lambs at Richmond shall be sent up on Friday [January 23] if possible. . . .[88]

So into the grounds of Buckingham Palace, at that time those of The Queen's House, came the forty-two young Spanish Merino rams from the unhealthy river bend near Richmond to be cured of their 'distemper'. Some six weeks later William Moorcroft pronounced them fit, and on 16 March 1807 they returned in good order to Kew.[89] But for the next few years both the lung-worm and the scab mite remained as recurrent nuisances from which the flock was never entirely free. These pedestrian complaints, however, were for a brief while eclipsed when in March 1809 Richard Stanford, among all the confusion of the new Paular accessions, had this to report:

. . . And ther[e] was thirty Couples in the bushy Lawn and there was a Dog got among them and bit as many [as] nine Lambs and they all died through the bite of the dog and four of the Ewes that I know of and we have had seven Ewes go mad since.

Mr Dunstall was in the Gardens at the same time and he thought it was not a mad dog and I said it was a mad dog I [have] taken my Pony and I rode after the dog and Killed him in the Gardens and Marked them all and kept them by themselves throught that I have proved it to be a mad dog

Dr Dundas have been and Proved it as well as myself.[90]

So, to the manifold ills which afflicted His Majesty's Spanish flock there must be added the more than slight suspicion of rabies as a final ingredient of the involved clinical history of its struggle to survive. It may perhaps also serve as a reminder that these were the days before the protecting device of quarantine had been added to the formalities of animal importation—a system that might well have had some difficulty in 1809 of surviving intact under the strains which the Peninsular War alone would have created. But even the dramatic appearance of rabies was soon submerged under the flood of other problems which were so soon to engulf Richard Stanford.

CHAPTER VII

The Royal Fleece, 1788–1809

I

In the month of April 1784, as the disputes in the Royal Society of England were drawing to an end, the Académie Royale des Sciences of France listened to a paper read by Louis Daubenton, *Sur le premier Drap de Laine superfine du cru de la France*.[1] Augmented by further contributions in June and again in August that year the French savant was reporting a triumphant end to nearly eighteen years of experimental cross-breeding and careful selection among the sheep of his flock at Montbard. He could announce with clear confidence the proven success of his long labours in the first cloth of superfine quality made from wool entirely grown in France—four hundred and four kilogrammes of fleece wool, washed on the sheep's back. For this the manufacturers were now prepared to pay a price not inferior to that given for the most valuable of the fine wools imported from Spain into France. They had at last conceded that it was not less fine to the eye and not less soft to the touch than the most superior Spanish wools; that not only was the spun thread as fine but that the tensile strength was greater than the Spanish; that although spun and woven in the depth of winter the French superfine had withstood a harder fulling than the usual Spanish cloth made in France. In fact, it had manufactured into a very superior cloth which bore comparison with the best English product. This, said Daubenton, was an event of the utmost importance to the manufactures and the general commerce of France, pointing the way to ultimate freedom from bondage to the Spanish wool trade. The impact of Daubenton's first memoir on this subject was such that de Calonne, Controller-General of Finance, eagerly brought the matter to the attention of Louis XVI and caused it to be printed as a pamphlet for the public benefit.

Then on 16 November 1785 Daubenton stood before the Académie again and reported more exactly with *Observations sur la comparaison de la nouvelle laine superfine de France, avec la plus belle laine d'Espagne, dans la fabrication du drap*.[2] The subject of his discourse had been opened more than two years earlier when Bertier de Sauvigny, anxious to consolidate the foundations of rural economy at the rejuvenated École Royale Vétérinaire at Alfort, had persuaded Daubenton to bring four rams and nine ewes from his flock at Montbard. These were to be the first

148

material at this institution for experiments there on the improvement of the fine-wool sheep under Daubenton in his new capacity as Professor of Rural Economy. The sheep were established by him in the small park attached to the school and in 1784 they were shorn, yielding a total of 17·5 kilogrammes of fleece wool, washed on the sheep's back before shearing. This was sent to M. Van Robais, a noted manufacturer at Abbeville, and from it a piece of cloth was produced measuring 30·17 metres long and 0·74 metres wide. This was in effect equivalent to 32·7 yards of an English narrow cloth 29 inches wide, derived from approximately 31 pounds of clean-scoured wool. The fabric was sent to Bertier de Sauvigny and by him exhibited at the Société Royale d'Agriculture of Paris. Later it was presented to Louis XVI by de Calonne as a superfine cloth from wool entirely grown in France. Van Robais was emphatic that there was no discernible difference between the spinning performance of this wool from Alfort and the true Spanish sort of the finest qualities, certainly none that he, as an expert, could appreciate.

This was by no means all. Daubenton sent to M. Jean-Baptiste Decretot, a clothier of Louviers, thirty kilogrammes of washed wool from his own flock at Montbard to be compared at all stages in its manufacture into cloth with a similar quantity of Spanish wool. For this experiment 30 kilogrammes of the best Leonese imperial was also chosen, valued at 5 francs 68 centimes per livre (=0·5 kilogramme) or about 4s. 7d. per pound. A similar amount of the inferior Spanish wool termed 'Molina' was the third sort, valued at 1 franc 49 centimes per livre or about 14d. per pound. To ensure the authenticity of the experiment a suitable sample of each of the three kinds of raw material was lodged with the Inspector of Cloth at Louviers, with the Warden of the Clothiers' Trade Corporation, and with M. Decretot. To ensure the exactness of the final comparison of the finished cloth all three kinds of wool were processed at the same time by the same skilled workers. In this way were avoided any slight differences in the manipulations and any due to the variation in atmospheric conditions throughout the period of manufacture. This precaution was carried through to the final fulling and dressing of the three lengths which were dyed a light olive. Such a colour was in itself an exacting test as one likely to reveal any slight defects in the original material most clearly. But the experiment as Daubenton reported it in November 1785 was not quite finished. It was possible to say that the wool from Montbard had fulled as easily as the Leonese imperial from Spain and that it had spun more finely by about one-twenty-fifth. On the other hand, the Montbard cloth was shorter by fifty-nine centimetres or half an ell. This deficiency could be attributed to the greater amount of grease in the French-grown wool, and hence to its lower yield of clean wool. M. Decretot at that point had not much more to add except to indicate that the dressing of the cloth was complete and that the French wool had compared well with the Spanish Leonese. It was not until 29 March 1786 that Daubenton was able to read before the Académie the final details which set the whole experiment in its proper light.

From equal weights of the original raw material there were evident differences in the finished cloths. The important points were those in the comparison of the raw wool from the Montbard flock with that from the Spanish Leonese. Here the final tally showed clearly that Daubenton's sample produced an appreciably shorter length of the narrow cloth of a lighter weight than did the same original weight of the best imported Spanish. This result, at first glance discouraging, was not displeasing either to Daubenton or to M. Decretot. The experiment had in fact succeeded admirably by showing clearly not only the extent but also the probable origins of the differences in the end result of the manufacturing test.

First, it was clear that by washing the fleece on the sheep before shearing, as Daubenton practised at Montbard, his sample had approximately ten per cent more grease in it than had the fine Leonese wool which had been washed after shearing more thoroughly in the traditional Spanish manner. The effect was in part exaggerated by the absence of any 'triage', the sorting into first, second, and third qualities which was the usual division of the Spanish pile. Daubenton had submitted his wool in the unsorted state, and it included much of the naturally soiled and inferior parts of the fleece normally withdrawn in the second and third sorts. By contrast the Spanish Leonese in this experiment belonged to the prime or first sort only. On two counts, therefore, there was likely to be a lesser yield of clean wool for spinning in the sample from Montbard.

Next, the absence of any sorting and the inclusion of the whole fleece in the experimental sample from Daubenton's flock meant that there was an inherently greater variation in the fibres from fine to coarse in the French wool as compared with the Spanish importation. Apart from any other effect, as M. Decretot was careful to say, this mixture of fibres could explain why the fulled cloth was not as strong as that from the Spanish wool, being not so well felted. Moreover, this mixture of the sorts in the French sample might have been one factor, in his opinion, causing any slight difference in the evenness of the dyeing as between the two cloths. He was, however, ready enough to say that this might well have been due also to slight differences in the temperature of the dye-baths or the time of immersion of the wool in the vats.

On both points it was agreed by Daubenton and Decretot that the comparison was weighted rather against the Montbard sample. It was the more encouraging, therefore, to find that not only did the French wool take the dye on the whole as brightly as the fine Spanish but that it actually had been spun into a finer thread and woven into a cloth of a quality as intrinsically beautiful. Though, for an equal period of fulling, it had resulted in a cloth of rather less strength and of a summer weight (*drap d'été*), Decretot was sure that, unsorted as it was, the Montbard wool could have been easily matched with Spanish wool of the first quality. Any slight defects in his opinion could be readily overcome by sorting out the inferior second and third qualities in the first place and by increasing the time of fulling by a small amount for the woven cloth. To Daubenton, as the breeder of sheep and grower of the wool, it only seemed necessary to add that proper care and attention to the washing of the raw wool in the first place would have eliminated any important difference in the yield of the finished cloth. In effect, then, there was no serious difference between the best Spanish fine wool and that from the *bergérie* at Montbard which a proper attention to sorting and washing (*triage et lavage*) could not eliminate.

All this was confirmed in principle and almost in detail by a report from M. Oger of the firm Julienne, Oger et Cie on 1 March 1786, concerning a piece of scarlet cloth made from another sample of fifty kilogrammes from Montbard.[3] These clothiers of the Gobelins under-lined their enthusiasm and their convictions by offering Daubenton the same price for this wool as for the best Spanish and requested that he reserve for them all that he had. M. Oger was further moved to add that he and his fellow-clothiers hoped that the lesson of the experiment would be noted by all French flock-owners and that they would imitate the example of Daubenton in attaining the same point of perfection in their wool by the same methods. This would be but a fraction of the tribute which was his due and a small part of the debt which all the clothiers recognized that they owed eternally to his efforts. Although they still must submit to paying enormous duties on the imported fine wools from Spain, they were now more than ever sure that they would not have long to wait before they were released from this heavy imposition.

To Daubenton, to the Académie Royale des Sciences, to France, the final seal, it seemed, was set on twenty years of hard and purposeful research to solve a national dilemma.

II

Five years at least had now elapsed since Banks first seriously turned his 'Thoughts towards the subject of wool and lamented that we in

England [who] are so Famous for that article were under the necessity of drawing our supplies for the finer Manufactures from Spain'. Throughout this time he had, as we know, 'attended much to the Flock managd in Burgundy at the Royal expence by M. Daubenton', and had studied all he could obtain on that subject with any pretence to authenticity. Now at last the industrious French savant seemed to have reached a logical and most satisfactory conclusion in his paper to the Académie Royale des Sciences. Again the Royal printing-house in Paris had been commanded to prepare it as a pamphlet for the public instruction. Again the President of the Royal Society in London sought a copy but, for a whole year, it eluded him, although he applied the instant he saw it advertised towards the end of the year 1786. 'Out of print', he was told—and well it might have been—though he was not to be easily deceived by such an answer. With the cunning of long experience now in the pursuit of his foreign intelligence he turned to William Eden on 20 March 1787.[4] In early May he had the satisfaction to receive the pamphlet from his old school-friend, hard at work on his diplomatic occasions in Paris. There was no mistaking the sense and importance of the message in this modest but eminently clear paper from France. The means of emulation at hand were slender, but Banks did not delay in setting them to work, pursuing the lead which French science had now so firmly established and so convincingly displayed. On 6 June 1787, at Spring Grove, Banks had shorn there, for the second time, 'Monsieur Ram' from Montbard, the ewe, and also the young ram lamb, their first offspring.[5] These three fleeces, with the two from the ram and ewe shorn on 7 June 1786, were sent to John Maitland in Basinghall Street in July 1787. Here on 14 August they were washed. The two fleeces of 1786 had been washed on the sheep's backs 'as customary in England' and were washed again in cold water, losing very little in the process —only about two to three per cent. The two fleeces of 1787 from the ram and the ewe had been shorn 'without being washd same as in Spain'. These were now washed in warm water first and then in cold. For the ram the loss or shrinkage on the original fleece weight of 7 pounds was 52·7 per cent. For the ewe the loss on her original fleece weight of 5 pounds 2 ounces was 58·5 per cent. The fleece of the ram hog was treated in a similar fashion and lost only 35·7 per cent of its original weight of 9 pounds 8 ounces. On 19 August 1787 the four adult fleeces were 'assorted by Mr Bell' of Bermondsey Street and then valued by Mr. Powell. These values for the ram and ewe fleeces of 1786 work out to be 11·75 pence and 18·90 pence per pound respectively. For the fleeces of the year 1787 the values are 17·00 pence and 23·90 pence per pound. It is clear that for all the sorting and washing, lessons well learned from Daubenton's experiences, these values are far below the figure of

55·00 pence per pound, which is the estimated sterling equivalent value of the Spanish Leonese wool with which the Montbard fleeces had compared so favourably in the French experiment.[6]

About the end of August or early September 1787, John Maitland sent the five fleeces away to be manufactured on general instructions received from Sir Joseph Banks who, on 20 September, wrote to Maitland hoping to recall the fleece of the Spanish tup hog for his own personal investigation. In reply Maitland sheds some light on the arrangements he had made:

. . . I am so triflingly concern'd in the Sale of Manufactures which require *fine* Combing wool that I am vex'd the fleece you mention is out of my Power to recall. The Person [J. A. Cole] to whom I had sent it I have written to acquaint me with the State it is in, and to proceed no further without my directions, but I fear I am too late—I have some doubts about his being able to have justice done to it in the Spinning but if he has succeeded in that Stage, I am sure he will Produce something worthy your Notice for I think him the most ingenious Manufacturer in the West.

The other four fleeces I have sent to another Person [Matthew Humphreys] who is esteem'd the best Superfine Clothmaker in the Kingdom, I inclose his Letter to me together with the Samples referr'd to therein, also a paper stating how I have & mean to proceed, by which you will observe Bell has assorted them rather after the English than Spanish Method, tho' I gave him the usual proportions and what Instructions were in my Power.

Powell said they were in so different a State to what Wool is which he is accustomed to put a value on that he was incompetent to the Task, however I made him give his Opinion, and his Valuations prove he did not plead Ignorance without Cause—Humphreys has not sent me the Acc[t] of what they lost in Scouring with him but as he is very correct, I have no doubt he has been as particular as I desired him. . . .[7]

Maitland's letter to James Cole of Trowbridge was partly successful. Of the tup hog fleece, Cole sent back to John Maitland for Sir Joseph just 1 pound 3 ounces of clean-scoured wool described as 'Superfine'. The rest of the 'Fine' or F sort had been used to make a length of cassimere, eked out by a small addition of warp yarn from some true Spanish wool to complete the cloth. Enough of the clean wool, however, had been kept back from further manufacture to find its own small niche as the subject of a classic spinning test at the hands of Miss Ann Ives the following year.[8] But however fine and beautiful this may have been it is to be noted that Cole described the T or third and lowest sort in this fleece as 'Coarse beyond anything [I] have been accustomed to find in Spanish wool'.[9] From this we may well infer that the son of 'Monsieur Ram' from Montbard left much to be desired in the general quality of his fleece, the T sort being described as 'very long coarse haired Wool'. Of the F sort, when picked and sorted Cole found that one-seventh remained of 'the same degree of Coarseness as [I] generally find in Spanish F Wools'. Of such stuff, then, was the fleece of the first authentic Spanish Merino lamb born in England, the sire of Lord Sheffield's Spanish-Southdown cross-bred lambs of 1788.

But of the first two fleeces grown in England by Daubenton's ram and ewe there was much more to be said at this early stage. Matthew Humphreys reported his first steps to John Maitland:

In one of this weeks Cloths you will find a small bit of each of the Sorts of wool, and, in the parcel, a bit of Coronet [=Patrimonio=Escurial] scour'd in the same wash, which you know gives a fair comparison. I have been particularly attentive (for I stood every moment of the time at the furnace) to have it nicely scourd, and kept apart, so that Sr Joseph may depend on each as it really appears, which I cannot but observe is very white and clean; but then, by examining, you will find the real Spanish has a cottony appearance, which the best of the [English] fleeces does not arrive at, and I am confident it will never work into Cloth as fine; however I have sent to the blue dyer the R[affino]^s of the two Ewe fleeces, and the R[affino]^s & F[ino]^s of the rams, for the R^s of the rams, alone, would have made so small a quantity of Cloth as to be of no use, besides, the difference between the R & F of the ram was so small that I did not think it worth keeping apart. I hope to get these parcels manufactured in time to shew you when I make my visit to weigh off my wool, and when, perhaps, you may give me an opportunity of making a few remarks to Sr Joseph in person which cannot be now so well made. . . .[10]

By mid-December the whole of this first experimental manufacture was complete. Two years after Daubenton's paper before the Académie Royale des Sciences in Paris, Sir Joseph had attained the conversion into English broadcloth of four fleeces from two sheep bred at Montbard itself. However modestly, he had certainly repeated the essentials of the French experiment and satisfied himself in the most practical fashion possible that the savant across the Channel had truthfully reported the general performance of the new fine wool of France. He could have done no more. His were the only two sheep of the Spanish fine-wool breed in England. From these alone could be got the material for such a test. What had it revealed? To Matthew Humphreys at least it had shown itself comparable to the best Spanish imported piles, and this he indicated in his letter concerning the matter to John Maitland:

In answer to your Letter this moment received—it is impossible for me to say with exact precision what each quantity of the wool wasted, but upon the whole I can assure [you] I found the wast[e] much the same as the best Spanish (i.e.) about three pounds to the score. I informed you when I had the pleasure of seeing you in town that it was impossible to keep such small quantities, perfectly separate, but, I again observe to you that the great perfection in every sort of it was the excellence of its scouring—in short— as for the Ewes of both years (for the difference was exceeding small indeed) I wish I had a quantity of it at 3/6. The whole of the Cloth was near $5\frac{1}{2}$ y$^{ds.}$ —$2\frac{1}{4}$ entirely Ewe at the fore end—$2\frac{1}{4}$ of the ram entirely at the latter end, and about a y^d in the middle of different Sorts. I beg you will make my respectful Comp^{ts} to Sir Joseph Banks when you see him and say how happy I shall be on all occasions to demonstrate to him that I am at his Service on any further Experiment he may choose to make in my way.... The Bristol bills shall be sent imm^y & placed to your acc^t when p^d I wish to have the bound plain Editions of both.[11]

This was followed the next day with a slight correction to note that the cloth length was in fact $5\frac{1}{4}$ yards in all, as nearly as could be determined.[12] With these and other details from John Maitland it is clear that Banks was in a position to make a fairly close comparison at least with the cloth made from the Montbard sheep sent several years previously to the park at Alfort. From the French wool Van Robais had made the equivalent of 14·9 yards of broadcloth, using 31 pounds of clean-scoured wool in the process. From the English-grown fine wool at Spring Grove Humphreys had produced 5·25 yards of broadcloth from 11·3 pounds of clean wool. Thus, in terms of broadcloth, the Alfort wool produced material at 2·08 pounds per yard and the Spring Grove wool stuff at 2·16 pounds per yard. That from Alfort was presented to His Most Christian Majesty Louis XVI of France and perhaps at some time adorned his Royal back. That from Spring Grove made two blue coats for the President of the Royal Society of London which he most certainly wore '& found as good as any made of Real Spanish Wool'.[13]

III

As far back as the spring or late winter of 1787 the concern of Sir Joseph Banks with the experiments of Daubenton and the Alfort wool was apparently a matter of general interest in Lincolnshire. His receptive attitude to all things relating to the growth and manufacture of the combing wools was by now established. It was therefore natural enough that Matthew Ives, corn merchant of Spalding, should seek to bring the prowess of his daughter as a spinster to the notice of an authority so discerning:

I have took the Liberty to inclose a Pattern of Stuff that was spun on the Distaff with the Spindle by my Second Daughter it was wove in Norwich. She had 18 Yards which weigh'd only 3 lb & $\frac{1}{4}$—near 60 Skeans to one Pound of Wool. 80 Threads in a Lea & 7 Leas to a Skean. know^g You was concern'd in the Alford [sic] Spinning thought you w^d like to see how fine Wool might be brought to perfection by industry. hoping you'll excuse me troubling You . . . P.S. it was made of Lincolnshire Wool.[14]

So it was that Miss Ann Ives, spinster of Spalding in Lincolnshire, became known to the man who would find in her a human instrument of some value for gauging the status of the Spanish fine wool of English growth, and in assessing its future as a possible fibre for combing as well as clothing purposes. Her dexterity with the distaff and spindle was immediately apparent in her conversion of the Lincolnshire wool into a thread that would yield 60 skeins or hanks to the pound of clean wool.[15] At Norwich it was considered that 70 hanks to the pound was superfine spinning for the worsted manufacture. And here was a young spinster capable of approaching this standard with the long and relatively coarse wool from the marshes! What might she not do with a finer wool? Sir Joseph was quick to perceive her potentiality as a piece of experimental machinery and to devise an early trial of her virtuosity. Ready to hand was the tup hog sired by the Daubenton ram out of a Lincoln ewe from Mr. Fowler of Retsby, fresh from being wintered in Mr. Walls's marsh.[16] Shorn that year at Revesby this first experimental cross of the Spanish fine-wool breed on the Lincoln long wool foreshadowed a new future for the wool trade and yielded its fleece for a test which would hasten its evolution. By November 1787 Ann Ives had spun from it a skein weighing $37\frac{3}{8}$ grains, equivalent to 186 hanks or skeins to the pound, and more than a threefold advance on her performance with the old Lincolnshire. In fact, it was beyond the limit of 150 hanks to the pound spun in 1754 by Mary Powley of East Dereham in Norfolk which 'was thought so extraordinary that an account of it is entered on the Registers of the Royal Society'.[17] Sir Joseph was delighted. He marked the occasion with material proof of his satisfaction. He further proposed to send more wool even finer to test the skill of his new protégée. What spinster could resist such flattery! Ann Ives was no exception:

Accept my sincere and most grateful thanks for your polite and very handsome present which gave me infinite pleasure as I flatter myself it was a proof I have attained what I most earnestly wished—Sir Joseph Banks approbation for my trifling exertions in spinning. indeed sir you do me great honour by your opinion that it may be of public utility. I anticipate great advantage from the next wool you were so obliging as to send me as I still keep improving in fineness. . . .[18]

The 'next wool' was the small sample of the superfine or Raffino sort from the young Spanish tup whose fleece had been sent to James Cole at Trowbridge, of which John Maitland had recovered 1 pound 3 ounces of the clean-scoured wool. In January 1788 Sir Joseph received the first proof from Ann Ives of the spinning performance possible with English-grown fine wool from the Spanish breed. She wrote with justifiable pride:

Sir Joseph Banks will not I hope think me too presuming in again addressing him on the subject of my spining [sic] having now arrived at the greatest degree of fineness I think it possible to attain the liberty will I hope be pardoned the Skain I have the honor to present weighs one dram 256 to the pound and could I receive any encouragement there was a probability of its being manufactured with infinite pleasure would spin a Shawl to that Standard the damp has such an efect on the Wool as to make two or three grains difference in a Skain should take it as a favor if before weighing this lay it a few minutes near the Fire my Father and Mother joins in most respectful comp[ts] with sir your very much obliged . . .[19]

Sir Joseph was at first disconcerted with the arithmetic of Ann Ives until he found that she had her own conventions. The Norwich skein contained 7 lees each of 80 yards which made a total length of 560 yards, the weight of which was the common basis for calculation. Ann Ives weighed her skeins each to the nearest one-eighth of a grain reckoning 28 grains per dram avoirdupois or 7168 grains per pound.[20] This consistently overestimated the number of skeins to the pound, and Sir Joseph always reduced her figures on the basis of the correct figure of 7000 grains per pound. At a weight of 1 dram per skein, however, the present figure needed no correction. His curiosity to see this new marvel was extreme, but it was not until 17 June 1788 that this was satisfied when Ann Ives wrote:

I am almost afraid from the length of time I have taken in sending the Skain which you did me the honor to request so long since you should be offended at my seeming neglect. but I hope you will pardon me when I acquaint you with the occasion of my not sooner complying with your commands. my visit at Lynn was much longer than I first intended and on my return my eldest sisters Marriage made it impossible to dedicate the time necessary for such fine spinning as I was anxious it should be. accept sir my most grateful thanks for the favor confered on me in presenting me with some of the most beautiful Wool ever seen and I beg your acceptance spun from that Wool a Skain weighing not quit 24 Grains which according to my calculation is three hundred to the pound. I cannot omitt relating a circumstance which has given me the most exquisite pleasure the Society of Arts &c, have done me the Honor to present me with their Silver Medal. indeed my sincerest thanks are due to you for all the praise I have received as I never should have attempted arriving at the perfection in spining I now have had not you Sir by your condesending to notice me emulated me to persevere in endeavouring to attain your good opinion . . . my Father and Mother beg their most respectful compt. . . .[21]

Banks himself seems to have reckoned this skein to weigh twenty-five grains and, therefore, by his more correct computation, to have made two hundred and eighty skeins to the pound. Later in September 1789 when Ann Ives looked back on this achievement she wrote:

... I have never spun any finer than that I had the HONOR to send in June [17]88, it weighed exactly 24 grains which I calculate would be 300 to the pound but I have known the Weather to have such an effect on a Skain that it would gain 2 grains in the weight till laying it before a Fire has reduced it to its original standard. . . .[22]

Such, however, is the spirit of emulation and ambition to succeed that eventually arithmetic tends to erode at the edges. Even with Ann Ives's figure of 24 grains per skein exactly and her 'long' pound of 7168 grains the result was nearer 298 than 300 skeins to the pound of clean wool. But with the true pound of 7000 grains the figure becomes 292 approximately. Nevertheless, it was at 300 skeins or a total length of 95 miles to the pound of wool that the reputation of Ann Ives as the English spinster *par excellence* was generally proclaimed. Nor were the vagaries of the weather and their possible effects on the calculation more than noted at the time. Certainly these small errors and approximations were unimportant in the magnitude of the advance in skill, and the efficiency with which it was now shown that the fine-wool fibre could be combed and used on the worsted spinning system.

The first impact of these demonstrations was on the manufacturers of Norwich. It had been noted that 'tho' this Young Lady has carried the art of spinning combed Wool to so great a degree of perfection, she does not despair of improving it still farther'. These gentlemen, 'zealous to encourage MISS IVE'S ingenuity', were 'desirous of improving their Looms in such a manner, as will enable them to weave her delicate Yarn'. In 1789 John Harvey of Norwich had already manufactured some of her fine yarn and was even then 'engaged in weaving her finest sort into a Shawl, the texture of which is expected to equal that of the very best that have hitherto been brought from India'. The ultimate success of this new branch in the wool manufactures of the kingdom was recorded less than three years later when John Harvey wrote to Banks on 23 April 1792, in a manner which sheds some light on the closeness with which the first modest efforts were pursued to an effective practical end:

As I cannot but consider you the Patron of the Manufactures of this Kingdom & particularly so of the Woolen & Worsted, I hold it a duty as a Manufacturer to lay before you any Specimen of superior excellence or extraordinary workmanship.

It is with this view that Hon: H. Hobart has kindly undertaken to bring you a Long Shawl made with the fine spinning of Miss Ives of Spalding, which is [a] full yard wide & four yards long & weighs only six Ounces— it is to be regretted that the extreme delicacy of finger this Lady possess should not be exercised on a finer wool, such as Sir John Sinclair's beautiful Silky Shetland—Mr Hobart will likewise show you a Shawl Counterpane nearly 4 yards broad & 4 yards long Weight lb 3. 10 [ounces] probably the broadest work ever woven by one person only in this Kingdom, & I might possibly add in Europe & by the same simple mechanism I would undertake to make one double the breadth if required—

I have the less scruple in addressing you, Sir, as I had the honor of some conversation with you when you passed through Norwich some years since. at the time I had just begun the then newly invented Shawl Manufacture & I was indebted to some of your observations for the improvement of the Top & yarn—Should you be of opinion that a Specimen of this broad work would be acceptable to the Society for the Encouragement of Arts & Manufactures &c. I shall consider myself honored in being permitted to send them a piece of the Shawl Work for that purpose. . . .[23]

IV

The forethought and the curiosity of the savants continued its quiet fermentation. The leavening effect of the small introduction of Spanish fine-wool sheep from France to the domestic pastures of the Spring Grove villa in Middlesex worked its way deep into the solid centre of manufacturing conservatism. Towards the end of 1790 George Chalmers, Clerk to the Board of Trade, conveyed a message to Banks from a most unexpected quarter.[24] Through this mutual friend John Anstie of Devizes, lately Chairman of the Committee of Manufacturers supporting the Wool Bill, had expressed a desire—a spontaneous interest, be it noted—to judge for himself how far the keeping of fine-woolled sheep in England might be expected to succeed. The cloth of Matthew Humphreys and the spinning of Ann Ives from wool entirely of English growth, though on sheep of French breeding, were enough as practical demonstrations already to raise prickly doubts in at least some strongholds of British complacency. Hard-spun fine wool for the worsted looms of Norfolk was but a short step from the cottage looms of Yorkshire. John Anstie of the West Country was no doubt prescient enough to sense the first stirrings of a far-reaching change in the broad structure of the woollen industry. The tussle over the Wool Bill of 1788 had raised issues enough to shake traditional foundations. Now the slender experiments at Spring Grove seemed to carry a message—hopeful or ominous, who could say?—which the West Country could not ignore. The passing incident of John Anstie and the fifth fleece of

'Monsieur Ram' from Montbard has its significance in British commercial progress. It also sheds a pleasant light on the characters of two of the late adversaries in the long-drawn-out Wool Bill contentions, ended scarcely two years before in the passage of the Act.

Early in December 1790 Sir Joseph Banks sent two fleeces to John Anstie 'by Clarke's Waggon from the White Swan Holborn Bridge'.[25] His letter covering the dispatch of this material is illuminating:

I have great pleasure in Fulfilling your Desire Expressd by my Friend M[r] Chalmers in Furnishing you with an Opportunity of Judging how far the experiment of keeping Fine Woold Sheep in England is likely to succeed having the utmost Confidence however I may differ from you in Opinion Relative [to] the Commerce of wools that [you] ever acted under a conviction that your opinions were just & true

You will Oblige me by letting have your Sentiments on the wool as fully as you conveniently can as no one has a higher respect for your Judgement or your integrity than myself they will be of the utmost use towards the guidance of my Future Speculations

I send you two Fleeces the one of my old Ram who came to England in Aug[t] 1785 & has now given me 5 fleeces of which this was the last clipd in June 1790. the other of a Spanish wether Sheep of 3 years old of which this is the second fleece. the original Ewe died two years ago The first fleece of the Ram was made into cloth by M[r] Humphries I send you a pattern of it the best means in my power of shewing you what the wool then was

I need not say to you that Rams wool is always Coarsest Ewes next & wethers finest but it may be necessary to inform you that no pains has been spard by me to make the wool coarser by keeping my little Flock always upon Land very rich & constantly manured in Short as unpromising to the growth of fine wool as possible but this has been done under an opinion that breed alone directed the Fineness of the pile & that Keep when the pile really was Fine had had little if any influence in making it Coarser[26]

The extensive concerns of John Anstie it appeared afforded him very little leisure and had obliged him to postpone answering Banks's letter until New Year's Day in 1791. But he would not have Banks think that his time had not been well employed on the subject of wool. As a witness to his industry there was his letter to Sir John Sinclair on this theme which the Scotch Baronet had promised to submit to Banks's perusal. However, in the midst of these distractions some progress with the wool from Spring Grove had been made. It had been scoured, and, as the quantities were too small for dyeing, he proposed to make them into white cassimere. This would give him an opportunity of comparing the draft of the wool with that of the best Spanish. Some had already been scribbled and found to work very freely though it was longer in the staple than the usual run of Spanish wool. He raised the common obstacle so frequently conjured up by wool valuers in these circumstances—that it was almost impossible to appreciate the true value of such a small quantity, though his assessment would be better when the different sorts were spun. However, at that stage he did not think the value of the fleece as a whole would 'prove equal to one of our Common Wiltshire Fleeces'. A friend engaged in the wool trade had in fact given his opinion that the ram's fleece was not superior to the best Sussex wool. Anstie could not agree, especially as he had now seen the wool scoured and found the quality even better than he had at first supposed. It had, he observed, also retained the qualities of Spanish wool, but could still only be denominated as second or third rate of that kind. Altogether he considered the ram's fleece 'to be in very good Condition as to the fineness of the Wool but full of Grease owing to its not being washed Clean'.[27] He noted that, although the staple was much longer than the usual Spanish, it was 'strong enough for Combing'. He felt sure it had declined from its original quality during the five years on the Spring Grove pastures and would become even coarser if the ram should survive for two or three more. None the less he could not 'but be pleasd to find the decline in the Quality of the wool much less than [he] could have supposd would have happend in the course of five years'. The essentials of his opinion he had now embodied in a letter to the Secretary of the Bath and West of England Society.[28] He had charged George Chalmers to give Banks a copy of the paper. Finally he reverted to the matter of past differences:

. . . I am much obliged to you for entertaining such favourable Sentiments respecting the rectitude of my Conduct. I have my own Opinion on the Commerce of Wool which is formed without attending to the prejudices of the two opposite parties. It will give me pleasure to see a Spirit of liberality prevail which will prove to be for the mutual benefit of the Wool Growers & the Manufacturers. My experience however has convinced me of the difficulty of effecting this with large Bodies of Men. . . .[29]

Science and the Manufactures were for the time being at least partially reconciled as John Anstie wished Sir Joseph a 'happy recommencement of the New Year'.[30]

V

Bridging the interval between the first experimental blue cloth from Spring Grove in 1787 and the first pieces of magnificent scarlet from 'the pure Spanish Breed' of His Majesty's 'patriotic project' at Windsor early in 1793 lay five years of apparently desultory experiments in different parts of the kingdom. These were all activated from the same source and eventually integrated in the same inquiring mind spreading its influence from Soho Square.

First, perhaps, there was the cross-breeding at Sheffield Place.[31] The summer relaxations on the South Downs with the Holroyd family and, occasionally, with Edward Gibbon, the racing at Lewes and at Brighton, the earnest correspondence on the commercial problems of a much-disturbed national economy—these had all in the end fostered a small practical experiment with the first son of 'Monsieur Ram'. Relieved of the fleece that was to achieve fame at the hands of Ann Ives, the young Spanish tup from Spring Grove added another small sprig to his laurels in the autumn of 1787. For one brief season he ruled in a seraglio of Southdown ewes at Sheffield Place, twenty of which were bought and kept there for the purpose by Sir Joseph Banks in a joint breeding experiment with Lord Sheffield. In the spring of 1788 he died leaving, from Sir Joseph's ewes alone, twenty-one progeny, and probably at least as many again from those of Lord Sheffield.[32] In 1789 the washed fleeces from sixteen of the Southdown dams and sixteen of their ewe tegs were sent to Thomas Bell, the wool stapler of Bermondsey Street.[33] Here Bell 'broke this Wool according to the Custom of his Trade, which is not to make any assortment for a higher value than twenty one pence halfpenny a pound'. But 'he observd that in breaking the half Spanish Fleeces a considerable quantity of Wool of higher value was put into the 22 penny assortment'. In the end the pure Southdown fleeces were found to average 1·91 pound in weight, 2s. 10d. per fleece, or 17·8 pence per pound. The half-Spanish fleeces from the tegs averaged 2·56 pounds in weight, 4s. 7d. per fleece, or 20·0 pence per pound. A second son of the French ram was sent to Sheffield Place and, in 1790, it was possible to submit sixteen fleeces, some half-Spanish and some three-quarter-Spanish to the partnership of Thomas Bell and John Buxton for a similar valuation. For these the average fleece weight was 2·94 pounds, the average fleece value 5s. 9d., or 23·5 pence per pound. In this latter consignment from Sheffield Place Bell was asked to treat them according to the Herefordshire practice, first trinding and then sorting them so that they could be matched against some of the most choice of the native fine wools. Of these that year the picklock or finest sort was valued at 32 pence per pound. Gauged by these standards the advance in fleece weight and quality in the Spanish cross was very satis-factory—especially when we recall how coarse and hairy for a Spanish fine-wool sheep the first son of Daubenton's ram really was.[34]

From the short-wool sheep of the South Downs to the fine short wools of Sherwood Forest was no great step for the perambulating Squire of Soho Square and Revesby Abbey. In 1788, therefore, Banks purchased twenty of the small 'forester' ewes and established them with Major Cartwright at Marnham in Nottinghamshire.[35] To them he sent another son of his old French ram and ewe and, in 1792, he was able to repeat his earlier experiment by sending twenty of the original Notts ewe fleeces and twenty from their half-Spanish progeny to John Buxton for valuation. The original 'forester' fleeces averaged 2·55 pounds and 3s. 7d. per fleece or 16·9 pence per pound. Their half-Spanish progeny by comparison averaged 4·15 pound per head, 6s. 5d. per fleece, or 18·5 pence per pound.

In a similar fashion Banks established in 1789 an experimental flock at Woodmansterne near Banstead in the hope of improving the sheep of Epsom Downs in Surrey. But of the results in this case no record seems to have survived.[36]

Then in 1790 Banks acquired two 'blackfacd Norfolk Ewes belonging to Mr Coke of Norfolk' which he mated with a son of the French ram, perhaps the same one used at Marnham. The fleeces from the two Norfolk dams averaged 2·82 pounds and those from their two half-Spanish progeny 5·56 pounds.[37] The comparison of values here was vague and inconclusive, for John Buxton offered only 33s. per tod of 29 pounds (13·7 pence per pound) which was much less than Southdown wool sold for in the year in which he received it (1792). Banks noted in relation to this that 'he does not say that it is inferior in Fineness to the South down but uses the old Staplers argument that it is heavier & ought therefore to be cheaper'.[38]

The search for truth and light on the obscurities of the wool trade was no easier then than now. Sir Joseph found confusion no less confounded when he turned to John Maitland after the fleeces from the first-cross Spanish progeny of the two Norfolk ewes had been manufactured into cloth by Messrs. Waring and Davis of Alton in Hampshire —cloth on all counts 'well Suited for Either Waistcoat or Breeches'.[39]

Mr Maitland on Seeing the cloth admitted readily that it was extraordinarily Good Cloth but said that the goodness of the cloth was no Proof of the Excellence of the wool it had been made of but only of the diligence & ingenuity of the manufacturer who made it—Mr Coles he declared had made as good Cloth of wool for Sir John Sinclair which had no such pretensions to being superfine as mine had.

The value of different wools said he is only to be ascertained by the Facility & cheapness with which they can be converted into Cloth there are some piles which tho to appearances ^{d}6 a Pound worse than others are in reality as much superior for they will almost make cloth without workmanship

how are experimenters to proceed they are not allowd to be Judges of their progress in any one of the necessary Steps they are not allowd to be judges of the comparative fineness of the wool that they are told can only be known by the Cloth made of it (such was the language when I began my experiment) & now the Cloth is no criterion one thing only I have Learnd which is not to appoint any persons who are dealers in Spanish wool of the party who are to decide on the merit of mine[40]

By the autumn of 1793, in spite of the evasiveness and the equivocation of wool merchants, clothiers, and wool staplers, Sir Joseph felt that he had, by the variety of his experiments, 'tended to prove that Spanish Wool had not degenerated in fineness, even on his Pasture at Spring Grove, tho' particularly unfit for Sheep'. All the wool which he had kept since the year 1788 for the purpose of comparison he finally determined to dispose of to Messrs. Buxton and Buxton, now the successors of Thomas Bell, of Bermondsey Street.

. . . not expecting to hear any more concerning it, except by receiving a fair price, which he was certain from the liberality he had observed in the dealings of those Gentlemen would in due time be remitted to him . . .[41]

On 11 January 1794 he was, however, agreeably surprised to receive a letter from Messrs. Buxton and Buxton begging his acceptance of a piece of cloth produced by Mr. Henry Wansey from three grey Spanish fleeces which together had originally weighed 8 pounds. These were derived from two coloured ram lambs probably sired by the old French ram from one of the three *métis* ewes given to Banks by the King and drawn from the flock got from Daubenton in January 1788.

The first Grey Lamb bred by Sir Joseph was dropd in 1789 and clipd in 1790, at which time the Spanish breed had been 5 Years in England & 14 Years out of Spain, this & one more both Males were kept for Castration which is known to ameliorate wool but Sir Joseph did not chuse to obstruct his experiments which were carrying on in several parts of the kingdom by castrating White Lambs of the pure Spanish blood.

Henry Wansey the clothier who had organized its manufacture considered it an excellent piece of cloth but, as it was wholly of undyed wool in its natural colour, thought it would fade in the wearing. Sir Joseph was greatly impressed with this unexpected specimen. On 14 January he sent it to John Wallace, woollen draper of Bedford Street, 'a Gentleman whose integrity of dealing he had long been accustomed to', and sought his opinion 'respecting its value per Yard & its degree of Fineness compared with superfine Broad [cloth]'. On 18 January 1794, at Soho Square, he received his draper's remarks on the small piece of manufacture which, for all its undyed state and natural colour, set the high-water-mark of quality and at the same time the effective end of the Spring Grove experiments:

I have had the favor of your Note, & have examined the Cloth you sent for my inspection very minutely, & find it in every respect very excellent. The Wool is remarkably good, though I have Cloth which, in my opinion, is made of rather finer wool, tho' that may admit of a doubt, as judging from the feel of the Cloth depends much upon the Dressing, & cannot be so correct as from the wool itself. The Spinning is very fine, & upon the whole it may I think be ranked with the best superfine Cloth Manufactur'd in England, if I except a few pieces made at a very high price & merely out of curiosity. I find it stouter than our superfine Cloth in general & I am of opinion that such Cloth from the Manufacturer is well worth 19^s p^r Yard or more. I return the Cloth by the Bearer . . .[42]

After nearly nine years this was at last a satisfying turn in the long maze of hedging and mystification through which Sir Joseph had patiently travelled. It was a much-needed antidote also to the strange pills he had been made to swallow by John Maitland, Thomas Bell, John Buxton, and all who were dealers in Spanish wool. Doubtless it was with a light heart that the next year he sent all his Merino flock to Arthur Young as a present and turned to His Majesty's Spanish flock, single-minded and encouraged in the pursuit of a fine-wool fleece for England.[43]

VI

The induction of Sir Joseph Banks into his working association with the Royal fleece was modest enough. It was also instructive. But it had little to do with Spanish wool in 1788. The Spanish flock had certainly been established with the French importation in January 1788 and with the ram and two ewes from Lisbon in March the same year. On 4 April 1788 His Majesty and Sir Joseph had together viewed this nucleus of the Spanish flock, the fruits of more than a year of planning. But on 24 May when Banks surveyed the Royal flocks at Windsor, Richmond, and Kew the 'true Spanish' and the French *métis* Spanish scarcely numbered fifty in all among a total of nine hundred and twenty-two of all ages and sexes. These were dominated by no less than seven hundred and sixty-nine Wiltshires of which two hundred and fifty-one were breeding ewes. Matching the new importations in number, there were also forty Herefordshire and forty Gloucestershire breeding ewes. It was with the clip from this very mixed flock that Sir Joseph was concerned when on 26 July 1788 he 'weighd up his Majesties wool' for the first time.[44] The experience was enlightening in many ways as a practical procedure to Banks. In nothing was it more so than in its bearing on the custom of the London wool staplers. It was doubtless a long and tedious day. The clip was weighed by drafts of 61 pounds each, four drafts making a pack of 240 pounds for the purposes of payment. In the case of oddments of more than 20 pounds an allowance of 1 pound was also made, whether the wool was sold by the pound or by the pack. But Banks was quick to note, 'Notwithstanding this allowance which is evidently intended as a compensation for the turn of the scale at each weighing that advantage is taken & a Quick one expected at least $\frac{1}{4}$ sometimes $\frac{1}{2}$ a pound a draught'. For cotts, black, and cast fleeces half price was allowed and the buyer took all the locks and sweepings—15 pounds that day. From this it is evident enough that Mr. Thomas Bell of Bermondsey Street had a sharp eye for the main chance.

The Wiltshire wool of 1788 totalled 6 packs and 140 pounds or 1603 pounds of saleable wool of which 1580 pounds were bought by Bell at $10\frac{1}{2}$d. per pound with an allowance of 23 pounds for draft. In addition there were 16 pounds of cotts, cast, and black fleeces at half price, the latter, oddly enough, being from two Gibraltar rams belonging to Mr. Evan Nepean.[45]

The Gloucestershire wool of 1788 totalled 197 or 194 pounds of saleable wool and 3 pounds of draft bought by Bell at $7\frac{1}{2}$d. per pound.

The Herefordshire wool which weighed 92 pounds in all was not in an attractive state, and Bell offered no more than 13 pence per pound where the current value was nearer 21 pence per pound. It was, therefore, sent off by Vaughan's wagon on 1 August to Major William Price (who had originally bought the sheep for the King) at Mancell in Herefordshire to be trinded and sold at Ross Fair. Too late for this occasion the wool, after trinding which reduced it to 76 pounds or 6 stone 1 pound (at $12\frac{1}{2}$ pounds per stone), was sold for 11s. a stone or slightly less than 11 pence per pound—clearly a very bad piece of business.

The average adult fleece weights that year for these three breeds were: Wiltshire, 3·05 pounds; Gloucestershire, 7·04 pounds; Herefordshire, 2·30 pounds. In 1789 all had increased, being respectively—3·62, 8·00, and 3·12 pounds.

The clip from the small Spanish flock in 1788 was left in the care of Goddard the shepherd. So also was the clip of 1789. Both were supposed to be kept separate though in the one place. In this Banks was not obeyed. Nor was he in 1790 when the clip of that year which he 'many times desired might be kept separate but the whole wool was mixed in bringing it from Windsor to Marsh Gate, where it now is as well as I could pick out the Fleeces', as he noted on 5 August 1791.[46] The disposal of the general clip of the King's sheep to Bell and Buxton could go on even during the sad period of the King's illness and even though Goddard neglected the whole business of the sheep at this time. The Spanish wool, however, was stored until the times appeared more settled for an appraisal of its value. Goddard's carelessness, over which Banks had no control, defeated him in this objective. In the end, as he stated in his first report to the King on 11 August 1792, as

. . . the wool had never been kept separate he has therefore sold the wool of the former years [1788, 1789, 1790] in its mixd state to his wool stapler

[John Buxton] who is highly delighted with the Samples of the Finest & Sʳ Jos: hopes to encourage him to wash the whole & sell it as Spanish wool having no doubt that the greatest part of it is Equal in all good Qualities to such Spanish wool as is usually imported[47]

In these circumstances we have no means of knowing what the productivity of the Spanish flock was during these first three clouded years. The domestic skies were clear enough by the summer of 1790, but the fleeting incident of Nootka Sound was disturbing the international scene and Banks held back both the Spanish and the Spanish-Herefordshire cross-bred wool,

as the Price of Wool owing to the uncertainty of war or peace is at present in a state of fluctuation & the staplers seem inclind to depreciate it . . .[48]

By the spring of 1791, however, he was determined there should be no further impediment to the progress of his observations on the Royal fleece for the flock had by now attained a useful number. It was indeed tantalizing after the shoe-string operations at Spring Grove to have nearly a hundred and fifty Spanish or near-Spanish sheep under his supervision and yet to be defeated by the neglect of a feckless shepherd Therefore that year he had determined to be present at the shearing of the flock for the first time and to arrange in advance for the experimental treatment of the clip. Samuel Lysons, F.R.S., a fellow-member of the 'Antiquary Society' (Society of Antiquaries) and well known to the King, had arranged with John Hawker, clothier of Dudbridge in Gloucestershire, to assist Banks 'in Carrying on the Experiment his Majesty has put under my direction for the purpose of ascertaining whether Fine wool can be produced in England . . .'.[49] On 5 August 1791 he not only visited the sheep at Windsor but packed up the wool of that year's clip in three bags ready for dispatch. Later that day he 'Saw H. M. on the terres who was graciously pleasd to approve' what he had done and all the arrangements he had made for the future progress of the experiment. Without further delay Ramsay Robinson was ordered to forward the wool bags by Tanner's Stroud wagon to John Hawker. In his covering letter on 8 August the matter was clearly put:

. . . The Large bag Contains wool Cut from Sheep of the Pure Spanish Breed most of which have been imported from there.
  one of the Smaller bags Contains the Wool of Sheep of the Spanish Breed imported from France where Government has carried on experiments for the amelioration of wools at Considerable expence & it is said with great success in this a peice of paper markd N° 1 is placd withinside under the part on which the word wool is written

in the other small bag you will find wool shorn from Sheep of the Herefordshire breed with one cross of the Spanish & in that is a paper markd N° 2

You will be pleasd to observe that as the Fleeces have been washd upon the Sheeps backs & managd in the English way they are not at all the appearance of Spanish wool but I have no doubt that when they are sorted & washd that some of them at least will produce very fine Cloth

from the Pasture in which they are fed being richer than I could wish the wool is become considerably Longer than the Spanish wool. I do not observe however that it is at all coarser.

as the English mode of washing is not nearly so good as the Spanish the Fleeces will Lose as much weight in scouring as English wool does Possibly 3 times as much as the Spanish wool exported to us Loses

The Spaniards as you know Sir Sort their wool into three denominations R F & T. a good Flock I understand yeilds 10 parts R. 2F. & 1T. I should wish you to have an eye towards the proportion of fine & Consider the Real Spanish Fleeces upon this system . . .[50]

Not much more than six weeks before Sir Joseph dispatched the wool clip of His Britannic Majesty into the West Country for manufacture His Most Christian Majesty Louis XVI of France had been arrested at Varennes and finally imprisoned.[51] The ten years of dwindling peace since the Treaty of Versailles were lost in the gathering crises of the year 1792 as France swept away its own Monarchy and turned against Europe. In the New Year of 1793, the Year I of the Republic, France executed its King, and on 1 February declared war against Britain, Holland, and Spain. Not much less than six weeks thereafter Sir Joseph received, again by Tanner's wagon from Stroud, three bales of cloth from John Hawker's brother George Hawker of Lightpill. On him the main task had fallen in the making of the fabric and in preparing a report on the performance of His Majesty's Spanish clip. Quickly Banks submitted the cloths to the scrutiny of John Wallace, his draper in Bedford Street, who gave a succinct judgement on each piece. Primed with these and the several reports by George Hawker, Sir Joseph prepared a short statement for the King on 18 March 1793. These papers he put into His Majesty's hands the same day with others of a more appropriately war-like portent concerning fire-arms. With them also he included a book by Sir Benjamin Thompson,

. . . the author whom H. M. may remember in Ld. Sackvilles office. his ingenuity as a Philosophical reasoner is allowd to be above par, he last year receivd the medal of the R[oyal] S[ociety] for Papers printed in the P[hilosophical] T[ransactions] on the subject of conducting heat . . .[52]

Although Sir Joseph may have been 'in hopes before now to have been honoured with an answer concerning them', it was not surprising from 'the multiplicity of business which the present eventful times produce' that His Majesty had not expressed any opinion by 9 April when Banks wrote in acknowledgement to George Hawker.[53] Technical problems in the boring of cannon and matters of fire-arms, the mobilization of Science to the aid of the nation—these were subjects which clearly had precedence in the minds of both the King and the President of the Royal Society. None the less Banks wrote carefully and appreciatively to George Hawker, considering himself 'as materially obliged by your very intelligent reports and the great trouble it must have given you to consider the small quantity of wool I sent with the accuracy and attention you have done'. Certainly, as far as the experiment permitted, George Hawker had contributed as clear and comprehensive an account as Banks ever received. It bears comparison favourably with the French experiments reported seven years earlier in its details. These permit some useful inferences to be drawn about the general character of the flock at that time. His remarks on the wool of the pure Spanish clip of 1791 convey much about the contraband acquisitions through Bilbao, Oporto, and Lisbon:

. . . Excepting a few fleeces which were remarkably fine, the wool in general proved pretty much the same with regard to quality, one third of which was well wash'd & pretty free from animal oil. The remainder proved extremely full of it & appeared as if not washed at all. It also appeared to be covered with a composition which had been smeared all over the wool when on the back of the sheep, and which probably, if ever wash'd, might have occasioned the impossibility of separating the yolk in any degree from the wool in that process. The wool however was by no means injured by it, but it rendered it impossible to ascertain the quantity of yolk it would lost had it been well washed, and thereby to compare it in that respect to either English or Spanish. . . . The fleeces were extremely fine and far superior to the best Herefordshire not only in being much finer, but in having a much straighter hair, which is a great perfection, and peculiar to Spanish Wool. The best of it however marked R was not so fine as the finest Spanish, but I think very little inferior to their second best R. . . .[54]

This is a brief but admirable summary against which his comments on 'the Wool of the Spanish Breed brought from France' stand in a clear contrast:

. . . The fleeces appeared pretty equal in quality and were very fine, much more so than what is produced by any sheep in this Island.
   The prime part of the fleeces, I thought rather superior to what I have called R. in the pure Spanish but still they did not upon the whole produce so much fine wool. In consequence of being better washed than the pure

Spanish, it did not waste so much in scouring, but its loss exceeds English wool by about 2 lib. in 20.

Finally, there were the important comments 'on the Wool of the mixt Breed'—the Spanish × Herefordshire cross—the first examples in any quantity of a product that would have a large place in the future discussions of British wool improvement:

. . . The fleeces were not so fine as Herefordshire but the fibre of the wool had that excellent quality of being very straight, which I presume it derived from the Spanish Ram, and which the other does not possess. It was also remarkably soft, and I have no doubt had the sheep been fed in Herefordshire they would have produced much finer wool than any that county ever yet boasted. It wasted in scouring about two pounds more in 20 than English wool does . . .

All these and many other points of contrast with the usual home or imported wools of commerce Sir Joseph discussed with George Hawker who responded with constructive interest, offers of further assistance, and a commendable willingness to accept Banks's reasonable explanations.[55]

Banks elaborated the substances of these explanations on 6 August 1793 in what was in effect his third annual report to the King. This announced without equivocation that

. . . it appears that the wool of the Spanish Flock answers the purpose of the manufacturers & has actually been converted into Broad Cloth far superior to any that can be produced from the finest British wool

That the Rafinos or finest Portion of the Wool when sorted is not equal to the best Spanish Rafinos imported is not to be wondered at, a Quality of wool equal to that of the best Merino Flocks which sells for much higher prices than that of the inferior ones could not be expected from sheep collected at different times & in various places by smugglers utterly ignorant of the nature of wool.

The Loss of weight complained of by M[r] Hawker S[r] Jos: apprehends is owing to the excessive quantity of Grease with which Spanish wool naturally abounds & this it will be difficult if not impossible to remove by the English method of washing the sheep before they are clipd, in Spain the wool is washed after it is shorn & it is said to Lose in that process half of its original weight

The Fact of the Proportional Quantity of the Finest Wool being Less & that of the second & third sorts Greater than in Spain S[r] Joseph attributes to the Richness of the Pasture at Windsor but he has great Pleasure in remarking that notwithstanding Luxuriance of Pasture is always inimical to the Fineness of Wool the Rafinos or finest portion of the wool has not abated from its natural Quality which is provd by a few fleeces (no doubt those of sheep purchasd by the smugglers from a good Flock) being of a Quality remarkably Fine

The Observation of Mr Hawkers that has given Sr Joseph the most pleasure is, that the Cloth made from the wool of the French breed of Sheep is Finer than that made from the wool of the imported Spanish

The King will be pleased to recollect that these Sheep were bought in France & brought into England in the 1787[56] at which time the Flock they were taken from had been 14 years at Montbard in Champaign, in the year 1791 then when this wool was shorn the sheep had been 18 years out of Spain & consequently passd through 3 or 4 generations, the Fact then of their Wool continuing to be superfine is a strong Proof in opposition to the Prejudice of our manufacturers that Merino wool may [not] be grown beyond the limits of Spain without losing its appropriate excellence.

That Monsieur Daubenton should originally procure from Spain Sheep of a better Quality than Sr J. B. has been able to do is not a matter of wonder the application from the Court of France to that of Spain for procuring Sheep was direct & the answer perfectly favourable, he had it therefore in his Power to chuse from the best Flocks in Spain & these the French manufacturers who have always been able to Procure finer piles of wool from thence than ours can obtain easily Pointed out to him; that he kept the original Quality of his wool or if he is to be credited rather improved it was doubtless owing to the variety of shepherds & other assistants paid by the French Government who were constantly upon the spot to aid him in selecting the best woold sheep from the inferior ones.

if the King approves the mode of ascertaining the value of the wool of the Spanish Flock by having it annually manufactured & a report of its Quality made by the manufacturers as was done with the clip of 1791, Sr Jos: Banks who knows of no other way so likely to put the question of its value beyond a dispute will be much gratified by H. M. Permission to send the two years growth he has now in hand to Mr Hawker, he is aware that this mode of trial appears to be expensive but as by receiving the cloth he will always have value in hand he has no doubt when he sells it at the termination of the experiment, of reimbursing much the greater part of what he may be permitted to expend in this manner of carrying on the business . . .[57]

Though we may well believe that the King was as gratified as Sir Joseph in the outcome of this practical trial there was some delay before 'H. M. Permission' for its extension was actually granted. The war itself was enough to defer much serious thought about it on either side. The next step was finally authorized by His Majesty on 14 July 1794.[58] Sir Joseph, nevertheless, did not see fit to convey the King's commands 'on the subject of his Experiment of growing in England wool capable of producing when manufactured Superfine Cloth' to George Hawker until it was nearly the spring of 1795. The reason for this hesitation was clear. After the scarcity of 1793 there was 'a glut of Spanish wool in Gloucestershire in the autumn [of 1794] This Spring it is scarcer & they will pay more regard to the importance of the Experiment'. Or so Sir

Joseph reasoned to his own satisfaction, in a small footnote to his draft of the letter. The substance of the letter itself, however, was well designed to win the support of any loyal clothier:

. . . his Majesty has Conceivd just Ideas of the integrity of your Character as a Man & of your Skill & Judgment as a manufacturer & has therefore orderd me to Lay the subject before you in as full a manner as I can continue to do

I Shall therefore if you will allow me Forward to you the whole of the Wool producd by his Majesties Spanish Flock for the 3 last Clips [1792, 1793, and 1794] Requesting you to Examine it with Care in order to determine what Proportion if any of deterioration it has sufferd from the Climate & pasture to manufacture it into such goods as you think most Suitable & when the goods are finished to allow such Price for it as you can afford to give to the Grower allowing to yourself the customary Profits of your Trade which I do not wish in any sense to Enquire into the Whole Question being whether the Price a manufacturer can allow for the wool is a sufficient recompense for the Loss sustaind in growing it owing to the Carcase of the animal not being moulded in what our Graziers & Butchers are in the habit of Considering a Fashionable Shape . . .[59]

George Hawker was 'much flatter'd by the confidence' His Majesty was pleased to repose in him and in no state of mind to refuse. He was on all occasions extremely happy to render Sir Joseph every service in his power.[60] But Sir Joseph was soon after confined by a fit of the gout, rendered unable to do any ordinary business, and thereby compelled to depend on the King's servants to send off the Spanish wool. These he manifestly distrusted, for he hoped there would be no mistakes owing to his unavoidable absence. However, eventually the clip of 1792 from the ewes shorn at Windsor and the rams' wool of 1792, 1793, and 1794 from the same place were gathered and sent as one lot to Stroud. As a second lot there followed the wool from the ewes and wethers of 1793 and 1794, shorn at Kew 'in the Barn opposite the Pagoda' and stored at Marsh Gate. All this was done some time in April 1795 with the injunction that 'What his Majesty wants is to have the real value of the wool ascertained in order that it may be known whether or not the breed will answer in England'.[61] Sir Joseph expressed his conviction that it would be impossible for Hawker to be certain what price he could pay for it until it was worked up into cloth and sold in that form. He was, therefore, in no haste for a definite answer respecting price, 'for that if you are so good as to buy it you must take your own time'. With this valediction the wool clips of these three years disappear from our further knowledge. George Hawker so far took his own time that five years later Sir Joseph, on 13 April 1800, taking stock of the 'Proceeds from the Wool of His Majesties Spanish Flock' noted that he had not yet accounted for the sale of the cloth.[62] From what is known of the clips of 1792, 1793, and of 1794, however, we may estimate the total amount of wool dispatched to Hawker as 1150 pounds of washed fleeces approximately or about 645 pounds of clean wool. This would produce about 308 yards of broadcloth which if sold at the prices of the period would have yielded a return of about £318 or 20s. 6d. per yard. With manufacturing costs at the rate charged in 1795 by John Walker —approximately 10s. 6d. per yard—we achieve an estimated price of about 2s. 9d. a pound for the fleeces in their washed state after the English style equivalent to about 4s. 3d. a pound in the Spanish state, a value somewhat above the average figure for imported Spanish wool at the outbreak of the French War in 1793. By contrast at the rates charged by George Hawker for the manufacture of the clip of 1791 the estimated price would have been about 2s. per pound in the English and about 3s. per pound in the equivalent Spanish state before the war. The cost of manufacture per yard was then about 8s. 1d. and sale price per yard about 15s. 6d.

VII

In the year 1795 the wool of the Spanish clip weighed 589 pounds, compounded of 177 fleeces—3·33 pounds per head, washed in the English way. This was packed in two cloths and sent to Mr. John Buxton for safe-keeping after he and Sir Joseph Banks had weighed it at Marsh Gate Farm on Saturday morning, 8 August.[63]

The arrangements for its disposal this year were to be different. Buxton undertook to sort the clip into three lots after the Spanish manner, and from this operation we are able to assess the relation between the English and the Spanish systems of sorting the fleece:

Raffinos	Prime
	Choice Locks
	Super
Finos	Head
	Downrights
	Seconds
Terceros	Abb
	Livery
	Short Coarse[64]

Having done this, Buxton was to send the wool to John Walker, clothier, of Painswick in Gloucestershire. Walker was to manufacture it into cloth which was to be sold at Blackwell Hall. The value of the wool was to be calculated from the profit obtained. In the process no one of the persons concerned—apart from John Buxton—was to know that the wool had come from the Royal flock. This new exercise proved to be more protracted than perhaps Banks had calculated.

It was not until July 1796 that the clip was sent to John Walker at Painswick. The amount was then recorded as 568 pounds or 2 packs 4 stone 8 pounds. This had been sorted by John Buxton in the following way:

Best Sort [=Raffinos]	292 lb.
Second Sort [=Finos]	226 lb.
Coarse [=Terceros]	50 lb.[65]

By 24 December 1796 four ends of green cloth had been finished and sent to Messrs. Fryer, Telford, Liddell and Smallman, Blackwell Hall factors in Alderman's Inn, 'to be disposed of to the best advantage'.[66] Before 13 February 1797 this had been followed by the remainder— four ends of blue, two ends of mulberry, one piece of black, and one piece of blue beaver—251¼ yards in all. For this the account rendered by John Walker to John Buxton for manufacturing was £84 10s. on 19 May 1797, to be paid 'seven days after sight'. This was reimbursed by Sir Joseph on 19 August 1797, with a gratuity of one guinea to Buxton after he had scrutinized the detailed statement of the costs of manufacture involved.[67]

The disposal of the full tally of ten ends and two pieces was slow— but not, apparently, unusually so for the system at Blackwell Hall. On 24 September 1798 John Buxton, now retired from Bermondsey Street and living at Highbury Place, returned from three weeks' absence to acknowledge receiving from Banks 'a remarkably fine Haunch of Venison'—no doubt from Revesby Abbey.[68] He also announced having that day seen Messrs. Fryer and Company who had paid him the first proceeds of sale—£26 13s.—for which, however, Banks did not trouble him at that date.[69] By 10 June 1799 a further sum of £42 0s. 9d. had been received by Buxton, but this again Banks asked him to retain until the whole business was completed.[70] The last ends of cloth were not disposed of until late in the autumn of 1800, when on 11 October John Buxton communicated this fact to Sir Joseph. The account was finally closed at a total return of £163 2s. 3d. to His Majesty or an average of slightly less than 13s. per yard. Some of the superfine green had sold at 16s. 6d. while the one piece of 29 yards of blue beaver, evidently made from the 'coarse' or 'Tiercero' sort, sold at the low figure of 8s. per yard. Following Banks's method of estimating the effective value of the raw wool we may on these figures assign a value of about 2s. 5d. per pound for the Royal clip of 1795 in its washed state as received and sorted by John Buxton. The cost of manufacture on the available figures may be assessed for the main stages in the process:

			Pence per yard
1. Scouring, picking, scribbling, etc. ..	..	..	8.8
2. Spinning, spooling, and warping ..	..	..	19.0
3. Weaving	..	..	14.7
4. Burling	..	..	2.0
5. Dyeing and listing	..	..	12.5
6. Fulling and dressing	..	..	12.2
7. Pressing	..	..	1.8
8. Miscellaneous (list yarn, folding, etc.) ..	..	..	4.2
9. Clothier's time and trouble	..	..	4.7
			79.9

To this must be added the cost of carriage and the cost of selling at Blackwell Hall:

10. Carriage both ways (between London and Painswick) ..	1.8
11. Selling charges (commission, insurance, etc.)	8.0
	9.8

Total cost per yard=7s. 6d.[71] approx. or   89.7

On the average 2·26 pounds of wool washed on the sheep's back in the English fashion or 1·63 pounds clean was in 1795 required from the Royal clip to produce 1 yard of finished broadcloth at an average 13s. per yard. With costs of manufacture and sale at 7s. 6d. per yard the net proceeds were therefore 5s. 6d. per yard or 29·2 pence per pound, by Banks's method of calculation. If we assume a clip yield between the washed and the scoured state of seventy-two per cent—a value found later over the years 1798–1804—then we attain a value of 40·5 pence per pound for the clean wool of the Royal Merinos at this time. At the values of the year 1795 this is almost equal to the average price of the imported wool from Spain itself washed by warm water in the *lavaderos* of that country after shearing and as a pile. The imported Spanish wool lost about ten to fifteen per cent on scouring and we must conclude that the Royal fleece of 1795 was less in value by about that margin.

As the business of the manufacture into cloth of the 1795 clip dragged to its end in 1800 a new relationship of great importance to the future conduct of the flock and its affairs gradually shaped itself. The wool-stapling business of Thomas Bell had become the firm of Bell and Buxton in 1790. By 1792 it had become the partnership of J. and J. Buxton, and so it remained until it was acquired by James Newsome of Russell Street, Bermondsey early in 1797.[72] When this change occurred John Buxton left his house in Bermondsey Street, where the warehouse was, and moved to the choicer environs of Highbury Place far north of the river beyond the City. From here he conducted the concluding phases of the sale of the experimental cloth whose manufacture he had arranged from the last wool he was to sort for Sir Joseph Banks from the Royal flock. As the figure of John Buxton gradually recedes into the mists of respectable middle-class retirement, the unassuming shape of his foreman Henry Lacocke appears in 1796 to grasp the torch and continue the long association of Bermondsey and the Royal fleece. He is to be found first among the sheep themselves as he attends 'H. M. Clip at Kew' on 18 June 1796, bringing his shrewd old eye to bear as each ewe was shorn, noting the finest and best fleeces, marking the ewes that grew them and culling out those with the coarsest and worst from other points of view.[73] For this he receives his first guinea, in common with the shearers from Sir Joseph. We glimpse him again on 20 June 1797, evidently performing the same service as 'he observd that the Tegs of this year had more kemp on their Polls especially than usual'.[74] Again he receives a guinea as gratuity for his trouble, but the days of his servitude now end. In 1798 Henry Lacocke steps forward as his own man.

VIII

When James Newsome acquired the wool-stapling business at Bermondsey Street from John Buxton he seems also briefly to have enjoyed the services of Henry Lacocke as foreman. This did not long survive the changed régime and on 18 July 1798, in delivering his account for the 'scowering' and sorting of the two Spanish clips of 1796 and 1797, Henry Lacocke made this clear to Banks. He inquired about the two years' wool collected at Marsh Gate from the rest of the King's sheep, saying 'I will Sell it for you or buy it of you which you please I have nothing to do with Mr Newsome having left his Service I have employ to Seek for my Self'.[75] This was not Lacocke's first letter to Soho Square, but we may regard it as the real beginning of another file of charmingly natural and blissfully unpunctuated documents in that comprehensive repository.[76] The tide of Henry Lacocke's working life was at that moment of pause before the ebb. Retirement and a secure old age were not for such as he. Almost inevitably he turned to the one source of patronage he probably knew. But he knew also that it was one which would not deny him a hearing. Therefore, a month later, he gently pressed the point home:

Your wisdom and good understanding I Know will pardon my Troubling you with these lines wishing you to acquaint me whether the Kings wool

Plate IV

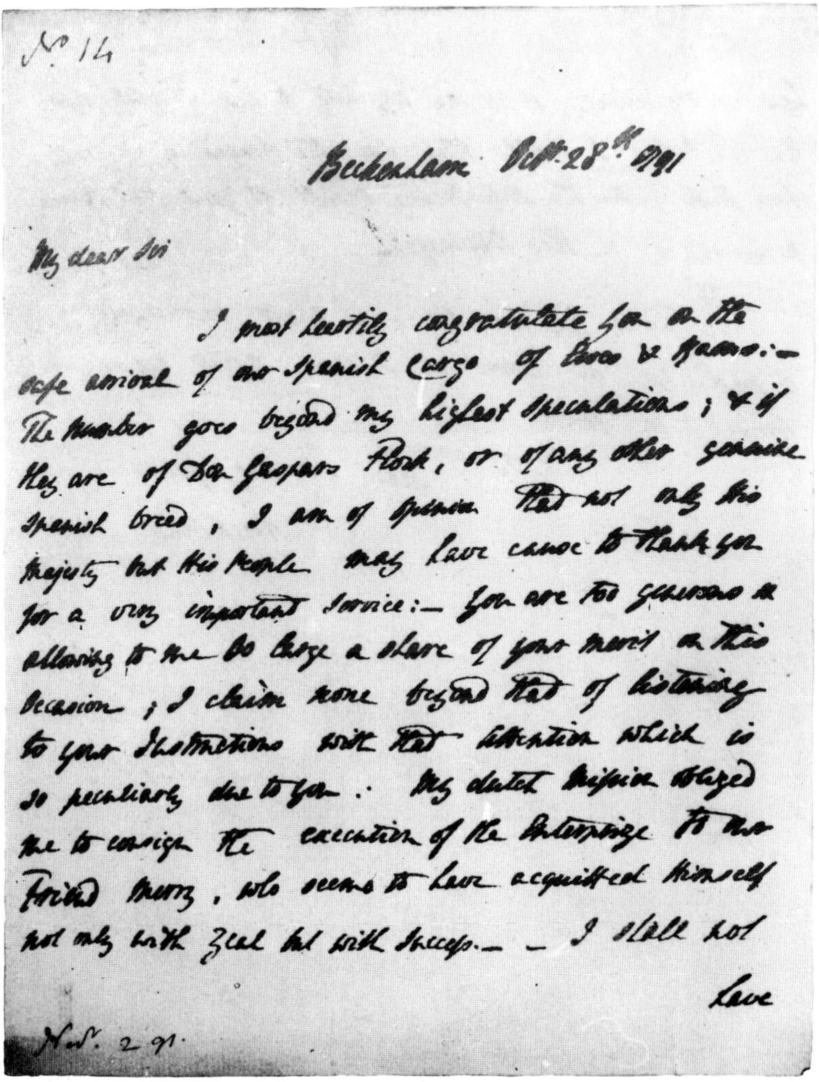

No. 14

Beckenham Octr. 28th 1791

My dear Sir

I most heartily congratulate you on the safe arrival of our Spanish Cargo of Ewes & Rams:— The number goes beyond my highest Speculations; & if they are of Don Gaspar's Flock, or of any other genuine Spanish breed, I am of opinion that not only His Majesty but His People may have cause to thank you for a very important Service:— You are too generous in allowing to me so large a share of your merit on this Occasion; I claim none beyond that of listening to your Instructions with that attention which is so peculiarly due to you.: My dutch Mission obliged me to consign the execution of the Enterprize to our Friend Murray, who seems to have acquitted himself not only with Zeal but with Success.— — I shall not

have

Novr. 2 91.

William Eden, 1st Baron Auckland, to Sir Joseph Banks, P.R.S., 28 October 1791, concerning the arrival of the first Negretti sheep from Santander.

Plate V

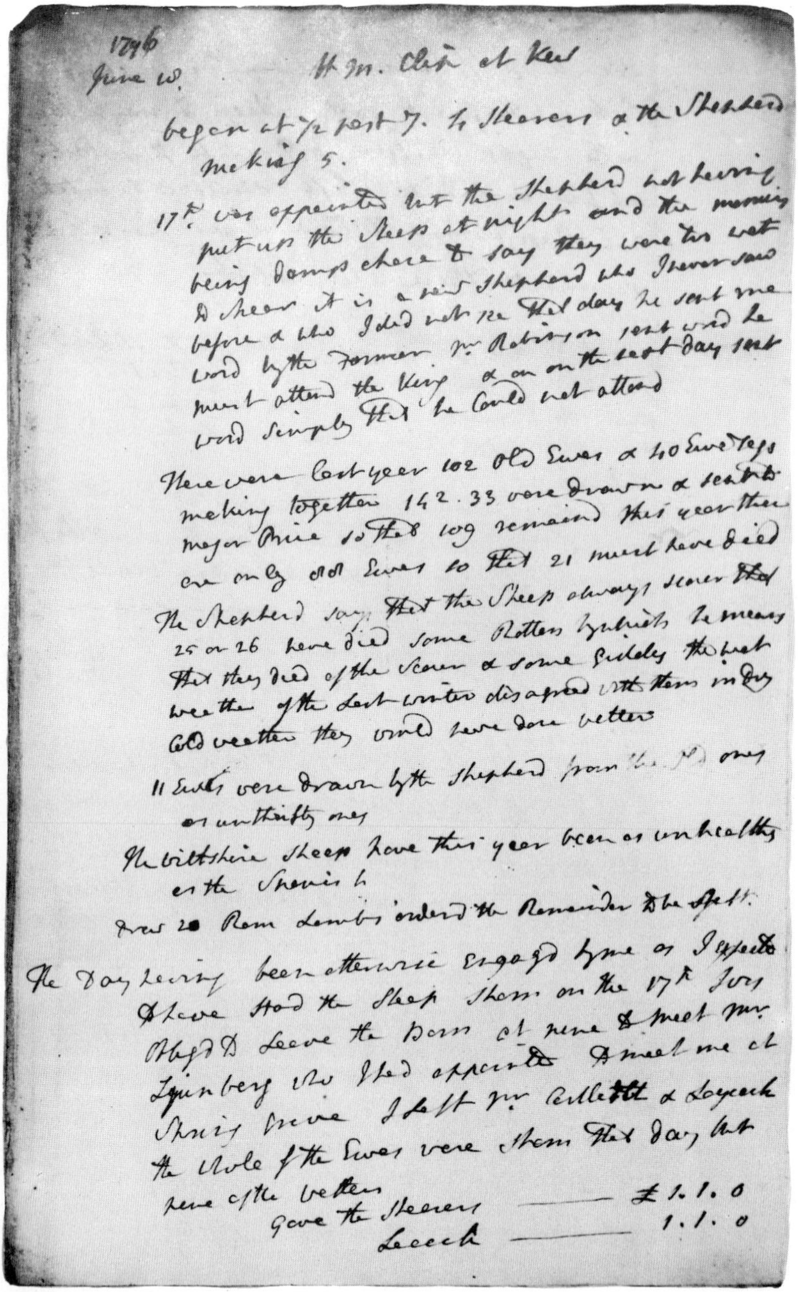

1796
June 18.   H. M. Clin at Kew

began at ½ past 7. 4 Shearers & the Shepherd
making 5.

17th was appointed but the Shepherd not having
put up the Sheep at night and the morning
being damp chose to say they were too wet
to shear it is a new shepherd who I never saw
before & who I did not see that day he sent me
word by the former, Mr Robinson sent word he
must attend the King & on the next day sent
word simply that he could not attend

Here were last year 102 Old Ewes & 40 Ewe Tegs
making together 142. 33 were drawn & sent to
major Price so that 109 remained this year there
are only old Ewes so that 21 must have died
The Shepherd says that the Sheep always shear that
25 or 26 have died some Rotten by which he means
that they died of the Scour & some Suddenly the wet
weather of the last winter disagreed with them in dry
Cold weather they would have done better

11 Ewes were drawn by the Shepherd from the others
as unthrifty ones
The Wiltshire Sheep have this year been as unhealthy
as the Spanish
& was 20 Ram Lambs ordered the Remainder to be spelt

The Day having been otherwise engaged time as I expected
& have had the Sheep shorn on the 17th was
obliged to leave the Barn at nine & meet mr.
Lynberg who I had appointed & meet me at
Shris Irene I left mr Collett & Doyenk
the whole of the Ewes were shorn that day but
nine of the betters
          Gave the Shearers ————— £ 1. 1. 0
          Leech ————— 1. 1. 0

Notes by Sir Joseph Banks, P.R.S., of the shearing of the ewes at the barn opposite the Pagoda at Kew, 18 June 1796.

at Marsh gate is Sold or Not, if not Shou'd be glad to Weigh it up Soon as I've Nothing at press^t to Employ my Self About, Cou'd Sort it out and give you the particulars of What it wou'd be worth, or if you please wou'd take it on my own account and pay you as Soon as I've Sold it, which I Suppose wou'd Not be longer than Three or four months

I hope, Sir Joseph you'l Not be Angrey with me, by my Saying, you'l Not forget one if you have an Opportunity to get for Me some little Employment in the Mint as I hear you intend making an inlargement in that office, it wou'd be Very acceptable and Gratefully Rec^d & Acknowleged.[77]

Banks had already acknowledged to himself a personal indebtedness to the old foreman, and this had taken the outward form of small sums as commissions on work done apart from gratuities for interest, civility, and zeal. He was prepared to receive Lacocke's plea with sympathy. He was also clear in his own thinking by this time on the part that Lacocke could play in relation to the King's Spanish flock. He was quite sure, leaving aside any principle involved, that Henry Lacocke was better wool-stapling in Bermondsey than place-seeking at the Mint. He replied with firmness but in a constructive fashion that settled the matter in the best possible way for them both:

The Kings wool at Richmond & Kew is not Sold if you will meet me on Saturday next at 9 in the morn at the Kings Barn at Marsh Gate we will consider about the mode of disposing of it & see if we can agree be so good as to Send down Sacks & let there be plenty as there is Two years wool & I believe the Flock has been increased as there has been an addition to the Farms.

if you will ask any one who knows he will tell you that the business I am employd in at Present at the mint is to abolish useless places but few of which I believe will be savd you may readily understand however that upon such an occasion it is not likely that a Place of any Kind should fall into my disposal.[78]

So it was on or about 24 August 1798, over the subject of the King's Wiltshire wool at Marsh Gate barn, that Henry Lacocke and Sir Joseph Banks consolidated a relationship mutually of value to them both— security for the one, expert assistance for the other. Out of the close association between these two men there slowly grew a mass of small precepts and practices that set a pattern for the future guidance of all who became 'amateurs' of the Spanish breed in England and disciples of the Spanish fine-wool fleece wherever it was grown under British hands. From an obscure position as a foreman wool stapler in Bermondsey, Henry Lacocke in his old age found a modest fame and a small but significant place in the history of the Commonwealth wool trade. In the following year, on 17 April 1799, we have the first-fruits of this association becoming evident as Henry Lacocke raised the matter of the Spanish wool in hand at Oatlands and at Windsor:

Respecting the Spanish wool that you have by you if I had it in the ware-house No Doubt that I cou'd Sell it for you prapps at 2^d or 3^d p^r pound more than I sold the last for, But if any Spanish wool Shou'd Arrive in England Shall Not be able to get any More for it than I did the last in the grease Not Scowerd as the year Before—I'm very Sorry to hear you are so lame that you cannot Exercise y^{r}self as you generally do I Know you love to be imploy'd I have latly heard there's a M^r. Gardner who lives in long-acre will undertake to cure the Gout in any Gentleman.[79]

This brought an instant reply from Soho Square the same day, agreeing to have the wool 'scowerd' and sold by a procedure which set the pattern for the next ten years. Some semblance of order had now at last been established in the manner of disposing of the Royal fleece, whether of the Spanish or the Wiltshire or any other kind. Banks had also acquired another correspondent on the perennial subject of gout, a fellow-sufferer who worried thereafter as much about Sir Joseph's health as he did about his own, and almost as much as he did about the numberless ills of the Spanish flock itself. By 22 April, Lacocke had received the clip from Robert Dickson at Oatlands sent down the river by Charles Fencock, the Walton waterman.[80] On 31 May he was able to report that he had sold the Spanish prime (Raffinos) wool of the 1798 clip to John Poole, clothier of Rode in Somerset, for 5s. a pound at six months' credit.[81] Again, on the same day, Lacocke received a short but clearly delighted reply which must have relieved the mind of the old man in several ways:

You have done very well by me in the Sale of the Spanish wool better it is impossible for any man to have done better. If it will be any convenience to you to keep the money that will be paid for it in 6 months, for 6 months Longer & pay it to me the day Twelve months from the time the wool was sold you are very welcome[82]

This transaction was soon followed by the Oatlands clip of 1799 sent down the river with Charles Fencock as before.[83] Of this the prime sort of 207 pounds was sold to Edmund Crabb, clothier of Tilsford in Somerset, at the excellent price of 5s. 6d. per pound. Crabb also took the 181 pounds of the prime sort from the accumulated rams' wool sent from Windsor—at 4s. 6d. per pound. The choice and fribbs, equivalent to the Spanish Finos and Terceros were sold for 3s. 6d. and 2s. per pound. These sorts went to a hatter's for carding. Lacocke's charges on the handling of this wool, which included 84 pounds of moth-eaten wool unwashed from Spring Grove, was 3d. per pound for scouring and drying and 1d. per pound for sorting, i.e. £3 and £1 per pack for each operation.[84] These prices could not have been much bettered. In the lean period after the failure of imported Spanish wool supplies during 1798 arising from the war with both Spain and France, this was one of the more fortunate transactions in the wool trading of His Majesty's Spanish flock. This was made clear by Henry Lacocke on 8 October 1799, in a letter to his distant patron at Revesby Abbey, with informative comments on business with some other distinguished clients:

No Doubt bu[t] you thought I had forgot my promise to you, Not giving you the State of our Marketts in London, one Reason amongst many was cou'd not properly get the Statement of the prizes of the Sorts of wool so Near as I cou'd wish, wools of Descriptions having its fluctuations in the Marketts. Since I saw you last I Shall give you Sir on the other Side the prizes of Each Sort that has gone through my Hands this Season, I've Rec^d from M^r [Arthur] Young Such a lot of Fleece wool that I think no Gentl^m wou'd wish to own as their Growth or Clip Some of the fleeces half wash'd others Not at all in the Spanish wool as Mr Young call'd it was all Sorts together, so that I cannot make a proper Trial any how, Likewise his Down wool as he call'd it is much the same, I have Not Begun his Bakewell as yet Can't Say any thing to that at pres^t I'm Sorry it was sent to me by way of Trial. I Shall get Neither Credit nor it may be a good word by Sorting it as I Suppose Mr Young cou'd Not be aquainted with the State of the wool or Condition. Lord Egremont's wool has come to hand, have Not as yet Examin'd [it] Not getting time having So much Business from Gentlemen in the Commision line I've taken care Sir to Sort your Kew wool first as wools Rather Drops in price for want of money in the Trade at pres^{nt}— your three Clips of Spanish wool is all Sold Except a few fribbs, have Settled the Business with M^r [Edmund] Crabb to whom I sold the prime Spanish wool at 3s./6 p^r pound and Likewise Sold him the Rams wool that was Shorn at Windsor for 4s./6 p^r pound at 6 mos Credit from the 5 of September which you'l say is Long Credit, cou'd Not Settle the Business any way besides without an abatement in price which I did Not like to do, I have waited Like wise to hear from M^r [Robert] Dickson Respecting the Spanish Sheep at Oatlands whether it would be Necessary of my coming to assist in putting the Ring on the Sheep—we have had great arrivals of Spanish wool from Spain which has lowerd the price Considerable. Some Spanish wool have Sold as low as 2s./ p^r p^d and Some at 2s./6 p p^d and good wholesome wool such as have been Sold as high as 3s./6 or More if another Arrival of Spanish Shou'd come, it will be very Cheap indeed which will be the Means to lower the price of our fine wools and then Wo to the woolstaplers that have given such great prizes for Sussex Down wools

I hope Sir Joseph I shall have the pleasure of Seeing [you] well in Soho Square in the Month of November, and I trust I shall be more able to inform you of all my Conduct Since I saw you last and what has Anoyd in y^r Absence, we just Nick'd the time for the Sale of our Spanish wools.

Sir, Shou'd be glad if you'd Trouble y^{r}Self to Drop me a few lines whether it wou'd be Necessary for Me to go or write Down to Oatland, and Shou'd be Glad to hear of y^r well Being and family may my God and Father whom I love Bless you and family Remain Respectfully . . .[85]

Revealing as this letter is on the general nature of the business and the personal relations between Banks and Lacocke in 1799, it is amplified by the details of one small account:[86]

1799	Expences going to oatlands an windsor &c.	£		
June 14	oatlands to Sheer the Sheep	0.	11.	0
do 28	windsor to do the Rams	0.	14.	6
July 8	oatlands to look at Ram Lambs	0.	9.	2
do 26	Expenditure at Lewes fair	2.	1.	2½
Augt 9	oatlands with the men to Ring the Sheep	0.	10.	3
		£4.	6.	1½
8 Days	.. ..	8.	8.	0
		£12.	14.	1½

This was settled by Sir Joseph on 17 April 1800 when he called personally at 12 Magdalen Circus to receive the money for the clip of 1799, part of 1798, and the rams' wool of both years—a net amount of £96 11s. 9d. after deducting £18 4s. 9d. for sorting and scouring. The services of Henry Lacocke at this time were not a charge upon the King's purse for Banks disbursed the sum 'on my own account as I ought to pay for the assistance he gives me in doing what I have undertaken to do'.[87]

Waiting at Magdalen Circus also for his inspection and approval were twenty-one yards of good blue broadcoth made of the Raffinos sort of the ram's wool from Windsor. Henry Lacocke had written to him during the winter about this and there had been a lapse of nearly two months before the invitation could be taken up:

I was in hopes of Seeing you in Bermondsey Street Before now, if you Shou'd be in the City on Monday Shou'd take it as a favour, you Cou'd Call as I have Received the piece of Cloth from [Edmund] Crabb as I mention'd to you when at Soho Sq^r.[88] I've been Rather Doubtfull in my mind not seeing you, that the Gout have Relapse'd and you are Not well knowing you are very punctual to y^r promise, I wish you to See the Cloth Before any one have the Sight of it, as he writes me word there's not an ounce of other wools but what I Sent him last, which is the Rams fleece wool Shorn this year at Windsor. I have not any Doubt But you will be pleas'd to See the production of the wool into So good Cloth as it appears to me, I Shou'd be glad of your Approbation how it may be Dispos'd of and to what purpose you may think Best . . . I hope I shall See you well Monday in Bermondsey S^t89

Edmund Crabb had suggested that this cloth should be bought at 17s. per yard which Banks readily agreed to and from the piece he 'spard M^r [John] Buxton 4 yards for Two Coats & gave 4½ yards to Mr Lacock to make him a Compleat Suit'.90

If Sir Joseph had been apparently slow in visiting Bermondsey Street it was by no means for lack of an interest in anything that Henry Lacocke may have had to say or to show. Far otherwise it would seem, for the first months of the new century—and of the Consulate and of the Republican Year VIII—were ripe with Banksian plans for the future of the Spanish breed. Scarcely a week before he viewed the blue broadcloth from the Royal rams' fleeces grown at Windsor his endlessly busy pen had been drafting a plan for a show of 'Spanish Rams of the pure Merino blood . . . in Their wool on the . . . day of May next at Smallbury Green for Particulars Enquire of A. Young Esqre Sec. to the B[oard] of agriculture at the house of the board in Sackville Street'.91 This was to be but the earliest step in 'A Project for Extending the breed of Spanish Sheep to such parts of the Island as may be most suitable to the Production of Fine Wool'.92 There were busy calculations to establish a 'mode of estimating the Value of a Spanish Ram' and more for gauging the value of a ewe. There were worried glances across the Channel at the proposals of Lucien Bonaparte who, as Minister of the Interior, was planning to sell no less than two hundred and twenty ewes and rams from the national farm at Rambouillet.93 There was an urgent throb everywhere as the pulse of the nineteenth century gathered its rhythm and strength. It is almost as though Sir Joseph divined the year 1800 as 'The year of the Merino' and was determined to lose no time in celebrating the event. His spring thoughts blossomed into print during the summer, enshrined for ever in the hallowed pages of *The Philosophical Magazine* as 'A Project for Extending the Breed of Fine Wooled Spanish Sheep, now in the possession of his Majesty, into all parts of Great Britain, where the Growth of Fine Cloathing Wools is found to be profitable'.94 And, as it were, to seal his devotion to the task he now saw clearly before him he performed a small personal sacrifice. This perhaps was no less symbolic for all its outward trapping of practical goodwill towards the man whose assistance and support he was always ready to acknowledge. In the last week of May 1800, therefore, he drafted a deed, legal in form but benevolent in spirit:

I Sir Jos: Banks of Soho Square London do hereby promise and agree that I will Pay to Henry Lacocke of Bermondsey Street Southwark the annual sum of Twenty Pounds Quarterly on the Four usual days of Payment as

Long as the said Henry Lacocke Shall continue to Sort for me as he has hitherto done, such wools of the King's growth & of my own as I shall Send to him for that Purpose, & Shall dispose of them by Commission on my account Paying to me the amount of the Sales after His Commission of a guinea a Pack has been deducted out of the Same & Shall Render to me an account of Each of the Sales of the Said wools, according to their several sorts, with the Price of Each sort after the manner of the Trade of a wool-stapler, & as he has hitherto done, The first Quarterly Payment of the said annuity to become due & Payable to the Said Henry Lacocke on Midsummer day next ensuing.

I do moreover agree with the Said Henry Lacocke that in case he serves me in the capacity of a woolstapler to my Satisfaction for the Term of his natural Life, which he Shall be presumd to have done unless I give him notice in writing that I am dissatisfied with his Proceedings, I will Continue to pay to . . . Lacocke wife of the Said Henry Lacocke the Said yearly sum of Twenty Pounds for the Term of her natural Life as aforesaid & in the Case of my Death happening to Fall out before the Death of the Said Henry Lacocke or of . . . his wife or of Either of them, I hereby bind my heirs Executors or assigns to Continue to pay to the said Henry Lacocke and his wife and to the survivor of them the said yearly sum of Twenty Pounds as aforesaid for the Term of their natural Lives & of the Life of the survivor of them Provided I have not during my Life by writing under my hand declared myself to be dissatisfied with the Conduct of the Said Henry Lacocke in his Capacity of a woolstapler towards me, in witness whereoff I the said Sir Jos: Banks &c. have put my hand and seal this . . . day of June in the year of our Lord 1800 in the Presence of . . .[95]

No man knew better than Banks how to blend patronage with pragmatism, though his disbursements and dispensations were always far sighted—or mostly so. Usually it was Man, rather than one man, who gained. He was more than commonly possessed of the material means for open benefactions. Of these he was known to give freely. But he was no mere public philanthropist. It is hard to measure the wealth of quiet help he gave in places and on occasions where no public acclaim was ever likely. With Lacocke there would seem to have been no reason why a system of *ad hoc* gratuities should not have continued as tantalizing refreshments to the payment for services rendered or of commission earned. We may justly credit Banks, however, with a social conscience and a broad human sympathy—even though at times there remains a suspicion that, in his organizing drive to gain some scientific end, flesh and blood were sometimes almost forgotten. He expected much but he gave greatly himself in more ways than in money. His own energies were expended and his own physical comforts sacrificed as freely as his guineas. Beyond this, also, there were few men who had as full a store of friendship to offer for itself alone. It was from this rather than from

Sir Joseph's pocket that Henry Lacocke was enriched to the end of his life. It is true that the friendship of the great is an implied flattery to humbler men and at times to them it is worth more than gold. Lacocke was patently gratified to have such a close personal association with Banks, and through him to gain some sense of contact with Royalty. There is perhaps small harm in such conceits at any time. Here, however, there was positive good in the long years of service achieved for the King and in the general public benefit which we can at last see in clear perspective. Old Lacocke, who had already in his own way committed himself to Sir Joseph's service, was genuinely overwhelmed by the annuity and more than usually inclined to incoherent lapses in his letter of 27 May:

I Scarce Know how to Express my feeling of Gratitude to you for so generous an act of Benevolence in communicating the inclos'd deed for the Support of my Self and wife in old Age by the Gift and Donation whereof you were not ask'd by me for, the Contents of that agreement (I hope) which you have therein Express'd, be inabled to fulfill to y^r Satisfaction as I've I trust done in times past, for you, my wife Desires her Sincere obligations and g[r]atefull thanks to Sir Joseph Banks for his Benevolent thoughts Towards her—I will get the agreement done according to y^r Directions By the Coppy [writer] and take the Liberty to Bring them unto you for y^r Approbation with the original Copy Sent me. I have Sir this day Rec^d by y^r Cart 4 Small Bags of wool which I Suppose to be y^r LinconS^r Clip have not look'd at them But Shall Sort them as Soon as possible to See what they will Make and give you the Contents[96]

In this way Henry Lacocke entered the last and perhaps the happiest and most rewarding phase of his otherwise obscure life, assuring Sir Joseph again before the year was out—'I will Strain every Nerve of my understanding for y^r interest and Honour'.[97] No idle words were these, for the next ten years are replete with evidence of many kinds that the old man gave his heart to the task as well as 'every Nerve' of his understanding both to His Majesty's Spanish flock and 'all that appertains to my Best friend the Rig^t H^{le} Sir Jos. Banks Bar^t'.[98]

The first year of the new century with all its personal significance and comfort for Henry Lacocke was not to end before he had recorded one small but important point of general significance and rather less comfort for certain gentlemen in New South Wales. At some time during the year the first small lot of wool of whose existence we are sure had reached England from that distant Colony, but by whose hand or by what ship we do not know. It may well have been from Governor Hunter with his dispatches by H.M.S. *Reliance*, under the command of Captain Henry Waterhouse, which arrived at Plymouth on 26 August

1800.[99] This at least is possible and not unlikely. If so the specimens may have been laid to one side until Sir Joseph returned to Soho Square from Revesby Abbey in late October or early November. Soon after this he may well have made a preliminary examination of the colonial wools with Henry Lacocke for, on 10 December, the old man wrote to Soho Square from Magdalen Circus:

... —I have this day Examined the Bottney Bay wool and find there's but very little of that Kind which we took on the Table to look at will let it Remain in the Bags untill I See you as the hairey wool is but little worth ...[100]

This glancing reference to the contents of what may have been the first bags of wool from New South Wales—however 'hairey' and of 'but little worth'—was hurriedly interpolated between the account for sorting the King's Wiltshire wool of that year from Kew and word of the arrival that day from the Belle Savage Inn on Ludgate Hill of a 'Remnant of Cloth from the Country', a capital piece of broadcloth for a greatcoat, from Mr. Edward Tovey. This appears to be the 8 yards of 'Double milld Drab' whose manufacture Henry Lacocke had managed for Sir Joseph from 20 pounds of the best prime Sussex wool picked from about two bags and worth 3s. a pound. Banks reckoned it 'worth to a woolen draper 17/ a yard' but 'if dampd & cold Pressd' it would be so advanced in price that a 'taylor' would have charged him 23s. a yard.[101] It was evidently a fine piece of cloth from the native Southdown breed, albeit from carefully selected material, rivalling the best from Spanish wool.

These transactions between Lacocke and Banks matured in their own good time—the sale of the Royal clip from Kew, the manufacture of the double milled drab, the legal expenses in drawing up the deed for the annuity, the manufacture of eight pairs of stockings—all were presented and settled on one final account when Henry Lacocke visited Sir Joseph at Soho Square on 9 July 1801.

IX

It is perhaps not unreasonable to mark this date as one of the significant moments in the commercial annals of the world. Seldom can we identify a particular day as that on which historical conception occurred but this summer morning in Soho Square has just that element of mild romance, briefly noted as a journal entry of most unromantic tinge:

July 9 Mr Lacock call'd upon me & paid me the balance of his account £36. 1. 6. I deliverd to him 8 Fleeces from N. S. Wales to be examind and Reportd upon[102]

Since 17 October 1800 H.M.S. *Buffalo* had been lumbering home under the command of Captain William Kent, bearing his uncle Governor John Hunter into retirement with dispatches, letters, and a diversity of specimens from Acting-Governor Philip Gidley King. At the end of June the *Buffalo* dropped anchor in Portsmouth, and both uncle and nephew were prompt in discharging their duties to Soho Square.[103] The long letter from King written on 28 September 1800 was delivered before 29 June 1801 to Sir Joseph, who noted:

Received: One small square case of seeds and crytogamia; one larger, containing specimens of plants; one large box with fleeces, from Capt. McArthur[104]

For ten days or so the fleeces remained at Soho Square until—quite in the ordinary way of business—Henry Lacocke called, cash in hand, to settle his debts with his benefactor, friend, and fellow-expert in sheep and wool. Together they viewed and discussed in a preliminary way the first identifiable fleeces from the southern continent whose future would so largely be determined by their opinions thereon. Henry Lacocke did not delay long in setting about his closer study of this colonial novelty which was altogether an advance on what he had noted during the previous December. Returning to Magdalen Circus, he hired a porter for 1s. 3d. to carry the specimens from Elizabeth Farm across the Thames from Soho by way of London Bridge to Bermondsey:

please to deliver to the bearer those 8 Fleeces which came from Botney Bay that Sir Joseph and myself look'd at this day and not take the wrap[p]ers of from them as they are numbered[105]

Within the next week he had finished his examination of them, and no doubt had recorded his remarks for the benefit of Sir Joseph—those same remarks which on 26 March 1803 were published under his name in the *Sydney Gazette*.[106] On 20 July Lacocke scoured 24 pounds of the best sorts (prime, choice, and super) at the same time as the 220 pounds of the Spanish rams' fleeces from Windsor. His account for all his operations submitted to Banks on 14 September included the values of the wool from 'Bottney Bay' with those of His Majesty's clips of 1801 from Oatlands, Kew, and Windsor. From these accounts and his published comments we can clearly see that the best of the colonial wool, from the stock presumed to be of the real Spanish breed, was certainly as good as the rams' wool from Windsor and little inferior to the best of the ewe clip from Oatlands. On value this was about twice the price of the Wiltshire clip from Kew. All told the 36 pounds of wool sent by Captain John Macarthur realized £4 14s. 1d. of which 6 pounds of the best were valued at 5s. per pound clean scoured. This was mainly derived from the first two fleeces which Lacocke emphasized in his remarks—'if they could preserve Nos. I and II for their breed in the Colony I think they may make good progress in their Breed and Wools'.[107]

Henry Lacocke had at last inscribed his small but indelible mark in the annals of the Commonwealth wool trade. John Macarthur had also made the first of his far more widely known contributions in the same field. Presumably the two men eventually met and discussed the significance of all these operations after Macarthur had reached London on 21 December 1802,[108] though of this there is as yet no direct clue. We may also speculate on another small point—whether Sir Joseph Banks ever paid John Macarthur the few pounds owing for the '8 Fleeces from N. S. Wales'. But whatever remains hidden from us at present on this score, there is no denying that these slight transactions in the summer of 1801 are the definitive beginnings of the nineteenth-century pattern of Great Britain's wool trade and what we might almost classify in this sense as the 'century of the Merino'.

X

In all the essentials Banks and Lacocke had now between them established the methods by which the general economy of the King's Spanish flock was pursued for the next ten years if not actually to its problematical end. In the manner of dealing with the annual wool clip this is now made clear as Banks summarizes it in a manuscript note of 12 May 1803:

The Plan of Selling wool adopted by Sr Jos: Banks on his Majesties Account & in which I have been employd for Several years is Quite different from the usual one it is more profitable to the grower & it has the advantage of giving him information every year of the Real State of the wool but on the other hand the Credit is necessarily much larger

in the usual way the buyer takes the wool at a Price agreed upon & Pays at an early period also Settles between him & the Seller & makes his money by retailing the wool to those who buy the sorts for their use who are a Set of People who expect & who are usd to have long Credit

Mr Lacock who takes the King's wool Sorts it in the first instance & Sells it to these people charging only commission for his Labor in Sorting & Selling it he therefore Cannot Pay for it [n]or indeed can he be expected to Pay for [it] till these people have paid him which never has been less than 8 months & sometimes more than ten[109]

Such a system would, of course, have been impossible for Henry Lacocke as a 'little master' in the wool-stapling business had there been no benevolent baronet in Soho Square. As it was, he managed not only to dispose of the King's wool consistently to advantage over a period of recurring military and economic crises but also to build a modest business using the same principle with a small but select clientele—the Earl of Egremont, the Marquess of Exeter, the Earl of Sheffield, Sir Richard Sutton, and others who had been drawn into the orbit of the Spanish sheep in various degrees.

In relation to the affairs of the Royal flock, however, Lacocke established himself in a unique place. By the time the Spanish breeding ewes returned to Kew from Oatlands Park in October 1802 and Richard Snart had succeeded to the place of Ramsay Robinson that summer he had consolidated his status as 'Sir Joseph Banks's man' by a multitude of small practical services in relation to the sheep as well as the wool. He himself rated this clearly as equal to the style and dignity of being in effect 'the King's woolstapler'.[110] In both capacities the world accepted him. Even Richard Snart learned very soon to respect him as a fountain of knowledge and experience in the matter of Spanish sheep. He had by then received the benefit of more than five years' association with Sir Joseph at sheep washings, at shearings, at reviews of rams, ewes, and lambs, at the selection of individual sheep for matings or for sale, and at a miscellany of other occasions. Whatever he may have known or understood before this about the sheep as an animal it is certain that he was thoroughly indoctrinated afterwards, especially in the peculiarities of the Spanish fine-wool breed. With sheep-lore added to his skill as a wool stapler and with both concentrated round the Merino, the old man became in the last decades of his life a prototype of the sheep classer in those distant colonies from whence would come finer and better wool than ever he or Sir Joseph would live to see—and in quantities beyond the vision of any of their fellow-Georgians.

From 1802 to 1804 Henry Lacocke was apparently tireless. There was no activity or concern relating to the Spanish flock at Windsor or at Kew which escaped him. By coach, at His Majesty's ultimate expense, he ranged out from Bermondsey 'on Sundry times'—to shear the ewes and lambs in the sheds near the Pagoda, to shear the rams at Windsor, to cull the ewes or to select a sheep for some worthy suppliant, to weigh the Royal clip at Marsh Gate, consulted by Richard Snart, disposing and arranging the clip for sale, or the lambs' wool for manufacture into 'Lady's Cloth', writing long autumnal letters to Revesby, keeping a watchful eye on Richard Stanford at Kew, bemoaning the outcast and neglected state of the rams in the Little Park—all this on the whole apparently in a harmonious relationship with Richard Snart which left Sir Joseph at last comparatively free from the practical urgencies of the flock management for three years. Each year Lacocke attended to the Spanish clip in the same way—sorted it into its three

sorts (prime, choice, and fribbs) after scouring, and sold it at comparatively long credit—until 1805. And then, about the usual time of shearing in June, Henry Lacocke suffered his 'misfortune'—the hey-day of
the Royal fleece was past. Just what form the old man's illness took we
cannot quite assess—some form of 'stroke' in the language of today it
almost certainly was—but from then on he never had the use of his
right hand nor the full use again of his right leg. The tally of human
infirmities was rising to a point where the security of His Majesty's
Spanish flock was seriously endangered. Sir Joseph could no longer rely
on the prop whose support he had enjoyed for the past eight years. The
weight of management was now falling on Richard Snart as Sir Joseph's
own health began to fail, but the sudden withdrawal of Henry Lacocke
undoubtedly hastened the crisis of 1805 and the long tension and silence
of 1806 between Windsor Castle and Soho Square.[111]

In July 1805 John Buxton emerged from his seclusion at Highbury to
the assistance of his old employee at Bermondsey Street and wrote on
his behalf to Soho Square requesting that the clip of that year be sent
from Kew as soon as possible. Lacocke was fearful that he would not
be able to obtain the same price as the previous year.

On 11 August 1805 Banks had occasion to advise Lacocke not to
undertake further business on behalf of the King—even though pressed
by the Honourable George Villiers superintending the Windsor farms
from Cranbourne Lodge[112]—'in Your Present State of Health' and
'Especially when I consider the Present disposition of your Nephew
[John Ewarth]'. By the end of the year, however, Henry Lacocke had
sufficiently recovered to write a 'left Handed Scratch' asking Banks to
drop him a line 'to Say Whether you've granted M.r Campbell of
Edenboruh the Receipt to cure the Scab in his Sheep'.[113] He apologized
that he could not wait upon Sir Joseph, 'being much the same in my
lameness as when you Saw me'.

From this year on until Lacocke's presumed death or final disability
in 1811 the Royal clip was handled in a less elaborate fashion being sold
washed and sorted but not scoured, disposed of by the most direct
negotiations and with the shortest terms that could be arranged. The
old frequency of personal contacts in London and at Kew and Windsor
between Banks and Lacocke diminished year by year as the health of
each became more uncertain. Communication was maintained by brief
notes across the river conveyed by John Ewarth or a maid-servant,
while the daily affairs of the flocks at Marsh Gate Farm and at Windsor
Castle were increasingly managed by Richard Snart who, after his
mysterious neglect of 1805–6 from 'Some peculiar Circumstances of a
private Nature', maintained a suitable liaison with both of these ageing
experts.[114]

We finally lose sight of Henry Lacocke in the summer of 1809 on Tuesday morning, 18 July, about eleven o'clock 'at the Sheds near the Pagoda' where Snart had arranged to meet him for the purpose of selecting the sheep for the sale of that year.[115] The system of dealing with the Royal fleece, which he had done so much to establish, was also about to change. The old wool stapler himself must have known this, for that very day Snart had written to Banks on the same occasion, telling him that

A M.ʳ White, a Manufacturer of Frome, having been recommended by a Person at Windsor to purchase some of the Wools, I took the Liberty of mentioning the Circumstance to His Majesty, who approved of the method as demonstrative that the Wool is in Repute, and that Purchasers can readily be procured for it at a fair Price—I shall have the Honor of Shewing you Tomorrow a Letter received from M.ʳ White Yesterday Evening—It matters not to whom, if a Substantial Person, the Wool is sold, and as there is no Wish to take the Commission out of M.ʳ Lacocke's hands, he can set the value upon it—If sold on the Spot, it would save a great deal of Trouble and time & no objection that I can see can be made to it—A ready Sale and prompt Payment are at all times desirable, and more so at this time from the increased Number of Sheep, and consequent Expenses attending them—

But by the evening of Monday, 17 July, Snart had received through Banks a note from the Admiralty 'respecting the arrival of Spanish Sheep at Portsmouth', and therefore thought it incumbent upon him 'to be at Windsor very early in the Morning, in Case His Majesty has any Commands to give on the Occasion'. Snart was therefore unable to meet Henry Lacocke who thus for the last time selected the sheep for sale alone, but for the assistance of Richard Stanford. For Snart on the other hand there were, indeed, commands from His Majesty who had ordered the naval transports with the new Negretti sheep from Cadiz to leave Portsmouth for Deptford. It is, therefore, in the bustle and confusion of the arrival of one of the last remnants of the flock of the Countess del Campo di Alange that Henry Lacocke moves out of the history of the Royal flock. Snart's letter to Sir Joseph of 17 July 1809 very effectively marks the end of the experimental phase in the life story of His Majesty's Spanish flock. With the passing of Henry Lacocke from an active part in its affairs the following day so also may we mark the occasion as that on which the Royal fleece became an article of ordinary commerce in the wool trade of England. After nearly twenty years of assiduous study by Banks, with thirteen years devoted assistance by Henry Lacocke, the Royal fleece had played its part in setting the foundations of Great Britain's commercial prosperity throughout the nineteenth century.

CHAPTER VIII

The King's Grace, 1791-1799

I

By the summer of 1791 the Royal flock of fine-woolled sheep in the Little Park at Windsor Castle numbered over one hundred and fifty. This was the achievement of more than four years' assiduous correspondence and tortuous negotiations with France, Spain, and Portugal; with men of science, the sea, and the counting-house stool. From north and south of the Pyrenees the sheep which composed the first phase of His Majesty's Spanish flock—half brought honestly from France, half as contraband from Spain—had clustered in their little shiploads under the Castle walls. Since that first week in January 1788 some nineteen rams and ninety-six ewes had been gathered from Burgundy and Provence, from Old Castile and Estremadura as chance had largely determined. Of these some twelve rams and eighty-eight ewes survived the English seasons to become the parents of the lambs of 1791. But these dividends of 'Daubenton's Flock', of 'the Bilbao plan', of 'the Lisbon plan' were destined to give way before 'the Treasure of infinite value' that was so soon now to be the outcome of 'Lord Auckland's undertaking'. The first importations were all to be scattered far from the Royal precincts to pursue the Royal plan in odd ways and among surprising people. It is not always easy to discern the circumstances or the reasons that determined their outward paths from Windsor. And yet it is instructive to try. We can almost mark the day when the Merino genes began to move into circulation under the impetus of His Majesty's 'patriotic plan'.

It began on New Year's Day in 1791, almost casually, in a short note of inquiry to Banks from a fellow-Trustee of the British Museum, the genealogist and antiquary, Sir William Musgrave, F.R.S.:

Being prevented from waiting on you at Breakfast this morning as I intended, I am obliged to trouble you in this way to enquire where Sir John Sinclair lives in London? and also what becomes of the Male lambs of the King's Spanish Flock? it is to be hoped that they do not cut all those which they do not want for his Majesty's own use but rather that they save some surplus Rams every year to be distributed among those publick spirited persons who may be desirous of improving the English Wool.

A very worthy Nobleman of my acquaintance is already possessed of

some Ewes of the best Herefordshire & Southdown breeds and wishes to
procure a Spanish Ram if you can point out the proper channel by which
it can be obtained.

Wishing you many & happy revolving years . . .[1]

With this note the first written plea of which we know for sure was
made for a sheep from the Royal flock of Spanish Merinos. Whatever
other verbal promises or half-promises emanated from the King or from
Banks before or after this we are at least certain that Musgrave's inquiry
placed that 'very worthy Nobleman' the 2nd Earl Bathurst at the head
of the private memorandum of arrangements for distributing the spare
rams which Banks prepared for the King's approval on 6 August.[2]
The surviving draft of the letter whereby Banks conveyed the news of
this first manifestation of the King's grace to his enlightened subjects
well displays the pattern of other similar transactions in the next few
years:

I yesterday Receivd his Majesties Final Commands relative to the distribution
of the Spanish Rams that are not wanted for the use of the Experimental
Flock /kept in the Little Park at Windsor/ & take the Earliest opportunity of
acquainting your Lordship that one is destind for you

it is a three year Old Sheep & was imported from Estremadura in the year
1790 & I have no doubt it is one of the True Merino Breed its wool since it
has been in England has become somewhat Longer in the Staple owing to
the Richness of the Pasture in which it has been kept but I do not Observe
it to be at all Coarser & I have no doubt /that/ if your Lordship puts it upon
Pasture when the grass is short & sweet that the wool will be restord to its
original Shortness of Fibre

Mr [John] Robinson of Windsor who has the Care of H.M. Flock kept
in the Little Park will deliver it to your Lordship's order whenever you chuse
to send for it & as the Proper Season of Putting Ewes to the Ram is not till
St Lukes Tide I trust your Lordship will have ample time to suit your own
convenience . . . /Sir Wm Musgrave mentioned to me that your Lordship wishd
for some Ewes I can only say on that subject that his Majesty has 5 of the true breed
that are taken from the Flock on account of their teeth being bad they are capable
however of bearing a Lamb each/[3]

Second thoughts dictated the scoring out of any reference to the five
cast ewes which eventually seem to have found their way to another
quarter. Lord Bathurst therefore received only the ram, numbered 2
on the horn, about which nothing remarkable seems to have been
recorded—except many years later, when Dr. C. H. Parry who sent
ewes to him in 1792 stated: 'He was, surely, the most hideous of his
kind.'[4] But before this impression could burn itself into the recollection
of the good Doctor or make any impact on the noble Lord it was

enough that the King's bounty should be suitably acknowledged—whatever the peculiarities of the gift itself. Therefore on 10 August from Cirencester the Earl replied:

I was honor'd by the last Post with your letter communicating to Me his Majesty's Goodness in having destined for me a spanish Ram; you will be so good as to make an opportunity of expressing the gratitude I feel for his gracious remembrance of Me. I have provided a Seraglio of Ryland Ewes to receive the Spaniard into their Cotts for they never lay out at night in open Air. their Wool this last season sold at 2ˢ. 2ᵈ p pound . . . will send a carefull Driver as soon as the Weather gets cooler.[5]

II

Second on the list of 6 August was Arthur Young of Bradfield Hall, Suffolk, then on a tour of Leicestershire hobnobbing with Mr. Robert Bakewell and his nephew Mr. Honeyborn, in full cry after material for volume sixteen of his now well-established *Annals of Agriculture*.[6] There is no need here to seek far for reasons why Ram No. 3 should have been destined for the farm-yard of the most voluble agricultural writer and quasi-experimentalist of his day. Sir Joseph and Mr. Young had been running in double harness for several years in the matter of the Wool Bill of painful memory. The *Annals of Agriculture* had been almost half-written for several volumes with the arguments and distresses of the long-wool growers of England. Arthur Young had supported Banks enthusiastically during the period when wool was his hobby-horse as much as it was the more sustained interest of the President of the Royal Society. His name, high on the list of recipients of Spanish rams, is therefore no surprise. A letter in much the same form as all the others was duly sent to Young on 7 August and doubtless he found it waiting at Bradfield Hall soon after his return from Dishley on the 14th.[7] The industrious editor was delighted; he was ecstatic; he soared into an eloquent paean that few kings and no sheep have inspired—at least in the English language.

How many millions of men are there that would smile, if I were to mention the sovereign of a great empire giving a ram to a farmer, as an event that merited the attention of mankind; the world is full of those who consider military glory as the proper object of the ambition of monarchs; who measure regal merit by the millions that are slaughtered; by the public robbery and plunder, that are dignified by the titles of victory and conquest, and who look down on every exertion of peace and tranquility, as unbecoming those who aim at the epithet *great*, and unworthy the aim of men that are born the masters of the globe.

My ideas are cast in a very different mould; and I believe the period is

Plate VI

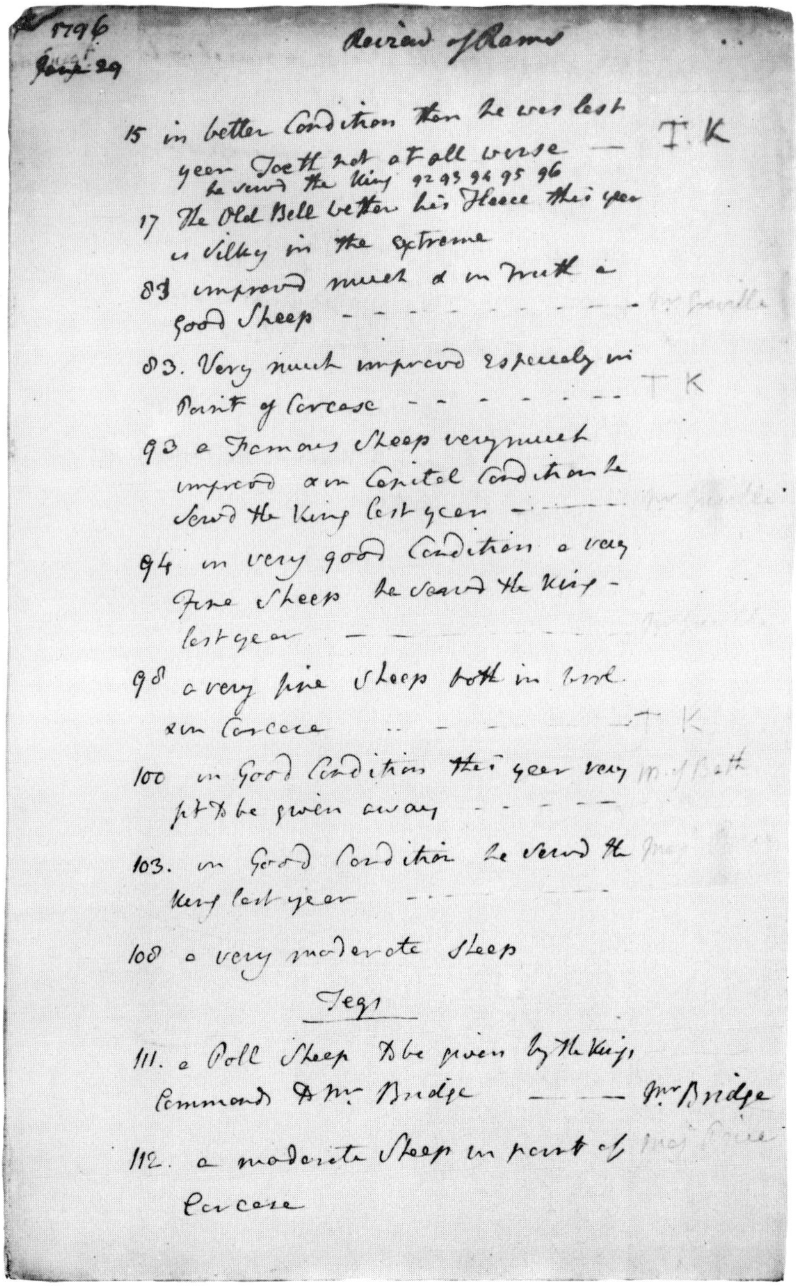

1796
June 29   Review of Rams   T. K

15 in better Condition then he was last
   year doeth not at all worse —
   he serve the King 92 93 94 95 96
17 The Old Bell better his Fleece this year
   is Silky in the extreme
83 improved much & in truth a
   Good Sheep - - - - - - - -   Mr Greville
83. Very much improved especially in
    Point of Carcase - - - - - -   T K
93 a Famous Sheep verymuch
   improved a in Capital Condition he
   Serv'd the King last year - - -
94 in very good Condition a very
   fine Sheep he Serv'd the King -
   last year - - - -
98 a very fine Sheep both in Wool
   & in Carcase   - - - - -   T K
100 in Good Condition this year very
    fit to be given away - - - -
103. in Good Condition he serv'd the
     King last year   - - -
108 a very moderate Sheep
                    Tegs
111. a Poll Sheep to be given by the Kings
     Command to Mr Bridge - - - Mr Bridge
112. a moderate Sheep in point of
     Carcase

Notes by Sir Joseph Banks, P.R.S., of his review of the rams at Windsor Castle,
29 June 1796.

Plate VII

Arthur Young's imported Spanish ram 'Don' (Ram No. 3 of the Royal flock) aged four years, with horns left uncut in the English manner, 1791.

Lord Somerville's imported Spanish ram (Ram No. 20 of the Royal flock) aged three years, with horns cut short in the Spanish manner, 1803.

advancing, with accelerated pace, that shall exhibit characters in a light totally new; that shall brand rather than exalt the virtues hitherto admired; that shall place in the full blaze of meridian lustre, actions lost on the mass of mankind; that shall pay homage more to the memory of a prince that gave a ram to a farmer, than for wielding the sceptre—obeyed alike on the Ganges and the Thames.

I shall presume to offer but one other general observation:—when we see HIS MAJESTY practising husbandry, with that warmth that marks a favourite pursuit;—and taking such steps to diffuse a foreign breed of sheep well calculated to improve those of his kingdoms;—when we see the royal pursuits take such a direction, we may safely conclude, that the public measures which, in certain instances, have been hostile to the agriculture of this country, have nothing in common with the opinions of our gracious sovereign: such measures are the work of men who never felt for husbandry; who never practised; who never loved it:—it is not such men that give rams to farmers.[8]

Such, in part, was the effusion elicited by the gift of one small sheep, a lone ram from an unknown *cabana* in Estremadura, smuggled down the Tagus, survivor of the cargo on the *Betsy* under Captain Michael Firth which reached the Thames in the summer of 1790, and now immortalized as 'DON a Merino Ram given by his Majesty to the Editor of the *Annals*'.[9] It was his fortune to achieve a publicity not accorded to any other individual sheep of the Royal flock and to provide us with one of the rare glimpses of the animal itself from which so much may be deduced. Here then was a four-year-old Spanish ram, rated by Banks as *b* for wool and *c* for carcass, measured and described by Young soon after its arrival at Bradfield Hall:

Measure of the Royal Ram

Girt, ...	42 inches
.. .. at chine, ..	36
.. .. of neck, ..	20
.. .. of leg, ..	$4\frac{1}{2}$
Thickness, ...	11 inches
.. .. at chine, ..	9
.. .. carcass, ..	23
.. .. of neck, ..	7
Breadth of loin, ..	6
Weight, ...	91 lb.

The thickness, *hardness*, and closeness of his coat, are singular; the colour to the eye very dark, dirty, and even blackish, arising from that superior degree of closeness; but when opened, for examining the wool, the extreme beauty of the staple is at once apparent. The fibre fine; twisted; full of that yellowish waxey grease, that distinguishes the Spanish fleeces; the skin oily to an extraordinary degree.

But though this is the first word-picture available, supported as it is
by an engraving, of any sheep from the imported foundation stock of
the Royal flock, the subject's ultimate contribution to His Majesty's
national project was small. This was in truth a 'remote and ineffectual
Don'. His performance was not equal to the rhetoric which had
wrapped him round in the pages of the *Annals*. He did less to establish
his kind to the contemporary benefit of British agriculture than did
Ram No. 2, his former shipmate on the *Betsy*, a younger animal of
three years old, rated *b* for both wool and carcass by Banks and as
'surely the most hideous of his kind' by Parry, who none the less made
him the foundation of a breeding project that lasted far into the next
century. No. 3 was put to forty of Arthur Young's finest woolled
Southdown ewes. No. 2 entered the 'Seraglio of Ryland Ewes' prepared
by the 2nd Lord Bathurst at Cirencester Park which presumably
included in the following year the modest few ewes of the same breed
sent by the Doctor, the mothers of offspring that would represent a
solid and enduring addition to our knowledge in certain well-written
papers about ten years on.

III

Next in serial order of the horn numbers was the Ram No. 4. This
was a French ram from Montbard imported in 1788 which Sir Joseph
had evidently ordained for himself in his private memorandum. It was
undoubtedly a mere formality thereafter to record of the King's
approval that 'he was also graciously pleasd to order me to take for
myself an A ram'.[10] This duly joined the tiny flock at Spring Grove
with the three *métis* ewes of the same French origin that autumn. This
allotment was no more than a just benefaction to the servant who more
than any other had laboured in the vineyard. Nor was there a man in
England more likely on the face of it to make such good use of this
mark of the King's grace. And yet this animal too would fade into
obscurity as its high-minded owner turned his own flock over to
Arthur Young a few years hence and became the single-minded
guardian of the King's Spanish sheep.

The disposal of the Rams Nos. 5 and 6, however, was attended with
much delicate negotiation ending in publicity of a high order, but
again somewhat out of proportion to the contribution made.

The matter had begun gently enough as far back as September 1790,
when Sir John Sinclair sent Banks a copy 'of a Report laid before the
Highland Society of Scotland, respecting Shetland wool'.[11] In the
fourth paper of the Appendix to this report was a plan prepared by
Dr. James Anderson 'of an association for the improvement of British

Wool' which Sinclair hoped would meet with Banks's 'countenance and support'. He hoped also that Sir Joseph would comment on the idea that there should in fact be two such societies, 'one for South, and the other for North Britain'. He thought they might profitably correspond together and assist each other 'and perhaps the rivalship between them might be of service to them both'. But in particular he hoped Banks would have leisure to look over the report on the Shetland wool, 'and to examine it with your usual accuracy'. He added,

The Highland Society, I have reason to believe, would be much flattered with a communication of your sentiments on the subjects mentioned in that paper, and of the lights which you have acquired, in the course of your patriotic exertions for the improvement of British Wool. We are yet young in the business, and therefore would be happy to put ourselves under the banners of an able and experienced leader. In particular regarding Spanish sheep and the possibility of that breed thriving in the Western Islands, it is altogether Theory and conjecture.

A fortnight later from Revesby Abbey Banks replied at some length, supporting the idea of two societies in principle—'if Societies for the improvement of wool are necessary'—with his guinea a year much at Sir John's service,

Provided however that by so doing I am not understood to coincide in opinion with our worthy friend Anderson on the subject of the mode of improvement as the little experience I have had on the subject inclines me to differ with him toto calo in some very interesting parts of his Memorial[12]

Whereupon Sir Joseph proceeded to expound his reasons for not accepting the Doctor's opinion on the possible value of the Shetland sheep as a significant aid towards the widespread improvement of British fine wool—adducing arguments as valid today and as worthy of support as when he first put them to Sinclair. But Sir John was not to be easily deflected from his Shetland enthusiasm and riposted cunningly with a 'Specimen of Shetland Wool properly prepared' for Lady Banks—'free from stitchel hairs'—and as nice a piece of advertising copy attached to it as a modern publicity expert could contrive:

N.B. Shetland Wool, taking all its *properties* together, is, perhaps, the completest article of the kind in the universe, possessing at the same time, the gloss and softness of silk, the strength of cotton, the whiteness of linen, and the warmth of wool.[13]

But to Sir Joseph himself he dropped the hint

Lord Sheffield has promised us some of the Spanish breed of sheep. Perhaps you might dispose of some of yours.

Banks, however, for the moment was content merely to advise him 'to have a Shawl made at Paisley of the Shetland wool'.[14] But no man could so easily escape the persistence of the long laird from Caithness. By the early New Year of 1791, within ten days of the formal birth of the Society for the Improvement of British Wool in Edinburgh, Banks found himself under the necessity to answer yet another probing letter from the north in which he ended with the following pregnant words:

your proposition that H M may have Spanish Rams for the asking of the King of Spain has been long ago considered & deemd Erroneous if your Society is Established & proper application made I think it very likely you will be able in the Autumn to Obtain one or two as by that time there will if no accident happens be 10 or 12 at Windsor[15]

Then on Monday, 31 January 1791, in a room of the Highland Society's premises, poised on the Bridges between the Old and the New Towns of Edinburgh, at a 'very respectable and numerous meeting' under the Chairmanship of Sir John himself—not surprisingly—the Society for the Improvement of British Wool was launched on its brief but not wholly insignificant career. On Monday, 4 April 1791, at the St. Alban's Tavern in London Sir John felt 'induced to call a Meeting, to consider the propriety of constituting a Society in London, for the purpose of promoting the Improvement of British Wool'[16]—an abortive exercise, for no such society was born alive that day or ever. Banks, for one, had withheld his support and presumably had drawn away the support of the 'many respectable Characters' on whom Sir John had relied.[17]

As my opinion relative to the Proper means of improving British wool are not very similar to those you have recommended in your Publications & patronised in those of Dr. [James] Anderson & as I differ from you Espeshaly in some of your political deductions on that Subject & in none more than the Expediency of Prohibiting the importation of Spanish in order to force the improvement of English Wool I shall venture to conclude that it will be more agreeable to your intended Society as well as more creditable to myself that I should remain unconnected with it than that as member of it I should be daily under the necessity of controverting in conversations resolutions & undertakings in the Formation of which if I belong to it I must appear to have acquiesced I shall therefore decline attending your Private meetings & if I come to the public one shall do so only for the sake of giving the reasons why I do not join a Society the Professd intentions of which I highly approve in case anyone should think it worth while to enquire what they are . . . P.S. as I have never given my consent to becoming an office bearer & my engagements would not allow me to undertake it were I inclind to become a member I ask that my name be struck off the List before it is offerd to the meeting[18]

On the subject of the southern society the two baronets agreed to differ and the matter quietly died. The northern society on the other hand thrived in the warm brightness of an early Edinburgh summer, and Sinclair kept the idea of the Royal sheep well nourished. On 16 May 1791 he hoped Banks would 'have the goodness to make an early application for as many as we can get of the Royal Flock'. He mentioned the great clipping day intended for the last Monday of June at Edinburgh and thought 'it would have an excellent effect if some of the Royal donations were present at that time'.[19] However, on 17 May, Banks, genuinely sympathetic but mildly reluctant under this form of pressure, told him,

it is I fear impossible for anything to be done relative to his majesties Sheep before your Clip day his Rams must be seen & examind without their wool before it can be determind which will be usd for the Windsor Flock besides I have not heard a syllable from him on the subject tho I some time ago mentioned that the Scotch society had an intention of making application for assistance[20]

Sinclair pressed the point because he intended to 'bend his course northward' in the next day or so. He hoped again that Banks would have the goodness 'to communicate in the most respectful manner, the wishes of the Scotch society to have a share of the Royal flock'. He was sure that Banks knew the most proper time to make the request. This was true. But Banks was inclined to be coy—truthful but tardy, polite but rather more laboured in his explanations than was his custom. Clearly he was struggling against a feeling that he could not wholly suppress—a touch of resentment perhaps at the fine public flourishes which Sinclair with his established Society was now able to make in the interest of national improvement in the home wool supplies and the spreading of the Spanish genes to that exalted end. He felt that somehow he was being asked to assist in a process designed eventually to bilk him of the credit due to him in the matter of Spanish sheep.[21] Sinclair could now work in the open glare of a public advertisement that Banks was denied in his own relations with the Royal experiment. At the same time Banks was called upon to give Sinclair public aid and comfort even to his own private discomfort. The guise of disinterested public service—which Banks was certainly pleased enough and proud to wear, even anonymously—occasionally has the bristles of a hair-shirt and its own subtle irritations. Blessed it may be to give and to serve, but even the most altruistic men occasionally find unstinting service— even to a cherished ideal—a drain on their instinctive generosity. The springs of goodwill may sometimes dry up when a certain form of heat is applied. Sinclair's pressures often raised that heat of friction and

Banks was almost as susceptible to its dessicant action as any other man. On 19 May he wrote,

... I mentiond in my Last that I had sometime ago when his M. did me the honor to converse with me said to him that I understood the Scotch society for the improvement of wool meant to apply for the Loan of a Ram or two if they could be spard & that I did not then receive any answer nor had since heard H.M. say a word on the subject

under these circumstances I dare not undertake to make the application but I will not fail if any opening is given to me to urge it I cannot however but be quite clear that if H.M. has seen the List of Directors he will not be pleasd if I take upon myself to make an application which so many persons of higher rank infinitely than myself are equally intitled from their connections as well as their rank much more calld upon than myself to carry into the R[oyal] Presence[22]

The indirect approach by the path of the inverted-U to his Royal prey was no hindrance to Sir John. The Society at Edinburgh was now in full bloom. It has staged its colourful Sheep Shearing Festival on 1 July 1791 in the garden adjoining Newhall's Inn at Queensferry in favourable weather where, to the fashionable company of about a hundred and twenty ladies and gentlemen, it 'exhibited a new and very pleasing spectacle'.[23] It was an innovation which had far-reaching effects in agricultural education for the hint was well taken and the idea expanded in the more famous occasions later at Holkham and at Woburn. As a piece of imaginative publicity for its intended purpose no modern public relations man could improve on it. As a reminder to Banks of the Society's wishes Sinclair ensured that there should be no mistake. After an elegant repast and many loyal toasts, came the climax to the afternoon—'The Royal Shepherd of Great Britain, and success to his Flock' —and the salute. Sir John's handkerchief fluttered from the window of the inn and from H.M. frigate *Hind*, under the command of Captain Alexander Cochrane, broke the firing of twenty-one guns, startling the sea-birds on the Forth and in time echoing along the Thames. After this there could be no less a messenger from the Society than the new Home Secretary himself, the Right Honourable Henry Dundas.

In such distinguished hands the last stages of the matter were concluded according to a formal protocol that may or may not have been really necessary. Banks probably thought so. Dundas almost certainly did—but whether for the honour of Scotland or merely as a minor political ploy, who can tell? The circle was closed as Banks wrote to Dundas on 11 August 1791,

I conclude if you Saw the King yesterday his Majesty informd you he had been graciously Pleasd to order 2 Spanish Rams to be deliverd to any person you shall authorise to receive them as a Present to the Society for improving British Wool I should have given you an Earlier notice of this circumstance had I not thought right as the application came directly from you to the King that his answer should likewise come first from his Majesty to you

the Sheep are at Windsor & will be deliverd to your order by M^r [John] Robinson the person entrusted with the care of the King's Experimental Flock in the Little Park[24]

Banks, however, added a small memorandum to himself as a private historical aside, a footnote to his draft in one of his rare comments of this kind:

as Mr Dundas Seemd desirous That the Whole business of Procuring Sheep for the Society in Scotland for improving British wool should rest with him I did not write to him Lest I should seem to arrogate Some of the merit the whole of which I wish to put into his hands

however I acquainted him that two Sheep were intended for the Society & told him how they were to be applied for

The tenderness of Scottish sensibilities had again been protected and no harm done. It was unfortunate, therefore, that for all the pother only one ram (No. 5) was actually shipped off from Hawley's Wharf on the Thames to Messrs. Sinclair and Williamson, merchants, at Leith according to Sir John's explicit instructions. Sir Joseph's autumn recess at Revesby Abbey was disturbed by a query from the Minister himself, ever active in the interests of Scotland, but not before the error had already been noted by a fellow-countryman just returned to duty. Ramsay Robinson wrote immediately to Banks:

On my Arrival from Scotland I found by John Robinson when I was at Windsor that there had only one Ram been delivered to the Steward of the R^t Honble Henry Dundass, instead of two, as marked in your List—The mistake proceeded from his either not Knowing or not advertising to Mr Dundass's being principal Sect^y of State—as principal Sect^y of State is wrote opposite to N° 6 and he delivered N° 5—And tho' both Numbers are Circumflexed he says he did not understand it—I hope it is an Error that can be rectified and if you will be so obliging as write me how to dispose of the Ram (N° 6) I shall take care to avoid any further Mistake[25]

The error, though noted, was never set right. For the next three years Ram No. 6 served the Royal purposes at Windsor and Kew. By the end of this time war and the attrition of interest in 'the Scotch Society', superseded in Sinclair's activities at least by the new Board of Agriculture, left little cause to send him to the north. Ram No. 5, however, probably also a Spanish ram from Estremadura brought over in the *Betsy* the year before, joined the ewes from Montbard which had preceded him by several months to the Society's fields not far south of Edinburgh. Rated by Banks as *a* for both wool and carcass he was on this evidence the best among the first distribution of rams. He, too, achieved a small place in the records of the age as his arrival on 1 October was duly noted:

Thursday, the Ram given by his Majesty to the Society for the Improvement of British Wool was safely landed at Leith. It does great credit to the Royal Flock, being on the whole the best Specimen of the true Spanish Breed that the Society has yet been able to obtain, uniting in the same animal, an excellent shape to a fleece equally fine and abundant. It is sent to the parks belonging to the Society at Bowbridge, near Morton, four miles from Edinburgh, Linton-Road, where the flock will be shown by the shepherd, every Saturday, to such as have an order for that purpose from the Directors.[26]

IV

There is a reasonably clear background also to the assignment of Ram No. 9 to His Grace the Duke of Grafton—a young ram, less than two years old, classed *b* for wool and *d* for carcass by Sir Joseph Banks and also one brought from Lisbon in 1790 on the *Betsy*. Five years earlier Augustus Henry Fitzroy 3rd Duke of Grafton, had made a public impression as a writer on the farm economics of a flock of sheep in a very fruitful discussion with Mr. William Macro of Barrow.[27] These exchanges were published in the same volume and number of the *Annals of Agriculture* as those of the King himself who wrote under the pen-name of Mr. Ralph Robinson discussing the mode of husbandry of Mr. Ducket 'the able cultivator of Petersham in Surrey'.[28] Both the sovereign incognito and the peer of the realm were duly blessed with the encomium of Arthur Young on their respective contributions. The noble Duke was awarded the higher honour as he received the full distinction of several pages of observations by the Editor opened by words that were praise indeed.

Since the first publication of this work, I have not inserted a paper that has given me more satisfaction than the preceding; nor have I the least doubt of the public uniting with me in opinion. It is by far the most important memoir on sheep that ever was published; throws the general oeconomy of a flock into the clearest light; explains a variety of circumstances dubious before; removes every hesitation concerning the profit of this branch of husbandry; and shews on what parts of the management it is, that this profit depends. I should be very backward indeed, in executing the office of editor of the work, if I did not congratulate the nation on such men as the Duke of Grafton, giving so marked an attention to agriculture. When men of the highest rank, of the most undoubted abilities, and who have filled with applause, the greatest offices of the state, do not think it beneath them to pay this public attention to the art, to what degree of perfection may we not reasonably hope to see it arrive![29]

Young expressed the greatest admiration for the exact accounts kept by the Duke in the management of his farm of four thousand acres at Euston in Norfolk. It was to be noted also that, considerable as the profit of the Duke's flock of black-faced Norfolks was, he was not prejudiced against other breeds. So far from it, indeed, 'that he has always been ready to try any experiment to the public good'. As examples, he had some years earlier procured sheep from Wiltshire and recently had done Arthur Young the honour of listening to his recommendation to try the Southdowns, a score of which he had accordingly obtained. And now, five years later, he was apparently still of a questing mind in the matter of sheep and had given Sir Joseph Banks sufficient grounds for supposing him to be a worthy recipient of the King's bounty with Spanish rams. The nature of the correspondence over this matter has its own light to cast on the motives involved. The situation is very different from that in which Sir John Sinclair had engaged. Here the initiative for the gift seems to have come from Banks and the King's approval received without the Duke's intrusion in any way. But Banks must have known that he had a willing party to the transaction when he wrote on 7 August:

his Majesty having done me the honor to intrust me with the care of a Flock of Sheep intended for experiments on the amelioration of British wools & there being at Present in it more Rams of the true Merino breed imported directly from Spain than are necessary for the number of Ewes I take the Liberty to mention to your grace that if you express the slightest wish to have one H.M. I am sure will immediately order me to deliver one to whomever your grace may direct to receive it

From the experiments I have already tried I have deduced that a mixture of the Spanish breed increases the Quantity as well as the Value of the wool in all the Clothing breeds I have tried & in none of them more than the black facd Norfolk on which if I rightly remember for I have not the Book at hand is the sort on the Subject of which your grace has favord the world with a most able Paper in the annals of agriculture.[30]

The King, of course, had already approved the Duke as one to receive a ram when he had met Banks at the Lodge at Windsor Castle on 6 August. The Duke's reply was delayed for some ten days by a mistake of his Steward at Euston who had failed to forward it. When the Duke received it 'near Stoney Stratford' he immediately wrote back to his Steward by the same post asking him, as he told Banks, 'to contrive the properest Conveyance for a young Ram in case his Majesty should be pleased on your Recommendation to consider me, as a Sheep Master, fit to be intrusted with one of the Breed from the true Spanish Sort'. He proceeded to explain his own viewpoint to Banks as a sheep breeder:

. . . The immediate Way of expressing the Sense I have of the Compliment you pay me, will be by turning the sheep to those Purposes for which I receive him, & according to the best of my Judgement, when I shall have seen him.[31]

My Flock at Euston is of the black faced Norfolks; not that I like their Shapes; but that because they appear to suit the Country, to meet with a readier Sale than any other, & to be pretty well for fineness of Wool.

To improve the Sort on every one of its deficient Points has been long thought by me to be the more reasonable than these; even preferable to the Introduction of a totally new one. Therefore it is particularly pleasing to me to hear of the effect of the Experiment you have already tried so successfully as to the Value & Quantity of the Wool, by the Spanish Cross.

It may not be amiss to mention one Experiment I can answer for, as having made it here, that the *Norfolk* on a lime Stone Land, *but* where the Surface is commonly approaching nearer to a Clay than to a *Loam*, can not stand the winter, altho' the County Sheep those from about Burford & the *Westerns* find on the same Spot perfect good Lying or Layer and thrive. And on the other hand these Norfolks would starve these same kinds on our Breeding heaths & fields—I am confident that their thin Coat counteracts in this country all the hardiness they have otherwise received from Nature

I am ashamed of the Length of my Letter, altho' the Subject is well worthy the attention of the President of the Royal Society . . .[32]

On 19 August 1791 Sir Joseph lost no time in acquainting His Grace that the King had directed 'a Ram of the pure Spanish Breed as imported from Spain in 1790' to be delivered to his order from the Little Park at Windsor. All this was according to the usual form of proceeding in the end, though it seemed to have taken a curiously circuitous path to that point. However, the correspondence had revealed some interesting facets in the attitudes and understanding of these two men at this early stage in the history of the King's Spanish flock on matters that were of wider interest than the mere delivery of one ram. Banks replied to the *obiter dicta* of the noble Lord with titbits of his own:

. . . I have observed the wool to grow somewhat longer in the staple than imported Spanish wool usually is owing as I think to the pasture in the Little Park at Windsor being too Strong I am not however able to observe any alteration in point of Fineness & have no doubt that your graces short sweet sheep pastures will restore it to its original staple

I beg leave to return my best thanks for the interesting observations relative to the properties of the Western & Norfolk breeds it supports an opinion which with some exceptions I have long held, That the experience of past ages has taught the agriculturalists of each county the kind of sheep best suited for their climate & soil of all those within their reach I have not however been able to Learn from either history or tradition that Merino sheep were ever imported into this Country till the arrival of those his Majesty now possesses[33]

There were some points of similarity between Banks's letters of announcement to the two dukes who received rams in 1791. He lost no time, he said, in acquainting either of His Majesty's commands. He also explained to the 2nd Duke of Newcastle, who received Ram No. 12 'importd in the year 1788', that as far as he could judge it had not at all declined in fineness since that date though its staple had grown longer 'in consequence of the Richness of the Pasture in which he has been Fed'. But he had no doubt 'that the short sweet grass of Sherwood forest will restore it to its original Shortness'. Our insight into the reasons why the Duke of Newcastle should have been so honoured by the King in this first year is far less than anything we know of the others and not much more than is revealed by his letter of acknowledgement on 11 August:

I yesterday receiv'd your very obliging letter; I must beg the favor of you when you wait upon his Majesty, to present my most dutiful respects, and grateful thanks for his condescending goodness in recollecting his kind offer to me some years ago to mend as he said, the wool of my Stock at Clumber. I have accordingly ordered my Servant to call upon Mr Robinson at Windsor, who I take for granted will deliver the Spaniard to him[34]

Unlike the arrangement with the 3rd Duke of Grafton that with the 2nd Duke of Newcastle was certainly the shortest distance between two points—and one is left to speculate why.

One more ram is now left to be accounted for from the dispersal of 1791. This was Ram No. 10 allotted to Sir George Yonge, the Secretary of State for War and Member of Parliament for Honiton in Devon. There are no papers to help us here in appreciating why Sir George was on the list. Sir George Yonge had been at the War Office continuously since December 1783. He had been in various ways associated with Banks during that period. The common thread of their relations was that of botany, of which apparently Sir George was an earnest amateur. Wherever the Army was to be found there he also indulged his botanical interests to some effect as a rule. Yonge had a finger in the establishment of the Botanical Gardens at Calcutta and at St. Vincent. He was involved in many plans for the transfer of plants, such as the mango and cinnamon, from India to the West Indies; he intruded into the business of the *Bounty* and the bread-fruit, at first to the annoyance of Banks, but later helpfully in the speedy fitting out of the *Providence* and the *Assistance* with which Bligh returned to Tahiti, sailing in June

1791. He was, therefore, much in the foreground as Banks prepared his list of persons in August of that year 'as proper to have Spanish Rams given to them'. But there seems to have been more to Yonge's claims than this, he had taken an active interest with Banks in the development of plans for the settlement of New South Wales prior to 1787 and perhaps as early as 1784. This in itself was almost enough. There was, however, his compelling interest and spirited attempt backed by his own money to establish a woollen factory at Ottery St. Mary in his own constituency. As recently as 18 April 1791 he had written to Banks inquiring where twelve to twenty packs of wether wool at £7 12s. per pack could be got for his friends—in Devon presumably.[35] It was no doubt his practical support of the woollen interest that finally secured him a place among the chosen few to receive Ram No. 10—a sheep with broken horns—and also, apparently, the five cast ewes which had been at first in Banks's mind for Lord Bathurst.[36] Where they went is not known for sure but it is quite probable that they found their way to Sir George Yonge's estates either at Colyton or Coplestone in Devon.

In the story of these first six sheep from His Majesty's Spanish flock and their scattering through Britain we have all the elements which in different ways were combined to account for all those rams and ewes that in the next eight years to 1799 were to be Royal gifts in the execution of His Majesty's 'patriotic plan'.

V

The key to the distribution of sheep from the Royal flock during these early years, however, lies especially in the relations between Banks and Colonel Robert Fulke Greville. In their persons the spheres of influence of the Royal Society and the Court of St. James's were integrated and to a degree expanded within the scope of a social background they had shared for many years—both rural and urban. One might almost go so far as to trace the origins of this early spread of Merino genes through Great Britain to the gentlemen of the Dilletanti Society of which Sir Joseph was the industrious Secretary for so long.[37] In this social consortium were many of his friends, and among them the Honourable Charles Greville, F.R.S., the elder brother of Robert Fulke Greville. Banks's association with Charles extended back at least to March 1773 when they journeyed abroad together to Rotterdam and a meeting of the Batavian Society. This friendship remained throughout their lives and it could not have been long before Robert, the younger by three years, also entered the convivial society of Sir Joseph. The group was completed by the long friendship with the uncle of the two Grevilles—Sir William Hamilton, F.R.S., Ambassador to the Court of

Naples, with whom Banks shared a fervent interest in archaeology as well as in horticultural matters.[38] Botany, indeed, seems to have been the common bond between them all and Wales and the counties of the Welsh Borders to have been their favourite ground for plant-gathering expeditions as younger men. It is not chance, therefore, which directed so many of the first sheep westward from beneath the Castle terraces at Windsor. Nor would the story be wholly complete without appreciating the other 'things of beauty' in the lives and interests of these four men. The Honourable Charles Greville, ardent horticulturist and mineralo- gist, had established at Paddington Green a fine garden which almost rivalled that at Spring Grove. But among the flowers and the gems the brightest ornament at Paddington Green was one not perhaps of 'the purest ray serene' and not, in any sense, 'born to blush unseen'. Emma Hart had found her second 'protector' in the Honourable Charles. From the secluded garden of Paddington Green the 'beautiful plant called Emma' was in 1786 somewhat heartlessly transplanted to a more exotic environment by the blue waters of the Bay of Naples under the cultivation of that other accomplished botanist, Charles's uncle Sir William Hamilton.[39] Then after five years of discreet impropriety Sir William was finally induced by Sir Joseph to recognize her 'infinite merit' and to give 'a public reparation'. In September 1791 at Marylebone Church the little nursemaid from Paddington Green became Emma Lady Hamilton, and Banks had earned her unfailing regard—'I do not consider you as one of his [Sir William's] common friends, and therefore love and esteem you more than you think I do'.[40]

Into this social pattern the Honourable Robert Fulke Greville brought the aura of a less profane romance and an ethic much nearer that of the code to which Banks gave service. To Fanny Burney the tall Colonel was the frequent solace in long hours of tedious waiting among other equerries who were often tiresome and even obnoxious: 'His gentle- ness, however, his perfect good-breeding, and a delicacy of manner I have rarely seen equalled, made it utterly impossible to decline his conversation.'[41]—'There is something in Colonel Wellbred so elegant, so equal, and so pleasing, it is impossible not to see him with appro- bation, and to speak of him with praise.'[42] Yet, though at times we know that he fluttered her heart she found him essentially shy, occasionally withdrawn, but never so much in this way as she recorded of his good friend Sir Joseph Banks whom she met for the first time in Robert Greville's company over the tea-cups at Windsor in March 1788:

... the party was Miss [Margaret] Planta, Colonel Wellbred, Mr. Fairly [Colonel Stephen Digby], Sir Joseph Banks, and Mr. Turbulent [Rev. Charles de Guiffardiere].

Sir Joseph was so exceedingly shy that we made no acquaintance at all. If instead of going round the world he had only fallen from the moon, he could not appear less versed in the usual modes of a tea-drinking party. But what, you will say, has a tea-drinking party to do with a botanist, a man of science, a president of the Royal Society?

I left him, however, to the charge of Mr. Turbulent, the two Colonels becoming, as usual, my joint supporters. And Mr. Turbulent, in revenge, ceased not one moment to watch Colonel Wellbred, nor permitted him to say a word, or to hear an answer without some provoking grimace. Fortunately upon this subject he cannot confuse me; I have not a sentiment about Colonel Wellbred, for or against, that shrinks from examination.

To-night, however, my conversation was almost wholly with him. I would not talk with Mr. Turbulent; I could not talk with Sir Joseph Banks; and Mr. Fairly did not talk with me. . . .[43]

Two years later she bade Greville farewell at the end of his term of waiting in 1790 after a closer and more confidential talk than she had ever before achieved with him, and it confirmed her best opinion 'of his honour and delicacy':

He has the misfortune to have two brothers who never meet—solely from dissension in politics. He loves them both, and with both keeps well; but while he has a place that devotes a fourth of the year to the King, his residence for the rest of it is with the brother [Charles] who is in opposition to the Government. Not small must be the difficulties of such circumstances, and his preferment is probably checked by this determined fraternal amity; though his moderation and uprightness secure him the esteem, and force the good word, of both parties, as well as of both brothers.

Much injustice, however, has I believe accrued to him from this mild conduct, which is not calculated for advantage in a station that demands decisive vigour, though in private or retired life it makes the happiness and peace of all around.[44]

But though Fanny Burney may have been Robert Greville's favourite among the maids-in-waiting at the Court and he her favourite equerry among the gentlemen this relation was for neither of them much more than the passing fondness of two people flung together in a crowd of less congenial company, under the accident of the circumstances. For all her admiration Fanny did not find in him the intellectual qualities she sought. In her there was perhaps too much of the blue-stocking for his taste—or even something disturbingly neurotic. There was, however, in Robert Fulke Greville's life—and perhaps something also in himself— a force that held him back from any entanglements. Unlike his brother Charles he was not one of the 'dilletanti'—not, it would seem, in the courts of Love. For him there was to be but one love and to that he was already committed. It was the love of his early youth and it was to be the love of his old age. During more than half of his life he was to devote himself to its romantic shadow. The woman who claimed his devotion was for twenty years the wife of another man.

His first cousin, Louisa Cathcart, had become the second wife, as a young girl of nineteen, of a man much her senior, David Murray 7th Viscount Stormont. As the Viscountess Stormont she had led the life of a diplomatist's and statesman's wife. As lady ambassadress in Paris she evoked the comment from Madame Necker: 'Lady Stormont is pretty, she holds herself badly, and has not a charming manner, but her expression is full of intelligence.' She was, however, generally acknowledged to be a most attractive woman, full of wit and humour. Something of this is found in Hoppner's painting of her, made in 1797 when she married her faithful Robert and he found at last the wife for whom he had been so long waiting. In later years he found also—as most men do—small cracks in the flawless mirror of his imagining. She had, it appeared in her mother's judgement, a quick temper— 'flurries' and 'little female indignations', to use the characteristic terms of her imperturbable and knightly husband—but nothing that could in his view detract from her lovable character. Music, horses, and the pursuits of the country were her life. Such interests she shared rather with her second husband than with her first. But her community of interest with her tall cousin and discreet admirer became openly evident during the closing years of her first marriage—from about that time when, just prior to the death of the aged 1st Earl of Mansfield, the new patent for the succession was issued in August 1792. In this twist of an oddly tangled legal sequence Louisa Cathcart through her first marriage became in March 1793 Louisa Countess of Mansfield in her own right.[45]

By this remote stroke of the legal pen it was determined that Merino sheep should graze at Ken (or Caen) Wood above the village of Hampstead and in the parks of the Palace of Scone in Perthshire beside the River Tay. The first step towards this was taken on 9 June 1792 during 'his Majesties Clip at Windsor', under the personal supervision of Sir Joseph Banks when 'at 10 H.M. was pleasd to come to us he ordered a Ram for Lady Stormont'.[46] Then, on 10 June, 'Lady S. the next morn chose N° 7'. This was a ram which Banks the month before had noted as having 'wool full of nature[47] and very good', and this too may well have been one of the *Betsy* lot of 1790 from Lisbon. It was followed the next year by the gift of Ram No. 31 among a group of ten whose distribution was arranged by Greville and which were 'all Tegs that is a year & a half old bred from Sheep importd from Spain of the pure Merino Breed'.[48]

Then in August 1794, just as the Reign of Terror in France was coming to its blood-stained end with some hopeful glimpses of returning sanity across the Channel, we have a contrasting picture of the Court life at Windsor and the background of the Spanish flock as Robert Greville chooses two rams for Lady Mansfield, his 'Friend' and, at that time, his hopeless love. So in his diary for Tuesday, 12 August he notes the scene and the first preparations for the Royal vacation at Weymouth:

Rose at our usual hour—Breakfasted a little after Nine. About ten attended His Majesty a quiet ride of some hours thro' part of the Forest & thro' His Norfolk & Flemish Farms—a most lovely day. In the Evening walked on the Terrace, from it saw the setting sun in the greater beauty. This Evening on the Terrace saw Miss [Ann] Ives the famous Spinner; was introduced to Her & begun my acquaintance by a profusion of Questions, She has spun ninety five miles in length from one Pound of Wool. She says it is not bad Spinning to extend the Thread from one Pound of Wool sixty miles. Seventy Miles is finer spinning than Common. She prefers the Lincolnshire Wool—She is self taught, & learnt originally from an old Picture She saw—
    This day sent My Horses from Windsor on their journey to Weymouth— The King leaves Windsor tomorrow—Evening cards as usual in the Castle—[49]

Banks, on 18 June, had seen the rams shorn at Windsor on a day particularly inconvenient to him. He had found that the washing, ordered by the King himself, had been abominably done; that the sheep had been much neglected and were 'full of Ticks & much struck with the Fly'. They were, however, mercifully, less affected with foot-rot that season and their feet were generally in much better order. He had also that day carefully examined each animal and selected those for the King's own use. Soon after, probably in the first week of July, Robert Greville had a sudden notice to attend the King during his six weeks' residence in Weymouth. He had written to Banks asking to be informed of the marks on the horns of those rams selected for His Majesty so that before he left for Weymouth he could choose two out of the remainder for Lady Mansfield.[50] But he misdirected the letter to Revesby Abbey and still had no information on 12 August when he wrote again to Sir Joseph giving him a recapitulation of how the King's mind then stood about the disbursement of the rams—and, among other things, announcing that:

You will be happy I know to learn that Charles [Francis Greville] will probably kiss hands tomorrow [at the Levee] on His appointment to be Vice Chamberlain to His Majesty & that He comes in to Parliament for Petersfield vacated by Welbore Ellis's promotion to a Peerage[51]

By now Banks was on his journey north at last and this letter did not reach him until he arrived at Overton in Derbyshire. So Greville took it upon himself to make a tentative selection among the rams in any case, including the process in a round of small activities in which his

'Friend' was much in his thoughts. The hours passed slowly but agreeably as he waited on His Majesty's convenience for the start to Weymouth while the last business of State was done on 13 August:

Abt. 7 o'clock this Morn'g Walked thro' the Garden with His M. to the Stables. His Horses had set out for Weymouth abt. six o'clock. Look'd at those which remained at Home. Return'd to the Queen's Lodge when His M. took me with Him to His Library & conversed with Me on various subjects till it was time to go to Chapel. Went with His M.ʸ & Pss. Augusta to Chapel & return'd to the Queen's Lodge to Breakfast. After Breakfast His Majesty sett out in His Chaise for His Levee in Town. I called on Dr. [James] Lind in Windsor where I saw Miss Ives who I found spinning with Her distaff a finer thread than any other Person in this Kingdom has yet ever been able to accomplish—To satisfy the enquiries of an absent Friend I took a long lesson from Miss Ives, & never did she give instruction which was more attentively listen'd to. I hope my Friend will profit by My report, & if I can but explain properly I am perfectly sure She will do ample justice to the art of fine Spinning.

   When at Dr. Lind's I saw a very handsome flowering Plant whose botanical name is Hydrangea Hortensia—It has large cluster Flowers & continues in bloom many weeks—From Dr. Lind's I walked to the King's Farm in the Home Park & continued my speculations on subjects connected with the distaff. The object of my Visit was to look at the Flock of Spanish Rams—There were here this day thirty four full grown Rams & thirty this years lamb Rams, all of the true Spanish Breed. The distribution which His M. is graciously pleased to make through his Kingdom of these Rams to improve the general quality of the Wool, being at hand, I looked over the grown Flock with attention as it had been intrusted to Me to chuse two for a Friend of Mine for whom His M. had given very particular directions that She should have the first choice from the Flock after those reserved for Himself should be fixed upon—

   Return'd thro' the Queen's Garden at Frogmore & looked at the new Ruins erecting in the Gardens; These are executed & with great taste by Mr. [James] Wyatt. Here I saw a very late invention from Birmingham & one quite new for the Covering of Houses, for Pipes &c. It is thin Sheets of Iron plated with lead. It comes very cheap & Mr. Wyatt approves of the invention. He recommends giving it one coat of Paint when made use of. The Copper plates cover'd with Tin, I think I like best.

   No Terrace this Evening which is not usual. His Majesty did not return till a very late Hour for Him viz. at 10 m. after Nine. An unusual press of business previous to His departure for Weymouth had detained Him. He very graciously communicated two very pleasing articles of intelligence. The one was a strong report & beleived, that Robespierre had been put to death,[52] The other that The Romney of 50 gs. had taken the Sybil french Frigate of 46 guns after an Action of 1 hour & 10 minutes in the Mediterranean.[53]

   The usual card Parties at the Castle finished the amusements of this day.[54]

When Greville received his much-delayed answer from Banks about the rams chosen for the King's flock the Royal party was already well settled at Weymouth, in Gloucester Lodge, 'very respectably protected' by Admiral McBride's Squadron at sea while 'On Shore We have ab.t 3 troops of the Royals & a Company of Volunteer artillery from the Town & ab.t a mile & a half at Wick Heath is the Bucks. Militia under the Marquis of Buckingham encamped—a fine & strong Regiment.'[55] Robert Greville had noted the numbers of several rams for Lady Mansfield at Windsor and, on receiving Banks's letter with those chosen for the Royal flock was, he said, a little flattered to note that his selection had included several of those preferred by Banks. However, from the remainder he was able to choose No. 58—noted by Banks as 'a bettermost Sheep Tolerable condition, rather Ticky'— and No. 77—'The Largest Sheep in the Flock & Tolerably form'd'.[56] On 30 August Banks confirmed Greville's choice in a letter from Gainsborough and at the same time sent confirmation of this to Ramsay Robinson at Kensington. At some time soon after this the two rams were sent to Lady Mansfield at Ken Wood. These were the last pure Merino rams we know she received, bringing the total to four.

Soon after she had been allotted the first ram, No. 7, Lady Mansfield had bought twenty-two half-bred Spanish × Herefordshire tegs and fifteen half-bred lambs at 21s. and 10s. 6d. per head respectively. This had been made possible by Sir Joseph Banks's recommendation and had enabled her to lay the foundation of a small three-quarter-bred flock on the 'upland lawns' of Hampstead.[57] To these were now added in 1795 a draft of pure Spanish ewes cast for age by Banks after shearing. As early as 4 April the King had in conversation shown that he was inclined to sell the old ewes to someone 'who wanted them for Breed than to the Butcher'.[58] Greville, a month later, said that he wished to buy the ewes at a guinea apiece. Banks told him there were twenty-three available and that they would be a good bargain even if only a few should produce lambs the following year. These with some wethers had all been put into Kensington Gardens upon turnips to fatten in the autumn of 1794.[59] Greville was immediately anxious to have them drawn for him but Banks refused Ramsay Robinson permission to do this:

I said that before Shearing there was no use in drawing as the Ewes could not be deliverd till their Fleeces were off, & that I did not Find myself able to do Perfect justice to the Kings Flock if I drew before I saw how the Sheep throve after Shearing which could not be till the middle of July

Soon afterwards these old ewes joined the Mansfield flock at Ken Wood, making it possible to breed the pure Spanish there at last. In the following year her Ladyship, hailed as 'a true patroness of husbandry', had sent at least a part of the Ken Wood flock north where she had

. . . also turned her attention towards improving the breed of sheep, by bringing to that extensive lawn, in which the house of Scone is situated, a flock, partly of the Warwick-shire breed, so much esteemed for their carcases; and partly of the Spanish, so remarkable for the fineness of their wool. The English breed answers very well; but the experiment with the Spanish has not yet been fully made. Except 30 or 40, all the sheep in the parish [of Scone] are her Ladyship's property. . . .[60]

Her double interest in the Warwickshire and the Spanish breeds was a perfect expression of the influence of Robert Fulke Greville on her life as the man who on 19 October 1797 became her second husband.

VI

Whereas Colonel Robert Fulke Greville had the most extended and widespread influence, among those of the Court group, on the dispersal of surplus sheep from the Royal flock, there was no one more assiduous in fostering their exploitation in one particular locality than Major William Price. Though he had resigned from the post of Equerry in 1787, his health unequal to the very considerable strain the duties entailed, he had always kept a close and friendly association with the King with whom he was a great personal favourite.[61] He had retired to his farm at Mancell in Herefordshire from whence he visited Windsor from time to time—perhaps in the less fatiguing role of 'Backgammon-player to His Majesty' as Fanny Burney had once affectionately suggested, 'a post which no one fills so much to the King's satisfaction'.[62] She was perhaps less aware of another part which he played even more to the King's satisfaction in the liaison he maintained with the sheep farms of Herefordshire. It was first due to him that the King procured the foundation sheep of his Ryeland flock. It was later due to him that the experiment of crossing this breed with the Spanish Merino was so generally prosecuted in Herefordshire itself, largely by the efforts of one of his tenants, Josiah Ridgeway of Upperton in the parish of Yazor, near Ludlow. During the nine years over which the King presented sheep from his flock as gifts, Major Price received no less than twenty-one of the hundred and five rams and thirty-six of the hundred and fifty-four ewes so dispersed. Of these sheep two of the rams (Nos. 33 and 103) were particularly good, having been used as sires in the Royal flock. Two rams at least were hornless or very nearly so. This preference was established with his first selection, Ram No. 27, which he chose on 9 June 1792 when he visited the shearing at Windsor with the

King. On 18 June 1794 Banks allotted Price Ram No. 78, a well-formed sheep with a good fleece and described as 'without horns but has stump of horns'. Among the others at least five, in the group of eight given specially in 1795 to Josiah Ridgeway, were noted as having black spots about the ears, eyes, and mouth. Of the ewes there are no particular records except that they were all drawn from the old ewes in 1795.[63] All these transactions were mediated with Banks by Robert Greville who as early as July 1794 made the comment to him:

. . . The best and *most attentive* Experiment now going on that I know of is by Mr. Ridgeway in Herefordshire for whom Major Price has already thro' You obtained 3 or 4 Rams—He is extending the cross exceedingly, so much does it answer, & His Son told me, that His Father should be most happy if He could obtain thro' His Ms favor one or two more Rams this Season— There is now every interest making with Ridgeway in his part of the Country for some of His New Breed, and all He means to part with this Year are already bespoke—You know that when Price first made interest for His Friend Ridgeway that He tied Him up to make the Experiment fairly, & according to articles stated & accepted—All which He has faithfully executed & with great judgement—[64]

Eighteen months later Greville was able to send Banks a copy of a report[65] made by Josiah Ridgeway to Major Price which casts much light on the trends in this particular enterprise:

Please to accept of my best thanks for your kind present of the Four Rams You last sent Me—They are all well as also the seven sent before—I have forty, which I have bred from them & one Hundred Ewes which are good wool & double in weight—They were bred from the Ryelands & Spanish Ram & in quality finer & longer, & in price 7.sh pr Stone [of 12½ pounds] more than the Ryeland—They stood the Winter better than the Ryeland tho' the last was the severest Winter We have had for this 56 years—1794-5[66] The Spanish Lambs stood the cold better than the Ryelands—Since I have had the Spanish Sheep, I have made it a point to sell my Wool to a Clothier a Mr. [Gale] Everett of Heytesbury Wilts—He does nothing but in fine Wool—He came two days together before Last Hereford Fair to see the Sheep & He is well satisfied with the Management as well as the cross breed —The Wool pays double, which is the great profit of our fallows by keeping it clean, as We can grow double crops of Wheat afterwards—The Spanish are tamer than the Ryeland. The foot Rot sunk the last lot much, but they are all well & near dropping lambs—I have 180 Ewes in Lamb & shall have no other breed next Year than Spanish & Ryelands— . . .[67]

That year Josiah Ridgeway could report with clear satisfaction that he had sold 28 stone of the Spanish cross and 34 stone 4 pounds of the pure Ryeland mixed together at an average price of 27s. per stone of 12½ pounds or 2s. 2½d. per pound, equal in Banks's opinion to 3s. for imported Spanish fine wool at the time, owing to the greater quantity of dirt in the English wool. The best Spanish marks that year were selling at, Raffino—3s. 9d.; Fino—2s. 9d.; and Tercero—2s. 3d. per pound. Ridgeway's price had been the highest at the Hereford market and the average fleece weight for his flock of three hundred and ten sheep had been 2.5 pounds or nearly twice that of two of his neighbours with Ryeland sheep only. He estimated that when sheep of the Spanish and Ryeland cross were three years old they would cut over four pounds per head of washed wool. His forecast was a sound one. And it was certainly gratifying to Banks that eight years later he was able to report to the public:

. . . This gentleman, whom his Majesty graciously permitted to have rams from the Spanish flock some years ago, has also shown by his accounts that the wool of his flock of about 16 score sheep, has been so much increased both in quantity and in value[68] by the Spanish cross, as to have produced nearly twice as much money for each clip after the Spanish blood was established in it, as it usually did before . . .[69]

Of the report on which this statement was based Banks commented to Robert Greville who had sent to him in August 1800:

. . . I have seen no Report in favor of the Spanish breed which equald his in point of interest, & as his account of wool sold supports it, I can have no doubt of its accuracy . . .[70]

Nor could he find any reason to doubt the evidence. Ridgeway's results were some of the few to be returned more or less formally. There was almost none with which to compare them.

VII

Far less happy in the outcome were the unsustained enthusiasms of the literati of Wales. The episode with Thomas Johnes was a bad start. From the first moves by Greville in the matter there was an element of confusion, lapsing into farce, that brought Banks as near to infuriated rudeness as he ever came in his correspondence. The whole business was perhaps the least felicitous of all Robert Greville's exercises in agricultural diplomacy. There was, first, his laboured duet with Johnes explaining their individual unpunctualities in not answering Banks's letters to them in the first week of July 1792 asking for some form of confirmation of proposals tentatively made at Kew somewhat earlier. Both of them sent their well-harmonized letters from Hafod on 25 July like two schoolboys, writing out excuses after an escapade, in evident fear of the wrath of the headmaster. 'You are Yourself so punctual in everything that I fear I shall be out of Your good Graces for my un-punctuality in not answering before this time . . .' said Greville, 'My excuse is, that really I wished to see Mr. Johnnes before I wrote to you . . . .'[71] Dutifully in tune, 'I am afraid you have often blamed me for my negligence in not thanking you sooner for your kind letter of the 7th, But I was obliged to wait for Col: Greville's arrival here to write to you satisfactorily . . .' said Johnes.[72] Then gradually it became clear that Thomas Johnes really did want to have 'this little Spanish Flock'— and Mrs. Johnes as well—and that both of them felt nothing but the greatest gratitude for all Banks's friendly attentions to their respective hobby-horses. With Mrs. Johnes it was her garden and

. . . She desires me to say how very much she is obliged to you, & hopes you will once more visit this place in order to see whether we have paid that attention your kindness has deserved—Her Seeds from the Cape & New Holland are doing exceedingly well and any of them are much at your Service. The Mimosa camelopardalis thrives exceedingly—

Johnes himself proposed to send a 'Taffey' from Hafod for his sheep on the 1 August who would 'probably take Six days in coming to you'. Well and good. But there was a complication for, at Greville's request, Lady Stormont had 'added to this importation a Bull Calf of the *Canley* breed', and the good Colonel had conceived his own solution to the problem:

. . . As Lady S. is now in great affliction at present, I shall from hence en-deavour to be of service, without giving Her the trouble of thinking of any arrangements, & what I have thought most likely to answer every object will be, to desire that the Bull Calf may be sent to *Spring Grove*, from Little Grove, for a night or two, & from thence join Mr Johnes's Flock & proceed with it as they proceed from Kensington towards Cardiganshire—

With this masterly stratagem established Greville then passed lightly on to other topical items of their tour in Wales—the summer that was so wet it was no summer at all, rain unremitting from the mountains of North Wales and Caernarvonshire with but 'one fine day for Llanberris, where We saw your old Friend John Close who was delighted to hear of You'. But when Greville 'asked Him ab^t the little *Aquatic* in the upper lake under Dolbaden Castle' he found he had no chance of assisting Banks in the search and knew of no one else in the country to do so unless it was 'Mr Lloyd of Havosdunas' or Banks himself.

No amount of charming botanical causerie from Hafod—whether on exotics from the southern hemisphere or aquatics from the sodden wilds of Wales—no genial trivia from Robert Greville could on the occasion have done much to relieve the irritations of a patently ruffled Banks. He exploded in a sharp fusillade of words whose peremptory rattle must have taken Thomas Johnes—and his wife—by surprise, but can have left no doubt that their kindly botanical visitor had a few hidden stings. Banks, for once, had let a few mishaps put him in a tizzy. He found relief in colourful narrative.

Your Shepherd arrivd at my house on Monday the 6th instant at night & was so drunk that my Servants would not admit him into the house but laid him on the Straw in the Barn The next morn I sent him to London to enquire after the Calf & to Kensington with a Letter to Mr [Ramsay] Robinson his Majesties Servant who has the care of the Sheep which were Lodgd in Kensington Gardens ready for marching & I orderd him to proceed with them & the Calf if he could get it toward Windsor where he might meet me on Saturday & take up the Ram that being the day which the King had fixd for this years distribution.

on Friday morning he came to me at Spring Grove & told me had driven the sheep from Kensington to Hounslow about 8 miles /that day/ & that he was sure he could not get them any further they being out of Condition & Footsore & insisted upon going to you for further orders

I made him come with me this morn to Windsor where I was to meet Mr Robinson & I learnd from him that the Sheep were not in good Condition & that their Feet were sore[73] but there was no doubt that if a Quiet man marchd them in the night they might be driven to any distance beginning with Short Journeys but that your man set out from Kensington at 3 in the afternoon of a very hot day the most improper start possibly of the 24 hours

at Windsor I met Major [William] Price who hearing the story of the Sheep /voluntarily undertook to/ wished me to write to you he has had some of the same Lot & met with some difficulty in driving them into Herefordshire but both himself & his Herefordshire neighbours are so much pleasd with them that he regrets the possibility of your giving up yours

They are now at Hounslow where they pay 1s / a day & night a score for their keeping there are 3 score & 18 Ewes & Lambs so that their board costs 28/shills a week which is dear but I could not get it from my exhorbitant neighbors at a cheaper rate

The Calf I have heard nothing about I judgd it impossible for a Calf & Sheep to travel together & so did your drover who declard he had never heard of the Calf till I spoke of it I expected [it] at Spring Grove for a week but it never came

Now my dear Sir you have the whole story of the Sheep & you may do concerning them as you chuse you may send a sober Quiet man to drive them by slow marches /or you may order them in waggons/ & you may surrender the whole or any part of them for as the price was intended to be the same as could be got from Farmers here the King will be no loser /& H M has allotted a Ram to you which you may have when you Please/

I should by all means advise that a Cart attends the Person who drives the Sheep to take up the Lame ones & it may Carry the Ram & possibly the Calf the whole way or as the Lot is Large a Light Waggon & 4 horses would be still better

as I am on the Point of Leaving this Place for Lincolnshire you will please to Correspond in Future on the Subject of the Sheep with M^r R[amsay] Robinson Junr Kensington Palace who will give you all kinds of facility as long as he stays he is going for his health to the sea but you had better apply to some friend in London to do for you as I would do if I was there [to] manage the whole business in the way you chuse it to be done[74]

Although Banks was sharp and to the point and not in the best humour on the business he was not inconsiderate. On 14 August, in spite of his haste to be away to Revesby Abbey, he visited the sheep where the Welshman had left them in an acre field, half of which was a gravel-pit. The thirty-six ewes and forty-two lambs had already eaten out the grazing and Banks ordered their removal back to Kensington Gardens 'so that your account for Board & Lodging with my Exhorbitant neighbor will close sooner than I expected'. He also told Johnes that the King had ordered a ram to be added to the flock should he take it. Banks had therefore chosen for him a very valuable sheep— 'he is of the Pure Spanish Blood rising two years old & a better woold one is not in his Majesties Flock he is markd on the Horn 21'. This was a donation from the King but Johnes paid for the half-bred Spanish and Hereford ewes and lambs 21s. and 10s. 6d. per head respectively, the same prices paid by Lady Stormont for her lot, by Major Price for his twenty-two ewes, and by Banks for his three.[75]

Banks also wrote on 14 August to Greville with a very abbreviated account of 'The scrape I am in about Johnes' which he found inexplicable. However,

...I have told the whole to the King who is very good humord as you know and he had not shewn any marks of disatisfaction Price says that if Johnes abandons the Flock as he possibly will do he will wish to have some of them & your Confrere [Colonel Thomas] Garth says he is sure Ld Clive will wish for the Rest

How this matter is to be finally settled I know not as I am going to Lincolnshire this week if you have any thing to say to me be so good as to direct to Revesby Abbey near Horncastle[76]

The matter was settled in due course, probably on the lines that Banks had suggested. Thomas Johnes later was given three rams in 1793 and four rams in 1795 from the Spanish flock which would imply some evidence of serious intent in Cardiganshire. For Thomas Johnes, politician, scholar, and botanist, was also of that class of 'improving' landholders to which Banks and so many others belonged. He had done much on his estate since 1783 to execute his theories—removing the poor to comfortable cottages and employing them in forestry schemes on the near-by mountains, forming an agricultural society in the neighbourhood, and, as a most radical departure, bringing Scotch farmers to settle there. But the private printing press of Hafod and the scholarly works which he issued from it in the cottage near his mansion evidently in the end rose above his interest in the sheep. The unhappy opening seems to have augured an ill-conducted enterprise and Banks was suitably bleak in his closing comments on the affair in his report to the King:

. . . Mr Johnes, in answer to the form of making a return of the success of experiments in crossing with the Spanish breed which he had received from Sir Joseph, verbally acquainted him that all the Spanish Sheep he had received from your Majesty were dead; he purchased in the year 1792 the whole remainder of the Metis Ewes & at different times had received from your Majesty 8 Rams, Four of which were given to him in 1795. Sir Joseph therefore ventures to suppose that the Spanish breed are very ill suited either to the hills of Cardiganshire or to Mr Johnes management[77]

There was another literary man in Wales who, by the King's grace, received as many rams as Thomas Johnes, but who made rather more of the talents he acquired and yet did not appear in any open report to His Majesty. Philip Yorke of Erddig (or Erthig) Park near Wrexham in Denbighshire, author and scholar, former Member of Parliament for Heston and for Grantham, shared Banks's archaeological interests and had also been mildly involved in the last stages of the struggle over the Wool Bill of 1788 as Sheriff of the County.[78] His name had been passed on by Greville as someone to receive rams during the last hasty weeks before he left for Weymouth in August 1794 in attendance on the King. Yorke's claim originally had been put forward by Lord Walsingham, Chairman of Committees of the House of Lords.[79] Greville had as usual been the genial intermediary. The results were more harmonious than with Johnes. In his reply to Lord Walsingham expressing his 'great obligation for the present of the Rams' Philip Yorke set the scene for his future hopes with the Spanish breed:

I wish I may be able in any degree to forward His Majesty's Benevolent dispositions to this Principality—A great many Sheep are bred upon an Estate I have among the Mountains in the upper parts of this County [Denbighshire] & as yet they have had very little choice or delicacy in the article of their Rams & it is supposed they have failed much on that Account . . .[80]

Profiting by the experience with Thomas Johnes's sheep two years before, Banks specifically recommended to Yorke to send a horse and covered cart for them to Windsor. This was done instead of entrusting the animals to the 'Wrexham waggon, which sets out from the Blossoms inn, Laurence lane, every Saturday at noon, and arrives the Saturday following at Wrexham'. On 3 October Yorke announced the arrival at Erddig Park of the two rams, Nos. 61 and 71, safe and well—after an expedition by the horse and cart of more than two weeks' duration. But he was uncertain on their best use.

. . . I wish I knew what the best, to make of them: I have bought a lot of Shropshire Ewes whose wool seems most to assimilate to theirs, and I have also a lot of Mountain Sheep to cross with them. I shall keep a strict account of the Event. . . .[81]

In the following year, 1795, six more rams were allotted to him and in 1797 the gift of six ewes made it possible for him to become a ram breeder himself with the pure Spanish stock. Unlike Johnes he did, however, make some attempt to fill the form of report that Banks had hopefully circulated. In February 1798 he had this to say:

The weight of Carcass in the Spanish Rams will be no very great advantage to the farmers of this country, as there are Rams in this and the adjoining Counties of greater weight than the Spanish, and hardier in their Nature, but there appears in the Spanish a stronger inclination to feed than any sorts we have in this neighbourhood, when kept on inclosed ground. The greatest benefit to be expected from this breed is in the superior fine quality of the wool, altho' at present the people of this country are ignorant of the real value of it, and will give but little more for it than the com[n]. wool, and the quantity being as yet too small to induce a manufacturer of fine cloths to come into the Country to buy it.—It appears evident that the Spanish breed are too tender, and their wool too short to enable them to stand the cold climate of the Welch Mountains, but may answer extremely well on low com[ns] & inclosed lands of Midling quality.[82]

In February 1799, anxious that Banks should know everything that he could with certainty communicate 'relative to the Cambro-Spanish sheep' he sent some details of cloth manufactured in Chester at half a guinea a yard. This was a piece of broadcloth in length seventeen and a half yards made mostly from the Welsh Mountain and Spanish cross with some wool from the old Spanish rams with it. The manufacturer had been disappointed in not making twenty yards from the fifty pounds he had taken and complained about the waste.[83] Banks, on the basis of valuations by two mercers, noted that it was worth 16s. 6d. per yard but wrote conservatively to Yorke on this point:

. . . The Cloth you have been so good as to enclose, is in my judgment at least worth 15[s] a Yard to the Draper, & if 2½ lb of wool will produce 15[s] in manufacture, surely that wool ought to receive 2[s] a pound in order to give the grower a fair share of profit; indeed your letter which states the cost of Manufacture to be half a Guinea a Yard seems to give a strong proof of the justice of my conjecture.

I rejoice to hear that you are likely next year to have a man from the Forest of Delamere to superintend your Clip, as I conclude the waste the Manufacturer complains of to have been owing to the Fleeces being ill washd; the Spanish breed are so full of nature as we call it (that is they perspire so much) that they attract more dirt than any other breed of Sheep, all Sheep however are said to perspire in proportion to the fineness of their wool, even in Lincolnshire where we grow the coarsest wool in all England, this observation has been long made, I was taught many years ago to distinguish the finest woold Sheep in a flock, when they are at a distance from me, which was done entirely by choosing that which had the blackest back . . .[84]

He closed his letter with an offer to renew the Spanish blood in the breed of Philip Yorke or any of his neighbours should they wish to have it—the King, he said, was fully sensible of the zeal with which he pursued a matter so close to His Majesty's own interest. No response to this appeared until the end of the year when the offer was tactfully declined and the Denbighshire experiment lapsed:

I should have much earlier acknowledged your kind favor, received long since, had I not waited the effect of a further acquaintance with the Spanish sheep; and I think I find, that being too tender for the Country in the mixed state, they would less succeed in a purer one; I still remain equally obliged to you for your recommendation, had their appeared a better promise of success . . .[85]

VIII

On the very day that Banks, from Gainsborough, confirmed for Robert Greville the choice of Ram No. 58 for Lady Mansfield in 1794 the Colonel himself set out to see the ram next in serial order, No. 59, which had been allotted on 18 June and sent down by the King's command to Mr. John Bridge of Winford Eagle on the Dorset Downs about sixteen miles north-west of Weymouth.

The morning of 30 August at Weymouth was one of mizzling rain and cloud with a south wind, defeating the King's hopes of going to sea in H.M.S. *Southampton* to view Lord Howe's fleet. The weather instead tempted him into thoughts of a long ride. He bathed in the sea at half past seven and after breakfast the horses were paraded before Gloucester Lodge on the front. His Majesty then signified his intention of visiting John Bridge by a route through Upway, Frampton, and Maiden Newton. The party consisted of His Majesty, Prince Edward Duke of Kent,[86] Lord Walsingham, General Goldsworthy, and Colonel Robert Greville. The King set his customary cracking pace leaving

Prince Edward to turn back from Upway and General Goldsworthy to haul his wind at Maiden Newton. His Majesty, Lord Walsingham, and Colonel Greville then continued over the Downs to Winford Eagle and on the way saw a large flock of polled sheep and some of the Dorsetshire Horn breed. The polled animals struck Greville as the handsomest in the flock. At Winford Eagle they were disappointed to find that John Bridge had but shortly before their arrival set out for Dorchester market. But, says Greville

I learnt from His Shepherd that the Flock I had taken notice of belonged to Mr. Bridge & that the polled Ewes I had seen were a cross between a Leicestershire Ram & the Dorset Ewes—The Ewe Lambs of this Cross He rears, the Poor Lambs He sells off—I enquired for the Spanish Ram [No. 59] which His M: had lately made Him a present of. He was at some distance, & turn'd in with fifty prime Dorsetshire ewes, to make the first experiment of the cross with the Spaniard in this Country. All the Ewes on this Farm had their full long Tails.[87]

On 5 September he was able to satisfy his curiosity further when he attended the King to review the Corps of Yeomanry for the County of Dorset at Longbury Hut near Winterbourne. It was another day of 'misling Showers of Rain' but

After the Business of the Feild was over, I conversed with Mr. Bridge of Winford Eagle one of the Serjeants of this Corps. From Him I learnt, that He likes the Cross between the Leicester & the Dorsets, & find that He has adopted the Leicestershire phrase, that they 'will thrive on the less meat', & quicker, & will become heavier Sheep in Weight, tho' less in size. On questioning Him further He acknowledged that the New Cross of Leicester & Dorset had less fat in the inside & that the Wool was considerably dis-improved. He told Me He should try, a cross between the Spanish & Dorset with the Leicester Ram, which He thought would answer Well & improve the Wool which has been much deficient in the other Cross. At my desire He will try this Season the Ryelands cross'd with the Hereford [sic], having from a Neighbour an opportunity of getting a few Ryelands.

This being quite a Sheep county I have desired Mr. Bridge to procure Me a good Sheep dog for a Friend of Mine—My instructions are that it is handy & good temper'd & not too large—He has promised to procure Me one.[88]

Here through the eyes and ears of the King's Equerry we have the first impressions and first intentions of John Bridge, farmer of Dorset, in relation to the use of the ram which was in a sense the by-product of His Majesty's holiday relaxation by the sea. It was followed in 1796 by No. 111, 'The Poll'd Ram' and in 1799 by No. 128. With two ewes given in 1795 this was the sum of the King's gifts to John Bridge but they had fallen into good hands and added more to the records left of this early phase than did many more pretentious gifts of sheep. His experiments are chiefly interesting for their comparisons of the performance in the production of mutton, wool, and tallow of crosses between three basic breeds as significant now as they were then—the Dorset, the Leicester, and the Merino. In 1796 he noted that the fleece of Ram No. 59 was worth annually seventeen or eighteen shillings where the average Dorset fleeces were not worth more than four or five. He thought that such a difference was well worth the consideration of the farmer for his own advantage as well as for the kingdom at large. He hoped that the cross between the Leicester and the Spanish would produce an animal as good if not better than the Dorsets were then— though 'We must not give up the Carcase & inclination to feed for the fleece.' The cross between the Leicester and the Dorset far exceeded any other sheep he had bred; their form was superior; they got fat on land where the Dorsets would not; and the butcher gave more per pound for them. As to the lambs got by the Spanish ram from the Dorset ewes he found their form very indifferent; from what he could judge they were not inclined to carry mutton; their wool was good but putting the whole together he did not think them as profitable as the Dorsets.[89]

The first report to Banks on the subject reached him in February 1799 but he was not able 'to take the King's pleasures on the paper' from John Bridge until 30 April. His ill-health for six months previously had completely denied him his 'customary occupations'. The report appeared in fact to prove that the half-Spanish and half-Dorset breed were in practice more profitable than either the whole-bred Dorset or the half-Dorset and half-Leicester cross. On which Banks told Bridge

I have the pleasure to tell you that his Majesty, expressed much satisfaction, not only at the Result, but also at the accurate & ingenious method in which the comparisons are stated.[90]

The second report came to hand in Soho Square in May 1800.[91] For reasons of State rather than of personal health Banks did not reply until 3 August:

it was only a very Short time ago that I had an opportunity of Conferring with the King on the subject of your valuable report his majesty has been so much occupied by his army this year that it was very difficult to find him in a humor to discuss matters of Farming tho his most Favorite Topic in times of Peace

his Majesty made however one very Judicious Remark which is that if the Wool of the Short woold breeds joind with Spanish had been valued at 2s/ a Pound the Price at which South down wool has been often Sold and which the mixd wool was no doubt with these Cross breeds would have yielded more profit on the whole returns than any others if you have any wools of the Spanish cross in your hands & will send them to me I will have them broken & sold & return you the amount which will be more than you can make of them in your neighbourhood & will ascertain their real value of the Leicester however I cannot say so much[92] because fine Combing wools are not wanted in our manufacture & cannot therefore bring their real value . . .[93]

In October 1800 John Bridge took up this challenge and shipped at Weymouth on 16 February by the *Martha*, under William Stone, 'Twenty Tods of Wool of Twenty Eight pounds each Tod of the Half Spanish & half Dorset' for London where Henry Lacocke duly received them.

the 2 Bags of wool which you Advised me of that came from waymouth have got them from the Wharf into my warehouse waiting for y^r inspection when you Shou'd think proper to Come over to see them, Shall be at the warehouse Every morning this Week untill one o'Clock[94]

And while expert judgement on the point was pending John Bridge sounded the note that was more urgent then that it had been when he first dabbled with the Spanish breed in 1794:

. . . A great thing for the grower as well as for the publick at large, a famous thing for the Island if we could do without Spanish Wool, which I am in hopes we shall be able to do If the Spanish Mixture goes on well . . .[95]

IX

The autumn of 1794 was, for 'His Majesty's Farming Secretary', a season of 'mellow fruitfulness' in rural knowledge gained and in duties well performed. The days at Weymouth that year had passed in a strange medley of naval, military, and agricultural affairs. The tumbrils of the Terror had not ceased to lumber through the streets of Paris. The prisoners-of-war and the *émigrés* from the insane excesses of the Committee of Public Safety were scattered in a negligent confusion along the Channel coast.[96] McBride's squadron was in and out of Weymouth Road prowling along the French coast. The Esplanade was replete with Ministers of State, Privy Councillors, an Envoys Extraordinary coming and going as portents of crisis. Reviews of troops on the Dorset Downs and Royal hunts were seasoned by weighty exchanges with Farmer Ham of Upway on the economics of folding and the merits of the Dorset and the Somerset sheep. Robert Greville had his own part in these things:

During the Hunt I saw one of the Dorsetshire Yeomen a farmer settled near Upway from Somersetshire (Mr. Ham) The King has often had conversation

with him ab.^t His Sheep. I put in my word this day ab.^t Them. I find he
is more partial to the Somersetshire sheep than to the Dorsets. The K[ing]
has commissioned Him to get two Prime Rams from Somersetshire I believe
to cross with His Wiltshires & give them breadth—as He says. If so, they
may improve the breed, as they are generally too long in the Legs & too
thin a sheep to please Me.[97]

The same day he received from the hand of John Bridge of Winford
Eagle—the rival to Farmer Ham in the Royal interest—the promised
sheep dog for the 'Friend' of his thwarted romance, to be carried home
and very soon no doubt to work among the Spaniards at Ken Wood.[98]

Mr. Bridge reckons it a handsome one. It is not quite so handsome as I
thought it would be by His Acc.^t of it, but its colour is notwithstanding the
common colour of the Shepherd Dogs of this county, & I suppose He is
handsomer than I think Him at first sight. If He is a useful & a steady one
it is such as I have been trying for.

But then those who buy sheep dogs must always reckon on the silver-
tongued deception of their breeders.

Meanwhile Sir Joseph was immured at Revesby Abbey, very much
occupied with the affairs of the county. When Greville sent him a report
on the state of 'the Ram Flock of Spaniards' at Windsor soon after his
return from Weymouth and the casualties therein from the fighting
among themselves[99]—especially the state of that incorrigible warrior
No. 16, the imported Negretti—Banks was inclined to apologize for
his tardy reply:

I have been in one uniform fidget Ever since I was here & what with
Elections in which I acted the double part of negociator & Returns officer
assise cavalry meetings &c have scarce had a moment respite I should not
however have delayd a moment an answer to yours had I been at home
when it came to hand for you well know that H.M. business always with
me supersedes all others whatever they may be that I am engaged in . . .[100]

His fidget may well have been somewhat relieved by the knowledge that
Greville was now on the scene at Windsor again, and to have some
assurance that a responsible eye was occasionally cast in the direction
of the sheep. Greville had used his initiative in this and had made it
clear that

. . . if I can by my residence on the Spot be at all useful to you I hope You
will command Me—As the Time of Your sending away the Rams to Kew
approaches so fast, I hurry away this despatch without delay—
I have cleared the 11 Acres of 9 Sheep 3 Cows & two Horses which I
found eating up the grass in it very fast when the pasture should have been
freshening whilst the Ram flock are now feeding at Frogmore—

We want looking after Here, & I intend to keep an Eye now & then on the *11 Acres* & the Spaniards— . . . P.S. All here is as well as You could wish, & *all abroad* on the Continent as ill as the Devil would have it—[101]

The Revolutionary armies swept on and Pitt's first Coalition crumpled. From the Queen's Lodge at Windsor Greville looked out in deep gloom at the international scene:

. . . I mention nothing of Campaigns—So much extraordinary disaster I suppose can not be met with in the whole History of War . . .[102]

And yet in spite of the collapsing policies of Britain abroad and the spirit of unrest at home—and not so far from the walls of Windsor Castle—there was a latent optimism in the small events of that very day as Greville reported to Banks what had been done on 27 October:

. . . This Morning His Majesty orderd the remaining full grown Spanish Rams to be collected for His inspection—They were seen in one of the Cow Hovels in the Dairy Farm Yard—The object of this inspection was to select two *unengaged* ones for Lord Egremont, who had wrote to Price, to endeavour to ask the *Loan* of one of the Spanish Rams as He was anxious to try a Cross with one—His M. on this being communicated order'd two to be given to Him— N° 38 & N° 75 are accordingly selected for Petworth— . . .

About these two animals there was little to say. At the shearing they had both been 'midling' and 'full of Ticks' but they were the beginning of a long train of events whose influence would spread far. They were the first sheep from His Majesty's Spanish flock to be planted on or near the South Downs. As pioneers they joined the offspring of the French sheep sent from Spring Grove to Lord Sheffield at Lewes. But they were obscured three years later by a more distinguished reinforcement of considerable weight both in numbers and quality. When, on 29 July 1797, Sir Joseph wrote to the 3rd Earl of Egremont he announced a gift that was Royal indeed:

I yesterday Receivd the King's Commands to acquaint your Lordship that in consequence of your Lordships wishes his Majesty desires your Lordships acceptance of Two Rams & 20 Ewes of the True Spanish Breed

his Majesty was pleasd himself to assist yesterday in drawing out the Ewes, they are not the Crones of the Flock but are regularly selected for your Lordship from Every Class of the Flock 13 are Ewes of different ages from 2 years upwards 4 are Tegs & 3 are Lambs

The Rams are N° 15 a Real Spanish imported by the King the only one now Remaining it is an old Sheep & sent more for Curiosity than for use The other is N° 98 a very Fine Sheep of 3 years old who servd his Majesties Flock last year & will be more than sufficient for the little Flock he accompanies

The Rams are at Windsor and will be deliverd by M^r [John] Robinson of Windsor

The Ewes are at Kew & your Lordship may arrange matters for their delivery with Mr Ramsay Robinson of Kensington I would by all means advise that a Waggon be sent for them which will carry the whole Lot as the weather is too warm for their being movd with Safety on Foot[103]

Banks did less than justice to the old Ram No. 15. At eight years old he was more than a curiosity. He was not only the last of the original four entire rams of the Negretti flock sent by the Countess del Campo di Alange in 1791. He was also the most used of all the sires in the Royal flock and after five consecutive seasons had imprinted more on the character of its stock than any other ram at any time in its history. His retirement into the great park of Petworth was a dignified close to a distinguished career.

X

There was a hint of telepathy in the opening correspondence between His Grace the 3rd Duke of Montrose and Sir Joseph Banks. On 19 July 1795 at Buchanan Castle near Glasgow His Grace sat down to give Banks an account of his negotiations through Colonel Robert Manners, another of the King's equerries, for sheep from the Royal flock.[104] He had been reminded by a recent local example that the King had told him—'the last time I had the Honor of attending His Majesty about His Farm at Windsor'—that he proposed parting with a certain number of his Spanish flock. He had accordingly written to Manners at Windsor only to learn that of the ewes none were available, but that the King had in fact offered him two rams meanwhile and a promise of ewes the next season. The Colonel had recommended that he write to Banks—'as the Flock is under your management'. He was persuaded that the Spanish cross, from what he had seen and heard locally, was 'admirably well suited to our Hill Sheep, which are well carcased for such ground, tho' miserably Clothed, with their, bad, short Wool . . .'

However, Banks had already on 18 July from Soho Square in London written his version of the King's lapse of memory about the number of surplus sheep available, confirming the offer which Colonel Manners had already transmitted. But he added now the details. His Grace was to have immediately the imported Spanish ram of the Negretti flock numbered on the horn 16 and a ram teg numbered 91 bred the previous year at Windsor. The next year he was by His Majesty's command to have 'the choice of the draught which will be a very desirable one as several of the Ewes of the negretti Flock the best that have been imported must then be parted with . . .'[105]

The two letters crossed in the post, the Duke receiving that from Sir Joseph on 21 July. He replied on 23 July[106] expressing his formal gratitude to the King through Banks and enclosing a copy of part of the letter 'from the Farmer in this neighbourhood who tried the experiment with the native sheep & also a little of the Wool'.[107] It now appeared that 'the Farmer in this neighbourhood' was Archibald Edmonstone, an extensive grazier on the Duntreath estate within the parish of Strathblane in Stirlingshire almost due north of Glasgow and across the Clyde from Buchanan Castle. He had written to Mr. Menzies, Factor to the Duke of Montrose, saying that he had pretty good proof of the hardiness of the Spanish sheep on the Strathblane Hills where they had been the previous summer with his other sheep though wintered on the low ground but neither housed nor hay fed. They had been again in the hills since the 12 May and when clipped in July were in just as good order as the other sheep and the lambs were heavier and fatter than the 'muir' ones. If they thrived on the high hills of Strathblane at about eighteen hundred feet, what would they not do in the fertile parks round Buchanan? He concluded:

. . . I have crossed the breed between the muir Ewes & Spanish ram, and have reason to think the experiment will answer beyond my Expectations both with regard to wool and Carcase. The wool of the pure Spanish Sheep I have sold at 3/6d pr English pound—The ram had five pound tron weight (6 lb 11 oz English) The Ewes 3½ lb (4lb 11 oz English) and a Ewe Hog 4 lb (5 lb 6 oz English) a sample of which I have sent you . . .[108]

Archibald Edmonstone himself had succumbed to the evangelical preaching of the 'Scotch Wool Society' from whom he had obtained his specimens of Spanish sheep. No direct evidence is available to fix the exact source. The best assumption is that he purchased a few from the nearest source for that part of Scotland—'the Parent flock from which part of Scotland is to be supplied'[109]—at Galloway House to which a very liberal part of William Conyngham's second flock had been sent from Ireland. These had been chosen in 1791 by the agent of Admiral Keith Stewart, a Mr. Palliser, 'peculiarly skilled in Sheep'. This was certainly the largest source of pure Spanish sheep likely to be available to Edmonstone and they were, moreover, specifically intended to stock the west of Scotland. It is said that the only hazard of which he was apprehensive was that the inclemency of the weather would hurt them. Of this he had been agreeably relieved for they stood two winters as well as the rest of his stock, one of them—the winter of 1794–5—being the most severe that had been known for many years.[110] The only precaution, as he had said, was to keep them on his low ground, without extra feeding, during the winter. In summer they were fond of feeding on the tops of the hills where they thrived as well as the native breed. He had found that when he crossed the Spanish ram with the Scots ewe, or the Scots ram with the Spanish ewe, the wool on the lambs thus generated was little inferior to the old Spanish sheep and they were expected to be even hardier being inured to the climate from their birth. In short, if he had sufficient low ground he would push 'this experiment to a degree which might prove highly beneficial to himself, his landlord, and, *as setting a useful example*, to the whole country'. In the autumn of 1795 he went further and crossed a few Cheviot ewes with his Spanish rams from which he expected to improve the wool to a still greater degree of fineness than the crossing with the common Scots ewes. But on this point the future had yet to decide.[111]

Meanwhile Sir Joseph, on 31 July 1795, passed what information he had on these 'laudable exertions' to the Royal patron of all such experiments:

I had yesterday the honor of Laying the contents of your graces Favor of 23[d] Ins[t] before the King who Receivd the warm expressions of Gratitude it Containd with his usual Consideration & Kindness

The intelligence from your Graces Factor respecting the very high Price M[r] Edminstone had procurd for wool of the Pure Spanish breed grown in Scotland was receivd by his Majesty as very interesting information as in truth it is, but I fear M[r] E[dmonstone] must not continue to expect so profitable a Return prevailing during the present system of affairs in Europe which by throwing the Whole of the Produce of the Spanish Flocks that usd to be concernd in the manufactures of France or Forwarded to those of Germany by the way of Holland into our hands has reduced the price of that article from 4/10 a pound to 3/6 & less

I shall have infinite Pleasure in Obeying H M Commands in the next season which direct me to allow your Grace a full choice both in Quantity & Quality of the Ewes drawn out of the Spanish Flock at Kew his Majesty properly says that no experiment can be more likely to succeed than one tried under your Graces directions & Founded on the experience of M[r] Edminstone[112]

The promise was made good when, on 27 June 1796, Banks announced to the Duke of Montrose, who was then at his house in Grosvenor Square, that he had that day finished the inspection of the King's Spanish flock and drawn the ewes which by His Majesty's orders were destined for His Grace adding that

. . . there are among them some of the originally imported ones and the whole Lot I hope will be found better than Cast Ewes usually are there is only one black which will please your Graces Shepherd as it is supposd that good Luck to the Flock is the Consequence of having one of that Color . . .[113]

What the Duke's shepherd thought of this whimsy we cannot tell. Nor have we a record of his impressions of the draft from Kew when at last they arrived at Buchanan Castle by the Clyde. For these were the forty-six animals of which there were '15 Ewes drawn by the Shepherd as the least thrifty & 22 by [Henry] Lacock[e] as the least fine' with '9 Tegs drawn by Lacock as the worst Fleeces'.[114] Of these sheep forty-one were finally allotted to the Duke—sold to the Duke, in fact, if the note by Banks on the same day means anything—and the other five were disposed of to the Right Honourable Charles Greville. These then were not a gift but, by His Majesty's orders of 17 June 1795,[115] they were, for the Duke, '. . . his choice of all the Ewes that will be draughted next year at such Price as is thought Proper Probably a guinea Each'. With the two rams of that year—Nos. 114 and 115, which were gifts—these were the largest single consignment of sheep sent from the Royal flock.

Within a week of being drafted by Sir Joseph and Henry Lacocke the sheep were on their way to Scotland. On Tuesday, 6 July 1796, forty-one ewes and two rams were penned early in the morning by the shepherd on Kew Green. Here at 5 a.m. they were delivered to Mr. Gibbs, the Duke's agent, who had come up the river with a barge on the previous evening and was waiting there to receive them.[116] Taken down the river that day they were trans-shipped to the vessel nearer the estuary which set sail on Wednesday, 7 July for Grangemouth well inside the Firth of Forth. Taken by cart through the Clyde valley they arrived at Buchanan near Paisley without loss, being attended in their entire journey, watered, and fed on hay and oats, by a servant of the Duke's.[117] Next year two more rams—No. 108 and one other—were sent by the same route to join the flock which the Duke used to implement his plan 'of making experiments in the Hills under different Tenants at the same time'. On the results of these he promised Banks that he should receive reports on the approved form—but these, if sent, are yet to be found.

Altogether six rams and forty-one ewes were sent from the Thames to the Clydeside in the three years from 1795 to 1797 and dispersed by the 3rd Duke of Montrose on his estates. Here, somewhere in the hills or valleys of the west of Scotland, perhaps in Stirling or in Renfrewshire, lie the bones of the old Negretti ram No. 16—'a Great Fighter'—whose continual affrays in the ram flock at Windsor left him alive, certainly, but so often physically battered that he was fit only for service in the Royal flock during two seasons (1792, 1794). He was evidently a most colourful character but unquestionably an intolerable nuisance. We can but suspect that Banks and Greville were glad to have the excuse to send him into the west of Scotland where 'the wildness of the Hill stock' was probably judged a better foil for his talents. Somewhere, too, in the same region many of the old Negretti ewes—like him of the original importation from Santander—found a cold wet end to lives that had opened in the warm valley of the Guadiana in Estremadura as far back as 1788 or 1789.

XI

In the list of those persons to whom the King had 'been Graciously Pleased to Present Merino Sheep in the years 1791–1799' there were forty-two entries. There were in fact forty-three if we accept—as there seems no reason to doubt—an important but unpublicized note that His Grace, Francis 5th Duke of Bedford, received two rams and fourteen ewes in the year 1797.[118] In the dispersals it would seem that most of the *métis* flock from France eventually found their way to Cardiganshire where they died either from the rigours of the Welsh climate or from those of Mr. Thomas Johnes's management. All the sheep imported by way of Lisbon, Bilbao, and Oporto seem to have found their destiny at length in the possession of Lady Mansfield at Ken Wood and at Scone; with Major William Price and his tenant Josiah Ridgeway in the Herefordshire fallows near Ludlow; or with the tenants of the 3rd Duke of Montrose in the hills and valleys round the Firth of Clyde. Among the latter must be placed probably most of the survivors of the classic Negretti lot, the passengers on the schooner *King George*, the diplomatic treasures of 'Lord Auckland's undertaking'. To these favoured few, therefore, went the lion's share of the King's gracious bounty during these formative and fumbling early years. But neither the aristocratic nor the philosophic lustre of the recipients' names nor the numbers or merit of the Royal sheep donated to them are suitable clues by which to deduce their probable importance to posterity. The laborious tracing out of every sheep transaction negotiated by Sir Joseph Banks in serving the long-range experimental intentions of the Royal flock may or may not be a justifiable pastime at this stage. There is, however, one further entry on the list with which it is profitable to conclude this cursory account of the bounteous years in the King's favours to his subjects, high and low.

'In the Autumn season of the year 1777, several Gentlemen met at the City of BATH, and formed a Society for the encouragement of Agriculture, Arts, Manufacturers, and Commerce, in the Counties of SOMERSET, WILTS, GLOCESTER, and DORSET, and in the City and County of BRISTOL.'[119] The geographical scope defined for 'the Society instituted at Bath' fixes for us that area of Great Britain where, from the most modest origins, perhaps more was made of the sheep sent out from the King's flock than in any other region. Eleven years later the Society entered the field of public education to fulfil one of its most important ends, 'the diffusion of useful information'. In 1788 the first volume of *Letters and Papers on Agriculture, Planting, &c. . . . Selected from The Correspondence-Book of the Society Instituted at Bath, . . .* was published. The *Annals* of Arthur Young were augmented by a very hardy annual, a competitor that would outlast that vigorous pioneer. A mouthpiece had been found for 'the landed gentlemen, and those daily enriched by commerce' who were 'now emulous in the study of agriculture'.[120] Then, four years later on 10 July 1792, William Matthews, Secretary of the Bath and West of England Society, sounded the note which found responsive chords through all the western counties and from Bath to Soho Square:

How far the *general improvement of the quality of British wool* is practicable, so as to supersede the necessity of a large foreign supply, is a question agitating elsewhere; and this Society cannot be inattentive to its solution. It might possibly be found that a general national alteration of the stock of sheep, in favour of fine wool, would be incompatible with the national interest, both with respect to the *quantity* of wool and of mutton. Whether the quantity, and consequently the cheapness of mutton, would not be in danger of being sacrificed to fineness of wool; or whether the coarseness of most of our wool, compared with Spanish, be, under all circumstances, an evil; are questions of no small moment. Some gentlemen of much candour and reflection, will not be disappointed if this Society should ultimately fix in a confirmed opinion, that there is no race of sheep in Britain but what has its advantages, for particular situations and exposures. We have no wool, however coarse, but what is useful. Our different manufactures for home and foreign trade, require the different sorts already known, consume them all, and even call for more. If it should be found that the present system of artificial feeding, necessary to increase the quantity of mutton, (and which consequently increases wool) is incompatible with a general improvement in the *fineness* of wool, still that increased quantity of human food, a proportionable increase of wool and manure, and the adaptation of sheep to the circumstances of the district, are objects of higher national importance, than a uniform fineness of wool. These points may now be considered as in a fairer train for investigation than heretofore; and the result may be expected at a future day. So long as British genius and advantages for manufacture, on a comparison with those of other European nations, continue what they are, so long must wool of some sort be imported. And the question then will most probably be, *which* may be imported to greatest advantage, that which is *most*, or that which is *least* compatible with the first of all objects, an improving agriculture? If the *latter* of the two, then it may be deemed a happy circumstance, that that sort is to be imported which from its compactness lies in least room; and that which may be paid for, in part at least, by the lighter and coarser manufactured articles made from the combing wool of our own country.[121]

From the West Country a voice of sober sense had been raised. It spoke from the heart of the problem. Nowhere else in the kingdom was it possible to see so clearly the nature of Britain's rising dilemma in the relations between her wool manufactures and her agriculture, between her import trade in wool and the qualities of her home-grown fibre. The Society for which William Matthews spoke comprehended all the elements of the conundrum within its membership—'the landed gentlemen' of the West Country and 'those daily enriched by commerce' especially that which flowed in terms of Spanish wool through the port of Bristol—all these were the living substance of 'the Society instituted at Bath'. Their collective and individual voices spoke in terms that were informed and realistic. In many ways they were both a powerful corrective and an essential supplement to arguments that were sweeping through the north as 'the Scotch Society' at Edinburgh moved into action and sent its evangelists to the four corners of the realm.

The introductory dedication of the sixth volume of the Bath *Letters and Papers* to the economic and agricultural problem of the improvement of British wool had a clear public message. But it also carried its own private significance to the prepared mind brooding and pondering the same intricate question in the big study at Soho Square. The restrained tone of the Bath Society manifesto on the subject of fine wool was to Banks much more of a piece with his own way of thinking than the strenuous preaching of hopeful self-sufficiency which reached him in doses, little and often, from Edinburgh and Whitehall as Sinclair reached the peak of his enthusiasm on the subject. Here at last was an established body of representative and deeply committed men in whose hands perhaps some well-balanced solution might be achieved. The subject of fine wool might have been critical—as it certainly was—but Banks in 1792 was not by any means convinced of the right path to follow. He knew that the Spanish sheep was the key to a door. But which was the door? There was much to be discovered and he was well aware that the Spanish Merino in Britain created almost as many problems in agriculture as it solved in the manufacture of woollens. It was some relief then to find a body of men, representing no mean order of business and farming acumen combined, rising spontaneously to face the problem with a spirit of critical inquiry not unlike his own. Worthy men, indeed, to receive the King's patronage in this patriotic exertion! And a useful foil also to the activities of the 'Northern society', it may be noted. It was, therefore, almost inevitable that on 14 August 1792, Banks should have written to the Secretary of the Bath Society in these terms:

I beg leave to acquaint you for the information of the members of the Bath Agricultural Society that the King on Saturday last [6 August] Commanded

me to select from his Spanish Flock Two Rams as a present for that Society
I have accordingly Chosen two. the one a young Sheep bred by his Majesty
at Windsor of pure Spanish blood markd on the horn with the N.° 26 the
other an older Sheep imported from Spain in the year 1790 & usd in his
Majesties Flock last year it is markd on the Horn with the Number 8

I should not have selected so Old a Sheep for the Society but under an
Idea that they would wish to see an original one & tho this Sheep is an Old
one I have no doubt he will be able to do his duty this year at Least &
possibly the next . . .[122]

It may have been a surprise to William Matthews and it certainly seems
to have startled the Society that so soon after their laudable sentiments
had been published in July His Majesty should have taken them so
literally so promptly. The Bath Society was set in a buzz. Their reply
in the hand of their Secretary was dutifully made on 18 August:

. . . I directly on the rec[t] of your Letter summoned our Committee of Agriculture, which having deliberated on steps most proper to be taken for
rendering his Majesty's Bounty most useful, directed me to summon a
general Meeting of the Society a week sooner than usual, viz. the first
Tuesday in Sep[t] and in the mean Time to commission M[r] Joseph Mighell a
very respectable Gentleman Farmer at Kennett,[123] & a Member of this
Society, to send for the Rams, from Windsor, and keep them safely under
his Care till the general Meeting shall determine concerning them.

I therefore write by this post to M[r] Mighell for that purpose, inclosing
him a Letter to be deliverd to M[r] Robinson

I have particular pleasure in communicating to you, the Thanks of the
Committee, for the part you have had in this Pleasing Business, and to
assure you that the approaching General Meeting will not fail to express
a suitable sense of the Society's Gratitude to his Majesty for his Royal
Attention to their pursuits.[124]

The general meeting seems to have decreed that the Society's rams
should be established with the Earl of Ailesbury—probably at Savernake
Forest near Marlborough south of the Old Bath road. Then in 1795 two
more rams were allocated by His Majesty's order for the use of the
Bath and West of England Society apparently on the application of the
Earl of Ailesbury, its President that year. On this occasion the Society
was to be honoured with two animals of the most distinguished lineage
the country had to offer and this was conveyed with proper formality
to the President himself by Sir Joseph Banks in a sentence of equally
distinguished length:

. . . his Majesty has moreover been pleasd in order that so Respectable [a]
Body of men may have the best specimens of the Merino breed he is able
to Provide for them to direct that one of the Original Rams of the Negretti
Flock which is Esteemd the Second Pile of wool that has Ever been imported

into this Country being inferior only to the Perales which Ram the King Receivd as a Present from the Marchioness del Campo di Alange the Proprietress of the Flock be one of the Two [No. 14] & the other a Teg [No. 110] of the Negretti blood Bred at Kew . . .[125]

And so Ram No. 14, second in importance to No. 15 for his influence on the first generations of the old Negretti flock, after serving His Majesty at Windsor and at Kew found a last haven on the grasslands of Wiltshire. It was acknowledged by His Lordship gratefully as President of the Bath Society to be a 'distinguished Mark of Grace & Favor conferrd by His Majesty towards the Improvement of the Wool of this Country which the Society have so much at Heart'. Sharing this patriotic adulation the young ram tag No. 110 may well have been the son of No. 14 himself—if not, then probably of No. 15.

Sir Joseph's formal letter with its breathless encomium had been sent on from Tottenham Park by the Earl to William Matthews at the Society's room in Bath on 27 July. Here on 28 July it was honoured with immediate attention and, as before, an extra general meeting called to receive it. On 29 July Matthews conveyed the sense of the meeting to his President:

. . . I have it in Command to beg that your Lordship will be pleased, in the way you judge the most proper, to communicate to his Majesty, the most respectful and grateful Sense, which this Society feels, for such a repeated and valuable Instance of his Majesty's Goodness: and particularly for the flattering terms of his Majesty's Royal Approbation, contained in Sir Joseph's Letter. —Your Lordship will confer an additional Favour by assuring his Majesty that the Society will not fail to endeavour so to dispose of those Rams, as to render them of all possible use, towards the Improvement of the Wool of this Country . . .[126]

Four rams in all, then (Nos. 8, 26, 14, and 110), were sent to the Bath Society. We must group with these the two rams sent to the 2nd Earl Bathurst at Cirencester Park (No. 2 and No. 121 in 1791 and 1798) and the four to the Marquis of Bath at Longleat (Nos. 46 and 55 in 1793; Nos. 100 and 118 in 1796). Against all the numerical strength of the gifts to those of the immediate Court circle mediated by Robert Fulke Greville these ten sheep at first sight were a feeble contingent. But it is an interesting point that in the history of Merino breeding the greatest successes were often achieved with slight resources in sheep. The King's 'Grace & Favour' to the Bath Society was not lavish but it was well bestowed. It was to be observed a few years later by a French writer of some note that 'Fine wool sheep may be kept wherever industrious men and intelligent breeders exist'.[127] Men of intelligence and men of industry were clearly to be found among those who 'laboured to render his Majesties patriotic views in importing Spanish sheep permanently useful to his subjects'. There were not many patriots, however, who sufficiently combined the two qualities necessary to complete success. As a crucible in which to forge such men the Bath and West of England Society proved its value in the years ahead.

CHAPTER IX

The Patriots, 1792–1803

I

IN November 1779, two years after the meeting of 'several Gentlemen' at the city of Bath to form 'a Society for the encouragement of Agriculture, Arts, Manufactures, and Commerce', a young man from Cirencester moved into 13 Catharine Place.[1] Here was Dr. Caleb Hillier Parry at twenty-four, fresh from the University of Edinburgh and armed with the scroll of an M.D. On the foundations of a noteworthy dissertation—*De Rabies Contagiosa*—he was about to build the practice in clinical medicine which became the consuming task of his whole life and bound him for ever to the classical precincts of that one city.

He had been preceded in his return to the West Country by his friend and senior, Dr. Edward Jenner, who at thirty, had already been established some seven years quietly in his home town at Berkeley about a day's ride to the north in Gloucestershire. Jenner, like Parry, was to live a life of almost sedentary devotion to one place and by assiduous concentration on the demands of a busy practice also to advance the scope of medical science. From the common ills of the countryside and the rounds of the country doctor Jenner would one day distil a single great discovery after years of patient observation, critical thought, and final courageous experiment. At Berkeley he would establish clearly the efficacy of vaccination and presage the future triumphs of immunology. At the age of fifty he would emerge from rural obscurity to struggle against human prejudice and professional jealousy. At seventy-four he would die with an international fame and a material reward from his own country that few men of science have achieved. But it was to his friend, Caleb Hillier Parry, correspondent and collaborator in many scientific researches, that Edward Jenner dedicated in 1798 his slim quarto volume on *An Inquiry into the Causes and Effects of Variolae Vaccinae*. . . . It was a significant tribute from one physician to another no less gifted.

For Parry, like Jenner, possessed a critical inquiring mind. From the curious ills of high society clustered about the Pump Room at Bath and from the wards of the General Hospital he filtered the evidence of his own acute observations into a few papers of classic importance in the history of medicine. Personable, charming, distinguished in intellect

235

and in character, Parry, at thirty-three, had achieved the glittering semblance of success in the world to which Jenner at forty could certainly not pretend. But the guineas which daily filled the pockets of his well-cut coat in growing profusion were the just reward for a medical practice honestly and brilliantly pursued. The fattening case-books were replete with unspectacular but endless details, critically assembled, to be digested in due time and added to the substance of medical knowledge. The recognition of his lasting contributions to human physiology and to the unripe field of endocrinology would be largely posthumous and known only to the most discerning among his contemporaries and his posterity. The mask of the fashionable physician obscured the face of the medical scientist. But at the age of thirty-three the guineas of the successful general practitioner created the scientific agriculturist.

Therefore, nine years after coming to Bath and in the same year that the first volume appeared of the *Letters and Papers on Agriculture . . . of the Society Instituted at Bath, . . .* Parry took the course that many other members of his own profession have since followed. In the year 1788 on Sion Hill he began to build a country-house to which was attached a small area of land—high, dry, unsheltered, unproductive.[2] Such as it was he felt obliged from an innate sense of business to stock it with cows and with Wiltshire sheep, the breed that had formerly grazed the hill. He then made the discovery that has so often since stimulated intelligent men in the same position—'that a cow was, in every possible form, ruinous to those whose avocations would not permit them constantly to superintend the application of its produce'. Moreover, he found by degrees that the sheep he had would not reimburse the rent as he had hoped. He parted by degrees with his cows and his Wiltshire sheep and substituted the small Portland breed which produced for him good mutton but whose fleece he rated as inconceivably coarse and in weight almost nothing. He had acquired four years of experience, so far unprofitable, when in 1792 he first learned from the 2nd Earl Bathurst of the King's interest and purpose in the Spanish breed of fine-woolled sheep—a crumb of information easily gleaned by a physician whose 'professional avocations' lay by the waters at Bath. To a mind already prepared it needed little further reflection to reach a conclusion. Parry swiftly decided that the solution of his practical difficulties with his land lay in 'a breed of sheep, the return of which would chiefly depend on the fleece'. His management would be made simple. He would not depend for his profit on the complicated vagaries of the season and the whims of the butcher. The wool could be easily weighed once a year and the value as easily ascertained by one of the numerous clothiers in the near-by western counties. The means to this end had already been shown by His Majesty, not only by the introduction of the Spanish breed itself but also by the clear benefit arising from its crosses with some of the English breeds, notably the Hereford or Ryeland. He therefore fixed, as the basis of his experiments, on that breed which had long been reputed for producing some of the finest wool in the island and as otherwise adapted 'by its hardiness and its habits of easily subsisting on a poor soil'.[3] He had considered, with much attention before reaching this conclusion, the common prejudice that Spanish fine wool could only be grown 'on that small space of earth, on which, in our time, it happened to be found'. Such a limitation he had rejected as 'unconformable to the fixed analogy of nature'. He had no doubt that with due care and sufficient time the properties of the parent fine-wool fleece might be transmitted to the hybrid progeny. For this purpose he could buy sufficient ewes of the pure uncrossed Ryeland race. His chief difficulty lay in procuring the Spanish male. However familiar young Dr. Parry may have been with the inner ailments of some of the King's friends, he thought that for an obscure individual like himself 'to obtain from Majesty the intire possession of a Merino ram, was utterly impracticable'. He modestly confined his ambitions within narrower limits and in 1792 was able to send two Ryeland ewes to Ram No. 2 at Cirencester Park and another four to the ram (either No. 8 or No. 26) belonging to the Bath Society at the park of the 1st Earl of Ailesbury. Of these six ewes one was stolen while in lamb. In 1793 he could send only four ewes to the Society's ram with the Earl of Ailesbury, but in 1794 he was fortunate enough to be able to send six ewes again to Ram No. 2 with the Earl Bathurst and four more to Ram No. 46 or No. 55 with the 1st Marquess of Bath at Longleat. In 1795 he sent no less than seventeen ewes to Ram No. 14 or No. 110 with John Billingsley at Ashwick in Somerset where the new rams of the Bath Society were that year being held. The following year in 1796 the Society recognized his singular merit by depositing one of its own rams with him—probably No. 14, the second most important survivor of the original Santander lot, and which died in the summer of 1797. It was replaced by either No. 46 or No. 55 which the Marquess of Bath first lent and then gave him, so that in 1797 Parry became at last the owner of a Spanish ram from His Majesty's flock. By 1800 he reckoned that in his flock of from three hundred to four hundred ewes and lambs he had a hundred and eighty producing very fine wool at about five pounds per head.

About the same time then, that his friend Jenner was strenuously engaged with the unbelievers, professional and otherwise,[4] on the matter of vaccination, Parry soon after set pen to paper to explain his ideas on the subject of 'producing in the British Isles Clothing Wool equal to that of Spain'. His was the first voice to speak on the basis of sufficient

independent experience and reasoning in support of the Royal experi-
ment. His paper followed soon after the publication by Sir Joseph
Banks of 'A Project for Extending the Breed of Fine Wooled Spanish
Sheep, now in the possession of his Majesty, into all parts of Great
Britain, where the Growth of Fine Cloathing Wools is found to be
profitable'.[5] To this, Parry's *Facts and Observations* . . . was an admirable,
long, and well-reasoned support clearly acknowledging a debt to the
King.[6] He described his theme as 'a collateral subject of Natural
History' which had served to invigorate his mind 'by an occasional
relaxation from severer studies'.

The subject to which I allude is that of WOOL, which has of late produced
much discussion, though not more than it deserves from its importance to
this country, of the chief manufacture of which it is the basis.

It was some time ago my intention to have considered this subject largely
in various points of view; but my professional avocations compel me to
relinquish that design; so that, at present, I shall confine myself to the
inquiry, how far it may be practicable to produce in Great Britain Wool as
proper for the manufacture of superfine cloths of different descriptions as
that of Spain; and what benefits may probably arise to the farmer, and the
nation in general, from the cultivation of a fine woolled breed of sheep.

The project of endeavouring to investigate, by experiment, the first of
these points originally suggested itself to me from his Majesty's patriotic
attempt to introduce into this country the finest woolled Spanish breed; and
as his efforts, soon after that period, happily succeeded, I was induced by the
importance, and at the same time the simplicity, of the pursuit, so well
adapted to my professional abstractions, to direct my agricultural views to
that object only.[7]

In Caleb Hillier Parry, then, we have the first of the patriotic few who
were directly stimulated by the Royal example to set about the breeding
of improved fine-woolled sheep by some means or other. No one was
more prompt in grasping the opportunity. No one reasoned or studied
the theme with greater clarity or carried it as far for so long. No man
wrote as much or as critically and to such purpose on the subject. Few
men among his contemporaries had as much to say that is almost as
relevant to the problems of sheep breeding now as when he wrote. He
became a Fellow of the Royal Society in 1800, but such an elevation
into the select brotherhood of science was not needed to seal his affinity
of interest with those of Sir Joseph Banks. This was already established.
It was, however, confirmed by the accolade of Sir Joseph's approval
in July 1803 when, in 'A Report of the State of His Majesty's Flock of
Fine Wooled Spanish Sheep during the Years 1800 and 1801 . . .'
reference was made to the 'commendable exertions of Dr Parry of

Bath in advancing his Majesty's patriotic view'. Banks could not have placed Parry more generously in his contemporary perspective:

Of all who have laboured to render his Majesty's patriotic views in importing Spanish sheep permanently useful to his subjects, Dr Parry, of Bath, deserves the highest commendation. Amidst the labours of a profession always toilsome when successful, and particularly so at Bath, where persons, whose diseases cannot be ascertained by the faculty elsewhere, continually resort, the doctor found leisure to employ himself in the improvement of the British fleece, by crossing various breeds with Spanish rams presented by his Majesty to the Marquis of Bath and to the Bath Agricultural Society.

The prizes the doctor has continually obtained from the judicious and respectable body from whom he borrowed rams, for cloths made of his own wool, in the midst of a manufacturing country, and amongst abundance of able competitors, prove to a demonstration, that he has brought the fleeces of the mixed breed very nearly to the value of the original Spanish; nor is this to be wondered at, when we recollect that the effect of a mixture of breeds operates in the following proportions.

Rate of amelioration of wool by the Spanish cross.

The first cross of a new breed gives to the lamb half of the rams blood or 50 per cent.

The second gives   75 ditto
The third $87\frac{1}{2}$
The fourth $93\frac{3}{4}$

At which period it is said, that if the ewes have been judiciously selected, the difference of wool between the original stock and the mixed breed is scarcely to be discerned by the most able practitioners.

More need not be said of the doctor's merit. His book which every man who wishes to improve wool ought to read, will give a more just idea of the acuteness of his discrimination, the diligence with which he pursued his purpose, and the success that finally attended his judicious management, than can be stated in the brief form of a report like this . . .[8]

Neither is it possible here to do more than hint at the range and substance of the Doctor's contributions to the literature of the Spanish Merino and its breeding. His reading was wide and his deductions from historical and contemporary records astute and critical. He was not only the most literate and scholarly of those who advanced 'His Majesty's patriotic view', he was the most persistent and, in every modern sense, the most scientific. The breeding of sheep, he was inclined to suggest, was to him a relaxation from more exacting disciplines. And so no doubt in principle it was, as all changes in the variety of work are a means of refreshment. His Majesty's Spanish flock was to Banks also a 'favorite hobby' and a summer easement from the cares of Soho Square. But to both men it was in practice much more. It was 'a subject of Natural History'. As such it claimed all the intellectual

power of which they were capable no less than did their 'daily avocations'. Parry himself took the same wide view as Banks of the field
before him. This he expressed clearly enough in explaining his interest
in the Merino and its place in his particular philosophy to the Board of
Agriculture:

... Agricultural oeconomy presents an unbounded, as well as an unbeaten
field, over which an enquirer will in vain loiter after knowledge. In order to
establish truth, he must search diligently, view all objects with his own eyes,
and scrutinise the qualities and order of phenomena with a precision not
inferior to that of the metaphysician or chemist. . . .[9]

Into this context his work with the sheep certainly fitted easily. Nothing
shows this better than his 'Essay on the Nature, Produce, Origin, and
Extension of the Merino Breed of Sheep . . .' completed in May 1807,
after fifteen years' working experience with the breed on which he was
by then no less an authority than Sir Joseph Banks himself.[10] But long
before this apotheosis was achieved he had been drawn into a profitable
correspondence with Banks who had thereby elicited nourishing
morsels of the Doctor's own clear and independent thinking with
which he was himself in complete accord. No animal breeder of the
eighteenth century in Great Britain has left a more complete and clear
account of his intentions and methods than the eminent physician of
Bath. On the motives and thoughts in such men as Bakewell and Ellman
there is but silence and occasionally the evidence sufficient for a wild
surmise. With Culley and some few others the conjectural cloud may
be half-lifted. But with Parry there is nothing confused or inarticulate.
Of this there is no better example than his explanation to Banks in
April 1800 of the reasons behind the conduct of his breeding plan with
the Spanish stock:

... In the inquiries which have been made on this subject, it has generally
been proposed to improve at once the carcase and the fleece; or at least to
preserve the symmetry and size of the former while means were employed
to increase the value of the latter. These certainly ought to be our ultimate
objects; but I much doubt whether they can be immediately obtained
together, if we mean to improve the fleece by an admixture of Spanish
blood; For as the form of the Spanish Rams imported into this Country is
not that which accords with the present opinion of beauty, it is evident that
this form will be communicated to their progeny; and it is reasonable to
suppose that it will be most prevalent in those of their young which most
resemble them in the fineness of their fleeces. This influence on the carcase
has actually taken place; and in such a degree as to make the common
farmers extremely averse to the introduction of the Spanish breed into their
flocks.

Plate VIII

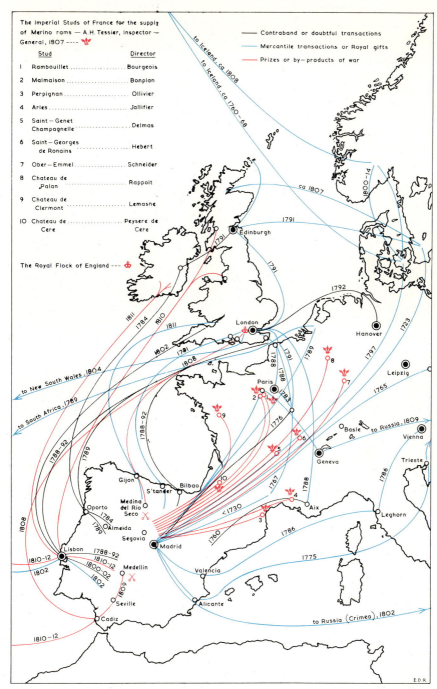

The Imperial Studs of France for the supply
of Merino rams — A. H. Tessier, Inspector —
General, 1807 ----

Stud	Director
1 Rambouillet	Bourgeois
2 Malmaison	Bonplan
3 Perpignan	Ollivier
4 Arles	Jallifier
5 Saint – Genet Champagnelle	Delmas
6 Saint – Georges de Ronains	Hebert
7 Ober – Emmel	Schneider
8 Chateau de Palan	Rappolt
9 Chateau de Clermont	Lemasne
10 Chateau de Cere	Peysere de Cere

The Royal Flock of England ---

Contraband or doubtful transactions
Mercantile transactions or Royal gifts
Prizes or by–products of war

The general pattern of the dispersal from the Iberian Peninsula of the Spanish Merino
from about 1720 to about 1820.

The question then which occurred to me was whether by repeated successive crossings with Spanish Rams we could not so far increase the value of the wool as to make the improvement more than counterbalance the deterioration of the carcase. This end I have endeavoured to attain in the quickest manner I have been able; and I have gone so far as to have sheep which are five sixths Spanish.

When I have carried the improvement of the wool as far as I can I shall then try to mend the carcase. This may be attempted in two ways; either by procuring from Spain fine woolled Rams with better carcases, or by constantly selecting from the flocks we possess, the best formed sheep, and preferring them as breeders. Whether the first method be practicable, I know not; as I have no opportunity of knowing whether Rams of better forms actually exist in Spain; but it is acknowledged that the second method is that by which Mr Bakewell in Leicestershire, and Mr Ellman in Sussex, have given their flocks the reputation which they have ever since continued to possess. If by these means we can eventually succeed in giving our breed superior form, and a constitution readily disposed to fatten, it will then be seen what effect this change of carcase will have on the quality of the wool. ....[11]

This exposition by Parry of his practical philosophy of sheep breeding ended with the news received from his son Charles in Göttingen concerning a very valuable cargo of specimens just received by Professor Blumenbach in that city. The collection included 'the very curious animal from New South Wales, which connects the Classes of Birds and Quadripeds',[12] one of the very first speciments of the platypus (*Ornithorynchus* spp.) which Banks had sent to the German comparative anatomist not long before. But of more immediate concern was the parcel of blue broadcloth and brown cassimere for the King and which this letter portended. Within the month this had been received by Banks and by him graciously acknowledged:

I received in due course your Favor [of April 26] & soon after a Parcel of Cloth & kerseymere intended for his Majesty, which I shall take the first good opportunity that occurs to Lay at his Feet, at Present the Lameness I have been subjected to from frequent returns of the Gout, renders it scarce possible to Remain in his Presence Long enough to do business, but as I now feel a Rapid amendment, I hope before it is [too] Long to draw his majesties attention again to the subject of Sheep & Wool both the Cloth & the Kerseymere are certainly fine Fabrics I have seen none so good from mixd wools, it will give great Pleasure to his majesty to see to what Extent the improvement which originated in the Royal Bounty has been pursued by you, indeed I am of opinion that your Wools are not discernably Coarser than those of the original Spanish which is very natural to suppose as I apprehend in 6 Crosses you have got more than $\frac{94}{100}$ of the male Blood.

I sincerely hope I shall soon hear of your Success in Improving the Carcas of the mixd breeds which I have no doubt you will be able to do, by judicious Selection of Breeding animals, I have already much improvd the Kings Flock, which being intirely Spanish, and of course in mould very discordant to the Popular opinion of the countrey, was a task of no small dificulty, I was fortunate in making a Sale of his majesties wool last year at very high Prices but whether I shall be able to Effect the same this year is a matter I cannot be sure of . . .[13]

Parry was the first of the breeders outside the Banksian circle to enter the field of experimental manufacture of his home-grown fleeces for the public instruction. This he continued for some years and gathered an impressive array of specimens and evidence to show what could be done in the production of wool 'not from *Spanish Ewes* with Spanish Rams, but from *English* Ewes with Spanish Rams . . .'.[14] These first cloths he offered as fair examples for the King's interest to show the current state of his progress in 1800 towards the distant goal he had so clearly defined to Banks. He regarded them as the finest cloth and cassimere 'that have ever appeared in England from wool so obtained' from what he had been told.[15] Banks was not deflected, however, from his usual custom of seeking a second opinion. He turned once more to John Wallace, his draper, of Bedford Street—the 'Gentleman whose integrity of dealing he had long been accustomed to'. On 28 June 1800 John Wallace delivered his verdict.

I have looked at the Cloth and cassimere made of Spanish wool *grown* in England. I wish I could say that the Wool was finer than it is—You are so good a Judge your Self Sir that I am sure you will agree with me in opinion that it is but indifferent, and very inferior to the best Spanish Wool imported here, and of which the best Superfine Cloths are made—I think the Cloth is 5^s/- p^r yard inferior, & it is much too narrow—
The cassimere is well manufactured but taken on the whole I think it is not so good as my best by 2/- p^r yard—
I shall be very glad, and much flattered if these observations will in the least enable you to make a report to His Majesty, and shall always feel myself very highly gratified in the opinion you are pleased to entertain of me . . .[16]

The view of John Wallace the draper Parry found hard to reconcile with the value assigned by Thomas Joyce the manufacturer. He made his own opinion clear:

. . . I will presume that the Manufacturer overvalues it and the Draper underrates it; and then it cannot be deficient in value more than $\frac{1}{2}$ a Crown a yard. Observe I do not say that Cloth may not be made from Spanish Wool, which will be worth 5^s a yard more than this. *I* too could have had cloth made of *my wool* worth 2^s 6^d a yard more than that in question. In both cases the wool would have been more nicely sorted; and such cloth does not get into the market for *indiscriminate use* as Superfine broad cloth. It is the same with regard to the Kerseymere. . . .[17]

He begged that Sir Joseph himself would decide how far the specimens were worthy of His Majesty's notice. But on 7 July 1800 Benjamin Hobhouse received a letter from Parry:

. . . I will trouble you to inform Sir Joseph Banks that I would wish him not to present the cloth [to His Majesty] & that I am very sorry for the trouble which he has had on this occasion . . .[18]

Grateful in the end of the practical interest shown by Banks in the matter he finally asked that the cloth be sent to Lord Somerville, the recently retired second President of the Board of Agriculture, for his inspection. Here it was that Parry's first essay in experimental cloth manufacture ended as Banks fulfilled his request in the last week of July 1800.[19]

If there was a tinge of disappointment in the outcome of his hopeful offering to the King there was surprise and satisfaction for Parry before the end of the year in the honours awarded by the Bath Society to specimens of cloth and cassimere made from his wool. Success was all the sweeter for being unexpected. In the two premiums offered by the Bath Society in 1799 for cloth and cassimere made before the September meeting of 1800 both had been won with wool supplied by Parry.[20] Thomas Joyce of Freshford had taken the premium for the best piece of navy blue broadcloth and Mr. Waldron of Trowbridge that for the finest piece of white cassimere. With delight Parry sent this piece of encouraging news to Banks on 10 September, secure in the knowledge that Banks would be equally pleased and share with him 'the highest gratification in having made so much progress on a sub-ject which has so deeply interested the Father of his People'.[21] At the same time he ventured to ask Banks, who was far away at Revesby Abbey, various technical questions relating to the Spanish breed and the management of the King's flock in order to complete his 'little treatise on the subject of fine woolled Sheep' of which some of the first sheets were even then about to go to the printer Cruttwell in Bath.[22] Banks was again free and informative even though he apologized, 'I can only answer your Question by memory my books &c. are in London'.[23] But these facts and the full story of the prize broadcloth and cassimere at Bath were included in the Doctor's first literary contribution to the waiting world on the subject of fine wool.[24]

The reward of all this virtue came two years later. The Bath Society itself had evidently been stimulated afresh by the success of its own premiums for cloth to raise the subject of Spanish rams again. On 10 September 1800 Benjamin Hobhouse as the recently elected President finding himself placed, as he said, 'in the situation of a beggar', conveyed to Banks the Society's petition for more Spanish rams from the King.[25] But the few which were available that year had all been distributed.[26] Banks promised that next year he would see what could be done, but again the Society was disappointed. Banks, who had found the rams at Windsor that year in such very bad condition, told Hobhouse

I am therefore ill inclined to send this year a Ram to the B[ath] Soc[iety] as I would wish to have the sheep sent to them in such Condition as would bear the Eye of a judge . . .[27]

So it was not until 10 August 1802 that Banks could write to Parry announcing that he had that day at last selected 'a Ram for the Bath agricultural Society & another for yourself'. He added

The one intended for the Bath Society is in better Case than the other owing to want of Care of the King's Shepherd at Windsor who plagues me extremely yours I have chosen as the best woold sheep I could spare I hope he will Suit you[28]

On 29 August 1802 Parry replied for himself and, in the interim before its next meeting, for the Society also.[29] As to the rams, which had arrived the week before, he noted that No. 151 for the Society was 'certainly the finest in point of make which I have ever seen, and was in very good condition'. His own ram, No. 146, he noted with sorrow

. . . if in flesh, would probably be equal to him; but he is not only poor, but has the foot-rot in each foot, so that I have some doubt whether I shall be able to use him this year. It is much to be lamented that the King should trust his Flock to so drunken and careless a man as Peesey seems to be.[30]

In reply Banks said he was glad to learn that the Bath Society intended to thank the King as he had never heard that his Majesty had received any thanks for the ram he had given them some years before, i.e. in 1795. He concluded with the cold reproof, 'if they have formed any opinion of the Probable success of the Experiment I think they could do well to express it'.[31] Parry, who had at no time ever dissembled his own gratitude to the King, saw to it that the point was well taken in the councils of the Society. At the first possible general meeting thereafter under Hobhouse as one of the Vice-Presidents that year the Society on 14 September formulated its thanks. Hobhouse in compliance with its wishes dutifully wrote to Banks on 18 September:

. . . I now take up my pen to intreat you on y[e] part of the whole body individually & collectively, 'to convey to his Majesty their warmest acknowledgements for his highly valuable present of a Spanish Ram', & also to request your own acceptance of their unanimous thanks for your politeness in assisting them to obtain the object of their wishes— . . .[32]

The demands of etiquette according to the Banksian view in relation to the King's bounty had now been satisfied in the case of the last dispensation ever made to the Bath Society from that source, and the first and last ram ever acquired direct by Parry from the same fountainhead. However, in the realization of the King's project Parry and the Bath Society are best considered as a unity and the Doctor himself as the guiding mind stimulating the corporate whole. In the matter of fine wool and sheep breeding for that product he had gradually become not only the foremost experimentalist of the Society but its acknowledged spokesman in that field. It was therefore in this dual capacity, with a touch of the expert medical clinician, that on 22 April 1804 he wrote to Banks

I am extremely sorry to be obliged to announce to you the death of both the King's Spanish Rams. That of the Society [No. 151] which certainly was much the finest that I ever saw, died paralytic from extravasation in the brain and mine [No. 146] of pulmonary inflammation. . . .[33]

He asked for another ram if the King had any to dispose of that year and enclosed five guineas in a London bill hoping that Banks would be able to select for him the one 'most conspicuous for the fineness of the wool'. He added the average price of eight rams he had himself sold during the season (£13 8s. 3d. per head) and the sixteen ewes of the second and third back-cross (£3 13s. 6d. per head)—prices that he could only regard as showing the improving credit of the breed when it was recalled that these were inferior individuals not wanted by himself for breeding. Then he presented the essence of his conclusions after twelve years:

. . . My present experience has, I think, enabled me to ascertain two facts; that the Cross of the Spanish and Ryeland, even to the fifth generation, is superior to the pure Spanish in hardiness and form of carcase, while it fully equals it in fineness of wool; and, secondly that fattening these sheep does certainly make the wool of the individual coarser, tho it increases its quantity. . . .

Sir Joseph promised to suit him with a ram should the sheep be sold that year again by private treaty but if by auction, which even at that date he expected would be the case, then he promised the Doctor early notice of the date of sale—a promise he certainly kept.[34] Sir Joseph was also greatly encouraged by the prices at which the Doctor's sheep had sold. But as to the final observation on the effect of fattening on the quality of the fleece Sir Joseph had these comments to offer:

. . . I have not Observd hitherto that the wool of the pure blooded sheep grows coarser as the animal grows fatter the Price at which the Pelt wool of the fat wethers sold by me fetchd is an argument in favor of my opinion that the wool of the Hereford breed grows coarser by good keep is certain I shall be mistified if I Learn that this Family failing is communicated to the half blood[35]

But before the date of the first auction sale of the King's sheep in August of that year Parry had changed his mind. Though he proposed to send his shepherd to bid at the sale for some Spanish ewes, he had been so elated by the value set on the wool of some of his rams by no less an authority than Edward Sheppard of Uley that he decided he needed no ram from Windsor that year. There is no record that he ever turned again to the Royal flock for pure Spanish stock—nor, indeed, to any other quarter of which we know.

On the controversial subject of fine fleeces and fattening sheep the brief exchange with Sir Joseph on the point lapsed in the waning of their correspondence. The point was, however, developed in the Doctor's classic *Essay* in 1807, recorded, and handed on to an unborn generation of scientists to revive and, one hopes, finally to have been clarified and settled.

II

John Southey Somerville of Fitzhead Court near Taunton in Somerset had been an original member of the Board of Agriculture from the date of its Charter on 23 August 1793. He succeeded his uncle on 16 April 1796 as 15th Lord Somerville and was elected the same year as a Representative Peer of Scotland in the House of Lords. Somewhat reluctantly in 1798 he agreed to stand for election as President of the Board of Agriculture against Sir John Sinclair, its single-minded originator of dwindling popularity in that office. Suggested by Arthur Young, supported with qualified approval by Pitt, he was elected by thirteen votes to twelve with the influential vote of Sir Joseph Banks tipping the scales in his favour. Thus, at thirty-three, Lord John Somerville attained the strategic point in his career from which his influence on the later course of British agriculture could effectively begin. His position was consolidated soon after when in 1799 he was made Lord of the Bedchamber, with a stipend of £1000. With this he gained the advantage of a close personal relationship with the King and his support as a fellow-agriculturist. His brief span as President of the Board of Agriculture was marked especially by his clear dedication to the improvement of British sheep and wool. Whatever else may have informed his differences of view with his somewhat prodigal predecessor at the Board, this vision at least he shared with Sir John Sinclair —and, of course, with the King and Sir Joseph Banks, and with Dr. Caleb Hillier Parry. His accession to the Chair of the Board had coincided with the crisis of 1798 in the supply of Spanish fine wool. As a West Country man he could see only too clearly all about him what were the effects of this strategic shortage. The crisis called forth the man and there was a crusading fervour in his address to the Board of Agriculture on 14 May 1799:

. . . The political situation of Spain may be such as to shut out, or at least materially increase the present difficulty of importing her wool into this country; in which case, it is a matter of the utmost national importance, that the fine woollen trade of Great Britain should suffer nothing in reputation. That this is speedily to be effected, I have no doubt; indeed the patterns now before my eyes[36] so absolutely prove the fact, that as an individual, bound in a particular manner to support the agricultural produce of my own country, I am resolved, from Midsummer-day next, never again to wear superfine cloth, or kerseymere, any part of which shall be of foreign growth.[37] It would doubtless be advisable to leave uncontrouled, the import of raw articles of manufacture here; for in a great commercial country like this, of what consideration is that million of money, annually paid for the import of Spanish wool? but the timely interference of those, whose duty it is, will probably teach the Hamburgh dealers in Spanish wool, to be cautious how they attempt any great advance in price, as we suspect they mean to do, preparatory to which, is the advance of 2s. per yard on superfine cloths; and this, without any thing like blame attaching to the clothiers, may be attributed to the limited quantities imported, and advanced price of the article; a damaged sample of which sold very lately for 4s. 6d. per lb.

To anticipate and ward off so severe a blow, levelled at one of our most valuable manufactures; to recal farmers' attention to the quality of wool, as well as the carcass; is a labour worthy of the Board of Agriculture, and must meet the concurrence of every woollen manufacturer whatever.[38]

All this high resolve and meritorious patriotism merely expressed, against the background of the most recent emergency, the basic creed of Sir Joseph Banks stated more than ten years before as his article of faith in the first struggles to secure for Great Britain the Spanish fine-wool sheep itself.[39] All that Banks feared then had now it seemed come to pass. The West Country at least, if not the nation, was at last alive to the nature of the problem. Lord Somerville himself in his secondary role as President of the Bath and West of England Society for 1799 had declared his intention to that body of moving the Board of Agriculture

'To become active in promoting the growth of finer wool in Britain, on a scale sufficiently extensive to check the exorbitant demand of foreigners for Spanish wool &c . . .'. This he had done in the last week of April, and although the Society did not wholly share their President's over-sanguine views that the industry could sustain much diminution in the supply of imported Spanish wool, it agreed that 'it is a subject which requires, and may in future more urgently require, the attention of the people of England . . .'.[40] He was also gently reminded by the Secretary, William Matthews, that 'It has been a subject very frequently touched upon incidentally in the meetings of this Society; and a subject which many men have much reflected on.'[41] This was true, indeed, but something more than reflection was now demanded. Lord John Somerville dedicated himself to the pursuit of a practical solution. He became like his senior and source of inspiration, Dr. Parry, another patriot adding his resources of time, money, and personal energy to augment and make real and effective the 'most national object' of his King.

Two months after Lord Somerville's address to the Board of Agriculture His Majesty's government at Westminster assembled gave evidence, in legal form, of recognizing the need for urgent action to facilitate the entry of Spanish wool. In the Act passed on 12 July 1799 the preamble intoned the Parliamentary view:

. . . And whereas, for the Encouragement of the Manufactures of this Country, it is expedient to permit the Importation of *Spanish* Wool from any Place whatever, in Ships or Vessels belonging to any Kingdom or State in Amity with His Majesty: Be it therefore enacted by the King's most Excellent Majesty, by and with the Advice and Consent of the Lords Spiritual and Temporal, and Commons, in this present Parliament assembled, and by the authority of the same, That it shall be lawful to and for any Person or Persons to import into this Kingdom, *Spanish* Wool from any Port or Place whatever in Foreign Parts, in any Ship or Vessel belonging to any Kingdom or State in Amity with His Majesty; any Thing in the said Act[42] passed in the Thirty-third Year of the Reign of His Present Majesty, or any other Act or Acts of Parliament, to the contrary in anywise notwithstanding. . . .[43]

Then, in October 1799, Lord John Somerville went to Portugal—ostensibly in search of his health after a bout of illness.[44] But here is a mystery. There is more than a mere suspicion that, even then, his main object was at least to see, if not also to import, some of the fine-wool sheep of Spain as a practical emulation of the Master whose stipend he received. The record is not yet clear but Parry, at least, seems to be explicit when, in his *Facts and Observations* . . . published in September 1800 he describes the staple length of his own sheep:

The average length appears to be about three inches and a quarter, or a half; *which corresponds very exactly with that of the specimens taken by Lord Somerville from his newly imported Spanish sheep.*[45]

Did Lord Somerville find something more than convalescent ease in the Peninsula on this occasion? The autumn of the year in Portugal was the season of opportunity along the Tagus if contraband sheep were being sought. And a licence to import could surely have been sanctioned readily under an Order in Council in the spirit if not according to the letter of the Act 39 Geo. III, c. 98 passed in July. Somerville himself says nothing directly about this, but in a memorial to the Bath and West of England Society of 1802 he cites the values of Merino × Southdown and Merino × Ryeland fleeces and pure Merino fleeces of his own growing whose average weight in the yolk was more than six pounds each and worth more than one guinea. He got no sheep from his King at any time. There is nothing to suggest that he had any from another British source, not even from Parry the most likely other donor—who, incidentally, would have been hard pressed to find a pure Spanish ram at that date in his own flock even to lease, still less to sell. No. What evidence there is supports the notion that Lord Somerville obtained at least a few Spanish rams in 1799 or soon after and that these may well have returned with him to Fitzhead. Full documentary proof of this is wanting but there is no doubt that in 1800 he is accepted as one of the chosen few, already initiated, ready to proclaim the Spanish Merino gospel.

In March 1800 he relinquished his Presidency of the Board of Agriculture to Lord Carrington. Then in July 1800 he received from Sir Joseph Banks the broadcloth and cassimere which was the first overt sign of Dr. Parry's success in the breeding of an Anglo-Merino. Soon after, from the scene of his service to Royalty at Windsor, he wrote briefly but significantly to Sir Joseph at Soho Square:

Lord Somerville presents his best respects to Sʳ Joseph Banks; He forwarded Dʳ [Caleb Hillier] Parry's letter to Sʳ Joseph at the Doctors' request not knowing its contents. Lord S. never saw any of the Spanish flock under charge of Sʳ Joseph Banks but having occasion to pass by Oatlands on Tuesday or Wednesday he is desirous to be allowed to look at them with Sʳ Joseph[s] permission[46]

After more than two years of his strong advocacy in the cause of British-grown fine wool it is surprising that Lord Somerville—a Lord of the Bedchamber withal—had not apparently set eyes on His Majesty's Spanish flock. There could have been no real obstacle to this other than

Somerville's own preoccupations. His first request for the privilege
certainly brought a free and cordial reply from Soho Square:

your Letter did not come to hand till it was too Late to send the order you
wished for I hope you had no scruple in visiting the King's Sheep without
my Letter They are the King's & his Majesty I am sure wishes you to see
them & he relies on your Judgement had they been my own I should
always wish your Lordship to see them[47]

But whether Lord John Somerville exercised this initiative as he passed
by Oatlands Park—probably on his way from Windsor to his Fairmile
Farm near by at Cobham—we do not know.

His wish to see the King's sheep at this period may have been
stimulated by his own first-hand study of the Spanish breed during his
recent convalescence in Portugal. It may even have arisen from a desire
to compare the Royal flock with the first sheep of his own importation.
It is difficult not to believe that he had such stock before 1802.[48] And
yet we have to hand no other direct statement on the origin of his flock
than his own:

. . . the author, in the spring of 1802, made a voyage to Spain, for the purpose
of bringing home a flock of Spanish sheep. This attempt is not easily
accomplished at any time, but is more than commonly difficult in a time of
war. It was an object, not only to attain the sheep themselves, but the whole
system of management adopted by those who had the care of these flocks
in Spain. In both these particulars, the author has been fortunate enough to
succeed. The sheep were selected from a Transhumante, or travelling Merino
flock, of undoubted high blood. The rams, twelve in number, were picked
from a flock of two hundred; for except the Manso or bell-wether, the males
are left entire, on a presumption that they carry more wool than wethers,
and equally fine. The couples (ewes and lambs) were selected from a number
proportionably large. Of the high blood and quality of this flock, the
admiration of those shepherds, through whose flocks, twenty-two in number,
they passed in the course of their journey, about the end of March, was
sufficiently indicative, if not otherwise established. . . .[49]

Whether these were the first or a second importation made by Lord
John Somerville there is no further question but that from 1802 on he
was a public leader in the Merino cause whose stature Banks was always
ready to acknowledge. This he made very clear when, in July 1803, he
noted 'Lord Somerville's active and judicious labours in establishing a
Spanish flock', in his public report of that year which also congratulated
Dr. Parry in the highest terms:

Much however, as Dr Parry deserves the gratitude of all who honour the
fleece, Lord Somerville's merit stands at least as eminently conspicuous.

Emulating the example of his sovereign, his lordship whose just discrimination of the value of different breeds of stock is admitted by the most experienced agriculturalists made a voyage to Portugal for the sole purpose of selecting by his own judgment from the best flocks in Spain, such sheep as joined in the greatest degree the merit of good carcase, to the superiority in wool which the Merino flocks are allowed to possess.

His lordship succeeded and brought home, more than two years ago, a flock of the first quality, which will probably repay with advantage the costs of the undertaking, as some of his lordships rams are said to have been already sold for 100 guineas each.[50]

Here is praise indeed for Lord John Somerville but no less confusion for his posterity in the suggestion clearly to be deduced from Sir Joseph's words that the foundation sheep of this note-worthy flock entered England in 1801. Without any further enlightenment from primary sources we are left finally with the more explicit statements of the unknown biographer of Lord John[51] which lead us to accept, on a balance of evidence, that both in the spring of 1800 and again in the spring of 1802 the energetic young nobleman was successful in bringing sheep from the Tagus into England to his farm in Somerset. What numbers were actually imported on each occasion is not clear. By his own statement on those introduced in 1802 it would seem that there were certainly twelve rams and possibly twenty-two ewes each with a lamb at foot.[52] And concerning these he had this to say:

Several rams, brought over with the flock, were of a shape unfit to breed from; notwithstanding the sacrifice was great, prime cost and heavy expences of the voyage considered, they were cut about the middle or end of October. . . .[53]

As a further footnote to this record of stringent selection towards a better carcass he added:

Out of thirty-three Merino rams, of pure blood, thirty were not fit to breed from, with a view to improvement of anything but wool, and one only, from which rapid approximation to that outline or frame indispensibly requisite in the eyes of every British farmer, could be expected.[54]

So firmly did Somerville pursue the often-toasted ideal of 'The fleece, covering a good frame with a sufficiency of fat'[55] that he was in the end prepared to acknowledge quite explicitly the measure of his critical selection:

From one animal [see Plate VII], he has drawn all his improvement; for whilst he was breeding from him, to obtain symmetry of form and early aptitude to feed, the Bath Society, as has before been stated, decided that his fleece was the finest which had come under its examination; and this attestation was confirmed within these few weeks, by an unsolicited and most candid declaration of Dr. Parry, that so perfect a sheep had not been imported into this Kingdom.[56]

Here, also, is praise indeed for Lord John Somerville's Ram No. 20 from the same discriminating source that had so many years before described one of His Majesty's true imported Spanish rams as 'surely the most hideous of his kind'.[57] The contrast, though extreme, is not without instruction and significance. In it is the whole essence of the difference between His Majesty's Spanish flock and that of His Majesty's Lord of the Bedchamber's flock. The former by 1802 had evolved from one source only—the Negretti *cabana*—and from sheep that were chosen by a Spanish eye to suit a Spanish ideal. The latter had been selected from many sources by an English eye—Lord Somerville's—to match an English notion of what a sheep should be in form as well as in fleece. Both in fact strove to achieve the same sort of compromise but His Majesty's flock had the greater handicap. Lord Somerville's flock in the search for beauty of form in a breed at that time not noted for any such pretensions had a flying start. From the beginning there was more intrinsic appeal to the English farmer in the Somerville flock. From the beginning there was also an excellent forum in which to display their make and shape in Lord Somerville's Spring Cattle Shows inaugurated in 1802. If Sir Joseph and the King were the pioneers of the breed in England and Dr. Caleb Hillier Parry the scientist and writer, then Lord Somerville must be accorded the distinction of being its most eminent and successful showman and promoter in practical farming.

III

In the green meadows where the Avon and the Severn meet lies the small village of Twyning, a few miles north of Tewkesbury. Here George Tollet had a farm looking out towards the mass of Bredon Hill over the River Avon. In these quiet precincts during the summer of 1800 he was informed through the medium of No. 199 in the thirty-fifth volume of the *Annals of Agriculture* that His Majesty had been pleased 'to spare some sheep of the true Merino breed to those who are desirous of improving the staple commodity of Great Britain'.[58] The ground-bait of Sir Joseph's well-conceived 'Project for Extending the Breed of Fine Wooled Spanish Sheep . . .'[59] had attracted another patriot. As the years proved no better fish was caught.

Tollet had already set out upon his own path to the improvement of the finer British wools when the Royal appeal, penned by Banks, first met his eye. Either from Lord Somerville or from Earl Bathurst he had secured the promise of a Spanish ram to further his experiments which had begun with the intercrossing of the Southdown and the Ryeland breeds. But now that open access to the Royal flock seemed assured he was content to wait for stock from that source—'as it is of much consequence to cross from the best Spanish breeds'. To Tollet the stock now to be had from His Majesty's flock 'appears to be as good as can be'. Eagerly pursuing the directions published in the *Annals*—'impress'd with the high importance of the project (so truly worthy of a good and patriot King)'—he hastened to apply to Sir Joseph for a ram and two ewes, emphasizing that wool was his great object, size a recommendation, but that symmetry of shape in his opinion 'has been outrageously over-valued'. He foresaw the extinction of the fine clothing wools of Herefordshire 'if the fashion of crossing with the Leicestershire continues', and said that it was even then a matter of difficulty to procure a few sheep of the true and uncontaminated Ryeland breed. This, he proclaimed, was 'a circumstance which adds to the importance of the object which many wise & good men have in view, viz. the improvement of the clothing wool of Great Britain'. While he relied on Sir Joseph's 'zeal on all occasions to promote the public good' for a favourable answer in the matter of sheep he thought it wise, no doubt, to add a botanical postscript. He was persuaded that *Dactylis glomerata* could be cultivated with great success as a pasture for sheep as they were uncommonly fond of it, especially in its young state—though he supposed all this had not escaped Sir Joseph's notice.

The following day Banks gently confirmed his knowledge of the palatable virtues of *Dactylis glomerata* as a sheep pasture but confessed himself so overwhelmed with applications for stock from His Majesty's Spanish flock that he could not provide Tollet with any ewes that year but only a ram which, if he decided to purchase it, would remain at Windsor until Tollet found it convenient to send for him.[60] But having made his point and lodged a claim for true Spanish sheep from the Royal experiment, Tollet was content to wait another year even for the ram. His reasons were clear and commendable. His plan required that fifteen Southdown ewes, as many Ryelands, and an equal number of the Southdown × Ryeland cross were to be mated together with the best Spanish Merino ram he could find. His cross-bred ewes, however, would not be in a condition for breeding until 1801. He proposed meanwhile to continue with the use of his Southdown ram, for his wool stapler had reported most favourably on his fleece and those of the cross with the Ryeland ewes which was rated even higher than either of the original breeds.[61]

Late in the summer of 1801 George Tollet was at last rewarded with Ram No. 144 from Windsor and two ewes delivered from the breeding flock at Oatlands by Robert Dickson, the Duke of York's Steward at Weybridge.[62] Though the recurrent foot-rot among the Windsor stock had caused some weeks' delay in its delivery, No. 144 was quickly set to work at Twyning—in spite of being still 'torn in pieces' by the disease. By the end of January 1802 Tollet reported to Banks that he thought him a valuable animal and even then had a good number of lambs from him. He had, however, lost one of the two ewes with her lamb—a great 'mortification' as he had taken into his hands no less than two hundred acres in Staffordshire to try his plans of producing super-fine wool in that county which he despaired of being able to do 'without a constant opportunity of resorting to the Merino race'.[63] On the other hand he was later able to report that the second ewe produced a ram lamb sired by the King's Ram No. 144—'My chance therefore of keeping up the true Merino blood rests upon a single thread.' In this situation he was no different to many another hopeful patriot who at various times drew from the Royal flock with its desperately small surplus of aged and unwanted stock as the only vehicles for dis-seminating the precious fine-wool genes. But Banks chose wisely when he confirmed his support of Tollet's 'views of raising fine clothing wool from the Spanish race and at the same time endeavouring to bring the Spanish carcase as near as may be to the English Standard'.[64] From the earliest beginnings this had been Sir Joseph's aim with the breed. Lord John Somerville had joined him in the same pursuit. Now instinct and good judgement affirmed that in George Tollet he had acquired a worthy recruit to the same cause. The 'single thread' was not left long un-supported for in August 1802 Banks selected from the flock at Oatlands Park four ewes 'marked on their Ears with the N°s. 13. 14. 15. 16.' by means of the new 'pastoral ear-rings'—with the promise of more in 1803.[65] But Tollet received no more ewes from the main source for, when the time came, Banks reported

I am disappointed in my wish to enlarge your Flock of Ewes this year by the King's Command to increase his own flock a Circumstance which Pre-cludes the Casting of any Ewe likely to bear a Lamb had it not been for this Circumstance I should I hope have been useful to you who I look up to as one of the best promoters of his Majesties Patriotic views[66]

In spite of this check in the matter of ewes it proved possible in the end for Tollet, in this last year before the system of dispersal changed to that of public auctions, to acquire one more ram, No. 157, for his own flock, and the joint use with Mr. George Talbot of Guyting in Gloucestershire of a ram numbered 148 which had been at Revesby Abbey in Lincolnshire.[67] Thus with two rams at five guineas each and six ewes at two guineas each from the King's breeding stock was the small Spanish flock of George Tollet established at Twyning. To these he added seventeen ewes from Lord Somerville, so that on 6 June 1803, just before he left Twyning to establish his new enterprise finally at Swinnerton Hall near Stone in Staffordshire, he was able to shear no less than twenty-four ewes and two rams of the pure breed. This was done in the presence of George Talbot of Guyting, John Darke of Bredon, George Perrott of Evesham among a number of others. A statement of the unwashed fleece weights on that occasion he was proud to show to Arthur Young at the Woburn Sheep Shearing just one week later on Monday, 13 June 1803. As one result of this Tollet was induced by Arthur Young to send an account of his flock to the *Annals of Agriculture* where it was published the following year.[68] Disappointed at the absence of Banks from Woburn he sat down instead to send him a long and full account out of the flood of his bounding enthusiasm:

I fully expected to have had the honour of meeting you at the Woburn Shearing and there to have had an opportunity of giving you (viva voce) a detail of my little Merino Shearing. Having been disappointed of that pleasure, and flattering myself you will rejoice at the success of your protege, I shall trouble you with an account of the result. Being about to leave this place [Twyning] for Swinnerton Hall in Staffordshire, I wished some of my neighbours here, excellent and experienced farmers of the good old school to witness the produce of these *outlandish* animals. The quantity and the quality of the wool astonished them, and they had before their eyes, such infallible proof of the profit that must result from such a concern as led them to form a different opinion to what they had hitherto entertained of my speculative exertions. My young Ram bred from the Ram [No. 144] & Ewe you first did me the favor to supply me with [in 1801], was by all acknowledged to be a very good sheep in every essential point in regard to carcase, and tho' only 12 months and three weeks old he was reckoned to weigh from 20 to 22 lbs per quarter—His fleece was taken off before then and was so thickly set upon him that it opened from the shears and had the appearance of spreading almost over the Barn floor. It weighed in the grease 11^{lbs} 12^{oz} The striking fact of such a fleece united to such a carcase bred from so small a Ewe tended I assure to raise the price of Merinos very considerably. I was offered *200 Guineas* for him which I refused and should have done the same thing *had 499 been* offered.[69] I was *offered 100 Guineas* for the use of him for the season which I also refused.[70] I was offered *30 Guineas* for the old Ram and *30 Guineas* for the Dam—but this price I could not think of taking as I consider them as a sort of donation from my Sovereign and can never allow myself to make a profit by the resale of them. However to do something I sold the Ram Lamb of this year as a matter of favor for *30 Guineas* and I think my friend has a good bargain.[71] Enclosed I send you an account of the general produce of my wool. I shall be proud to have you believe that his Majesty's patriotic views have not been retarded by my efforts. Constant attention and care are requisite in the conducting of so novel an undertaking and I assure you that the Master's Eye has had its continual effect upon my flock. Not that I think they require any particular care—But to mark their specific character, to examine their fleeces, to couple them judiciously &c. will require many years of constant attention to bring them to that perfection which I confidently expect them to arrive at—Sanguine as I am and ever have been in my undertaking, the results seem quite to out run all my expectations. . . . [72]

In this way then there burst briefly into the limelight the example of George Tollet's young Spanish ram, much quoted and much lauded as a paragon of excellence at the high-water-mark of the breed in Great Britain. Sir Joseph was entranced and at once sought Tollet's permission to make use of this bright hope for the future of the breed:

I am much gratified by your Report of the Success you have had in the Spanish Breed & sincerely wish you Joy of possessing what I can have no doubt is the best Spanish Ram in England & probably in the world

And then, almost as though this were the incident which confirmed him in his growing determination to see fiscal justice done to the Royal venture, he added the significant words

I intend if you have no Objection to insert in my Report of this year to be laid before the King & afterwards Printed the Contents of your Letter as far as Relates to the prices you have refusd & those you have taken if this is done I Have no doubt I shall Receive H.M. Commands to Sell the Spanish Sheep by auction next year in order that the Low prices at which they are now sold may not interfere with the high ones which gentlemen who breed successfully certainly ought to Obtain . . . [73]

This letter found Tollet in the midst of his final preparations for leaving Twyning and hastening to complete his harvesting there before departure for Staffordshire. Banks did not receive a reply, therefore, until about two weeks later when, in a first letter from his new home at Swinnerton Hall, Tollet returned in a few clear words a form of support that was balm to the troubled soul of Sir Joseph mourning much wastage of the King's bounty with the Spanish flock:

. . . As I am fully persuaded of the importance of the Spanish both in a public & a private point of view I shall be happy if any good effects can result from my experiences. I certainly can have no objection to your extracting any part of my humble communications that you may consider as likely to tend to promote a more general investigation of this project—
From patient and attentive investigations it must either be thoroughly established or deservedly abandoned. I am convinced that sale by Auction of the King's Spanish Flock would have a most beneficial effect. The price

of them would soon find its level & would certainly give an opportunity to the most zealous of carrying on their speculations in a superior style. A good price is necessary to ensure the degree of care and attention requisite for a new enterprise.

From those that were given away you did me the honour to inform me that in your opinion little or no good had resulted. This I can readily imagine: indeed I have reason to know that they were only considered as objects of curiosity & were turned out amongst the farrago of a Nobleman's or a Gentleman's Park to be shown amongst the Lions of the place as outlandish sheep from which the fine cloth was made. For my own part the facts which I daily see persuade me that not one Spanish Sheep should be neglected: That under British caution & British Skill the animal is to be greatly improved I can produce *already* the most positive proof. In regard to the quantity of wool in that view alone it is a great national object: and as to the quality I have every hope of preserving it, as soon as we can have a proper opportunity of selecting the individuals of our stock. What can be expected from a refuse flock without even the choice of a Ram! . . .[74]

There spoke Tollet the staunch disciple of Sir Joseph Banks and the devoted servant of the King. There also spoke Tollet the practical optimist of the breed; the evangelist of the faith ever eager to make 'proselytes of the whole neighbourhood' wherever he found himself; the ardent experimentalist with the Merino breed and its by-products in all its forms. A year later he was able to write and to congratulate his mentor on adopting the system of public auction for the breed as a plan that will 'tend to disperse them more than could be done by any other means, and will leave *free born Englishmen* unfettered in their views and give scope to their exertions—'. But he declined to be a participant in the bidding of that first auction—'It would have too much the look of monopolising and they may do more good in being dispersed into different parts of the Country'—though he hoped to renovate his flock the next year from the fountainhead.[75] This, however, he never did. The prices attained at the first auction exceeded Tollet's expectations and he confessed that he had not realized that the Spanish breed was sufficiently known to the public to produce that degree of competition for them which the results had established in 1804—even without the entry of himself and other established Merino proprietors. As it was in his view—'The marketable price of them has been in a great measure ascertained & I have no doubt His Majesty will receive much satisfaction in finding that the outcasts of the Flock have been so eagerly sought for—'.[76] He had his personal and private satisfaction in knowing that his own flock had in some measure contributed to the success of that notable event, for Banks had made full and effective use of the case of Tollet's own young ram, as he had proposed, in his 'A Report of the

State of His Majesty's Flock of Fine Wooled Spanish Sheep For the
Year ending Michaelmas 1803':

. . . Mr Tollet, a Gentleman of Gloucestershire, who has purchased Merino
Sheep both from the King and from Lord Somerville, has been very successful in improving the carcase without damaging the wool; he possesses a Ram
bred from a ram and a ewe both purchased from the Royal Flock in 1801,
which when clipped in June last [viz., 1803] yielded 11 lbs. 12 oz. of unwashed Wool. The carcase of this Sheep was estimated by good judges at
16 lbs. a quarter, and it was admitted to be a handsome Sheep.

    For this animal Mr Tollet has refused an offer of 200 guineas, or of 100
for the next season's use of him; he also refused 30 guineas each for the
sire and the dam, though old and infirm, being unwilling to part with animals
that had belonged to the Royal Flock; he however sold their Ram Lamb of
the last year [1803] for 30 guineas, and thus made some progress in ascertaining the value of this important breed.

    These facts, which prove an amelioration in the King's Merino Sheep, are
fully confirmed by the improved shape and weight of his Majesty's shearling
Rams of the present year, [1804] and give a Justifiable hope, that by a due
selection of Rams and Ewes, and a correct judgement in matching them,
Merino Sheep will in time be produced, with carcases perfectly fashionable,
and wool as perfectly fine . . .[77]

George Tollet had ample reason to feel proud at this honourable
mention in the report and acknowledged that it had raised 'my whole
flock 100 per Cent in my estimation'. There was, however, a small
example of Sir Joseph's human fallibility in respect to the young ram's
weight as a shearling in the report—'It their [sic] states him to have
been 16 lb a quarter whereas he was judged to be 20'—but otherwise
there is no doubt that the facts had been fully and fairly put before the
public.

    Among those who were caught in the chain reaction of the Merino
alchemy in British sheep breeding fostered by the wizard of Soho
Square was Thomas William Coke of Holkham—struck by the spark
from Staffordshire as the enthusiasm of George Tollet glowed in the
warm breeze of the King's and Sir Joseph's approval. The three ewes
which Banks had sent to Coke in August 1805 with the best of intentions as a sale by private treaty[78] may well have been mated to the two
Merino rams which George Tollet showed at the Holkham Sheep
Shearing on Wednesday, 3 July of that year.[79] It is certainly significant
that on Wednesday, 25 June 1806, 'This highly interesting *fête* concluded
by a shew of some Merino Rams, belonging to Mr. Coke, which
gave great satisfaction to all who know the importance of producing
superfine or Spanish wool, for the use of our broadcloth manufacture'[80]
—and that Tollet was again present to make 'some important remarks

to the company, on the superior advantages of the Merino breed of sheep' at dinner the day before. It is, one would think, fairly conclusive again that in the following year (1807) Thomas Walton, the acknowledged expert on whom both Coke and the Duke of Bedford depended in the selection of their sheep, should have written in this way to Banks:

> . . . I have had the pleasure of Mr Coke's Company to Mr Tollet's and he was so pleased with his Merino Sheep that he gave him 100 Guineas for a Ram lamb 8 Months old . . .[81]

It is certain also that at the Holkham Sheep Shearing of 1808 'the company adjourned to the sheep-house, where the Spanish rams were let by auction' on Monday, 19 June by Mr. Walton at fees from ten to forty-three guineas, which were in every way comparable with those for the more celebrated Southdown sires of that year.[82] George Tollet was present as usual and took part in the sweepstakes for 'naming the weight of Mr. Coke's three-shear half-bred Merino wether, from a small Merino ram, and a Ryeland ewe, which would not have fatted to more than seventeen pounds a quarter'. At slaughter the weight of the carcass proved to be 132 pounds (or 33 pounds a quarter) and the live weight 205 pounds. Merino rams were publicly clipped in the barn that year and fleece weights recorded up to 12 pounds 8 ounces.

At the Sheep Shearing which began at Holkham on Monday, 19 June 1809 the Merino breed was even more in evidence both pure and crossed with the Southdown and the Ryeland. Merino tups were let at prices from twenty-eight to fifty-one guineas where the Southdowns ranged from fifteen to forty. Mr. Coke and Mr. Tollet again appeared before the assembled agricultural intelligence of England in a harmonious duet in praise of the superfine Merino wool. The health of Mr. Tollet in that context was drunk before 'more than two hundred of the most distinguished Noblemen and Agriculturalists' at dinner.[83] But the apotheosis and the swan-song of the collaboration of Thomas William Coke and George Tollet in the Holkham Merino venture came at the meeting on Monday, 25 June 1810 when, at the usual great dinner, the subject was ventilated as it never had been so freely done before. Here Coke openly avowed his debt to Tollet 'who offered him the choice of his lambs from his Merino flock' which he, Mr. Coke, had accepted. Moreover, if 'ultimately the county should be benefited, the merit would belong to Mr. Tollett', in whose flock, incidentally, 'he saw more mutton on the carcasses than he had seen on any others of that breed'. In the exchange of views between Coke and Tollet both men paid full tribute to the President of the Royal Society who was present on the occasion, as for nearly every other Sheep Shearing held at

Holkham to that time. Coke declared that he was always willing to
try any experiment, 'and relative to that of the Merino flock, he was
greatly indebted to his worthy friend at his right hand, Sir Joseph
Banks, whose whole life had been a life of extraordinary service, not
only to this kingdom, but to the world at large'. Tollet declared that
'there had been doubts, whether a single yard of superfine cloth could
be made except from wool grown in foreign countries, but by the foresight of Sir Joseph Banks, and the efforts of the King, with the caution,
and the judgement so generally shewn by English breeders, it was
found that great object could be obtained'.[84] But there still remained
Tollet's heart-felt cry to Banks just seven years before: 'We must have
some Ellman or Bakewell in the Spanish line & I am confident we shall
new model the carcass so as to produce almost a miraculous change.'[85]
Both men clearly hoped that in Thomas William Coke and his far-
flung influence some such answer would be found. The patronage was
there but not the perseverence and, in this particular quest, Holkham
was only Cold Comfort Farm. It is probable that Tollet himself had
better claims than most men to the mantle of Bakewell as improver of
the Spanish breed in England if that is what he sought. The great landlord of Holkham Hall certainly had none. Yet his voice it was which,
by its very muted tones, assuredly set a slow curse upon the future of
the breed and its prospects of success as a meat animal on British farms.
Tollet shared with Banks the ultimate vision of a dual-purpose sheep
created from the imperfect and rough-hewn little monsters from the
mesetas:

To an English farmer's eye the generality of Merinos appear ugly; and
nothing tends more to create this effect than their tendency to produce an
exuberance of skin under the throat. This objection is more a matter of taste
than of positive defect, either in respect to fleece or mutton. The hollowness
between the neck and the withers, the flatness of their sides, and the pointed
coming off at the rump, are more solid causes of objection.

In Spain the fleece has been everything, the carcase nothing. Nearly all
the males of their immense flocks, some of them said to consist of sixty
thousand sheep, are kept unmutilated; because in that state they produce
more wool, and these are admitted to a promiscuous copulation. How then
can we wonder at the unsightly state of the carcase in most of the individuals
of that race? Have not many of our breeders gone to a contrary extreme,
making the carcase everything and the wool nothing? They are both
legitimate sources of public wealth and private profit; both articles of the
greatest necessity and why does not their joint improvement become the
object of every sheep-breeder?[86]

But to George Tollet in 1804 and to every improving breeder in Great
Britain, from His Majesty and Sir Joseph Banks at the fountain-head

outwards, the scope for advancing the standard of the Spanish sheep was severely limited. Of this Tollet took a suitably clear-eyed view:

At present there can be no choice but in the rams. I have never suffered any Merino ram to be castrated; and last year [1803] I bred thirteen rams, some of which are of great promise. The fleece will be the chief object of my attention; the improvement of the carcase appearing, from what I have already seen, to be likely to offer few difficulties. But for doing much with respect to either, we must wait till we can cull our ewe flock. These at present we must take rough or smooth as we can procure them. Next season I may probably have forty Merino ewes to put to the ram; but these will afford no great choice. Ten years must elapse before the business can be fairly tried with the thoroughbred flock; till then we must be content to fight with our hands tied behind us.[87]

Of the many hundreds who in time and for a medley of reasons were drawn to try the breeding of the Spanish sheep in the British Isles there were scarcely any to be found who matched Tollet in the balanced perspect.ve with which he approached the problem. He was certainly at one with Banks in his appraisal of the difficulties and the need for time and numbers in finding their solution. Such vision and such dedicated persistence and patience are always rare. Among the company of young agriculturists who frequented and supported the gatherings at Woburn, Holkham, and Smithfield in the very early dawn of the nineteenth century Tollet was one of these rare few, a man of 'sanguine imagination' who left few aspects of his favourite subject unexplored as far as the resources of a modest purse would permit. He lived long enough to see many of his own forecasts and expectations realized— not perhaps in his own hands nor even in Great Britain, but at least at the hands of British breeders somewhere with the descendants of His Majesty's Spanish flock.

IV

Among the 'proselytes' whom George Tollet claimed with justice and a measure of pride was Edward Sheppard, the influential and able clothier of Uley in Gloucestershire, who in 1800 was the expert on whom Tollet relied for his opinion on the wool of the first tentative crosses of Southdowns and Ryelands. Later in 1802 Sheppard was that eminent clothier who gave Tollet an opinion highly in favour of the fleeces shorn from the first few sheep acquired from the Royal flock in 1801—'indeed a most flattering one, and as he was at one time prejudiced against the measure I have the greater satisfaction from the result of his very accurate observation of them'. Sheppard was so far impressed as to pronounce the fleeces of the ewes 'much superior to the Negretti', a pile, which as a manufacturer of the West Country, he knew well. In practical support of this view he had paid Tollet 5s. 10d. per pound for the Raffinos of the ewes' fleeces and 5s. 8d. for the same sort of the rams', with 1s. less per pound in each case for the Finos.[88] The cloth made by Sheppard from this wool was sent by Tollet for Sir Joseph's inspection late in the winter of 1803[89]—but by this time Sheppard was himself as deeply committed to the exploitation of the Spanish sheep as George Tollet. Whatever his first reservations on the subject may have been Edward Sheppard was not long in setting to work as an experimenter, considering himself

from being largely engaged in the manufacture of superfine cloth, and in the practice of buying and working up considerable quantities of Spanish wool yearly, entitled to form, with some accuracy, an estimate of the relative quality and value of such wools as might be produced in this country in competition with the wools of Spain.[90]

Accordingly he sent twenty Ryeland ewes to a Spanish ram of Lord Bathurst's—doubtless No. 121 sent to Cirencester from Windsor in 1798. In the produce of the first cross he found a surprising improvement in the wool, approaching half-way in quality to the nature of the Spanish, and a substantial increase of one-half in the fleece weight. This experience and the association with George Tollet quickly brought him to the point of seeking a dispensation of Royal sheep for himself. His entry into the select circle of breeders of Spanish sheep was curiously circuitous but illustrative of the compact nature of the personal relations by which, almost casually, that circle grew. Sheppard's name was registered early in March 1802 at Soho Square by John Darke of Bredon, just across the Avon from Twyning, a near neighbour of George Tollet:

M[r] [Edward] Sheppard, a very considerable Glostershire Clothier, entirely in the Spanish Wool Line is very desirous of tryin the Experiment of crossing the Riland Ewes, with a Spanish Ram: this last Autumn, by favor of Lord Bathurst, with M[r] Tollet, he has had Forty Riland Ews tupped by the Spaniards; Sheppard having made a Connexion in my Family, (who am professedly both Grazier & Farmer) he applies to me to put him in a Method to procure a Ram from his Majesties Flock: at Hereford Fair in Oct[r] last, I met M[r] [John] Frost one of the Bailiffs at Windsor, from him I learnt my only Method was to apply to S[r] Joseph Banks, if I could get an Order from him, M[r] Frost would manage other Matters for me, & I will pay the value to your Direction.
    At the last Bath Meeting Dec[r] L[d] Somerville did me the honor to consult me on the Use of Salt to agricultural Purposes;[91] on consulting him on the Business of Spaniards Rams he immediately confirmed what M[r] Frost had

said, these collected Circumstances, I hope will induce Sr Joseph Banks to pardon this Intrusion. Should this Letter merit Notice, I shall esteem myself highly obliged . . . Mr Darkes Shepherd cured Tolletts Ram of an inveterate foot Rot.[92]

In reply Banks promised to deliver 'a fine woold Ram of the true Spanish Breed' to Frost for Sheppard 'when the Season of delivery comes which will be about 2 months after Shearing'.[93] But in May, when he was staying in London at 14 Albemarle Street, Edward Sheppard made his first direct approach to Banks, reminding him of the promise on his behalf to John Darke and adding a request for one or two Spanish ewes as well. Confident of his judgement as a clothier who dealt largely in Spanish wool he further proposed that he should call at Windsor on his return to the West Country and select the sheep himself.[94] Banks promised to do all he could to satisfy these aspirations, but as to the Windsor visit he had this to say:

. . . I have never thought myself Entitled to give orders for any person to see the Kings Flock lest accident should bring them into his Majesties Private walks & offence be taken it can however be of Little Consequence to you Sir to see them as you may Easily understand how impossible it would be for me to allow the Gentlemen who purchase Rams to chuse for themselves[95]

Sheppard accepted this situation with good grace and understanding, offered his services as a clothier to work up any specimens of wool Banks cared to submit, and volunteered information if needed relating to the manufacture or quality of the different Spanish piles. He was most definite in presenting his aims and his reasons for favouring fineness of fleece:

. . . if there is any difference in the fineness of wool in the original Stock imported by the King, I beg leave to say I should prefer Excellence in fleece to shape being convinced that to rival the Spanish wool in this country, extreme attention is to be paid to the original flock, as out of the great number of piles exported from Spain, I can from experience state that very few indeed are of the first class—I am informed that the Kings breed is from the Negretti flock which produces a prime though not the finest pile of Wool. . . .[96]

This clothier's preoccupation with the fleece to the relative disregard of the shape of the animal was a point of contrast with the equipoise between the two facets which Tollet was seeking. It caused him to comment to Banks—'I do not altogether depend upon this union of the manufacturing and breeding concerns.' Hence his cry for 'some Ellman of Bakewell in the Spanish line'.[97] There never was any question, however, with either Banks or Tollet but that Sheppard was a notable recruit not only for what he was but for what he proposed to do— 'being desirous of trying the experiment on a pretty large Scale'—for the great need now was for some form of commercial expansion. Who better than a capitalist West Country clothier to open this field for investment? What more cogent example could be wished to convince the unbelievers of the wool trade, and especially of the manufacturers, if not the nation as a whole? A sceptical clothier converted was, perhaps, best of all. Edward Sheppard was in all respects a man to be fostered and, true to his promise, Banks saw that he was almost as well endowed as the evangelical Tollet with stock from the slender surplus of the Royal flock. On 11 August 1802 Banks wrote the letter which announced the establishment of yet another important venture:

in Consideration of your intention of trying the Spanish breed of Sheep on a large scale I have selected for you from his Majesties pure Spanish Flock a Ram & 3 Ewes & if you continue this Experiment which I have no doubt you will find profitable as the Carcases of these Sheep improve with me every year. I hope to be able next year to Spare you as many Ewes at Least as the King has signified his Pleasure that a preference shall be given in the distribution of the Sheep to those who mean to enter Largely into the breed.

The Ram is markd on the horn 152 I do not know that there is a finer woold one in the Flock he will be deliverd to your order whenever you chuse to send for him by Mr Peesey the King's Cowman at the Lower Lodge at Windsor The Ewes are markd on the Ears 8 9 10 They will be deliverd to your order by the King's Shepherd at Oatlands Park or by Mr Dickson Bailiff to the duke of York at Weybridge in Surrey close to the Park gate

The Price of the Ram is Five Guineas. The Ewes are two Guineas Each No 10 has a bad mouth but a very good carcase She will bring you I think an excellent Lamb at Least if Care is taken of her 8 & 9 are also very fine woold you will please to Remit the money at your Leisure Convenient to you[98]

Sheppard hastened to acknowledge the liberality with which his wishes had been met and to remit the eleven guineas required through 'George Barclay Esqr & Co.'[99] The following year on 22 January 1803 he was delighted to announce to Banks that the three ewes had all yeaned—'having took the Ram on their journey from Windsor, which was sooner than I intended they should'—and that they had added a ram and two ewe lambs of the pure breed to his stock.[100] He craved more ewes—who did not?—but in the bad year of 1803 Banks had none to spare. One other ram at a price of six guineas (No. 143) sent down in August was the only other sheep ever received by Sheppard from the old Negretti flock of his King. Small wonder then that the first ram (No. 152) in his first season was mated to one hundred Ryeland ewes. Two rams and three ewes were a feeble origin for a new commercial flock but it was little different from the samples dispensed among the other patriots of the Royal plan. The cake was small and the claimants were many. Banks divided it with scrupulous fairness. Sheppard was grateful for his moiety and aware of the problem. In November 1803 he sent Banks a coat cloth of dark bottle green of his own manufacture from the wool of the sheep received from the King as a tribute of his gratitude and added

. . . As I think I shall now have Rams in proportion to my flock of Ewes I shall not trespass on your bounty when I know they are so much in request from all quarters, at the same time, I should always consider them as highly desirable at any price his Majesty might fix—[101]

This was a forbearance of which he repented the next winter when he announced to Banks the death of two out of the three original ewes—'so that my stock of Spaniards will be in great danger of being annihilated without your further assistance'—but the days of the auction sales were now close at hand and private sales were at an end. All this was 'of Serious Concern' to Banks but there was nothing he could do. It was not until 1809 that Sheppard was again able to refresh his flock with more of the pure Spanish blood from the Royal flock when he received another ram and five ewes. Meanwhile he made much of his opportunities in other ways to drive steadily towards his goal.

Between 1801 and 1803 he accumulated four to five hundred Ryeland ewes which he had personally selected with great care for their fineness, stringently rejecting nine out of every ten at his disposal from among the best flocks he could find in Herefordshire. Then during 1803 and 1804 he bought a considerable number of ewes from the flock of Josiah Ridgeway in Herefordshire which had developed in the past twelve years from the dispersals acquired from the Royal flock by Major William Price. In all he selected one hundred and ten ewes from this source—'a very mixed and unequal breed'—choosing such 'as were the least degenerated from the Spaniard'. To this he added forty ewes of the same description from the flock of Lady Caroline Price. By the year 1805 he was able to dispose of all his Ryeland ewes so that in 1806 his flock, nearly a thousand in number, were all cross-bred Spanish in various degrees with a very few pure Spanish. How far he had achieved his original aims at this date we may judge from the success of his claim for the Premium No. 15 offered by the Board of Agriculture 'for clipping the greatest value of Wool in part or wholly Spanish in the year 1806'. The substance is contained in the attesting certificate.[102]

291 fleeces 1st cross		2621 R wool at 5s.	610. 5. 0
186———2nd ditto	Ryeland ewes	327 F—3s.	49. 1. 0
110———3rd ditto	with	58 bottings 3s.	8. 14. 0
231———4th ditto	Spanish Ram.	[The above washed on the	
162———5th ditto		sheep's back]	
6 ditto of his Majesty's Merino breed		22½ R scower'd	
		6s. 4d.	6. 19. 0
		4½ 5s.	1. 2. 0
986 Total fleeces.	Total weight 3033 lbs.		£676. 1. 0

This must be reckoned a notable success. In five years Sheppard had established a large flock cutting more than 3 pound per head of washed fleece wool whose value of 53·5 pence per pound was at the same level as that of His Majesty's pure Spanish flock in the same year—though this was a fact not particularly noted at the time. Sheppard himself rated the quality of his clip from its price as rivalling that of two-thirds of the import from Spain and not disgraced in comparison with the soft and silky wool from Saxony which was just beginning to appear in the wool trade of England. Its value still lay well below that of the prime Leonesa at 81 pence per pound but this was not far above the value of 76 pence which was the price of the scoured pure Spanish fleeces of His Majesty's stock and the more correct comparison. There was certainly no cause here for any pessimism in viewing the prospect of growing a fine wool of a sort highly valuable to the broadcloth manufacturer— so long as there should be, as Sheppard emphasized, 'a depot of the real Spanish race carefully preserved, and protected from any mixture or degeneracy'. Such a flock he pointed out, was even now in His Majesty's possession and he at least was satisfied that they 'would remain for a century in the same state of fineness and perfection'. Indeed, he said, 'we have no experience that will assign any period to their decline'. To those who would seek a breed to cross with them for the same purpose as he had done he recommended a judicious selection of fine-woolled Ryelands in preference to Southdowns or any other. There was a similar variation from coarse to fine in both these breeds, he said, but 'the finest hair of the South-down sheep bears no proportion, in point of softness, to that of the Ryeland'.[103]

In recognition of this excellent achievement and its embodiment in a suitable memoir the Board of Agriculture awarded him a Gold Medal and the privilege of publication in its *Communications*—honours well deserved.

V

While Edward Sheppard laboured to establish his flock deep in the narrow valley at the headwaters of the little River Cam under the shadow of the high hill fort of Uleybury, another 'proselyte' of George Tollet matched his efforts a few miles east on the rolling Downs above the escarpment not far from Tetbury. Daniel Lloyd was another clothier whose imagination had been caught—'being connected largely in the Woollen Manufactory & at the same time possessing the means of keeping Four Thousand Sheep' he, too, wished to embark on the speculation of breeding the Spanish variety. Understanding, no doubt from Tollet, that the King had put the control of his Spanish flock under the direction of Banks he wrote on 25 September 1801:

. . . Presuming that this measure is in concert with the patriotic efforts of His Majesty, & that it may tend to effect the laudable purpose conceived by Him, of lessening our dependance upon Spain; I trust you will have the goodness to inform me, if you have any S[panish] Ram to dispose of by purchase or loan . . .[104]

His application was too late for that season and Banks could do no more than promise to spare him a ram and three or four ewes, if possible, the following year. Lloyd acknowledged feeling a strong sense of obligation for the intended favour and launched into a small homily on the virtues of the project:

. . . From circumstances trivial in their commencement, it is not unfrequent that great objects are derived; & from the prospect opening in consequence of Peace, there is a high probability that Spain will be incapable of supplying the demand of Fine Wool for the rival markets of England & France—& if by the Patriotism of his Majesty, we may be able to raise at home a supply which shall moderate the competition, it will eventually prove a more extensive benefit to the Nation than the more splendid achievements of millitary prowess—to desolate provinces & subdue Empire is not so honorable to the Sovereign character, as to cherish the means of diffusive comforts, & render them extensively accessible to honest & industrious industry—
I trust the ardent expectation of benefit expressed will not be conceived as the visionary effusion of an enthusiastic adventurer for the evidence so far as it has fallen under my notice justifies the most sanguine hope that labour to the amo^t of half a Million may be supplied, and one Million p^r An^m. saved to the Nation—without as has been insinuated producing a proportionate diminution of coarse Wool— . . .[105]

The claims of Daniel Lloyd were taken seriously at Soho Square, and in a letter on the same day and in the same form as that to Edward

Sheppard Banks told him on 11 August 1802 that he had set aside for him 'a Ram of excellent wool & 4 Ewes the largest number I am this year able to spare to any applicant'. The ram was numbered 142 and among the ewes was No. 3 which Banks noted had 'brought me Two Lambs last year a very unusual thing in this breed'.[106] With two more rams (Nos. 145 and 156) the following year[107] these were all the Spanish sheep that could be spared to establish the flock at Bowldown Farm for Daniel Lloyd in his

intention to persevere & put all the strong objections which have been made to this variety of Sheep to test of experiment, not with the view of strengthening my own conviction but under the expectation of producing facts which will carry it home to the bosoms of such who possess situations calculated for extending the breed.[108]

Lloyd followed the same general theme as Sheppard in his approach to the breeding of Spanish sheep as a clothier. But he had his own well-formed views of the path ahead and favoured the Southdown more than the Ryeland for a crossing breed as being 'the least departure from the most approved course of Agriculture' and the one more likely to meet the prejudices of the general class of farmers.[109] He was prepared to give more weight than Sheppard to general utility rather than special purpose in the sheep he bred, and explained to Banks that

. . . this course has led me to give a preference to the South Down Cross over the Ryland as the former has stood the severity of the Climate & the work of the Farm much better than the latter—[110]

Like Sheppard he laid tribute at the feet of Banks in 1804 as a specimen of cloth from 'British Wool grown on Spanish Sheep', aware, so he said

. . . that this is not equal to many which have been submitted to Sir Josephs inspection, but this is the product of the Animal under the usual conduct of Sheep upon Arable Land without any shelter or protection & though inferior to the First class of Spanish Cloth is equal to the Second, & is such as 9/10 of Mankind may be content to wear—[111]

In August 1805 he felt moved to give Banks an account of the progress he had made. His Spanish stock then consisted of four ewes, four lambs, and five rams. As additional sires he had sixteen half-bred rams 'selected with great care, & possessing with fine Wool great parfection of form'. Of the eight hundred ewes he proposed to mate that season with Spanish and half-bred rams four hundred and seventy were 'one dip of Span.ʰ Blood upon South Down & Ryland Ews'. In 1806 he intended that his whole flock would be of mixed blood. He allowed that the wool of the Ryeland 'dip' was superior to the Southdown in quality but he still preferred the latter as a general farm sheep. He had fattened in the previous winter his four-tooth half-bred wethers, twenty of which weighed 20 pound per quarter and forty over 16 pound per quarter, which were all good meat—'but not fancifully fat, & gave satisfaction to the Butcher & to the Market'. He judged the wool of his last shearing to be worth 4s. per pound as washed fleeces, among which on this basis the Raffinos would be near 6s. per pound. It is clear that he had not progressed quite so far as his fellow-clothier Edward Sheppard, but then he had not begun so soon and had not pursued so stringent a selection for wool alone. He had veered more to the school of George Tollet. He was none the less well advanced toward the convictions of Edward Sheppard as he expounded them to Banks in a sweeping summary:

I have not hinted at the political or commercial views affected by this effort to show the possibility of producing fine Wool in this Country, but it may be allowed me, feeling as I do from the facts before me to suggest its practicability, & to any extent circumstances may require—allowing the import of Sp^h. wool to be 30,000 Bags I have the fullest conviction they may be produced here, without any material diminution of the 700,000 Packs Annualy grown in this Kingdom—that there is no part of the 30,000 Bags finer than can be produced here in Conformity to the interests of tillage I will not assert; probably 10,000 of this Number are superior in quality to what can be produced without the help of Cotes & careful selection of feed particularly winter Keep but with discernment may pronounce that substitute for 2/3 of the import be attainable, an advantageous impression will be made upon the 1/3 & the great interests of the Nation materially promoted—[112]

These were typical and not wholly unreasonable figures—the Spanish imports at least were close to the mark. A thousand Edward Sheppards and a thousand Daniel Lloyds with two million sheep like theirs—could such men and such sheep have been found—might have released England from her contemporary dependence on the Spanish fleece but not for long. For these years concealed within them the point of inflexion in the upward rush of British commerce. The wool trade was already poised for its ascent on the wings of the morning of the nineteenth century. The old arguments of the eighteenth century lay dying and those of Lloyd were their parting breath—as he in a measure foresaw. Edward Sheppard had already—though unwittingly—pointed the way to salvation when he invoked the superior qualities of the recent influx of soft fine wools from Saxony as an example for British farmers. The light shone and the way was clear, but British feet found a different path through the commercial maze of the new century.

VI

By the end of 1803 some thirty-eight rams and forty-five ewes had been sold by private contract since the summer of 1800 under the impetus of 'A Project for Extending the Breed of Fine Wooled Spanish Sheep.' Including Sir Joseph Banks himself these had been distributed among thirty-five persons of many ranks and conditions as well as to the Bath and West of England Society. Some few on this list had already, during the years of the King's grace and favour, drawn stock from the Royal enterprise. But within three years thirty-one new growing-points had apparently been added to the Spanish Merino population of Great Britain. However, only about seven of these were in any sense potentially viable nuclei of the pure stock, by the possession of three to five ewes to mother the next generation. Even this number of fecund females was perilously insecure as everyone knew in advance and as the events soon confirmed. Old ewes mostly past their prime were all that could be spared from the King's breeding flock even during its hey-day at Oatlands Park. Death after one, occasionally two, rarely three years of private possession was the common tale even in the hands of good husbandmen. With less than eighty breeding ewes in the Royal flock itself at this period and an even-handed justice to be dispensed to many claimants, any hope of replacement from the main source was small. In the breeding of livestock ultimate strength usually lies in adequate foundation numbers. In extending the breed of Spanish fine-woolled sheep among the enthusiasts of England as a national project in 1800 only the determination was strong; numbers were tenuously small. There were few illusions on the risks ahead and hope was tempered with realism in most cases. But the motives and the means of the participants were mixed and the galaxy of personality and character always rich and varied. The patriots of the 'Project' were a recognizable sample of British agriculturists at work—a heady mixture of experts, eccentrics, and dilettantes—no stranger then than now to the British scene in almost any sphere of endeavour. His Majesty's national plan for the Spanish breed entered the nineteenth century feebly, perhaps for reasons that the French did their best to maintain. But it did not lack the good will of a sizeable and representative group of His Majesty's subjects—the enlightened, the befuddled, and the benighted in their just proportions.

John Maitland, wool merchant of Basinghall Street, Member of Parliament for Chippenham, and the Squire of Woodford Hall at Woodford Green in Essex was already an old friend of Sir Joseph's as one of his earliest expert advisers on the mysteries of the Spanish wool trade especially. In 1799 he had received a ram (No. 123)[113] as one of the last gifts from the flock, and had since craved two or three ewes as well as another ram feeling 'a kind [of] repugnance of putting his own Progency to the one I have got'.[114] Banks had sent him a copy of 'A Project . . .' as well as, somewhat earlier, some admonition on 'the Jacobine language' of the current Committee on the Woollen Trade.[115] In August 1802 Banks had sent him two ewes selected by Henry Lacocke 'who is as zealously inclined to serve you as I can be'.[116] This was followed on 16 August 1803 with advice that another had been set aside '& that old & infirm' and spared with difficulty.[117] One ram and three ewes of uncertain age but evident maturity became the sole foundation of the flock at Woodford Green.

John Fane, Member of Parliament, of Wormsley Park, near Stokenchurch, on the north edge of the Chilterns in Oxfordshire had, on 21 July 1800, received from his friend Sir Christopher Willoughby a copy of 'A Project . . .', which he had mistakenly attributed to the Board of Agriculture, declared to Banks that he had 'long wished for a Ewe of the Spanish sort but had scruples of troubling my Friends to make an application in My favour'—until Sir Christopher Willoughby of Baldon House had undertaken to do so the previous winter. He also reminded Banks that

Some years ago you were so obliging as to Make me a present of a Spanish Ram from the King's Flock, at the request of Major Price, & I have by him rais'd a small flock of the half breed, by putting him to some South down, Ryland, & a few fine Wool'd Bagshot Ewes, & the last Season with some of his own Family, which brings it nearer to the true breed— . . .[118]

Banks replied from Tetsworth, not far away, on 27 July, regretting he saw no way of meeting Fane's wishes but promising to bear in mind that, through their mutual friend Sir Christopher Willoughby, his application had been an early one. As to the ram he had received 'some years ago' as a present[119] he had this comment to make as a point of almost over-scrupulous nicety:

. . . I must beg you to Excuse me Sir for Setting right an inaccuracy in your Letter respecting the original Spanish Ram which Major Price procurd for you from the King's flock it was his Majesty & not me to whom you were obligd for that Present for willing as I should have been myself to have presented it to you had I had the power I never venturd to send a single Sheep from the King's flock without his Majesties Special command on the occasion Specifying the Person to whom it was to be sent.[120]

Nevertheless, John Fane received one ewe in August 1800; three ewes and Ram No. 136 in August 1801; and finally Ram No. 165 (with very short horns) in August 1802—a total of two rams and four ewes

under the mantle of 'A Project . . .', with one other ram as a gift from
the King himself through Major William Price. From these Fane was
able to raise a small flock which seems to have grown to his satisfaction,
for he remained a breeder for many years and an active exponent of
Spanish virtues in Oxfordshire. Sir Christopher Willoughby reminds
us of this and related matters when he addressed Banks on 24 July 1806:

I beg leave to remind you of your kind intentions to visit our Wool Fair
at Dorchester and that I fully depend on your assistance in setting us properly
going tho' I fear the fall in the price of Wool will be much ag.ˢᵗ us

    John Fane has promised to send some of his Spaniards to Baldon for your
inspection as likewise to meet you at dinner on Tuesday 29.ᵗʰ at four o'Clock
when plenty of Vegetables shall be served in Dame Willoughby's best
manner, and if you have any particular directions to give respecting your
eating, drinking, or sleeping, I shall be most happy to receive your
Commands[121]

VII

    John White Parsons of West Camel in Somersetshire may be
accounted one of the more curious mystics—if that is the word—without which no generation of British breeders is complete. Geographically
he lived between two of his close associates—the down-to-earth farmer
John Bridge of Winford Eagle in Dorset and the farming parson
William Quartly of Molland near South Moulton in Devon. Intellec-
tually he seemed to float somewhere between here and the hereafter—
perhaps a little nearer Earth than Heaven for he was not unsuccessful in
his day. He was certainly to be seen often enough at Woburn Abbey
where his earthly likeness was captured for us by George Garrard in the
company of the agricultural elect of this world in the early years after
1800.

    He was with Banks evidently at Windsor on 28 June 1799 when the
rams were shorn and three of them set aside—No. 128 for John Bridge
and Nos. 124 and 132 for himself and William Quartly—concerning
which John Bridge promised to see that proper reports were made for
His Majesty. He was sold a ram (No. 120) in August 1800 and an old
ewe; in 1801 he was allotted Ram No. 163. A total of three rams and
one old ewe was all he was able to acquire of the hot Spanish blood to
under-pin his high-flown tangled theories of the right road to animal
and plant improvement. In contrast to most of those who took the
Spanish breed into their farms it is difficult with White Parsons to know
just what he did make of them from anything he said himself, though
he assured Banks as early as July 1800 that he was his first 'and perhaps
as yet only true disciple'. His acquaintance with Sir Joseph had evidently
been much improved at the Woburn meeting in 1799 when he, John

Bridge, and the Reverend William Quartly had been able, all three, to converse with their eminent but distant benefactor.[122] He lamented the loss of his first ram (either No. 124 or 132) unfortunately lost soon after he had received him,

. . . I say unfortunately, as after a good deal of experience which I have had in Sheep of all sorts & degrees I feel bold to say that the 'ordinary coarse wool'd' degenerated Breeds of Sheep in England as well as in ffrance and also the Cott or kind in the most Southern elevated quarters by which I mean the old unadulterated Dorset—South-downs—Ryelands—are best to be regenerated with Spanish blood. I know how different I ought to be in advancing this new doctrine in direct opposition to the successful 'in and in' practice of Mr Bakewell as far and as fast as he dared exercise his genius on the right road for fear of not being followed—whose memory (as he persisted to the last in declaring that he had always done every thing by selecting the best of the old Leicesters) I should honor the more if I could but believe that he had practised what he had preached, for if the climate of Arabia produces Horses of Steel, capable of improving all others upon the Earth—If perfection in Soils, fruits, flavours—and Animals is best to be obtained by a most happy combination of parts from all Nations & Climates —If the most excellent of Men with Souls made of fire and the most beauteous of Womenkind are to be bred in England by blending with the Children of the Sun in preference to the Northern cold embrace—why should not Spain where the best Wool and Mutton in Europe is acknowledged to be grown be the best Country under the Sun for Rams? I also firmly believe that by keeping the *right blood* upon top we may entirely eradicate that now most prevalent & dreadful disorder raging 'in all directions' amongst Sheep called the Goggles—which I tell the Dorsetshire & Sussex ffarmers owes its origin to their bad taste & unnatural pride in crossing for large size, which Mr [Thomas] Davis in his 'Survey of Wiltshire' so justly condemns—and what is strange to advance in this one solitary case, to their having followed Nature in her spent course instead of embracing the Nymph at her first landing upon these northern shores—as I would prefer taking a Venus, 'fresh Arising from the foamy tide'—the fact is, that the disorder was never known in England, till the South-down Breeders up in Ether—not content with the best Wool and Mutton in England—the deer-like shape, bare small bone and everything that was essential to a good sheep naturally a Mountain Animal—descended from the Skys into Berkshire for Rams thicker fleshier and more beastly than any of the pure race.—And like the Great Dorsetshire Improvers impressed with the same beastly ideas went astray into Hampshire —Wiltshire—Leicestershire & other inland & midland Counties for some green heavy Rams as big as Apes—to put upon their small boned delicate rathripe Ewes, which I can well remember when Eyes were more in fashion than Horns—were as full of Nature as they could stare, and as light again in their offals—& better Nurses by half than they are now—By contaminating and oppressing Nature thus with lifeless clay, is it any wonder that so fatal a disease should have been generated—and that so many of the poor creatures with so much loss of blood to support their encreased bulk than they poss[ess]ed in their original state when upon a very small scale, should dye of a general wasting . . .

And so on for page after page, to conclude with a hopeful postscript

. . . I shall be highly grateful by your opinion on this truly interesting subject at your best leisure—in how far the stock of human sustenance & happiness may be encreased—& yᵉ Treasures of 'the Sun' commanded in this Northern Country 'without his Rage' by the importation of fruits—seed —corn—& the most useful Animals from hot Countries—[123]

After such a spate of verbiage and frothy notions Sir Joseph evidently shrank within himself, aghast at this man who called himself his 'perhaps as yet only true disciple'. He could only bring himself with difficulty to reply:

I respect your efforts for improvement I will do the best I can for you but I can promise nothing because 7 Ewes have died since shear time & several others earlier this year[124]

Such letters—and this was neither the first nor the last of them to emerge from West Camel—are always an occupational risk of the scientist or the scientific administrator. The ramblings of the mis-guided enthusiast can neither be wholly ignored nor wholly accepted as a serious theme for a lingering and fruitful correspondence. The dilemma is infuriating for good and useful morsels are so often hidden in the turgid flow. In any case the ideas can never be dismissed for they may at any time become the grounds on which a course of action is based, however wild or odd the notion. White Parsons's preoccupation with 'the Treasures of "the Sun" . . . "without his Rage"' and 'the dark bloodlike animals of Southern Extraction' to say nothing of the virtues of 'the Promethean heat' led him in practice not only to see more in the Spanish sheep than a clairvoyant but to bring such notions to bear on his cattle breeding—which was much more important to his posterity than anything he did or proposed with sheep. For White Parsons had much to do with the cattle of South Devon and for its improvement looked south to the Channel Isles, to Normandy, eventually 'to leap the Equator for Promethean heats' and to bring in the humped cattle of India. In all of this exotic philosophy he was not alone. The Reverend William Quartly, for all his sober cloth, was evidently at heart a sun-worshipper too, but of a more intelligible sect. Perhaps he clarified the issues a little when he wrote in May 1800:

. . . The different Breeds I have crossed with the Spanish these two years past are as follow: Dorset, Portland, Exmoor, Bagshot all horned—Ryeland, South-down, Devonshire Not[t], New Leicester, all no[t].—The Wool the produce of each of these various sorts I have shown to many of our first Clothiers, who all agree that it is of double value per pound to the wool of the females their Dams—But the circumstance which most surprised me in the experiment was to find that it was not only improved in quality but also increased in quantity. The Carcass likewise in most instances acquired fresh beauty and perfection contrary to the expectations and assertion of almost every observer prior to the experiment. The latter circumstance however I was sure must take place [agree]able to the well established infallible maxim of the most enlightened judicious modern Breeders.—viz. That all Animals (whether bullocks, horses, sheep, or pigs) having finer hair or wool, when transported from the more southern warm climates will, for all purposes greatly improve those having coarser hair or wool in the frozen regions of the North; give them renewed animation, life, and vigour; and render their flesh much superior in respect of delicacy flavour and nourishment as food for man. Nothing is more manifest than this when we apply it to the Indian Bullock, Arabian Horse, Spanish Sheep, and Chinese Pig, and compere them with the same animals in the North of Russia, whose flesh, being so very coarse, and of such inferior quality, an Englishman can scarce eat. The finest grain, the most delicious fruits, and the most nutritious vegetables are also the original production [of] those Countries nearest the Sun (an Emblem of the Deity) as the Soul of the Universe giving life and vigor to all material things—those then which are more immediately by its influence will consequently be the most excellent of their kind. However this theory may be received, a multiplicity of Experiments had proved that it is altogether romantick—After carrying you into the wild regions of fancy, doubt, and uncertainty, and troubling you with so much nonsense I have now to request that you will keep in reserve for me two Ewes of the true Spanish breed when you dispose of them after Sheartime and whatever the price may be I shall gladly pay with thanks and confess myself under the greatest obligation.[125]

It is an interesting speculation whether the Reverend William Quartly converted John White Parsons to the worship of Apollo—or was this a Mithraic survival—or whether they simply read the same books. At two very different levels of coherence they certainly struggled to express the same ideas. John Bridge seems to have been immune to their seduction. Sir Joseph seems to have listened. Perhaps that was all they sought. But how far, in practice, did they carry their perfervid notions of the 'climatic outcross'?

VIII

Near the town of Redruth in Cornwall—not so many miles after all from Land's End—at Tehidy House lived Francis Basset, 1st Baron de Dunstanville, the most recent of a long line of Bassets stretching far back to the first Normans. Bound to the Cornish soil by generations of intermarriage the Bassets were in fact the essence of Cornwall itself. Francis Basset, the 1st Baron, personified the family and its traditions. Under the threat of the combined French and Spanish fleets in 1778 he had been active in organizing the defence of the exposed peninsula. Like his father he had represented Penryn in Parliament in 1779 and was also Recorder. He had taken his M.A. at Cambridge in 1786. He had strongly opposed the peace with the American colonies, and became an active political writer. He did not, however, neglect the essential family assets and in their interest greatly developed the tin-mines which were the basis of his fortune. He was an improving agriculturist and a comfort to Arthur Young in the flow of his contri-butions to the *Annals*. It was, therefore, a natural thing for Sir Joseph Banks to send him in the summer of 1800, by the hands of a mutual friend, Dr. Wynne, a copy of 'A Project . . .'. It was, however, un-fortunate, that Dr. Wynne dawdled on the way and Sir Francis, who declared himself 'really ambitious' to cultivate the acquaintance of the Spanish sheep, resigned himself to wait a further year.[126]

Then on 6 August 1801 Banks told him that he was now able to furnish him with a ram (No. 141) and five ewes from the King's flock and that he knew of no method of getting the sheep safely to so great a distance but by sending a man with a light cart—'a method we Constantly take in the north when Sheep are valuable',[127] but perhaps Sir Francis would think of another way. Sir Francis, just returned from the Assizes, had no difficulty in this, and as the tin-ships sailed to Cornwall about once a fortnight he suggested on 11 August—'I think the new Colony you design for me had best come by that Conveyance.' Promptly then on 14 August Messrs. Wood and Cornish of 35 Broad Street Buildings wrote to Sir Joseph:

We have a Letter today from Lord de Dustanville requesting that we would forward to him at Tehidy Park a Ram & five Ewes which you have been so good as to procure for his Lordship.

A Vessel, the *Basset* Cap. Purchase, is now about to Sail—she will leave the Wharf Sunday Morning at 6 O'Clock—If you will please to order the Sheep to be at Foxalls Wharf Battle Bridge Tooley Street Southwark any time to-morrow they will be taken great care of . . . P.S. We have this instant seen the Captain of the Vessel—If the Sheep cannot be here till Sunday the Captain will take them on a boat to Blackwall where the Ship will be all that day—[128]

Banks replied, however, the same day that the sheep were not yet ready for delivery nor had he heard from Lord de Dunstanville.[129] But on 20 August he sent the order for the delivery to Wood and Cornish of the ram from Thomas Peasey at Frogmore and the ewes from Robert Dickson at Oatlands Park to be conveyed by a light cart to Southwark —evidently by the next ship sailing.[130]

Banks was apologetic—as he had so often occasion to be—about the sad state of the ram. It was much out of condition 'owing to the abominable carelessness of the person in whose charge the Ram Flock has been put but he is of an excellent quality'.[131] In October Sir Francis acknowledged the safe arrival of the flock but—the same 'but' of so many other letters—

I am very sorry however to inform you that the former [Ram No. 141] is Since dead: he arrived here very much affected by the foot Rot; the Ewes appear at present well but I am fearfull at mixing them with my flock, as I understand the disorder (of which we have no experience in this County) is very infectious: perhaps you may be able to procure me another Ram next year in case I should have no produce from my Ewes.[132]

The account he settled by a draft on Sir R. C. Glynn and Company for fifteen guineas. Next year he received 'a very nice Ram' (No. 140). By this time, however, he had lost two of the ewes and the remaining three were in a very bad state. He still hoped to make a fair trial of the breed in his home county but this 'I can hardly do in the present state of my flock'.[133] The ram he put to some Southdown ewes.[134] Next year he reported that his three surviving Spanish ewes were still lame from foot-rot and all his rams also. He had, however, acquired twelve lambs from the Spanish cross with the Southdown ewes. Another tenuous beginning had been made.

In the same year that Dr. Wynne's dallying on the road to Cornwall deferred the 1st Baron de Dunstanville's ambitions for a 'Colony' of Spanish sheep another one was safely established in almost the opposite corner of England at Alnwick far to the north. On 18 August 1800 Banks told Sir Hugh Percy, 2nd Duke of Northumberland,[135] that he had selected for him Ram No. 127—a very good three-shear sheep which had served the King's flock in 1799—and one old ewe whose mouth was still sound.[136] On 20 August 1801 Banks told His Grace that he had set apart three ewes of the King's Spanish flock such as he thought would suit him and that the following year he hoped to increase his flock still more. The price, as usual, was to be two guineas each.[137] His Grace, the old veteran of the Seven Years War and of the American War of Independence, his own private and perpetual opposition at Westminster, was relaxing at Tunbridge Wells when this news reached him. He was briefly thankful to Banks for his trouble but much more concerned with matters of health, the harvest, and what he regarded as episcopal hokum:

. . . It affords me such satisfaction to find that your Ginger regimen agrees so well with you. I am certain it is very beneficial to the Stomach as it greatly assists digestion. I am thank God pretty well, & get out for half an hour on horseback. The air here is very bracing & fine, & we have had the most delightful Weather possible, since our Arrival. I trust nobody who has Eyes will doubt the abundance of the present Harvest, & that the Almighty will not be accused for that scarcity which our good Diocesan, the Bishop of Durham has been foretelling in his Visitation Sermons, throughout the Northern Parts of the Kingdom. This with the present Harvest before their Eyes has given rise to strange Ideas & Conversation amongst the People of Monopolies—Corn sent out of the Kingdom &.ᶜ &.ᶜ &.ᶜ, which tho' the natural Consequence of such a Sermon, was not I apprehend in the Bishop's Contemplation when he preached it. Perhaps it would be as well if their Right Reverences would confine themselves to morality & Religion in their Sermons, without entering upon Subjects which have nothing to do with either. . . .[138]

Six months after this stricture on the vagaries of bishops was delivered, Major George Johnston sailed from Portsmouth on H.M.S. *Buffalo* returning to New South Wales with a release from his arrest and the court martial he had faced, bearing with him a Spanish ram from the Duke of Northumberland's small flock—at least so the slender record of this event would have it. There is however much more to be learned of this episode. The *Buffalo* arrived in Sydney Harbour on 16 October 1802 after an eight months' passage. The ram was still alive to enter history as the first authentic Spanish Merino to reach Australia. In this view it is for the moment assumed that the sheep of supposed Spanish origin from Cape Town landed in 1797 cannot claim the same undoubted antecedents as the ram from Alnwick. We are, however, left still with the speculation on its actual identity. If the Duke could spare the Major a ram so soon after the establishment of his own tiny offshoot—not much more than eighteen months—only two possibilities exist. Either it was the King's old ram No. 127 himself or a son of his out of the old but sound-mouthed ewe. In the latter case the ram would have been a shearling, an eligible and sensible beast to send to the Antipodes on such an arduous voyage. The alternative is to suppose that the Duke of Northumberland had Spanish stock from a source other than His Majesty—but of this there is no present trace and at this date it would seem unlikely though not impossible. Finally, it may be noted that while Major George Johnston was sailing south at the end of his arrest and abortive court martial, Captain John Macarthur was sailing north under arrest to face *his* court martial and to arrive in London on 21 December 1802. Military misdemeanour seems to have been a convenient means to a free passage home and the key to the door of opportunity for the recalcitrant officers of the New South Wales Corps—with Spanish rams from the Royal flock as their unlikely rewards.

IX

As the period of the private sales of the King's Spanish sheep drew to a close it became clear that at last the hopes of His Majesty and of Sir Joseph Banks were being realized. After years of struggle and obscurity the dissemination of the Spanish breed was now proceeding under the stimulus of its own power to create argument and investigation—but, above all, argument. The patriotism of the few was now to be assailed and tested in the polemics of the infant agricultural Press. This ordeal of ink-pots began astringently but, in its kind, modestly enough during the summer of 1802 when in the June number of *The Agricultural Magazine* some random darts were flung at the Duke of Bedford, at Lord Somerville, and particularly at Dr. Parry on the breeds of sheep which each was supposed to foster. The tone was set and the poison put to work in the following querulous taunts which the writer, under the cloak of anonymity, presented in the name of 'Practicus':

. . . Is quality forever to be the order of the day, and are we never to look to quantity? Only consider the present value of a pound of coarse wool, and of a pound of coarse mutton? Why should the fineness of wool be esteemed the chief object in our attempts to improve our stock? To direct our whole attention to such an object appears to me as preposterous, as it would be to reap a crop of corn before the grain is formed, merely to improve the quality of the straw; or to make straw bonnets of more consequence than bread. Is one pound of the finest wool that can possibly be produced here of equal value with five pounds of the coarsest? and will this fineness compensate for the diminution that must necessarily take place, both in fleece and carcase, by these new fangled, irrational crosses? Can a farmer ever hope to pay his rent with a flock of deformed, unthrifty, diminutive sheep, and a few tods of bastard wool?

This, it may be said, is only asking a few pert questions without giving a reason or stating a fact in favour of the argument which is here meant to be supported. These questions, I grant, may appear pert to such enthusiasts as Dr. Parry; but to every experienced agriculturalist in this island, I flatter myself they will be allowed to be at least pertinent. The Doctor, by the numberless daring affirmations with which his book on wool is replete, must have had the merit of first misleading Lord Somerville, and then of prevailing upon him to make the above extraordinary proposal;[139] or his Lordship surely would never have been induced to intimate to the world, that the British sheep, the best in the universe, can possibly be improved by crossing with the Spanish; or that wool, as good as Spanish, can ever be produced in England; or that one pound of high-flavoured mutton is of equal value with two from a coarse sheep . . .[140]

The text for many a year to come had now been given. A gage had been flung down and there were willing acceptors of the challenge.

Eleven years had now elapsed since the first Spanish sheep had been released from the precincts of Windsor Castle to make their way into what was then an apathetic and uncomprehending English world. Two years only had passed since Banks had published his 'A Project . . .' on the King's behalf as a summons to the nation to grasp the reed extended for the well-being of the woollen manufactures. Two years had almost passed since Dr. Parry had set out his *Facts and Observations . . .* whose good sense and even whose accuracy was now so heavily impugned. But it was now ten years since the Doctor had first set his feet on the path now so firmly trodden and so well defined by his Royal patron. The letter from 'Practicus' raised so many issues in a short space that were an affront not merely to Parry's loyalty but, more galling still, to his intelligence that he could not forbear to strike back—and that quickly. Perhaps in some respects the riposte was too quick and the Doctor's blood a little too hot. Rhetoric and scorn at times transcended reason—but this was in the spirit of the period. In any case it was less in proportion to the content of fact and sound debate than was in later years to clutter the pages of this and other journals. None the less it was the definitive beginning of what became for the next ten years 'the Merino controversy', a long and very tedious affair—a healthy catharsis, no doubt, but devilish long-winded and relieved only by short gusts of unintended humour. Parry's first contribution was his last. He turned to other and more constructive forms of reply and rebuke. 'Practicus' on the other hand continued to sweep the air with his inky quill for several years and to draw into the gyrations of this verbose argument a sequence of Latinized anonymities of whom one 'Rusticus' was early shamed into the open by the searing scorn of the Doctor for such a paltry device. This was the Secretary of the Bath and West of England Society, Mr. Nehemiah Bartley himself. For him there was, perhaps, no escape for his name—wrongly spelled—had been invoked by 'Practicus' and his example in a measure submitted to a ridicule that raised his hackles. Parry was content to allow him to bear the standard as a public defender of the faith. So Bartley went on to incorporate the essence of his contributions to this correspondence as *A Series of Letters on the National Importance as well as the Individual Benefit of Extending the Growth of Fine Clothing Wool by interbreeding with Spanish Rams and British Ewes*, printed in Bath in September 1804. From these beginnings we may trace a long sequence of polemical pamphlets and letters tending more to confuse than to clarify the issues, but not entirely unrewarding in their substance for the occasional sidelights on current questions and odd gobbets of useful information.

But in the summer of 1802 Parry spoke for all the high-minded patriots who had rallied from so many quarters to the support and proper exploitation of His Majesty's Spanish flock. No one had so much right as he to be its spontaneous mouthpiece on this occasion. His closing words to 'Practicus' will serve us well as a definitive view of the situation which he and his collaborators were proud to acknowledge and as a revelation of his own steps towards publication.

Those, indeed, who have read my book, must have seen in it an allusion to Lord Somerville's speech as President of the Board of Agriculture, and to the importation of his first flock from Spain. No one, therefore, could believe that Lord Somerville was misled by my publication except *Practicus*, to whose chaotic mind it may appear easy for an effect to precede it's cause.

What really suggested the course of my experiments, I have already told the public. Lord Somerville's design probably originated from the same source. This was the desire of his Majesty to make experiments with the flock of fine-woolled sheep, which he had procured, at a great expense, from Spain. Sir George [Onesiphorus] Paul[141] knows that I had not thought of any Essay on the subject of sheep, till he informed me that he had pledged himself to the King, that I should communicate to him the result of my observations. What was meant as a private communication grew insensibly into a pamphlet; but Lord Somerville himself had published on the subject before I had committed to paper a single thought.[142]

One word more, and I have done. *Practicus* accuses me of 'enthusiasm'. If by that term he means a strong inclination to propagate opinions conceived hastily and without due examination, I must tell him that such a temper is not very consistent with an occupation of thirty years in the study, and a very extensive practice of a profession such as mine. If, on the other hand, the term 'enthusiasm' indicates an ardent desire of diffusing, for the benefit, as it appears to me, of my country, that knowledge which I have gained by long and attentive experience, I glory in its appropriation; but I know not why I should thank *Practicus* for allowing me a merit, which I am conscious it is not in his power to deny me.[143]

CHAPTER X

The Pagoda, 1804–1810

I

IN spite of the war with France, so recently joined again after the brief Peace of Amiens, the summer of 1803 was remarkable in the affairs of His Majesty's Spanish flock for an unprecedented demand for its surplus sheep. The First Consul threatened invasion as he gathered his flotillas and his armies at Dunkirk, Calais, and Boulogne. From the Castle at Walmer near Deal, William Pitt, attended by his niece, the ebullient Lady Hester Stanhope, used his forced leisure from national affairs at Westminster in practical style, organizing the Kentish officers and gentlemen volunteers in defence of the invasion coast. These growing circumstances of national crisis entangled with the excessive loss of ewes in the spring all conspired to defeat His Majesty's 'patriotic exertions' and to disappoint the many claimants on his bounty. Sir Joseph Banks was impressed by the volume of the correspondence with which he found himself engaged, but chafed under the necessity to refuse so many worthy men. The demand for His Majesty's Merino sheep seemed to increase 'beyond all calculation'. It was, therefore, on a note of restrained optimism that he penned his report to the King for the year ending Michaelmas 1803 and concluded with the suggestion for a radical change in policy:

as Speculation upon the Price of Spanish sheep is clearly on the increase and as Reasonable probability now appears of the value of his Majesties patriotic exertions in Favor of his Subjects in introducing this breed being at Last duely appreciated, it is evidently improper that the views of those who have a right to derive advantage from the Sale of the Produce of Spanish Sheep Purchasd by them, should not be interrupted or in any degree impeded by a Continuation of the Sale of the King's Spanish Sheep at a Price inferior to their Real value, his Majesty has been advised therefore to Permit the Rams and Ewes that are in Future Parted with to be sold by Public Auction . . .[1]

So it appeared as he signed his first draft on 17 August 1803, and so it remained as he reluctantly set it aside in his preparations for the annual journey north by way of Overton in Derbyshire to Revesby Abbey. The Peace of Amiens had indeed passed. All about him as he travelled there was 'a general arming of the people'.

The preparations for repelling the invasion, with which we are menaced, continue with the utmost energy. The spirit of the country is roused to the highest pitch! every class of inhabitants has come forward nobly in the general cause with patriotic offers of personal service, as well as liberal contributions in behalf of the cause in which we are embarked! Indeed such a spirit of determined loyalty and resolute opposition to the implacable animosity and unlimited ambition of the Gallic despot has been excited from one extremity of the kingdom to the other, that instead of deprecating the threatened invasion, we ought to wish that it might be attempted.[2]

So the country prepared itself for autumn, that 'season of expeditions', taking all measures possible to achieve 'the most formidable state of self-defence'. The harvest of hay and grain had been got in and was found to be more heavy and abundant than for some years past. The south and east coasts were strongly manned and impregnated with defence works of all kinds. Plans for the evacuation from the threatened areas of the sick, the women, and the children by means of every form of transport were complete. The policy of a 'scorched earth' and of every measure 'to frustrate any hostile attempt' was fully established. The Volunteer Corps and Militia, nearly four hundred thousand men, augmented the Regular Army. The Navy was at sea continually probing the French invasion coast from Dunkirk to Le Havre.

By the wolds in Lincolnshire these things intruded only as a sub-dued undertone in the passage of letters to and fro as Banks relieved the worries of Richard Snart and Henry Lacocke involved with the importunate suitors for His Majesty's Spanish rams and ewes:

. . . Food & Credit is now very Bad in Town tho' there have been some quantity of wool sold off particular Sorts for the purpose of Clothing the Army and Navy and those fine Volunteers which are now as thick as Hops in every part of the City & Suburbs wishing Bonapart to come forward with his Terrible army as he say to Conquer England, if B. should make an attempt I think he'l have a hard Bone to pick from the English Volunteers & the Militia leaving out the Regular Troops, we shou'd not be cast down at the threat of a frenchman or any Enemy that wishes to destroy our lives and property . . .[3]

In this fashion Henry Lacocke ended his letter, of 22 October 1803, to Banks advising him to take early action 'to send for the Ram Lambs into Lincoln' as they were 'amazingly grown since we parted them from the Ewes'. However, the ram lambs did not reach Revesby until December, some weeks after Banks had returned to London. It was a winter of long bedridden months under the attention of Sir Everard Home who earned his gratitude for thoughtful care 'through a long and vexatious disease'.[4]

It was a bad season in other ways. The fear of invasion had for the time subsided but the nation was alarmed and the public mind again much agitated by the indisposition of the King. Doubt and despondency pervaded the cold gloomy days and it was not until March 1804 that the daily reports of the state of the King's health were discontinued and the nation could regard itself

... as having gained a tower of additional strength by the recovery of our most gracious and beloved Sovereign, from an indisposition which alarmed and afflicted us more than if an invasion had actually landed on our shores.[5]

None of these events was in any way helpful or likely to advance the proposals in Banks's report 'For the Year ending Michaelmas 1803'. Master and Shepherd, King and President of the Royal Society were in different ways suffering the stresses of advancing age which kept them from their customary exchange of views for many months. The national emergency and all the attendant 'unavoidable circumstances' deferred the final publication of the report and much further thought about its contents *sine die*.

In the early spring of 1804 'the hacknied rumours of invasion were still afloat'. A change of Ministry had altered the political scene. Henry Addington gave place to William Pitt who, leaving his Kentish Volunteers and the martial cares of Walmer, resumed his leadership of the nation for the last time. In France, the First Consul was preening himself to assume the Imperial diadem. The vaunted invasion of England seemed daily to fade as an imminent risk. Emerging from the shades of 1803, which had by no means stifled its rural energies, England seemed to enter the summer of 1804 with a great burst of agricultural *joie de vivre*. If we may believe the rhapsodies of its body of reporters this was a vintage year in the annals of agricultural education. In new-found health Sir Joseph Banks prepared to join the round of enlightened junketings that each year was becoming a more prominent and successful summer diversion for every agriculturist of property and spirit. For Banks himself it probably marked the zenith of his public work for British agriculture, a year of personal activity in that wide field he was never to repeat with quite the same vigour.

First, there was the Woburn Sheep Shearing. In all its varied activities that year, as for many past, he was a prominent, respected, and well-liked figure. As Treasurer of the Committee appointed to erect a monument to the memory of Francis 5th Duke of Bedford he could report a useful advance. On the opening day of the meeting, Monday, 18 June 1804, his first task was to show the assembled company 'a very good perspective view' of Russell Square with the intended statue, a colossal figure in bronze, the preparations for casting which were 'in great forwardness'. As a member of the Board of Agriculture he rode early one morning with Lord Sheffield, its President, and Arthur Young, its Secretary, to study the new water meadows at Priesley Farm four miles away. As President of the Royal Society and open-handed patron of all worthy scientific endeavour he subscribed £50 on the spot from a promised £100 towards the publication by 'Mr. Smith of Bath' of maps of the geological strata of England and Wales displayed at Woburn that year. As the tireless guardian of the fleece and of sheep breeding in all its branches he had the satisfaction to watch his very apt pupil, Mr. George Tollet of Staffordshire, show 'some very long wool produced from Spanish sheep, formerly of his Majesty's flock, and on which the wool had been suffered to grow unshorn for two years'.[6]

Next, after four days of intense discussion and strenuous social engagement with Woburn hospitality, four great dinners and many laudable toasts, he could at last leave in company with his good friend, Thomas William Coke, to post for three days a hundred and twenty miles north-east into Norfolk. As the miles rumbled away and ideas tossed to and fro between these two great landholders they did not neglect to pause on their way to inspect 'the newly-watered meadows upon Mr. Beck's farm at West Lexham'. By Sunday evening Banks was comfortable again in the great Hall at Holkham as Coke's honoured guest, while 'every inn and farmhouse in the neighbourhood were filled with visitors'.[7] Here, from Monday, 25 June to Wednesday, 27 June he engaged in all the rigours, intellectual and convivial, of that other famous 'rural festival', the Holkham Sheep Shearing. This year, however, he left Holkham before its usual conclusion, a decision hastened perhaps by the strain of these two great agricultural gatherings so soon after his long illness of the previous winter. Or, perhaps the stimulus of two unusually large and successful meetings with their shows and public auctions of outstanding livestock reminded him of his own report and recommendation to the King lying neglected in London. Neglected under the stress of illness and many other distractions during the winter, perhaps, but certainly not forgotten. The idea continued to germinate for, as he had written to Sir Henry Tempest Vane on 30 March 1804,

I mean to Recommend to the King to allow me this year to sell the Sheep by auction as the best means of Satisfying the numerous Claimants for them and increasing the public care of the Sheep for a man always takes the most care of the thing he gives the most money for . . .[8]

Perhaps the success of the New Leicesters for auction sale and hire at Woburn and the similar spectacle of Coke's Southdowns at Holkham confirmed him in his own intentions to experiment with the same technique of public advertisement for the Spanish flock. Perhaps he received encouragement from others at these Sheep Shearings; men such as George Tollet, Lord Sheffield, Lord Somerville, even Thomas William Coke himself may all this year have prompted him to bring forward the Spanish Merino on competitive terms. All these things may well have hastened his return to London, with the summer fast advancing, for he certainly lost very little time in resurrecting his draft report for 1803 and now bringing his firm advice for a public auction to the notice of the King. On 5 July he redrafted the text for publication having by then already carried the argument to His Majesty and received his assent:

This circumstance having been stated to the King, his Majesty was graciously pleased to permit the Rams and Ewes that are to be parted with from the Royal Merino Flock this year to be sold by auction in the same manner as is done at Woburn by his Grace the Duke of Bedford, and at Holkham by Mr. Coke, on the presumption of this being the most likely manner of placing the best individuals of their improved breeds in the hands of persons most likely to preserve and further to improve them.[9]

In this form now ran his final draft and the printed version, as he circulated it after adding a postscript on 10 July and a minor correction from Henry Lacocke to whom in his courteous care he had submitted it before publication:

As the publication of this Report has been delayed by unavoidable circumstances to so late a period, it is proper to add that the Wools of 1803 have yielded both raw and scowered much as usual. The Prime or R. of the Ewe Flock were sold for 6s. 9d. a pound, and that of the Rams for 6s. 6d. These enormous prices, however, depended on a scarcity of imported Spanish Wool, and are highly distressing to the manufacturer: they ought not therefore be allowed to enter into the speculation of the grower.

The Sheep that can be spared from the Royal Flock will be sold by auction this year at a barn opposite the Pagoda in Kew-lane, on the 15th of August next. Notice of the Particulars will be given as soon as possible.[10]

The play was at last on the stage; the scene was not quite set but the machinery was in motion; the actors were gathering in the wings.

II

If the first public sale of Spanish sheep from His Majesty's flock was to be properly inaugurated there was much yet to be done. Midsummer was past and there was little time left in which to organize. Banks had seen the King on 4 July. The next day he wrote to Richard Snart from Spring Grove calling him to a consultation there on the following Monday, 9 July, to 'fix on a proper place & the best manner of Carrying H.M. Commands into execution'.[11] The date of sale was then fixed for

Wednesday, 15 August. The place of sale was at first evidently to have been the barn on Marsh Gate Farm across Kew Lane opposite the Pagoda. These details were certainly entered in the postscript which Banks added to his report the next day. The printed *Particular and Conditions of Sale* . . . , also stated the site to be 'at a Barn nearly opposite the Pagoda, in the Road from Richmond to Kew'.[12] When the sale actually took place the common accounts support the placement of the site as having been 'in a paddock in Richmond Park, by the side of Kew Foot Lane, not far from the Pagoda', or in 'the field south of the Pagoda'.

Five weeks in which to prepare! Where were the sheep to be found that were fit for sale? As to the ewes there was no great problem beyond deciding which of the elderly matrons could best be spared after the mortalities of 1803. These were near at hand under the care of Richard Stanford. The main substance of the sale was to be the rams, and of these the shearlings and some others were far away at Revesby Abbey whither they had gone at the behest of Henry Lacocke the previous December to be wintered as an experiment. These must return in haste, but now Banks was in no condition to write to John Parkinson his Chief Steward in Lincolnshire. His familiar gout, never far away in these years and conjured up again among the fleshpots of Woburn and Holkham, returned to cripple his writing hand. Once more his sister, Sarah Sophia, became his amanuensis and wrote to his dictation. Then, on 17 July, at last came word from Parkinson that all preparations for the departure of the sheep had been made.[13]

With eight pounds in cash and bank-notes, old John Moor, the drover, was to set out from Revesby Abbey on 18 July to bring the sheep up to town. At twelve miles per day the journey itself was estimated to require eleven days. Sustenance for the sheep was reckoned at £3 9s. 6d. John Moor's wages were 2s. per day for himself and 4s. per day expenses, and assuming that he needed fifteen days for the task as a whole the cost for him was reckoned to be £4 10s. 0d.[14] To receive John Moor and his charges at the journey's end in Richmond, Richard Snart had made his own dispositions.[15] Word was left with the toll-gatherer at Kew Bridges for the foot-weary little flock to be directed to the house of Richard Stanford by the Blue Anchor inn, another mile and a half from Kew Green, but close to the agreed place of sale and nearer than the enclosures in Richmond Park. Thus eventually about 28 July John Moor from Revesby delivered the rams to Richard Stanford at The Orange Tree Cottage in Kew Foot Lane whence they were taken immediately into the Gardens where a piece of ground had been hurdled off to receive them. Here they rested during the remaining two weeks while other work to determine their historic fate went quickly on.

On 12 July Banks had sent the final draft of his report 'For the Year ending Michaelmas 1803' to Henry Lacocke with another copy for John Maitland to see and correct. Lacocke noted a small error in the weight of the fleeces in yolk[16] which was adjusted, but of Maitland's comments we have no record. It is very probable that Banks and Lacocke met at the shearing of the lambs on 17 July to discuss this matter and the urgent problem of the ewes to be selected and drawn for sale. Again, with no actual record to guide us, this was almost certainly the occasion when the one six-toothed and the thirteen full-mouthed ewes were set aside or marked for the sale. Without further delay the report was sent on to William Bulmer the printer of Cleveland Row, St. James's, who had done the report for 1802. The pamphlets were ready within a week and on 24 July the bundle was sent to Mr. Francis Freeling, Secretary of the General Post Office, to be franked and sent out by post in accordance with an offer of some long standing:

Sir Jos: has not before taken advantage of Mr Freeling's Obliging offer on this head because no occasion has occurred which he has thought of sufficient importance to warrant his giving Mr Freeling the Trouble on the Present [occasion] which is to aid his Majesties Patriotic Views of Distributing his Spanish Flock which improves rather than degenerates here, in such a manner as to Render England Less dependent on Spain for Fine wools than She has been, he trusts Mr Freeling will not think Sir Jos: has applied to him without Proper Reason.[17]

The list appended to this request contained forty-two names and addresses of men who had corresponded with Banks during the previous two years as applicants or whose names had been brought to his notice. More than half of these replied either to the effect that they could not be present or asking to act for them in making a purchase at the sale. Of those who did not answer it is clear from the events of the sale that most of them attended on the day.[18]

One man's name was not included. We are still left to speculate on the omission of Captain John Macarthur from those who were favoured with Banks's attention in this particular way. We need not assume, however, that any omission from this special list implies neglect or bad humour, deliberate or otherwise. Each and every man on the list itself had made, in one form or another, a serious and particular claim on the Royal flock for sheep. The report was in effect a circular answer and a reminder that a new system was about to commence. The claims of Macarthur on the attention of Banks were of another kind and almost certainly did not raise the question of Royal sheep in any specific fashion. Moreover, there were clear legal and other practical obstacles in the way to say nothing of immediate distractions which in the haste of final arrangements for the sale may well have prevented any late contact between Banks and Macarthur. For, during the very days in this busy month of July 1804 when the sale was being organized, evidence was being heard from 'Gentlemen who have been in New South Wales' by the Lords of the Committee of the Privy Council appointed for the consideration of all matters of Trade and Foreign Plantations.[19] The subject of the weighty proceedings in the Council Chamber at Whitehall was no less than John Macarthur's own *Proposal for Establishing a Company to Encourage the Increase of Fine Woolled Sheep in New South Wales*.[20] On 14 July the Lords of the Committee completed their inquiry, begun in the first instance largely on Banks's advice, by delivering themselves of an opinion of some consequence as time has proved, and whose effect may well have been decisive on the immediate intentions of John Macarthur by according him the official support necessary for his maturing plans. The opinion of the Privy Council Committee ends thus:

That from the information obtained from the Fleeces brought from the Settlement in question, and from the description given of the Climate of the Colony, the Lords of the Committee are led to imagine, and entertain hopes that wool of a fine quality may be produced in this Colony; and that as Wool of such fine quality is much wanted and desired by the Manufacturers of Cloth in England, it being mostly, drawn, at this time from a Country, if not dependent on France, then much under her influence, their Lordships entertain no doubt that it is well deserving the attention of His Majesty's Government to encourage the Produce of fine Wool, in the Colony of New South Wales.[21]

We need not at this point examine the complexities of the questions, arguments, and evidence surrounding this opinion and its background. We may note, however, that two streams of action with a common source, but which in 1787 had taken different channels, were about to join again.

From Banks's letters to William Eden in the spring of 1787 had come that flock of Spanish sheep from which forty-four animals were very soon to be offered for sale. Within days of these same letters to France, Captain Arthur Phillip had sailed from the Mother Bank at Portsmouth to establish the following year that small and distant Colony from whence had now come a memorialist to the Lords of a Committee on the subject of fine wool. Banks was in every sense the moving spirit behind the scenes of all these scattered phenomena—the Colony, the flock, and the Committee—and in a few weeks all were destined to attain a personal synthesis in the self-confident and controversial figure of John Macarthur. For eighteen months directly and indirectly Macarthur had been intermittently in touch with Banks on the subject of closest mutual concern to them both. From December 1802 when Macarthur had arrived not only with 'a valuable collection of natural history specimens' for Banks but also with some fleeces of his own wool there had been ample reason for both men to achieve some measure of personal contact. How far this went is not clear, but there was no more compelling reason than the very *Proposal for Establishing a Company* . . . of which Banks had received a copy and on which he had noted his comments. In the formation of such a Company at least one mutual friend of Banks and Macarthur was apparently to have been a participant. This was John Maitland, the influential wool merchant of Basinghall Street, to whom, for the past twenty years, Banks had continually turned for advice and discussion on matters touching the wool trade. Maitland was one of those favoured with a copy of *A Report of the State of His Majesty's Flock of Fine Wooled Spanish Sheep For the Year ending Michaelmas 1803* as an established breeder of the Spanish Merino at Woodford Green in Essex and as one of the principal promoters of the sale of British-grown Merino wool.[22] No doubt he had discussed the forthcoming sale of Royal sheep with Macarthur in all its implications. Even if Banks himself had not told Macarthur at some time, we have not far to seek if we are to find a channel by which he could have been encouraged to enter the 'field south of the Pagoda' with serious and well-planned intentions. Of the full extent of these plans Banks may well have not been aware.

Meanwhile John Farnham, the auctioneer, had taken in hand the advertisement of the sale in the country Press and in the *London County Chronicle*. Farnham had entered the growing cast of players as an old friend of William Aiton the younger, the Royal Gardener at Kew. As a resident of Richmond he had also heard about the sale from Richard Snart. With a fine detachment Snart had declared himself 'perfectly unacquainted' with Farnham, but Banks was evidently satisfied with his credentials. Thus the auctioneer and appraiser of Richmond, Surrey, and 80 Long Acre, London, became the first salesman of the King's sheep. He wrote his formal application to Banks on 18 July[23] and soon thereafter he was able to arrange the printing of five hundred catalogues of the sale and for the use of a room at the 'Blue Anchor near the place of sale' for the transaction of appropriate business. The *Particular and Conditions of Sale, of Some Rams and a few Ewes, from His Majesty's Pure Spanish Flock of Merino Sheep* . . . were printed by G. A. Wall of Hill Street, Richmond, before Banks could alter the title on the outer cover to 'a few Rams and Some Ewes',[24] a small point of strict accuracy that seems to have weighed slightly on his mind if we may judge from his *post hoc* corrections.

Everything was now ready for the day of sale but Sir Joseph's gout remained almost to the last moment as an intractable fiend that would not be exorcized.

III

The fine harvest weather that had been so general seemed to have withdrawn. From the eighty dragons on the Pagoda in Kew Gardens rain had splashed in fitful streams for some days. The morning of Wednesday, 15 August also dawned under low clouds and incessant showers, but as the morning advanced the sun at last cut through to bring rainbow glitters from the varnished iron plates of the ornate tower. High above the Royal parkland it now cast a beckoning gleam to the approaching carriages. Almost at right angles to the water-filled ditch of the ha-ha which bounded the Old Deer Park along the Kew Road from Richmond ran a pleasant avenue of trees under which the show pens for the Spanish sheep were now arranged. Near by on the damp pasture from eleven in the morning the horses and the carriages of 'a number of intelligent gentlemen' collected, about fifty 'amateurs and breeders' intent upon examining minutely the strange animals of which so much had been surmised but so little seen in public. No very large gathering was this to set against the crowded bustle at Woburn and Holkham not long past. It was enough, however, for the business to be done, for Banks had organized the affair with some discretion, on the whole, in spite of the apparent haste of his final arrangements. He was not, however, entirely pleased. He felt obliged to state in print on the catalogue:

All the Sheep are in Store Condition, and as high Prices are not wished for, the usual means of preparing Stock for a Sale by high keeping, have not been resorted to. The Shearling Rams are in a low State, owing to the Mismanagement of a Shepherd in Lincolnshire, where for experiment they were wintered, and possibly in some degree to the Soil, and Climate of that Country, but as Purity of Blood (which is fully warranted) is the principal Object of the Purchaser, it is hoped this Circumstance will be overlooked.[25]

That they should be valued for their true genetic worth, not merely for their appearance, was his fond hope—but 'Purity of Blood' was the nearest phrase in his vocabulary to express this. Their appearance on the other hand was paramount with most who gathered about the show pens and the impression they left was not untinged with doubt. Moreover, it would seem that whatever the 'low State' of the shearling rams from Lincolnshire, either the Surrey pastures or time and Richard Stanford had not dealt kindly with the elderly matrons of the flock also for sale, for these were remarked by John Lawrence, who saw them on the day, to be 'very low in flesh', the rams being 'in better case'. Further, as he also recorded, 'it was remarked by a dealer present, that in a country market and unknown, they would scarcely have fetched five shillings a head'. Thus the morning apparently passed in an atmosphere of critical appraisal of the sheep themselves and of the potential buyers as well as in wordy duels that would not be strange wherever the remote descendants of the Royal flock are sold today. Of this we gain another passing glimpse as John Lawrence continues:

Some of them were blind, from a cold caught in the winter and spring, a circumstance in itself sufficient to demand shelter for them throughout those periods, yet a Scottish gentleman present averred, that he had a Spanish ram which was exposed, throughout the whole winter, in his country, with no ill effect whatever: Mr. [Richard] Snarte [sic] exposes his Spanish stock in the same way in Essex, even during the snows; but on this Captain McArthur very rationally observed that a few solitary instances were insufficient foundation for general reasoning The Captain houses his immense flock, during winter, 300 in a lot. A farmer present observed, that his Spanish rams were equally hardy with his South Downs, that he kept them together in the same pasture, and they maintained an equal condition. The wool of the rams exposed to sale varied considerably, some individuals bearing a finer fleece than others. . . .[26]

Neither the threatening weather nor the residual twinges of 'his recent severe fit of the gout' could prevent Banks from appearing in the field at the earliest possible moment and remaining there until the business was ended, eager as always to enter fully into such arguments as these or to advise on the subject of Spanish sheep and fine wool as the occasion required. There was much to explain and much to defend, but there was also much to be learned. It was doubtless odd to find a President of the Royal Society in such a market place, but the contentious theme of Spanish sheep at such a time demanded all his wit both as savant and as sheep breeder.

About two o'clock the sale opened in the traditional way with a speech from the auctioneer. Mr. Farnham's exordium on this unusual day was short and neat, followed quickly by a recital of the printed conditions of sale:

I. The highest Bidder to be the Purchaser, and if any dispute shall arise between Two or more Bidders, the Lot in dispute shall be put up again.

II. No Person to advance less than Five Shillings, above Five Pounds, Ten shillings and Six Pence, and so on in proportion.

III. The Purchasers to pay down immediately into the hands of the Auctioneer, a deposit of 25 per Cent. in part of Payment, to give in their Names and Places of abode if required, and to pay the Remainder, and take away their respective Lots, with all faults, within Three Days after the Sale is ended.

Lastly. If any Lots remain unsettled after the Time limited, the Deposit shall be absolutely forfeited, the Auctioneer shall be at full Liberty to resell the Lots in question, either by public or private Sale, and the deficiency (if any) together with the Expences attending such second Sale, shall be made good by the defaulters.[27]

Banks then announced that two of his friends had commissioned him to buy if possible on their behalf: Sir Richard Worsley of the Isle of Wight, and Sir John Riddell near Berwick-on-Tweed in Scotland. Without further preamble the bidding commenced.[28]

The first lot was a shearling ram, 'labouring under a temporary privation of sight' which Banks and Richard Stanford stated was not uncommon among the flock at that season—a condition that the inquisitive eye of John Lawrence had already noted, and on which there had already been some debate. This sheep was sold to Captain John Macarthur for £6 15s.—a price not far from the standard for the private sales. The price itself was not spectacular but the buyer had already attracted some interest and had been prominent enough in the rural debates beside the sale pens. Here was someone from afar and beyond the charmed circle of Soho Square and Spring Grove. Here in fact at last was a colonial portent hopefully and with determination bidding in the face of strong and evident obstruction. There was a brief pause, therefore, while Banks very properly drew Macarthur's attention to one powerful and inclusive Act[29] of the Statute Books debarring the export of sheep from England in clear and definite terms and the sale went on. By a quarter past four it was over and Banks could tell the small assembly that the prices achieved had exceeded the King's and his own expectations. He had been impressed with the eagerness of the bidding and had no doubt that the King's intentions of putting the sheep in the hands of those who would most value and attend to the increasing of the breed would be realized. The sheep might stay on His Majesty's pasture for three days at the risk of the purchaser or longer if not convenient to remove them sooner. This offer seems not to have been much used for most of the sheep were removed that very day in carts. One enthusiast at least was seen to take his purchase away with him in his chaise.

Thirty rams had been sold at an average price of £19 4s. ranging from £6 7s. to £44 2s.[30] Of these animals Lots 1, 7, and 15 were blind on the day of sale and Lot 17 was suffering from foot-rot. Lot 2 had been withdrawn from the sale as sick, though the nature of the ailment was undisclosed. Lots 1 to 24 were all shearling rams; Lots 25 to 30 were all either four-toothed or full-mouthed sheep of which Lots 26 and 29 had both seen service with the Spanish the previous year at least. Lot 26 was in fact Young Snags (No. 148), aged four and a half, bought by

Mr. George Holme Sumner of Guildford, Surrey. He was the son of
Old Snags (No. 133) who had been sold in 1803 to a Mr. Cole. These
two rams were the only animals in the Royal flock to achieve historic
recognition by name and not merely by a number.

Fourteen ewes were sold at an average price of £8 15s. 6d. with values
ranging from £6 6s. to £25 4s. All of these seem to have been sound
and 'warranted to have good bags', being all proved breeders and aged
animals, except Lot 42 a six-tooth.

Time and the dust of controversy have blurred the image of these
sheep and the impressions they imprinted on the minds of those who
saw them that day. A faint semblance of them struggles through the
short record left in the words of John Lawrence, which is indeed about
the only eyewitness account of these particular sheep extant:

The size of the EWES, somewhat under our *pure* Ryelands, but above several
of our small breeds; heads sharp and well shaped, with, occasionally, a black
spot or two, wool externally having a dirty tinge, but without that red-brown
hue, which has been before mentioned; ears pendulous, perfect ewe-neck,
with the sinking or cavity, both before, and behind the shoulder, the top of
which is generally higher than the rump; capacious belly, the animals
standing wide and well upon the legs.

The RAMS generally of good size, some of them large enough for any
purpose whatever, and of great bone, but flat and symmetrical: several of
them were of as good useful form as need be seen, having compact, good
loins and shoulders, and streight backs. Two or three individuals resembled
very strikingly our Dorset and Hampshire stock. The characteristic velvet or
silken gloss on the shorn faces of the rams was remarkable, and their countenance put one in mind of the fair haired human complexion. Mouths by
no means fine.[31]

Eighteen buyers withdrew at the end of the day to settle their
accounts at the Blue Anchor with Mr. Farnham either on their own
behalf or for those whom they had represented. Some, like the Reverend
J. C. Beckingham and Mr. George Holme Sumner were to buy again
at later sales. Others, having bought once were to slip out of the history
of the Spanish sheep for ever. Of those who left the Blue Anchor to
return no more one man, and he only, carried the Spanish sheep to a new
destiny. John Macarthur hastened away to London with the problem
of an embargo on his mind, neither the first nor the last man to bear
such a burden for the sake of a few Merino sheep. Behind him at the
Blue Anchor in the room hired from mine host, Brooks, lay his settlement with His Majesty's auctioneer—£150 1s. for seven rams and three
ewes—and as sound a small piece of business as the dragons of the
Pagoda ever witnessed. In the seven years of the public sales on 'the

Ha! Ha! piece' only one man bought more sheep on a single day. No one man from so few talents made so much when we reckon the accounts of all those who drew from the storehouse of the King's Spanish flock.

IV

The sale had undoubtedly succeeded but it had not run its intended course. The Spanish breed, as was proposed, had been dispersed among His Majesty's dutiful and enlightened subjects, but further than anyone had foreseen. Of the forty-four sheep passed under the hammer ten, it would seem, were now under sentence of transportation to Botany Bay.[32] This cut heavily into a limited supply of stud animals for British farms at the very moment that the Royal gate had opened to the clamouring public. As he drove home to Spring Grove across the river that long summer evening Banks's own feelings were doubtless confused. There could be no doubt certainly about the impact of Macarthur's presence at the auction. His determined bidding had 'made the sale' in a financial sense: £697 7s. 6d. was beyond question a handsome return for thirty rams where formerly none had sold at more than 6 guineas a head, and for fourteen ewes previously valued at 2 guineas each. Even when John Farnham's commission at five per cent and other costs totalling £44 6s. 6d. had been deducted the net return to His Majesty of £653 1s. would look exceedingly well, bearing in mind the relative haste with which, in the end, it had all come about. A fat return to the Royal purse, however, was not the purpose of the auction. The primary goal was to make the Spanish sheep more freely available to those who would value and propagate the breed in the national interest. Was Macarthur, therefore, a worthy recipient of this rare stock? It is hard to believe that Banks did not think so and that he sought to place difficulties in his path. In his most secret thoughts Banks may well have been troubled to see his precious Merinos snatched away so far from his immediate influence and observation. Beyond this it would seem wholly out of character for Banks, whatever his honest doubts, not to connive at the opening of a new phase of development for the sheep which were in truth something more than his 'favorite hobby' and for the Colony in whose creation and growth he had been so deeply involved.

Macarthur, since his arrival in England in December 1802, seems to have enjoyed the opportunities and benefits of associating with two of Banks's most trusted intimates in the matter of fine wool—John Maitland the eminent wool merchant, and Henry Lacocke the old wool stapler of Bermondsey. We know also that Maitland was closely interested in Macarthur's proposed Company for the growing of fine wool in New South Wales and supported it in company with Hullett, who, as a dummy, had bought two ewes at the sale for Macarthur and was the owner of the *Argo* on which the sheep from Kew eventually left for the South Seas. In the vexatious year of 1803 Macarthur may in any case have had little opportunity for much direct contact with Banks himself, a man of large responsibilities at a time of national crisis, and also that year much bedridden and harried with gout. To the inquiring layman of fine Spanish wool, however, Maitland and Lacocke must have been deep wells of knowledge, freely available, on all aspects of the trade and the daily practice of breeding in the Royal flock and elsewhere. Later at the sale itself if Banks warned Macarthur about the obstructive Act of 1788 in the way to prevent the export of sheep, it may well have been because no one else present at the sale was in need of such instruction for no one else planned to send their purchases abroad. No one knew better than Banks the lets and hindrances of the traffic in live sheep, especially the fine-woolled Spanish breed, and his gesture on the occasion may as well have been a helpful one as otherwise. Legal obstacles certainly did exist. Banks himself on one occasion had sought advice about the re-export of Spanish sheep in 1792 from Lisbon via England to the King's Hanoverian estates.[33] If he seemed to raise a difficulty here it may well have been with the clear intention of finding means to dispose of it. Had it been his aim to obstruct Macarthur it seems unlikely that within two weeks after the sale he could write on 29 August 1804, in the following terms, to Governor King in New South Wales:

I do not think you need to trouble yourself about getting possession of the fine-woolled sheep for Government. If the project for breeding them succeeds, they must soon become so abundant that the genius of your people, who will not let a potato stay under ground until it is ripe, will soon spread them over the country.

A proposal has been made to institute a company here with a capital of £10,000 for the purpose of increasing the breed of sheep, which are to become the property of the subscribers—the wool I mean—and the mutton to remain that of M[r] Mcarthur, the manager. Government have been applied to to make grants of land for that purpose. I have advised that a grant be made of a million of acres in such parts as Captain Mcarthur shall chuse, at a proper distance from all settlements for the sole purpose of feeding sheep, resumable at the will of the Government, whenever any part of it may be appropriated to tillage or other purposes, on satisfaction being made for any stockhouses on the premises resumed, and an equal quantity granted at a more distant point, 100,000 acres at first and 100,000 more when 100,000 sheep are actually in existence on the first 100,000, and so on.[34]

If Banks made a point of inquiring about Macarthur in some personal detail, as he certainly did before he wrote these words to Governor

King, he was merely pursuing his own established custom applied in many other circumstances. It was entirely in his character as a wealthy man of large affairs in land and stock himself. It was equally so in his character as a confidential adviser to the King and to the Government on a host of similar matters. In all of these he was equally conscientious in seeking good grounds for a sound judgement. As a scientist he instinctively took a critical attitude to any new phenomenon and probed as deeply as he was able in his search for the truth. He collected the evidence as best he could and drew his conclusions. According to long habit he committed his thoughts and his opinions to paper as memoranda, mainly to himself. Some of these have survived and, taken out of their context in the sequence of his inquiries, may at times seem to bear the appearance of bias.[35] Viewed against a more complete background and against the finality of his subsequent actions, such notes appear in better perspective as steps towards an ultimate conclusion.

Macarthur, it must be remembered, was unknown to Banks as a person before December 1802. During much of 1803 and 1804, stimulated by Macarthur's persistent presence in London and his determined efforts to bring all matters concerning the fine-wool growing potentialities of New South Wales before the Government, Banks had ample need to satisfy himself about this new colonial phenomenon. Macarthur was in arrest and under a cloud for shooting his commanding officer in the arm in a duel—Colonel William Patterson, F.R.S., protégé and old correspondent of Banks on matters of natural history. Macarthur was at the same time a man of some wealth, by his own confession acquired during his professional career as a comparatively junior officer of His Majesty's New South Wales Corps. This was altogether a strange person to be advocating the floating of a large pastoral Company with English capital. At no time could such a man pass without some sort of investigation. In this context Banks's discreet inquiries were perfectly correct and on the whole conducted with an impersonal judgement of the kind he was wont to administer. Large issues were clearly involved and Banks was manifestly determined that no hasty conclusions would be reached for lack of ascertainable facts. It was necessary that some of this needed information should concern the character and person of Macarthur. If, in acquiring this knowledge, certain things were told to Banks and recorded by him in his desk-notes it argues no personal bias against Macarthur that he should have set them down. They were the case-notes essential to the final diagnosis.

It is not easy yet to piece together the scattered evidence of the relations between the two men into a clear sequence, but it is on balance, so far, hard to accept the idea that at this stage Banks and Macarthur were adversaries. That Banks let personal vanity obscure his eminently constructive interest in the extension of British fine-wool growing, wherever it may have been, seems unlikely and not least in relation to the Colony so close to his own heart. At all events, after Macarthur and his six surviving sheep from Kew landed in Sydney on 7 July 1805, Governor King could write to Banks:

Macarthur intends writing to you and speaks highly of your politeness to him at the sale of Spanish sheep in England.[36]

On this note we may for the moment let the problem rest.

V

For Banks himself there were several matters to be completed before the sale of 1804 could lapse into the historic past. He required John Farnham to deliver Lots 7, 18, and 20 to Sir Richard Worsley or his agent and Lots 16 and 23 to Sir John Riddell for both of whom he had himself acted at the sale.[37] Reckoning that, as these gentlemen lived at a distance, it would be probable that they could not send for the sheep for a long time he asked Farnham to order the King's Shepherd to deliver them in his absence if necessary. Of Worsley's sheep we hear no more. Of those for Riddell we do not know much beyond their owner's intentions for them:

... by their means I can try a comparison between the pure Spanish [the] Spanish & South Downs (of which I have a very large Flock), Spanish & Cheviot, & Spanish & Blackfaced Highlanders
    The result may be highly advantageous to some infant manufacturers in the County of Roxburgh, which are struggling into consequence & which I wish to assist[38]

Sir John Riddell replied to Banks's advice about his purchases on 22 August 1804:

An excess of visitors, who according to the blessed custom of the North, considered their own amusement in coming rather [than] that of their host, has occupied me so fully that I have not been able until this moment to reply to your obliging letter of the 17th. I now enclose a Draft for 42£ & beg you to accept my thanks for the trouble you have been good enough to take on my account. I shall write to a person in London to remove my Rams & hope to receive them safely here. For this year I will be content without any Spanish Ewes.[39]

On 18 August Richard Snart called at Spring Grove twice, but found that Banks was away on other affairs and so could not discuss the

financial state of the Spanish flock.[40] Banks in fact was with the King
during the morning until one o'clock, almost certainly presenting a
detailed account of the sale. Later that same afternoon he was deeply
engaged at Kew inspecting a cargo of new plants from China which
had arrived by the evening's tide. All of this had prevented him meeting
Snart as he had intended. He therefore instructed Snart by letter to
receive from John Farnham the profit of the auction sale which he had
estimated at about £660 and which Farnham had agreed with Banks to
do on sight of the letter itself.[41] He also expressed a wish to pay one
per cent on the sales to Richard Stanford, the King's Shepherd, subject
to His Majesty's approval. The net proceeds of the sale revealed in fact
by John Farnham's account[42] agreed well with his own first estimate:

Account of the Sale of his Majesty's
Merino Sheep August 15.th 1804.

				697 : 7 : 6
Commission on Sale at 5 p[r] Cent ..	..	.. 34 : 17 : 6		
Printing 500 Particulars as p[r] bill ..	..	.. 4 : 19 : 0		
Bill at Blue Anchor Day of Sale ..	..	.. 1 : 8 : 6		
Country Advertisements ..	..	..	.. 2 : 0 : 6	
London County Chronicle Postage &c. ..	..	0 : 10 : 6		
Gave Booth as a compensation for the use of his				
Room during my attendance to deliver the		0 : 10 : 6		
respective Lots ..	..	.. ..	..	44 : 6 : 6

Paid in at Herries & C° £653 : 1 : 0

Faithful to his intentions Banks later paid £7 to Richard Stanford on
the basis of one per cent of the total proceeds. With this transaction the
sale of 1804 may be said to have closed. Other widely divergent preoccupations were now crowding the King's Spanish Merinos to one
side. The proposals for an expedition to Africa were germinating with
speed and a communication to Lord Camden on the subject was shaping
in his mind. Mungo Park had returned from Peebles in Scotland to
accept the leadership of his last expedition, under some pressure from
Banks, but now with the final consent of his wife. At the same time
Banks's thoughts were far away with Matthew Flinders, imprisoned
on Mauritius by the French General de Caen and then in close confinement. Camden had agreed to his attempt to procure the liberation
of Flinders entirely on his own statement to the French Institut National
free from Government intervention, and these things were taking
effective form as August and its agricultural excitements gave way
once more to the domestic problems of autumn at Revesby Abbey.

VI

No rain splashed from the dragons of the Pagoda on Friday, 16 August 1805, as the second exhibition and sale of rams and ewes took place.[43] Some invisible *muezzin* of the Merino faith must have called faint but compelling in the early dawn of that mild summer day for almost from sunrise some enthusiastic amateurs were already treading the green lawn in search of knowledge. In particular, it was noted that Mr. Nehemiah Bartley, the energetic and voluble Secretary of the Bath and West of England Society, was early abroad with his two sons, Messrs. G. and R. Bartley of London. The pens separating each lot were again set out under the shade of a row of trees, forming an 'agreeable promenade'. Mr. Bartley remained all day in the forefront of this 'numerous mixed company of agriculturalists and breeders' eager to seize this 'excellent opportunity for examination and discussion of the merits and defects, both in wool and carcass of these highly valued strangers'. The show was appointed to begin at ten in the morning, but long before that time the seventeen rams and the twenty-one ewes were surrounded by a critical company. Not all, by any means, were impressed with what they saw. The sheep themselves were all said to be in high condition 'but the wool was not equal to the general expectation'. Several samples were produced from among the company of staples from Merino-Ryeland and Merino-Southdown crosses 'which were not degraded by specimens plucked from the finest parts of the Royal Flock'. Nor was beauty of form by any means a prevalent feature among these 'highly valued strangers', as Sir Joseph Banks himself was heard to remark jocularly during the course of the day. High condition did not conceal that angularity of form so painful to the breeder of fat stock; 'the shoulder and hip bones were prominent'. As we review the evidence before and after the event, in fact, we come to doubt the existence of this 'high condition'. We can appreciate the inner conflicts and the expressed doubts of the 'intelligent gentlemen' collected about the show pens. 'A very great inclination to buy appeared in the company although many fears were expressed in the pursuit of the breed of losing all the advantage of carcass without obtaining an adequate encouragement in wool.' There can be no doubt that 1805 was not notable for the attractive state of His Majesty's Spanish sheep. As an occasion the sale of this year was financially and socially a huge success. As an episode in the progress of the Spanish flock it was a public disaster. There was more than one hint of this during the day. It is clear that Banks knew that all was not right. It is clear also that he did not fully know how far things had gone wrong.

The morning passed in the best fashion of all Merino ram sales then or since—in argument, discussion, and speculation about prices. The previous year seemed to have set a standard and many had come in hopes that such prices would rule again. Many would leave the field near the Pagoda at the day's end disappointed and surprised at the soaring values. It may be too much to suggest that this was due to the persuasion of 'the rural Christie', John Farnham, who was again on the field to sell the sheep. We must, however, recognize the merits of his rousing exordium as a model of what an auctioneer's opening appeal could be.

The day was warm and bright. By the early afternoon a great concourse of carriages had assembled. The Royal sheep became the mute, quivering victims 'of a large number of spectators, including some of the fair sex, whose forms might well vie with those who observe the flocks of Arcadia'. Sir Joseph Banks appeared on the field but lately recovered from a further attack of his almost habitual gout. With him were many 'noble and conspicuous persons' in whose company he gradually moved towards the southernmost pen. To this he conducted the 'fair nobility', the Countess of Jersey and her sister-in-law, Lady Caroline Villiers,[44] and here the attention of every eye and ear was now directed. At two o'clock the sale commenced as Mr. Farnham, 'with much justice and eloquence' rose to the exalted level that seemed to be required:

Gentlemen: In addition to the high honour which I have in appearing before you on this occasion it gives me extreme pleasure to see myself surrounded by so many gentlemen who favour'd me with their attention at last years sale. I have, therefore, great satisfaction in informing you that the individuals at present offered to your notice, are, I believe in most instances much superior to those of last, year, and that they are selected almost indiscriminately from the King's capital flock of the pure Spanish breed, some of the rams of which have been successfully used in his own flock, and all the ewes produced lambs. I need scarcely observe to my present auditory, that in the establishment of this annual sale his Majesty is influenced by that gracious consideration which has actuated all his conduct for so many years, creating a wish to disperse by the only possible means through every part of his dominions, a breed which may tend to enrich his subjects, and render them more independent. I shall add no more than to hope that with your wonted liberality, you will meet the gracious views I have stated, keeping in sight that no other opportunity will be afforded you till this time next year.[45]

The first lot, a shearling ram (and the worst in appearance of his fifteen brethren) with small horns, opened at 6 guineas and astounded the company by being knocked down at £22 11s. 6d. This sheep excited the comment from Mr. Farnham 'that what is sunk in the horns is saved on the shoulder'. The point led to some ripe argument about the virtues of polled sheep, but Nehemiah Bartley would have none of it and declared stoutly that horns were characteristic of the Spanish breed. Lot 15, the last of the shearling rams, was a contrast to the first being a remarkably fine sheep who would have been retained in the Royal flock for breeding but for a diminutive black spot on the face. He was sold for 46 guineas to Mr. Bell of Norfolk. Lot 17, the second of the two four-toothed rams used in the flock, and the last of the rams sold was declared by Mr. Farnham to be a descendant of Old Snags—a sire now almost as famous in the Royal flock as Eclipse was among racing stock. The semblance of a hurt appeared on its head. This was explained but no doubt served to lower its price for, despite its exalted ancestry, this ram only brought 33 guineas where Lot 16 topped the sale at 64 guineas.

The sale proceeded briskly to its end with seventeen rams sold for an average of £34 14s. 2d. and twenty-one ewes for an average of £24 3s. capped by a smart shower of rain from which the President of the Royal Society refused to flinch.[46] As on the first sale day the scene of business became confused as vehicles of all kinds were produced to convey the sheep away. In one corner of the field 'the celebrated, respectable, and good Mr. [John Julius] Angerstein, reckless of Lloyds' was to be seen cording up his cart full of sheep. Elsewhere a man of fashion was observed helping a ram into a carriage, 'with an enthusiasm of the most laudable kind'. Everywhere it was 'a picture of the greatest hilarity'. As before, all this haste was unnecessary for it was again announced that the sheep could remain on His Majesty's most excellent pasture at the convenience of the purchaser.

Among all this genteel levity of the successful buyers other groups were forming to exchange views on many things. Sir Joseph Banks 'with his usual affability' found himself closely engaged in contraverting many opinions and rumours circulating about the selection of the King's sheep, not least about those which had been exposed for sale that very day. No! The President of the Royal Society would not admit the superiority accorded to Lord Somerville's flock. Yes! Some of the young rams had died on near-by land of the King's that had been over-flown by the river during the past winter of a disease that Sir Joseph believed arose out of the locality. No! Sir Joseph could not agree with complaints about the unproductiveness of the wool. Dr. Parry had obtained as much as 17s. 11d. per fleece. Sir Joseph had received 19s. 4d. to 19s. 6d. and one gentleman who had complained heavily about this unproductiveness had at the same time announced he had got £1 1s. per fleece! Yes! Sir Joseph always clipped his lambs which is according to the Spanish custom.

Mr. Nehemiah Bartley, tireless and disputatious to the end, was observed to expound his practice in the breeding and management of

the Spanish Merino to Sir Joseph at some length and to win his approbation. A Spanish ram in his possession had clipped $11\frac{3}{4}$ pounds of wool
which when scoured fit for the manufacturer had yielded $6\frac{1}{2}$ pounds
equal or superior to any Spanish imported wool and worth 8s. per
pound! Splendid! Mr. Bartley's charges about the deficiencies of the
wool staplers (an eminent one standing near at the time), however,
'rather embarrassed the politeness and good nature of the President'.
It was rumoured also that the celebrated Thomas William Coke had
lately purchased a Merino ram from Mr. George Tollet with a view to
crossing with some of his English fine-woolled sheep—his Southdowns,
it was believed. Mr. Tollet was not present at the sale this year to confirm this so no one could attest to this marvel. Somewhere among the
pens Mr. George Garrard, the well-known animal painter and sculptor,
was quietly sketching such of the Royal sheep as he could find in relative seclusion, thinking no doubt of their place in his great work, the
picture of the Woburn meeting, in which he was making 'considerable
progress'. Mr. Franz Bauer, the botanical artist was also there bearing
in his hat a mildewed ear of wheat which Sir Joseph had promised later
to examine with proper attention—for the conversation was not all on
sheep and wool. In fact the President of the Royal Society had just performed a brilliant diagnosis for the same person whose other infected
specimen Mr. Bauer was preserving so carefully. In this other head of
wheat the cups were quite empty and it had been studied with much
curiosity by some bystanders when Sir Joseph, with his usual affability,
undeceived them, by pronouncing it as a depredation of the birds—
what had been considered a defect of nature!

The rigours of this enlightening occasion were by no means ended for
the devoted enthusiasts of the Spanish breed. At five o'clock that afternoon a select party, including Mr. John Julius Angerstein and Mr.
Nehemiah Bartley, 'the eminent advocate of the Spanish breed', sat
down to a 'petite dinner' with Sir Joseph Banks at 'his seat at Small
Borough Green', the forerunner, it was hoped, of others to be repeated
annually on a larger scale. As it was reported, 'the feast of reason and
the flow of soul commenced and many subjects connected with the
business of the day discussed with much attention'. After the cloth was
removed, the following toast, agreed upon to be the annual one, was
proposed by the irrepressible Mr. Bartley and drunk with much
enthusiasm: 'The Royal Fleece, may the King live to see it flourish in
every province of his United Kingdom.' This and many others were
'intermixed with many sensible and valuable communications from all
parties relative to their native districts'. The day ended happily at ten
with the company 'perfectly satisfied with the object of their meeting,
and each other . . .'.

VII

In such a state of euphoria have many stud sheep sales ended. Then later has come the reckoning, sometimes next day, sometimes many months after. Where had the sale sheep of 1805 found their new homes? One thing was certain, none had gone to New South Wales. Still, compared with last year, they were more widely dispersed in Great Britain. Two rams and five ewes were going to the estate of Mr. Angerstein in Norfolk; a ram and two ewes were purchased for Lord Mansfield's estate near Scone in Perthshire; Stanford, the King's Shepherd bought a ram and two ewes for Mr. George Evans to go to his farm near Rathdrum in Ireland; three ewes were destined for Mr. J. Fector near Dover in Kent; another two ewes for the Reverend J. C. Beckingham at Bourn near Canterbury in the same county; a ram and two ewes had been acquired by William Aiton the younger the King's Gardener at Kew for Lord Powis on the borders of Hereford-shire; Mr. George Holme Sumner near Guildford in Surrey had taken one young ram; Mr. John Woods of Sussex had bought one ewe; Mr. John Lucas of Somerset a young ram. So were the Spanish Merino genes scattered from the field near the Pagoda in the summer of 1805.

Banks could look back on the record of this sale with much satisfaction, pleased to see that the sheep had sold for more than their estimated value, delighted that now the Spanish sheep seemed at last to have achieved a tangible and solid public appreciation. For twelve years, he confessed to Snart,[47] he had been obliged to appeal to the King to have patience in the outcome and at last in this year's response to the public sale it seemed that the nation appreciated the patriotic action of His Majesty in introducing the Spanish breed. Moreover, his calculations just before the sale had shown that the whole flock in 1804 had brought the King more than six guineas a head, a larger profit he ventured to suppose than any individual has made by a flock except those who traded in the letting of rams.[48] What more could he have done?

There was one thing missing that had always worried Banks. None of the leading agriculturists had attended this year's sale except one, and he did not buy because he said the sheep were too dear.[49] Banks, however, before the sale, had done something to rectify this too evident flaw in an otherwise well-executed design. Some two weeks earlier he had asked Robert Fulke Greville, now the King's Groom of the Bed-chamber, to look in on him at the barn opposite the Pagoda in Kew Lane where he intended sorting the sheep to be sold, evidently with the idea of broaching his plan.[50] Greville seems not to have been able to keep the tryst and, on 4 August 1805, Banks found it necessary to disclose by letter to Greville that his good friend Thomas William Coke was anxious to make a trial of the Merino breed if he could but get some ewes.[51] Banks felt that Coke's patronage of the breed would do more to interest the general public in it than the attention of any other agriculturist in the country. He had, therefore, allowed Coke to have three ewes before the sale by private treaty and he hoped the King would approve. This piece of news, however, did not reach the King at that stage, as he was apparently suffering much from his eyes and the 'flying rheumatism' and was not to be worried more than necessary. So the matter rested until after the sale, when Banks hastened to send Greville who was now with the King at Weymouth, two marked catalogues setting out the financial success of the sale, with the buyers and the prices. These were laid before His Majesty on 18 August. The King was greatly pleased with the result but on finding that Coke had bought privately before the sale became suddenly very angry and accused Banks of not keeping faith with the public to whom it had been made known that all the sheep would now be sold by auction only and none privately. Neither Greville nor Snart who was also there when this tirade broke were given an opportunity of explaining the full reasons for Banks's well-intentioned deviation.[52]

Perhaps at no other time in his life did Banks ever suffer such a devastating injury to his self-esteem. Out of the clear sky of Royal blue under which he basked on the full tide of success Jove's thunderbolt had struck him down. The friendly association of twenty years seemed to have evaporated in one burst of hot and, so it seemed to Banks, unreasoning anger. He could not be comforted or in any way reassured by Greville who wrote:

I am happy to say *all is calm again*. A little fret of Wind you know often flutters a sail, suddenly, but it soon fills again, & We glide away delightfully —So it has been with us here since I wrote to You yesterday—H.M. at the King's Lodge yesterday Eveng. came up to me in the Music Room, & in *great good humour* said, 'I now understand the business of the Sheep better'. This Encouraging Exordium brought on further conversation, & He talked fully on the advantages of the Spanish Flock—& on the Sale.[53]

Within five short days of what had seemed his moment of undiluted triumph everything had crumbled. The enjoyment of his, and the King's, 'favorite hobby' had gone. On 20 August he sat down in Soho Square and wrote three long letters to Greville explaining and justifying his conduct but in no way won over to think of the episode as a 'flurry' or 'the ebulition of a moment'.[54] To Banks the trouble ran deeper. He had noticed an increasing irritability in the King's attitude and would rather be dismissed than remain on sufferance only. He had felt the blow conveyed by Greville's first letter very poignantly as he had at all times done his duty to His Majesty with zeal and fidelity.[55] The case of Mr. Coke's ewes had seemed clear to him. If Coke had not bought them from the King he would have acquired them from Lord Somerville. In the King's interests he had deemed it wise not to make a rival of so able a breeder and had allowed the private sale accordingly. He had avoided troubling the King in this matter as His Majesty had earlier approved the similar case of stock for the Duke of Bedford without demur. In the midst of this apologia came that long letter from Greville of 19 August setting out more details of what had passed, leaving him assured that matters were at least no worse but not assuaging his bitterness in any way. His spirits were raised but he hastened to make it clear to Greville that he could not take pleasure any longer in managing His Majesty's concerns. Up till now the confidence reposed in him by His Majesty had been unbounded and in no case abused. He felt now that he must resign a trust from which that confidence had evidently been withdrawn. He had no wish to meet again a reverse as unexpected as it was undeserved. He valued Greville's friendship in the affair for 'how rare was the man who, time and again, in the teeth of (he was sorry to say) a capricious master would seek to avert an unprovoked vengeance falling on his friend's head at the risk of diverting it to his own'. He hoped that after some rest his feelings would subside, but thought that time would confirm and patient reasoning approve the plan he had suggested.[56]

Banks for the moment had emptied the deep well of his inmost feelings. The annual pilgrimage to Lincolnshire was near and soon he set off northward away from an enterprise that had suddenly turned to ashes under his hand. Before he left Soho Square he wrote to Richard Snart declaring his intention to resign the management of the Royal flock as his increasing infirmities prevented him from continuing his labours to perfect it, and asking Snart to intimate this to the King at the first favourable opportunity.[57]

At Overton in Derbyshire a letter from Greville overtook him, written at Weymouth on 25 August:

However we may have been grieved at the tenor of our late correspondence I have now the happiness of informing you that the issue has been most flattering, & must necessarily afford you the most heart-felt satisfaction & the most lasting comfort.

The Justification You were pleased to confide to me, I have very carefully attended to Ever since I received it, & I was anxious that so clear a statement of the circumstances which had given rise to it, should at a favourable moment be made known to His Majesty, according to your Wishes—

The distribution of time & situation here might have deprived Us long of an opportunity, had I trusted to what was within my own reach; but at present, the more favourable & more frequent opportunities I was aware, were thro' Mr Snart who His Majesty sees daily, & often converses with on agricultural business—

I read over your Paper with Him, & with a few hints thereon, I confided it to his kind offices, & He promised to avail Himself of the first favorable opportunity of acquainting His Majesty, that I had put him in possession of a Paper from You, which contained a plain narrative of the whole transaction.

This Morning Mr. Snart had His Majesty's permission to read it, & it called forth from H.M. Every kind attention, & flattering Expression towards You that You could wish. His Majesty *was quite affected*, & much greived [*sic*] that You should have felt so much, & He was pleased to add, that what You did, You had done with the best intentions, but that as *You* had proposed to have *all* sold by Auction in future, He had not expected any deviations & that this had occasion'd his surprise—His Majesty was pleased to desire Mr Snart to acquaint Me with this conversation, & of His wish that You should think no more on the Subject.

I hasten to send You My Dear Sir Joseph these glad tidings, as pleasing to Me as they can be to Yourself, & I am sure You can now, have no other Wish, or Intention than to continue with confidence & cheerfulness Your useful & kind Exertions in the future Management of His Majesty's Merino Flock, and that You will never recollect hereafter, the Pang You have so lately felt—[58]

This courtly emollient did much to ease Banks's mind of the more acute irritant. His intention of resigning the management of the flock, however, he would not alter. Greville's friendly efforts through the whole painful affair he valued most highly but at the last they had cast salt on the very wound they were intended to soothe. For Banks felt deeply hurt that the vindication of his personal character to his Sovereign and old friend had been entrusted to Richard Snart, a man who was not in his eyes a gentleman either by birth or by education. Even in writing to the gentle and well-meaning Greville words almost failed to express his inner horror at this turn which 'makes my soul tremble'. It seemed that all discretion was at an end when the servant was admitted to the secret embarrassment of the master.

Banks was right. Something had changed most radically in the delicately balanced but complex pattern of human relationships which Time had woven about the Spanish flock. A heavy silence of nearly a year now fell abruptly over communications from Windsor Castle and Marsh Gate. No word from Snart came to Banks about his proffered resignation from the care of the Royal flock. No word came about the settlement of the annual accounts for 1804. No word came to Sir Joseph about anything concerning the Spanish flock except scab! On this subject there were words enough but all from far outside the Royal circle. Trouble seemed to breed trouble. His gout recurred and re-curred again. His integrity had been impugned by the King. General Campbell's ram purchased in 1804 seemed to have introduced scab into his flock in Scotland, and now the Lincolnshire quicksilver cure was proving worse than the disease itself.[59] Mr. George Evans's young ram bought at the recent sale in 1805 had died unsound, the 'lungs in a state of rottenness'.[60] Mr. Fector of Dover was complaining bitterly that his three ewes bought at the same sale had also proved to have the scab which from various circumstances he believed was present in them at the time of purchase. He was demanding sound ewes in their stead.[61] Still firm in his intention to relinquish the daily business of the flock Banks passed these complaints and inquiries on to Snart, making it clear to the complainants that he was no longer in charge of these affairs, but offering every reasonable advice.[62] The silence of Mr. Snart continued, dense and impenetrable. Sir Joseph's gout plagued and immobilized him to the point of incapacity, exacerbated by the more subtle torture of being utterly ignored by 'the man who was not a gentleman by birth or education'. The affairs of the Spanish flock were drifting into a deplorable confusion. Everything about it was charged with odd psychological conflicts.

As the months passed and Sir Joseph's first hard feelings subsided, it became gradually more clear to him that somehow his intentions had been misconstrued. To resign from active management of the flock for whatever reasons did not, to him, mean complete and utter segregation from its affairs. For nearly a whole year he lay in a sort of limbo. On one side he was assailed by the epistolary darts of an injured public, on the other he was chilled by a Court reticence that went beyond even his own varied experiences in that quarter. Unable to sustain this form of suspense any longer he turned again to 'Colonel Wellbred'. On 22 July 1806 he wrote at length to Greville asking him to intercede in some way to break the barrier of silence, reminding him of his letter to Richard Snart nearly eleven months before and which with five sub-sequent letters remained unanswered.[63] Greville's quiet and easy charm again smoothed away difficulties. One week later on 29 July Snart was constrained to write under command from His Majesty, hoping that Sir Joseph's health would improve and enable him to continue his management of the flock which no one else could do to such general advantage. His Majesty was pleased also to express his unqualified approbation of the zeal and ability he had always displayed and to thank him for the offer of advice which would always be accepted whenever necessity demanded it. Snart was also commanded to wait upon Banks to settle the accounts of the past two years.[64]

All of these kind sentiments Banks acknowledged but, while conceding that his health was better, remained adamant in his intention to resign the charge which had been 'his chief pleasure and principal honour for many years'.[65] There was by now no longer any doubt that, however much his feelings may have been lacerated in the painful incidents of the previous summer, Banks was sincerely aware that his physical handicaps alone were sufficient to make such a resignation necessary. The same truth was by now clear to Snart as inescapable. Nor was Snart by any means sure that after all he would relish wearing the mantle of responsibility for the Spanish flock whatever brief and grandiose delusions he may have enjoyed in the months of Banks's most acute discomfiture. Just what odd thoughts had been exercising Snart's mind during the past year we can only guess, but he clearly had much of which he was glad to be rid when he burst into a form of confession to Banks on 11 August:

> It is impossible, Sir, that I can attempt to offer an apology for the Neglect I have most unfortunately been guilty of, in not answering your former Letters—Some peculiar Circumstances, of a private Nature, have indeed occasioned me the most poignant uneasiness, and rendered me inattentive to those Duties which ought in no wise to have been neglected—I have frequently attempted to address you, and the Sensations arising from the consciousness of my previous Error have as frequently rendered me unable to proceed—I am so fully sensible of the Impropriety of this Conduct, that I cannot expect your entire Forgiveness of what is past—but I trust you will at least believe me that it has not been occasioned by any want of respect towards yourself—
>
> I have hitherto had it in my Power to pay so little attention to the pro-perties of the Merino Sheep, that I feel myself quite unequal to make a due selection of the Rams and Ewes for the ensuing Sale—I should therefore esteem it a particular Obligation if you would have the goodness to under-take a Task which your unremitting Attention & Judgement would render so serviceable to His Majesty—[66]

Ignoring this elaborate *mea culpa* Banks chose to conclude that the request for aid in selecting the sheep for the sale of 1806 was made by His Majesty's orders. As such he could with honour and alacrity rise to the emergency. On 15 August he drafted the sale sheep and set the state of the Merino flock for the ensuing year. There was no time to be lost if proper faith with the public were to be kept. He left full directions with John Farnham for his guidance in the management of the sale as though there never had been any unpleasant rift during the past year. Appearances were further preserved by the news of his restored health and his selection of the sale sheep finding a place in the news of the day. However, there was no change in his resolve to separate himself from the active care of the experimental flock. This point he repeated again to Snart on 16 August and with it his opinion and fears on the prospects for the sale:

I deem it proper that I Should absent myself from the Sale this year as the properest means of making the Public acquainted that H. M. has been graciously pleasd to allow me to Resign the Care of the Flock, which in Truth has been for several years so ill attended to owing to my infirmities [that] had not Mr Laycocke assisted me I must several years ago have begd the Permissn I have now

I Fear the very untoward circumstances of the Sheep having been Last year infected with the Scab when they were sold & the still more unpleasant one of Several of the Ewes sold being then with Lamb which has spread the Knowledge of the Shepherds extreme ill Conduct far & wide will have an ill Effect on the Sale of this year I Sincerely hope these circumstances will not be so disadvantageous to it as my fears prompt me to suppose[67]

VIII

The *Particular and Conditions of Sale* for 1806 were arranged by John Farnham with more than usual dispatch.[68] On Friday, 15 August, Banks had selected the thirty-one rams and twenty aged ewes for sale. On Tuesday, 19 August, the auction took place.[69] The proceedings followed the pattern now well established, but the forecast made by Banks the previous week was only too well sustained by the event itself. Few buyers attended. The bidding was far from eager though the sheep were admitted to be in unexceptionable condition both in point of wool and of carcass, and certainly better than at the previous sale. The results were in the end well below those of 1805.[70] To the buyers this seemed to be a distinct gain on what had seemed to many to have been excessive prices, 'exaggerated by the competition of amateurs in this art'. To Banks it was a clear recession arising from bad management at all points.

This year a total of thirty-one rams was sold of which as usual the majority were yearlings; three only were four-tooths and two were full mouthed. Of these last one was the famous Old Snags himself bought by William Aiton on behalf of Mr. Cole for a paltry 18 guineas where one of his sons the previous year had brought 64 guineas from Mr. Angerstein. The average price for all the rams was £17 4s. and for the twenty aged or full-mouthed ewes £12 7s., in both cases one half of the averages for the previous year, 1805. The sale itself was as unremarkable as Banks had foreseen; a diminished company, few bidders, and they lacking in enthusiasm. There is little doubt that the gossip of the countryside had spread the tale of scab-infested sheep. We cannot doubt either that the absence of Sir Joseph deprived the event of a dynamic element that could in other circumstances have done much to offset the eroding effects of such gossip. Altogether it was a strange anticlimax to the soaring optimism of 1805.

It was, however, a year in which many salutary lessons were learned by all concerned with the Spanish flock. Although public interest may have waxed and waned as it eventually did to the point of extinction, the fiasco of dissension and disease was never repeated. The remaining sales proceeded to the predestined finale four years later with a reasonable mutual understanding on all sides. The first sign of this renewed harmony came quickly after the sale. Banks had received a letter from the Duke of Richmond too late for effective action at the sale:

> On every Account, but particularly as a fellow Sufferer from the Gout, I rejoice to see in the Papers what I hope is true, that you are much recovered. as they also mention that you have selected His Majesty's Marino [*sic*] sheep for Sale on Tuesday next, may I hope that without Indiscretion I might beg of you to have bought for me one Ram and two Ewes that you could recommend for their Shape as well as the Fineness of wool, as make is very essential to enable Sheep to stand the cold of our Hills, [at Midhurst in Sussex] the distance they must travel for their food, and the constant folding they must be subject to, besides the Benefit to be derived from the Butcher. I believe my Flock of South Down is as perfect as any, in all these particulars, and though I wish to cross with the Marino Breed for the still greater Improvement of the wool yet I should not like to do so at the Expence of other Merits. I therefore should particularly wish to have the shape of such as you may have the Goodness to chuse for me as perfect as possible. The Price must of Course be that of the Market at the Time of Sale.[71]

Promptly on 20 August, the day after the public auction, Banks transmitted this request to Snart for His Majesty's notice and a suitable determination, recommending that this favour should be granted for the credit of the Royal flock as His Grace was a considerable breeder and a judicious sheep master.[72] For the ram he suggested that the Duke should have 'the one with the least horns between the numbers 21 and 26 inclusive' at 20 guineas; for the ewes it was to be two fourtooths of good shape at 15 guineas each. To this Snart replied the following day piously agreeing that the Duke should not seek sheep elsewere[73] and a week later was able to tell Banks that the King had granted this dispensation to the Duke.[74] There was no 'flurry', no 'ebulition', nothing but the quiet granting of what was in essence the very same request that, in the case of Thomas William Coke's ewes exactly one year ago, had produced such a devastating reaction. Banks's motives were never again called into question by the King. Snart's relations with Banks fell quietly back into those of servant and master and no further 'peculiar Circumstances of a private Nature' produced any 'poignant uneasiness' in Snart's breast or rendered him 'inattentive to those Duties which ought in no wise to have been neglected'. Only Banks's gout remained thereafter as the devil that would be cast out.

There still remained also certain problems of restitution and recompense to the afflicted purchasers of sheep from the sale of 1805—General Patrick Campbell of Bude in Scotland; Mr. George Evans of Rathdrum in Ireland; and the egregious Mr. John Fector of Dover. The King at Banks's recommendation was pleased to assign a ram each for Scotland and Ireland, but Mr. Fector was deliberately ignored as he wrote in a tone that Sir Joseph did not like—a point that seems to have made itself apparent for we hear no more from Dover.[75]

There was a brief confession, too, by Snart that he and John Farnham had connived (with the most noble motives of aiding the prices in the sale) in buying some of the rams. In this action Snart seems to have assumed that Banks would wholly approve. But Banks begged Snart to understand very clearly that he had given *no* opinion about any such action.[76] Whatever the ethical deviation it is by no means easy to determine who in fact bought what sheep in this sale of 1806. Neither Farnham's nor Snart's names appear on the final list of buyers and it is to be presumed that they bought the rams with the time-honoured assistance of a dummy. But who? We can account for the purchases of all but two men with reasonable certainty. The two in question are William Aiton and a Mr. Eden. General evidence suggests that Aiton's three rams were bought on behalf of a Mr. Cole who had Old Snags (Lot 30), while the other two (Lots 11 and 31) went to Lord Powis (2nd Lord Clive). By elimination we are left to suppose in the absence of any other evidence that the unknown Mr. Eden operated on behalf of Farnham and Snart. Eden in fact is the one man who bought more sheep in a single public auction at Kew than John Macarthur and it is noteworthy that until he began to intrude in the bidding the prices for the young rams were much below the average obtained. We may on the whole suspect Eden of being the cover-man though no single document is available to prove it. Nor have we a clue to the ultimate disposal of the twelve rams he acquired.

IX

The year 1807 opened with the young rams again in low condition and suffering from an obscure 'distemper'. Mr. William Moorcroft, the veterinary surgeon, was called to consider the matter.[77] After removing two of the more advanced cases to his establishment at 220 Oxford Street for observation and experiment he considered there was some hope of success in curing the remainder. At his request they were transferred to the Queen's gardens in Buckingham Palace grounds to be more convenient of access for the purpose of his treatment.[78] After about two months in this quarter Moorcroft pronounced them fit enough to return to Kew.[79]

In May, Banks received news of Farnham's death from Joseph Hall and the immediate offer of his own services:

I have the melancholy misfortune (as Executor) to acquaint you of the death of my late friend Mr. [John] Farnham; and as I have attended the Sale of his Majesty's Spanish flock every year to receive the deposits, I beg leave to offer my services to sell the flock next August for the benefit of Mr. Farnham's Widow; I have not the vanity to plead the abilities of my late worthy friend but I shall be happy to exert my endeavours for the benefit of the Sale[80]

Within a week came another approach for this morsel of patronage on behalf of a Mr. William Stanton of Hitchin who, it appears, was 'very desirous of the appointment not on account of its intrinsick value merely, but as it leads to most respectable connections'.[81] Sir John Sebright called in person upon Sir Joseph to add his commendation,[82] but in the end neither William Stanton nor Joseph Hall were chosen to bear John Farnham's torch. Mr. Daniel Smith of Windsor, not insignificantly, inherited the task and carried the public sales through for the remaining four years of their established course.[83]

A somewhat plaintive postscript to a letter of 22 July—'Pray tell me when the King's Sale is to be'[84]—produced a visit from Snart and Daniel Smith to Spring Grove the following day but Banks was absent. These gentlemen then went on to Kew alone to ascertain the numbers of the sheep available for sale after Henry Lacocke had made his accustomed selection. The sale day this year was to be Tuesday, 11 August, the date determined, so Snart averred, at his last visit to Banks. No shearling rams were to be sold on this occasion for in spite of the ministrations of William Moorcroft they were not considered fit to be exposed to the public gaze. So the sale stock consisted of fourteen four-toothed and two six-toothed rams, one six-toothed ewe and twenty-four full-mouthed ewes to which another very fat old ewe was added at the last moment— forty-two head in all.[85]

Daniel Smith opened the sale at half past one after a brief auctioneer's spiel which seems to have been of a traditional but not an inspired or lyrical quality.[86] It was to be noted more for the few pieces of useful knowledge cast at the feet of the small company of faithful supporters intent upon business. Though the day was fine it was not the social occasion of former years, but it was marked by the return of Banks once again to the field near the Pagoda. The sheep were said to have fleeces as fine or finer than those of any so far sold and to be visibly improved in size. Moreover, Smith stated the the rams on sale that day had 'sheared ten pounds each of washed wool and the ewes four and a half pounds on the average, the wool having this year been washed on the sheep's backs according to the English custom'. Perhaps with an eye to the presence of Sir George Mackenzie from Ross-shire some further statements were made about the hardiness of the breed and their ability to withstand the climate of Shetland or the most northern and exposed of the British Isles as their success in Sweden, for example, well testified. This theme was certainly the keynote of the day for at the end it was seen that the young Fellow of the Royal Society had acquired eight sheep (three rams and five ewes) for his small flock at Coul—a purchase that bore comparison with that of John Macarthur at the first sale. To be noted also was the small group bought by Charles Henry Hunt for his flock near Christchurch in Hampshire—one ram and six ewes. Both these men were within the next few years to leave their mark in the literature of the breed with their small treatises. The prices for rams ranged from £14 3s. 6d. to £43 1s. and averaged £24 15s. 6d. Those for the ewes ranged from £10 10s. to £32 11s. and averaged £20 3s. 1d. This was altogether an excellent recovery from the depressed values of the former year. It was stimulated perhaps by the informative presence of Sir Joseph Banks and by the keen competition of a few intelligent men who were clear in their objectives and determined to make the most of the present opportunity to get their experimental material. The day closed on a note of mild levity with Lot 42, the fat old ewe, passing under the hammer to Mr. John Tharpe of Chippenham in Cambridgeshire at £21 to general laughter at Mr. Smith's description of her as that '"rara avis" a fat Merino ewe'.

The next day Snart sent Banks the details of the sale as set out by Daniel Smith's clerk with the news that Charles Hunt had agreed to take one of the 'refuse' or cull rams with the black spots at the approximate price of the sale, £24. Hunt had also agreed to take twenty of the 'half bred ewes' (Merino×Ryeland cross most probably)—ten at 3 guineas and ten at 50s. each. Moreover, said Snart:

No Gentleman having expressed a Disappointment, otherwise than in Consequence of the high Prices. I did not deem it prudent to name our Intention of parting with more of the Flock—Lest any Applications should however be made, I shall Leave Directions with the Shepherd when I return to Windsor on Friday, to sell the three remaining Refuse Rams & likewise Six or eight [refuse] ewes—With respect to the latter although the average of those sold has been £20. 3. 0. yet the average of the thirteen lots from 21 to 33 both inclusive was £26. 10. 6. & as the Ewes remaining are fully equal or even better than those sold we may be depreciating the Value of them by asking less than five and twenty guineas each—Should you be of a different opinion and will have the Goodness to favour me with a Line, I shall not fail to act accordingly.[87]

Banks immediately concurred with these arrangements[88] though it is difficult to reconcile the prices set for these private treaty sales with the earlier description of these 'refuse ewes'—'8 are coloured, 4 useless, I barren'.

A week later Snart was troubled to receive a letter from Hunt conveying his disappointment at the ram (Lot 1) he had bought at the sale, declaring that it was below his standard 'as a prominent breeder from His Majesty's Merino sheep'.[89] He proposed that he should return it in exchange for 'the sore-backed ram' if a lower price than £25 were asked. Snart appealed for Banks's judgement, 'feeling anxious for the Reputation of His Majesty's Merino Flock'. Whereupon Sir Joseph replied:

I went yesterday morn by appointment with the Shepherd to take my Parting view of the Merino Flock intending to have made some memorandums about matching them but as he had savd himself the trouble of bringing Hurdles my visit provd of Little use.

I Examind the Sore backd Ram & Nº 1 which Mr Hunt wishes to get rid of how Mr H came to chuse the first sheep in the Catalogue if he meant to buy a good one is for him to decide all I can say on the subject is that the first & consequently the worst sheep in our opinion in the Catalogue is the Last we should wish to take back

I have no doubt however as Mr Hunt is a good Customer of the Prudence of Letting him Ease himself of that Sheep if he wishes to take the Sore backed Sheep instead of him at 25 guineas for after the success of this years Sale which portends a still further advance in the next year I would not advise the abatement of a Farthing as I have no doubt now that the Sheep will bring more than 25 next year This is just what you propose So let him Leave his Nº 1 & Take Sore back paying the difference[90]

Once again the delicate equipoise was maintained between the ethic of the sale ring and the spirit of public service and scientific detachment —but obviously not without some difficulty.

X

It now seems fairly clear that 1807 was the year in which Banks intended finally to withdraw from an active physical part in the management of the flock and that he was seeking the means to establish effective substitutes for his own personal contributions. What he referred to as his 'Parting view of the Merino Flock' seems to have been on 20 August when the shepherd 'savd himself the trouble of bringing

Hurdles' and his visit 'provd of Little use'. Since that abortive occasion he had arranged for Thomas Walton from Lincolnshire to look over the sheep, arrange the matings for the ensuing year, and in particular to select the rams, and to advise thereon. All this was rendered the more important as Henry Lacocke's health was declining and his activities of former years not to be counted on. Walton accordingly had sorted the ewe flock at Kew into three breeding groups about the time that Banks set out for Revesby. He had also inspected the young rams at Richmond and found them in such a miserable state that he could not perform any satisfactory selection. When this examination was attempted again in late November it was only to find that the King had ordered that no more rams should be castrated. Banks found this news unpalatable and wrote to Snart accordingly:

> From Some misunderstanding which I cannot understand Mr Walton who I orderd to Look over the Rams of Last year & give me his opinion about them did not see them he tells me the King has orderd that no more Rams are to be Cut
>
> I shall always pay implicit Obedience to the King's Commands & never think myself justified in Enquiring into H M Reasons I confess however that I see no means we can have of meeting the Competition which is now fast Rising up from Ld Somerville Mr Tollet & others unless we make considerable selection & Employ a proper person Mr Walton is the Properest man in England all who manage valuable Sheep in the Parts of England most Curious in Sheep well know it was for that Reason that I took him as my assistant to enable me to give good advice about the Flock when my advice was asked for.[91]

On this unquiet note the matter seems to have ended and Thomas Walton 'the Properest man in England' to advise on matters affecting the Royal flock seems to have retired defeated by circumstances beyond his control.

The winter passed and summer brought old Henry Lacocke from his chair to hobble loyally among the flock choosing the rams as had for some years been his custom about the time of their shearing (on 15 or 16 June 1808), setting aside the rams for sale. This year also he was asked by Snart 'to Select out the Handsom's Ram & Ewe for the painter to take their Likeness to present them to his Majesty'.[92] If old Lacocke was abroad in spite of his lameness it was not long before Banks was again confined by gout and his failing limbs which prevented him from attending the public sale for that year. Snart commiserated with him according to the well-established formula, on 14 August sent him the particulars of the Spanish sheep, and informed him that the applications had been more than usual.[93] Among other things John Tharpe, who had bought the fat old ewe at the last sale, was now anxious to buy the black ewes and for this Snart sought Banks's advice as he himself doubted the propriety of selling them and wondered if perhaps Banks would not prefer taking them to Revesby Abbey as he had done on former occasions. Snart also recorded that Lord Somerville was to inspect His Majesty's flock on the morrow, 15 August. Banks regretted 'it will not be in my power to attend as I am Still very indifferent & have not yet ventured out of the house' but he added:

I wish you by all means to Sell the Black sheep to Mr. Tharpe age and infirmity increases on me & prevent me from taking so much Pleasure as I usd to do in my Former Favorite occupation[94]

The sale of 17 August 1808, therefore, passed quietly away, the least noticed and the least notable of these seven public occasions except as the last of those at which the old original Negretti flock alone composed the lots. Forty-two sheep were again sold; four two-toothed, ten four-toothed and three six-toothed rams, and twenty-five full-mouthed ewes, one of which was in fact broken mouthed. The prices more than fulfilled Banks's expectation and prophecy of the previous year.[95] The rams ranged from £18 18s. to £74 11s. and averaged £33 10s. 2d.; the ewes ranged from £12 12s. to £38 17s. and averaged £24 17s. 8d. These prices almost exactly equalled the values attained at the sale of 1805. No one, however, seemed to rejoice in this restoration of public confidence and interest—or what seemed to be so. Banks himself was apparently so far from taking pleasure in his 'Former Favorite occupation' that it was not until 22 December that he roused himself to chide Snart mildly:

I shall be thankfull to you for a List of the Last Sale of H M Merino Sheep with the Prices upon it I was not furnishd with one at the time of the sale as has been hitherto done & now I have occasion for it to Finish a Report upon the Spanish Flocks intended for the use of H M[96]

Christmas intervened and the New Year also before Snart, who seems to have had his own distractions, was moved to answer with what sounds suspiciously like a lame excuse:

I have to apologise for your not receiving a Catalogue sooner, but your favor on the Subject came here [Windsor Castle] during my Absence, & was mixed by the Maid Servant among some loose Papers and was not discovered by me till last Night—
The new Spanish Ewes are now lambing [13 January 1809] and although many of them are deficient in Milk, yet I trust there will be more Lambs saved than might have been expected—The Sheep have pretty well got the better of their Voyage . . .[97]

These new Spanish ewes were the first fruits of the long struggle on the Peninsula that had begun effectively on 2 May 1808—the tragic 'dos de Mayo'—when the Spaniards in Madrid rose against the French and the War of Independence began. From that day the Spanish Merino became a small four-footed refugee in the path of the armies that for the next six years ravaged its ancient grazing grounds. Of these there is much to be said but here we must think of them as the new Paular flock which, in the sale of 1809, were to outnumber the stock from the old Negretti flock which for eighteen years had been His Majesty's Spanish flock alone. The problems and excitements of their coming had in fact been one reason for Banks's apparent failing interest in the particulars of the public sale of 1808. He had returned from Revesby according to his well-established custom in early November to find the new flock at hand after its voyage from Gijon and, for the first time in his long association with the Merino, himself face to face with Spanish shepherds. Stimulated by this sudden accession of new sheep and of sources of new but above all of first-hand knowledge about the Spanish Merino he wasted no time in setting down all he could elicit. In the last months of 1808 his final report began to take shape calling for those details about the sale that Snart had omitted to give him. Thus, in February 1809, with the King's approval, was published his paper, under cover of a letter to Sir John Sinclair, again President of the Board of Agriculture, and entitled: 'Some Circumstances relative to Merino Sheep, chiefly collected from the Spanish Shepherds, who attended those of the Flock of Paular, lately presented to His Majesty by the Government of Spain . . .'. For the second time, and the last, Banks had set pen to paper in a manner best calculated to enhance the public sales of His Majesty's sheep.

As a separate pamphlet this paper was circulated among the Merino *cognoscenti* during the spring. Snart had aided in its distribution, confessing himself in no doubt of the observations it contained 'having a sensible Effect in extending the Breed in This Country'.[98] In July he conveyed to Banks His Majesty's ideas for the sale.[99] The date was to be earlier than formerly in response to the expressed wishes of many gentlemen and was to be advertised for the 26th of that month. One hundred sheep were to be sold that year—as many of the old Negretti flock as could be spared and the remainder made up from the new Paular acquisitions. Banks had no obstacle to raise and the Royal wishes prevailed. Henry Lacocke, somewhat recovered from the lameness which had immobilized him all that winter, was to make the final selection in which Banks had offered to assist. At the last moment Snart was prevented from participating in this business by the need to attend His Majesty at Windsor concerning the arrangements to be made for the large flock of Spanish sheep on British transports from Cadiz. These had arrived at Portsmouth and had turned out to be for the King from the Junta Central. For the second time the affairs of the annual public sale were complicated by new treasures from the war on the Peninsula—in this case the arrival of the new Negretti flock, of which more is to be told.

On Wednesday, 26 July, 'in the Paddock opposite the Pagoda in Kew Gardens' the sixth public sale of His Majesty's Spanish Merinos took place.[100] This year 'a very numerous company of Agriculturalists assembled', drawn almost certainly by the excellent pamphlet which Banks had prepared and which set the new ornaments to His Majesty's flock in an attractive perspective. Moreover, here were some tangible proofs that perhaps the long struggle with Napoleon was at last turning to Britain's advantage. The sale followed the course now so well established and 'closed at about a quarter before five o'clock, when the purchasers retired to the Blue [Anchor], with Mr. [Daniel] Smith to dinner and to settle their accounts'.[101] Thirty sheep (ten rams and twenty ewes) from the old Negretti flock were sold that day, the rams ranging from 37 to 56 guineas and the ewes from 14 to 28 guineas. Seventy sheep from the new Paular flock (thirty rams and forty ewes) brought prices ranging from 25 to 75 guineas for the rams and prices from 30 to 47 guineas for the ewes. The new stock had certainly carried the day, partly from novelty but almost without doubt due to Banks's high rating of them in his paper as first among the Spanish fine-wool piles in the estimation of the English merchants.

This was the last public sale attended by Sir Joseph and when Snart, a week after the occasion, sent him the particulars it is clear that he was happy in the result:

I thank you for the List of the Sheep Sold on Wednesday Last There never has been a Sale at which Sheep sold as these have done not even in Leicestershire where every sort of Trick is used to Enhance the value of the New Leicester breed.

had it not been that many people have an Idea that C. Johnstons Sheep must arrive Some time to be sold in Large Quantities the Prices would still have been higher, I did not see one of those people who value themselves in being noted agriculturalists at the Sale most of them indeed are readers of Cobbets Register The Duke of Bedford I hear has Purchasd a Ram from one of the Persons who brought H M Sheep from Gihon, it was one of the supernumeraries brought down by the Shepherd to make up the King's number in case of accidents of course those left for other people were Culls & yet the duke gave 100 Guineas for this offal animal

I did not see at the Sale any one of those ministers or Lords of the Bed-chamber who asked the King for Sheep Lord Camden Employd me to buy a ram for him but limitd me to 20 Guineas of course his Lordship could not

have one Lord Westmorland Employd his Country neighbour Mr. Walcot
to buy for him but the Sheep were too dear for my Lord & he did not buy[102]

In various ways it is clear that the King's sale was little affected by
Dr. Parry's sale of his fine-woolled sheep at the farmyard at Summer-
Field House on Sion Hill near Bath on the previous day, 25 July 1809.
Snart's fears on this account were not confirmed by the result which
established the highest level of prices so far attained by the Royal flock.
Banks's point that prices may well have been even higher but for the
rumours of further flocks of sheep from Cadiz was more cogent.

XI

The last public sale in the field near the Pagoda was held on
Wednesday, 25 July 1810. It was the largest and the most rewarding in
financial returns, but of the hundred and three lots offered only ten rams
were from the old Negretti flock and therefore of the King's breeding.
The other ninety-three lots were either from the Paular importation of
1808 or the new Negretti importation of 1809. The stock were arranged
in separate pens under the trees by Kew Foot Lane near Richmond,
while a convenient range of sheds and pens had been erected on the
opposite side of the paddock next to Kew Gardens in case the weather
had proved unfavourable.[103]

At exactly twelve o'clock the sale commenced with a short speech
from Mr. Daniel Smith, appearing for his fourth and last casting as the
King's auctioneer. He made much of the military threat by the French
to the Merino flocks of Spain as a factor tending to diminish the
quantity and enhance the price of fine wool. He mentioned this, he
said, to show the certain advantages of speculating in Spanish sheep in
Great Britain. To show how much dependence could now be placed on
the fine Spanish wools improving instead of degenerating in England,
His Majesty had on this occasion directed a ram, a son of Snags and a
descendant of the first lot of Negretti sheep imported nearly twenty
years earlier, to be exhibited in a separate pen for the examination of the
company present. Last year some of the sheep had been lame but in the
present lots there were none with this defect. If the rams looked smaller
than last year, he also said, it was because this year they had been shorn
before the sale. However, he had every expectation of high prices and on
the whole great advances on former levels. He was encouraged to
expect this both from the high prices which had been realized at the sale
of Lord Somerville's Merinos in May and from the 'highly respectable
company before him'.

The 'highly respectable company' rose to the occasion and the values of 1810 clearly exceeded those record figures of the previous year. Mr. Daniel Smith's faith in the speculative fervour of his audience was vindicated. Thirty-three rams (eleven Paular and twenty-two Negretti) were sold at prices ranging from 30 to 173 guineas and an average of £65 6s. 8d. Seventy ewes (forty-eight Paular and twenty-two Negretti) were sold at prices ranging from 16 to 92 guineas and an average of £35 10s. 10d. One hundred and three sheep at the end of the day had brought £4714 10s.! At Lord Somerville's sale on his Fairmile farm at Cobham, not many miles away, in May, two hundred and twenty-eight sheep had brought no less than £9210 5s. 6d.[104] His Majesty's average of £45 15s. 5d. compared very well with that of his Lord of the Bedchamber—£40 0s. 10d.!

From the field near the Pagoda the seed had now been scattered for the last time. The Blue Anchor had seen its last and its most impressive settlement of accounts between the King and his subjects in the matter of the Spanish sheep. The pinnacle of success in the Royal experiment seemed to have been reached and its benevolent intentions seemed now assured of a secure place in the economy of the nation. The temporary domination of the Spanish Merino pastures by the French who were then at their most threatening strength on the Peninsula seemed only to set the seal on the whole fine-wool project if England was to be self-sufficient in this now critical raw material. No one of 'the highly respectable company' turning homeward from the Pagoda that day perhaps thought much of the future or whether the sale marked the beginning or the end of anything. Or did anyone, perhaps, think back to an evening just one month before at Holkham when the celebrated, wise, and good Mr. Coke rose to address the guests of his hospitality on the Merino breed and in the nicest and most dispassionate way to pronounce judgement and doom upon it?[105] Did Sir Joseph himself, who that evening sat on the right hand of the oracle, recognize the words and the occasion for what they were? The seventh and last public sale of sheep from His Majesty's Spanish flock may now in retrospect serve us to mark the zenith of the Merino in its brief transit across the face of British agriculture.

The words of Thomas William Coke at the Holkham Sheep Shearing of 1810 may have turned public opinion in the end strongly against the Spanish Merino as a breed but they had no immediate effect in themselves on the affairs of His Majesty's flock. The sales ended abruptly in 1811 even while preparations were being made for the eighth such occasion in July of that year. If there were no other cause (and the war provided many), the tragic changes which were shaping behind the walls of Windsor Castle set a final end to whatever was in hand. Sir Joseph Banks knew well that the times had altered and ventured his opinion that for many reasons a sale that year was perhaps not wise. Snart replied as was required in words that leave us in no doubt that what the Court and the nation had long feared was at hand:

Reflecting on the opinion you were so obliging as to give me I thought it right to prevent Mr Smith advertizing the Sale of His Majesty's Merino Sheep till I could either have an opportunity of making the case known to His Majesty or could get some other authority how to act. On my Arrival at Windsor I unfortunately found it impossible to make any Communication to His Majesty, and am under the Necessity of acting from my own Judgment. From the very unpleasant Situation in which I am thus placed, and considering the unfavourable Result of all other Sales as well as that we have had but one solitary Application for a Single Sheep, I have thought it most advisable to postpone the Sale for the present at least. Should you however be of opinion that a Sale might with propriety be made I shall be happy to have it advertized whenever you may think proper.[106]

This decision never came, for the matter was not in the power of Banks to make it. The national situation and the state of trade were serious enough, but the King himself was no longer in a state to care for His Spanish flock. Neither Sir Joseph Banks nor Richard Snart ever again communicated with His Majesty on the subject. Beyond any further question the Regency had begun.[107]

CHAPTER XI

The Spanish Shepherds, 1808

I

On the high Leonese plateau in the clear heat of early July 1808, near the border of Old Castile the Battle of Medina del Rio Seco was fought. The best of the Spanish armies under General Cuesta supported by a fringe of armed peasants was defeated by General Bessières and the French path to Madrid was again open. As Joseph Bonaparte entered the city on 24 July the rising of the 'dos de Mayo' must have seemed to the Madrilenos a vain sacrifice. But over the whole country the new spirit born that day in the capital was alive and vigorous. Napoleon was now for the first time confronted with the resistance of a whole people. Typical of the nation were two volunteers at the Rio Seco under the infirm and inept General Gregorio de la Cuesta. Miguel Prieto and Juan Colado, shepherds of the Mesta in Leon, were ordered to leave their ranks and quietly set about another business less military but in many ways more vital than battles in achieving the final defeat of the French.[1] The time had come to save what could be saved of the Merino flocks now widely scattered over their summer pastures and an open prey to the invading army. To the common soldiers the fine-wool flocks were no more than good fresh meat. To the French commissaries and merchants gleaning in the wake of the armies they were prizes of war whose value was high among the good things the invasion had to offer France. More than ten years earlier the Spanish Merino had been established by a secret Article in the Treaty of Basle as plunder well worth taking.[2] Therefore, Miguel Prieto and Juan Colado among other humble Spanish patriots were required as skilled shepherds to play their part in removing the best of the flocks as far from the French forces as could be contrived.

There was little choice in the line of retreat for the transhumance flocks in Leon during the summer of 1808. A British army under Sir Arthur Wellesley broke the French army at Vimiero. But the Convention of Cintra in August, blunderingly allowed Marshal Junot to evacuate Portugal. His retreat from the south-west blocked the path of the normal autumn migration into Estremadura. Napoleon himself with a picked army was preparing to enter Spain from the north-west driving straight towards Madrid to the aid of his brother Joseph. The flocks could only move with some hope of escape to the north and somewhat west across the Cordillera Cantabrica into Asturias. So toward Oviedo and the port of Gijon the Spanish shepherds slowly drove what flocks they could salvage from a countryside that was already hazy with the dust of marching foot columns and clattering patrols. Across this high and naked land the flocks stirred their own slow dust clouds and the *arroyos* echoed their protests at this affront to their old migratory instinct calling them south. Autumn at last stilled these yearnings among the soft green meadows of the damp Biscayan coast.

Earlier in June the representatives of the Junta of the Province of Asturias had arrived in London. The help they sought was quickly forthcoming. George Canning at the Foreign Office well realized the importance of the Spanish rising of which the Asturian delegation was the visible proof. Between Spain and Great Britain peace was made. Sir John Moore was sent to take command of the British forces and to move in support of the Spanish armies barring the advance of Napoleon on the line of the Ebro. As this first disastrous campaign began in October (to end four months later with Moore's death at Corunna) the Spanish shepherds Miguel Prieto and Juan Colado were already in England with rather less than the original two thousand odd sheep they had helped so carefully to gather in the confusing weeks since the battle at Rio Seco.

Among the medley of flocks grazing that summer over the *meseta* in Leon was one whose sheep carried on their sides a large and flaunting M[3] where once the far more famous sign was borne of the Carthusian Monastery of Santa Maria del Paular. The sheep, whose wool was of such pre-eminence among the piles of Spain that it seldom left the country as a raw export,[4] now carried the pitch-brand of Manuel Godoy, Prime Minister of Spain, Duke of Alcudia and, since the Treaty of Basle, Prince of the Peace. The former guardsman and present lover of the unlovely Spanish Queen Maria Luisa had acquired the flock from the monks of Paular for something less than a just price in 1796 to ornament his upstart status as a Spanish grandee. Now this much-hated adventurer had been deposed during the insurrection of 2 May at Madrid, maltreated by the mob and, with the Spanish Royal family, at length caught in the French usurpation. All his accessible property was confiscated by the new Spanish Junta of the nation in revolt. Of this the old Paular *cabana* was a considerable part, though it is now hard to establish how many were acquired by the Spanish patriots from a flock that was once rated as high as thirty thousand head. On the evidence of the shepherds themselves who brought the Paular sheep to England it seems probable that no more than about seven thousand five hundred were gathered all told, but mostly breeding ewes. These came from eight contiguous *dehesas* in Leon, the accustomed summer grounds of the flock.[5]

There were probably few gestures of friendship and appreciation within the power of the Spanish people to make as a return, if any were needed, to Great Britain for her support against the French invaders. Certainly the Junta of the Asturias chose wisely when they ordered a carefully selected flock drawn from the *cabana* of the Prince of the Peace to be presented to His Majesty the King of England. Was this a spontaneously happy thought? Or had some well-informed hint been dropped in the ears of the delegation in June or later that some of the choice fine-wool Spanish sheep would do much to nourish British enthusiasm in the new Spanish cause? The origin of the gift is now lost in the forgotten intricacies of this old crisis in the struggle with Napoleon. Not much more remains to record the passing event, apart from the sheep themselves and their descendants, than the material worries and bemusement of twelve Spanish shepherds inarticulate and alone in London, their small contribution to the cause concluded but not rewarded.

Under the supervision of the experienced Don José Alvarez y Suares, *mayoral* of the Paular *cabana* for fourteen years and a former servant of the monastery, the sheep for England were selected. The youngest and the finest woolled of the breeding ewes and the rams were taken, the ewes being in lamb and due to yean in early December. As it left Gijon the flock consisted of two thousand two hundred and fourteen head in all—two thousand for His Majesty King George III and two hundred and fourteen to be divided among four members of the Cabinet, the Duke of Portland as Prime Minister, George Canning, Lord Castlereagh, and Lord Mulgrave.[6] To distinguish the several lots, those for Mr. Canning were marked on the poll; those for the Prime Minister were marked across the shoulder; those for Viscount Castlereagh across the loin; and those for Lord Mulgrave down the rump.[7] The flock sailed from Gijon under convoy on 4 October 1808 for Portsmouth where they were landed and then driven along the roads across the South Downs and over The Weald to Richmond. Here on Sunday, 30 October they passed under the care of Richard Stanford who recorded the arrival of 'about 1680 ewes' and '120 Rams and there are a vast Number of them Rotten'.[8] A more complete reckoning later revealed that of the two thousand two hundred and fourteen sheep which had been originally chosen for the King and his Ministers no less than four hundred and twenty-seven had died in Spain, on the passage, and on the road until their arrival at Richmond. The King chose to take this whole loss upon himself so that when the full two hundred and fourteen had been assigned to the Ministers there remained one thousand five hundred and seventy-three for the Royal flock besides twelve *mansos* which do not appear to have been reckoned with the original number. However, on 12 November Banks recorded eight more than this according to the following summary of the numbers allotted:[9]

The King's Flock	Rams	111	
	Ewes	1458	
	Wethers	12	1581
Mr. Canning	Rams	6	
	Ewes	84	90
Duke of Portland	Rams	6	
	Ewes	84	90
Lord Castlereagh	Rams	4	
	Ewes	26	30
Lord Mulgrave	Ram	1	
	Ewes	3	4
Sheep in all			1795

At that date five only had died since their arrival, but in the ensuing month fifteen more of the King's lot (twelve ewes and three rams) had in the words of Richard Stanford 'died Rotten'. By June 1809 the Paular importation had apparently been reduced further by mortality to one thousand two hundred and seventy ewes, one hundred rams, and eleven wethers or *mansos*. The number of lambs which was born to the imported flock from the mating on the summer grazing grounds in Spain does not seem to have been large. At most only three hundred and ten seem to have been recorded and these had dwindled to two hundred and forty-nine in June 1809. From that month onwards the number of the flock extant at any given time is hard to estimate from recorded figures which are often difficult to reconcile with each other. The sudden flooding of the parks and farms at Kew, Richmond, and Windsor with so many hundreds of new stock followed by a further consignment of almost equal magnitude in the summer of 1809 clearly gave Richard Stanford a major problem in keeping his monthly returns in good order. The mere physical task of counting his charges under the improvised conditions with which he was suddenly faced could not be done with great accuracy even had he been accustomed to the handling of large numbers of agile Spanish Merinos for this purpose. He was, however, more accustomed to smaller numbers of more phlegmatic stock and we must on that account take a lenient view of his numerical discrepancies. Moreover, the complicated movements of sheep to and fro in the continuous effort to find grazing and sustenance on the Royal estates for a flock grown embarrassingly large by any standards must have added its own confusion. As we look more closely into the circumstances of the closing years of the Spanish flock before the King's insanity altered everything we are inclined to wonder that any records were kept at all rather than to quibble on questions of accuracy.

II

The new Paular flock had scarcely arrived at Richmond when Banks received a letter from Benjamin Thompson of Redhill Lodge at Nottingham.[10] The news of the importation with its impressive number of ewes had spread quickly to all the enthusiasts among the breeders of Spanish sheep who hankered after the 'pure blood' and who had so far been unfortunate in their efforts to secure sufficient female stock. From far north in Ross-shire Sir George Steuart Mackenzie had also promptly applied.[11] George Tollet of Swinnerton Hall near Stone in Staffordshire and one of the most successful of Merino breeders put his case:

I have been informed by the newspapers & thro various private channels that 2000 Merinos have been received by His Majesty from the Spanish Government. Now in recollection of former kindnesses & considering myself as one of your earliest disciples I am emboldened to hope that thro the medium of your kind offices I may be furnished with a few in order to carry on those experiments which I have ardently pursued for nearly ten years past. In regard to Rams I am in a state of such forwardness that nothing *now* that can be imported from Spain could without detriment to wool & carcase be admitted into my flock: But it may chance to happen that a cross with my Rams with some of those Ewes & unless I had some of them, others by purchasing or hiring my Rams would reap all the advantage.

This makes me desirous of adding about a score of fresh Ewes to my flock if I could do it upon reasonable terms. My Merino flock has been kept together for publick objects to a great private loss—I have never parted with a single Ewe tho' I have been often tempted by outrageous prices well knowing that till we had sufficient numbers no great improvements could be made either in the wool or the frame of the animal—Under these circumstances I am not prepared to give high prices: but would rather go on with my old concern with patience & perseverence. I have too a very sanguine & excellent pupil a Mr. Thompson near Nottingham who has applied to me under similar circumstances to my own & if you can extend your kindness to him I shall be particularly obliged.[12]

The suppliant voices for the Royal bounty grew in numbers and were
by no means of insignificant weight. Nehemiah Bartley, former
Secretary of the Bath and West of England Society;[13] John Fane of
Wormsley in Oxfordshire who would have been 'happy to take charge
of a hundred or more';[14] Lord Macclesfield, Lord-Lieutenant of Oxfordshire, offered to winter a hundred to two hundred of them for His
Majesty;[15] Thomas William Coke of Holkham displayed an interest;[16]
Mr. T. G. Elliot of Salviston near Ottery St. Mary in Devon with his
Merino-Ryeland flock built on rams 'hired at a very great expense of
Lord Somerville';[17] Mr. Edward Sheppard of Uley in Gloucestershire
with one of the largest flocks of Merino cross and back-cross sheep in
the kingdom[18]—all these men had good and persuasive arguments to
support their hopes of largess from the King. Many more had also been
encouraged by the contemporary Press to seek or at least to hope for a
generous sharing of the new Spanish flock—the largest single group so
far to enter the country and possibly the best as a source of general
breeding stock. All these patriotic expectations were, it seems, falsely
based as have been many visions created by the popular Press in the
public mind. To each earnest inquiry Banks gave a courteous answer,
of which that to Edward Sheppard may serve as a model of the rest which
only varied according to the details of the correspondent and his
particular case:

that you are a worthy applicant for a Share of H M. Bounty in the Case
of a distribution of the Spanish sheep lately recd by the King cannot be
doubted & you may depend up[on] having your name brought forward
whenever such a measure is proceeded upon in the Case of my being advisd
with which will most probably be the Case at present however no such
design appears to have Enterd into H M Mind many persons of high Rank
have Solicited for a Share of the new Flock but all have met with an unqualified Refusal what the Reasons of this may be & whether there is any possibility
of an alteration in H M present dispositions on the Subject I am not able to
inform you The Flock is a Draught from the Famous Paular Pile & is well
Selected The Sheep have sufferd much in their voyage 200 have died &
several more will be Lost They begin however to improve Fast[19]

There seems to have been no alteration from this view in 'H M Mind'
and no general distribution of the new stock took place at this stage.
Not long before the public sale in July 1809 Banks was given another
glimpse of the Royal opinion on the subject when Snart wrote:

The King's Intention is to keep the Breeds of Negretti and Paular pure,
and also to have a mixed Sort between the N: Rams and the P: Ewes—600
of the latter were put to Rams of the same Kind on the 30th June [1809] by
His Majesty's Desire and the others will be lambed down at a later Period
by which Means greater attention will be paid to them at the time of lambing.[20]

It was very clear that His Majesty intended to guard the Paular gift with great care and to see that it was valued appropriately.

III

Four months after the Battle of Medina del Rio Seco the twelve Spanish shepherds led apparently by Miguel Prieto and Juan Colado as their spokesmen went to 32 Soho Square.[21] Here they came to meet and to be interrogated by 'a Gentleman eminent for his superior Knowledge in Natural History' as so many men from strange and distant parts of the world had done before them. After more than twenty years during which Banks had become a breeder and notable authority on the Spanish Merino he was at last to meet some of the men without whose co-operation on many occasions there would have been no such sheep in England and no Royal flock at Kew and Windsor. Sir Joseph had prepared for this meeting with his usual care. Pen and paper were at hand and on his great desk perhaps was lying that sheet with its long list of questions about the Paular flock and its circumstances to which he hoped to find answers on this November day.[22] Then, too, there was the difficult problem of an interpreter. The obstacle of communication between Banks and his visitors seems that day to have been well negotiated by Captain José de Mendoza y Rios, F.R.S., in the Georgian opulence of Soho Square at this odd gathering of Merino shepherds.[23]

Few men were now better informed than Banks at second hand about the general conditions of Spanish sheep husbandry. More than twenty-five years of extensive reading, correspondence, and conversation had created a fairly clear picture of the background of the Spanish Merino in his mind. But, for Banks, this was not enough. What, now, were the particular facts and circumstances of this large and unexpected gift to the King? When the shepherds left Soho Square, possibly still bewildered at the persistent sequence of questions that seemed to have little relevance to their own plight, Banks had completed the series and could relax content. He now had the essential notes for the report to His Majesty which the occasion clearly required.

Of the twelve shepherds who came with the sheep nine, including Miguel Prieto, Juan Colado, and one other from the Mesta, were from Leon. The remaining three were Asturians. They confirmed that the sheep they had brought were indeed formerly the property of the Prince of the Peace and that originally they had belonged to the Carthusian Monastery of Santa Maria del Paular in the valley of Alcudia at the foot of the Sierra de Guadarrama near Segovia. The flock for the King had been chosen with particular care and regard to the texture of the wool from eight *dehesas* and were all young sheep. The ewes were with lamb and due to drop their lambs about 8 December. A *dehesa* was an estate or farm for sheep breeding, varying in size from one-half to two miles round and capable of supporting from about four hundred to one thousand sheep. For the Paular flock there were eight contiguous *dehesas* in Leon and a similar number in Estremadura. No fences used to separate the *dehesas* from each other, the boundaries being simply land-marks, usually stones. In Leon during the winter the *dehesas* lay under snow and were therefore of little value. In Estremadura in the summer when the *transhumantes* were absent in the north the proprietors 'gisted' (agisted) the vacant land to the owners of *estantes* or stationary sheep. In summer on a *dehesa* maintaining about a thousand sheep, the flock would be composed of nine hundred and fifty ewes, fifty rams, and a few *mansos* or wethers, the latter having their respective masters among the shepherds of that division.

From the middle of November until the beginning of April the Paular sheep remained on the *dehesas* in Estremadura. They then set out for the northern pastures the flock from each *dehesa* travelling separately under the care of seven or eight shepherds and as many dogs in constant attendance. At a place called the Esquileo de Tres Casas the sheep were shorn each year. This *esquilio* or shearing-shed was about one Spanish league from Segovia and the delay made necessary by the shearing lengthened the northward journey to forty-six or forty-eight days. From June to September the flocks remained in Leon. Each flock after shearing was branded with a well-formed pitch-mark of the letter M, the proprietor's mark of Don Manuel Godoy, the Prince of the Peace. This brand was placed on different parts of the body according to the *dehesa* to which a sheep belonged so that it could be easily identified by the shepherds. Early in October the flocks migrated south again, performing the journey unhindered in about thirty-six days and reaching Estremadura about the middle of November. When not travelling only four or five shepherds and the same number of dogs guarded the flock on each *dehesa*. During the period of lambing, however, the shepherds and dogs were increased to seven or eight again. In Leon or in Estremadura each flock regularly returned to its particular *dehesa* and never changed. The lambs were born from December onwards and only enough lambs were kept alive to replace those culled for old age. The remainder were killed as soon as they were born and often two or three ewes were used to suckle one lamb. The rams were castrated on the new moon of March. No sheep were ever sold from the *cabana* except for the purpose of increasing another that had been depleted by disease or some other cause. The sheep were supplied with salt in summer during the months of June, July, and August, but this was stopped in September. The shepherds believed that in winter salt was liable to cause abortion.

The shearers were paid for their work by the day and were fed with the mutton of the drape ewes and others culled for old age. The value of this meat was deducted from their pay. The shepherds themselves ate the rest of the culls and the lambs that were killed. The only sheep sold were those that represented an increase beyond the grazing capacity of the particular *dehesa*, but this rarely happened as the shepherds themselves decided the number necessary for slaughter each year. Such sheep as were sold were disposed of in Leon only to other *cabanas* of *transhumantes*, never to butchers. Each shepherd received for his maintenance 4 pounds of bread a day out of which the dogs had also to be fed. Three dogs ate 2 pounds of bread twice a day. This left about $2\frac{1}{2}$ pounds of bread a day per man.

It appeared also that at night the shepherds and their dogs lay on the ground under the stars beside the recumbent flock or in crude huts that afforded little shelter from inclement weather. This was their custom all the year round, except that each in turn was allowed a holiday of about a month which he spent with his family. The families of these shepherds it seemed lived entirely in Leon.[24]

So the long interrogation ended. The eminent *curioso* at last pushed his pen and paper to one side. He had thoroughly explored the past circumstances of the shepherds and their sheep. He could not, however, quite assess the problems of their present and their immediate future. As they retired from the awesome dignity of 32 Soho Square the shepherds left with Banks some questions of their own.

IV

When Miguel Prieto and Juan Colado and their companions were ordered to leave their ranks at the Rio Seco and to come with the sheep they had been promised that no punishment would be inflicted. On this question they expressed to Banks their own very serious doubts and asked for his protection from any unhappy consequences of their patriotic defection. They had embarked at Gijon on 4 October without any further agreement beyond that which applied to them in Spain during the long task of bringing the sheep to the port for embarkation. During this period they were to receive 16 reals vellons or 3s. 6d. approximately a day each. The Commissioners under whose orders they had acted deducted twenty-five per cent of the sum due to them for a reason that is not clear at this distance in time. Since their embarkation at Gijon they had received some advance on their English pay, but how much does not appear. Apart from these points the shepherds a

few days before their interview with Banks had drawn up a petition
in their own language which José Mendoza y Rios, F.R.S., had translated, literally, as he said 'to preserve the strong sense of the original':

The Spanish shepherds with the greatest veneration and respect possible
represent and make known to your Excellency that they are ignorant of
any determination concerning their return to Spain and other matters
because their superiors who came with them from Spain D^n Juan Arango
and D^n Francisco Arango do not see them, and your memorialists consider
them with great distrust, they being persons who command much but give
little even very little; of which they have some instances. . . . We request
that our interest and gratification may be given into our own hands and to
know the decision respecting our return home. . . .[25]

The two Arangos appear to have had private business of their own
for sheep were brought over from Spain with the King's consignment
in their name.[26] These commissioners or captains, if such they were, had
certainly been content to leave the shepherds to their own amusements
under the beneficent care, nominally, of His Britannic Majesty and his
servants. For their accommodation Richard Snart had made available a
cottage named the Call-House in the grounds of the Queen's House,
now Buckingham Palace. This was situated in that part of the grounds
on Constitution Hill nearest to Hyde Park Corner, and the King had
given directions for them to remain here as long as they cared to stay
in England. On this point they had expressed to Banks their willingness
to stay on until March the next year (1809) if necessary to instruct the
King's shepherds in the management and care of the new Merinos.
Seventeen years earlier no doubt this would have been accepted with
delight. Now the idea had not the same force. Instead of spending their
time in earnest instruction at Kew and Richmond they found themselves
free to see London at the King's expense.[27]
    Their housekeeping was simple and in the manner to which their
shepherd's life in the open had inured them. Scorning the beds that
were provided they preferred to sleep on straw on the floor or the
ground as commonly with men who have lived close to nature. Two
labourers were at hand to attend them, procuring their food and assisting
in its preparation. They were allotted one pound of meat each for their
dinners and suppers and were not pleased if it were fat. This they
cooked in their own way with the enormous quantity of a peck of
onions at each meal. For a guide and interpreter in their exploration of
London they had the services of an old sailor who understood Spanish.
He took a broad view of his duties. At his insistence they stood up after
every meal, joined hands, put their toes together and sang 'God Save
the King'. In mild retaliation, apparently, they also sang a Spanish

national air. Furnished with money for the purpose the old sailor conducted them to such entertainments as seemed to him most amusing. Inevitably this early course of London tourism brought them to Westminster Abbey. Here, it is said, they were highly amused and astonished at 'the curiosities to be seen in it'. Nor is it surprising to find, as they walked through the streets of the city with their crooks and their outlandish clothes, that they in their turn should have attracted the nods and smiles of mirthful Londoners.

However, these were twelve sad men. The amusements of the city could be no sustained diversion from their thoughts of home and of their families now caught in the developing mesh of the first campaigns of that cruel winter in northern Spain. They had come from a battle. They had perforce to return to a war that was to be their country's ruin for the next six years. In their anxiety to end their brief exile and to resolve their doubts about payment they addressed another petition to Banks. Translated by Mendoza y Rios this ran:

The Spanish shepherds under your Excellency's protection represent to you the same things they did the other day, and that D^n Francisco and D^n Juan Arango are in possession of our money, which we desire may not be the case, and that it may be put into our hands before we leave England, and this business settled by the english and not by the above mentioned gentlemen. We desire to know the specific sum total that His britanic Majesty has deigned to bestow upon us, in order to be free from doubts, and that we may have some document on our arrival home, not in the hands of the said gentlemen. We pray your Ex^{cy} most fervently to deign to favour us and take us under your protection as we have no other resource, favour which we hope to receive from so high a character and we pray God to preserve your life many years for the protection of the poor.[28]

In presenting this translation on 17 November Mendoza y Rios went to Soho Square but found that Banks had gone out. In a short note, however, he expressed his fears that, from the exalted idea which the shepherds seemed to have acquired about the wealth of the King of England, they would be dissatisfied with whatever they were to receive.[29] A month of ease and relative luxury in London as guests of His Majesty was perhaps bound to create some such illusion. We cannot be surprised if their expectations had become somewhat inflated. Banks has noted that they hoped for 3000 reals vellons, the equivalent of about 150 dollars or roughly 34 pounds sterling at the ruling exchange rates, and that they were in fact offered 7 guineas each. The latter sum is a close approximation to payment for six weeks' service at the rate of 16 reals vellons or 3s. 6d. per day, the agreed rate at which they were paid in Spain.[30]

On 18 November the Spanish shepherds found themselves in

Portsmouth waiting for a ship after a bewildering and hurried departure from London with no interpreter and no clear knowledge of how they stood. Their Spanish captains, the two Arangos, had evidently taken swift action to prevent further encroachment on the protective influence of Banks. Each shepherd did indeed receive 1333 reals vellons or the equivalent of £13 6s. 8d (as it was noted) from the Arangos 'without being able to know if it ought to be considered as appointment or gratification. These Gentlemen wish to vex us.' Eventually 'these Gentlemen' arrived in Portsmouth themselves and reimbursed the shepherds the expenses of their journey from London and no more. Their third and last petition to Banks, translated by Lopes Martinez of Cardigan Place, Kennington Cross, expressed great trust in his word that the 3000 reals vellons would be forthcoming.[31] Whether this sum was in fact promised or how it was computed by the Spanish shepherds cannot now be discovered. Whether it was ever paid is even more in doubt. It is clear only that about the end of November 1808 the twelve shepherds left Portsmouth on their voyage of return to the dangers and disasters that were to mark the closing months of that year as Sir John Moore retreated to Corunna across the very paths which they had traversed so recently with the Paular sheep for His Majesty's flock at Kew.

V

The dismemberment of the Paular *cabana* which began in effect with the Battle of Medina del Rio Seco in July 1808 may be said to have ended in Estremadura two years later. The remainder of this celebrated flock now consisted only of about four thousand sheep in all, and in the summer of 1810 were unseasonably still grazing the low undulating hills in the valley of the Guadiana near Badajoz. Again the flock was in retreat before the feet of the French armies, now on their last and greatest southward thrust into Spain. The Supreme Junta directing Spanish affairs, desperate for money to continue the War of Independence, had been persuaded to sell some of the many thousands of sheep from the confiscated flocks of several great *cabanas* still in their possession before it was too late.

On 24 June 1810 the last remnants of the Paular flock were sold by the Junta to the British Commissary-General, Colonel John Downie, by a formal decree of that body from its temporary seat of authority in Badajoz. On 25 June the transaction was certified by Firmin Coronado, Secretary to the Junta. The sale comprised two thousand eight hundred and fifteen ewes, eleven hundred and thirty rams and wethers (three thousand nine hundred and forty-five sheep in all), eighteen dogs, five shepherd ponies, and five mess kettles and these were to have a free passage to Lisbon or any other convenient port. That same day the Marquis of Romana, Captain-General of the Spanish armies, granted the flock a passport from Badajoz to Lisbon requiring all civil and military authorities to grant it every assistance on its way.

By a prior agreement the purchase was to be shared between the British Commissary-General and the Consul for the United States at Lisbon, William Jarvis. As soon as the business was known to be consummated Jarvis sent a clerk and two men to assist in the precarious task of extricating the flock from the path of the armies and across the border into Portugal. In small flocks of about two hundred and fifty and travelling only at night and in the early morning by various roads the whole *cabana* arrived at Lisbon, each lot complete with a certificate of sale and an assurance of pedigree. Among these papers was one dated 27 June 1810, two days after the sale at the Castle of Piedra:

I, Don Jose Alvarez y Suares, mayoral of the fine Transhumante Leonesa *cabana*, called the Paular, certify that for ten years previous to the sale of this flock I was its assistant mayoral, during which time it belonged to the Carthusian order del Paular; that in the year 1796 it was sold by the said Carthusian order to Don Manuel de Godoy, Prince of Peace, in which year I entered upon the sole charge of it, and so remained for fourteen years, making in all twenty-four years, previous to the confiscation by the Government of the property of the said Godoy, that I have had charge of it; and during all this time there has been no admixture of any other *cabana* with this; and that at this date there has been sold by the governing Junta of the province of Estremadura to John Downie, colonel of the royal armies of Spain and commissary of the British army, 2815 ewes and 1132 males (in all 3947), all of the best quality and condition, from the said flock, this *cabana* being the choicest and best of the Kingdom, and its wool being held in the highest estimation in foreign countries.[32]

Don José Alvarez also certified, on 10 July 1810, that he had come with this flock to Lisbon and that in his presence Colonel John Downie had delivered to the United States Consul, William Jarvis, seven hundred and fifty ewes and two hundred and fifty males of the Paular *cabana*. A similar certificate to this effect was made by Colonel Downie with the statement that he had sold them on that day to William Jarvis. On that same day also a ship sailed out of the Tagus from Lisbon bound for Port Glasgow and the Clyde with one hundred and three rams and a hundred and forty-six ewes of the Paular flock consigned to Mr. Charles Downie of Paisley in Scotland. Colonel John Downie was losing no time in putting his own share of the purchase beyond the risk of loss in the uncertainties of the Peninsular Campaign. These were followed, on 6 August 1810, by a further hundred and fifty rams and two hundred and fifty ewes from the same source and for the same destination.[33]

In the end William Jarvis himself seems to have secured about fourteen hundred of the Paular *cabana* and trans-shipped them to various ports of the eastern sea-board of the United States. Another thousand were apparently sold by Colonel Downie to Goold Bros. and Company of Lisbon who also sent them to the United States. The remainder were sold by Downie to various buyers, and all found their way across the Atlantic as ships could be found for this purpose during the frenzy of renewed trade with Europe that followed the Act of Congress of 1 May 1810, removing the embargo on such activity.

The last days of the Paular *cabana* were those of a woeful remnant of the thirty thousand head it had once been accounted to number. At the time of its confiscation from the Prince of the Peace it seems very unlikely that it consisted of more than about seven thousand five hundred—the number which, according to the evidence of the Spanish shepherds to Banks in 1808, seven or eight *dehesas* could support in a Leonese summer. Of these we can account for about six thousand and one hundred and sixteen head as having left Spain. The remaining thirteen or fourteen hundred head must be accounted as likely casualties in two years of the Peninsular War to which must be added those many hundreds which did not survive the sea voyages. On balance it would seem that Great Britain and the United States shared almost equally in the survivors— probably about two thousand three hundred each.[34]

CHAPTER XII

The Wicked Uncle, 1809

I

IN the pleasant warmth of an Estremaduran spring among the northern foothills of the Sierra Morena General Gregorio de la Cuesta with thirty thousand men and six thousand five hundred cavalry faced Marshal Victor and a French army of equal size. Since the defeat at Medina del Rio Seco nine months earlier Cuesta and the Spanish army had sustained relentless pressure from the French in the slow retreat southward. Now, beaten again at the Battle of Medellin in the valley of the Guadiana, the Spaniards prepared for the defence of Andalusia. The end of April 1809 found them camped on the heights of Monasterio and Santa Ollala barring the direct road from Badajoz to Seville. Somewhere near by were grazing the sheep of the Count and Countess del Campo di Alange—the remaining twelve thousand head of the Negretti *cabana*, prevented by the events of the War of Independence and the defection of its owners to the French from setting out on its normal spring migration to the northern *meseta* of Old Castile. In the fighting that shortly ensued the Spaniards were able to secure the whole *cabana* and to carry it south behind the Sierra to the safety of Cadiz and the heat of the Guadalquivir valley.

Sir Arthur Wellesley was even then at sea on his way to Portugal with a fresh British army of ten thousand men to set about retrieving the military position so heavily damaged in Sir John Moore's calamitous retreat to the coast at Corunna during the winter. In Seville, however, there sat already a Scotsman whose genius was of another kind, but who meanwhile posed as a self-appointed adviser on military and other affairs to the Supreme Junta now in Andalusia under the aged Floridablanca. Andrew Cochrane-Johnstone—ex-Member of Parliament, ex-Navy Agent, ex-Colonel of the 8th West India Regiment of foot, ex-Brigadier of the Leeward Islands, ex-many other things—could perhaps lay some claim to a form of military knowledge but of this it is impossible to judge—except perhaps his skill in the manipulation of regimental funds. It is certain, however, that he himself had no doubts as he penned his 'Memoranda relative to Measures which in the humble opinion of the undersigned ought to be adopted in the present situation of the Affairs of Spain' on 21 April 1809. Until Sir Arthur

Wellesley arrived Cochrane-Johnstone was evidently quite prepared, and quite unasked, to set the Spanish position in order. He advocated the defence of the Sierra Morena as the true defence of Seville and advised the Junta on its details accordingly. He strongly urged that all livestock should be driven south of the Guadalquivir in the event of the enemy forcing the passes of the Sierra. He noted with sorrow the unarmed state of the common people and generously offered to subscribe a hundred muskets with bayonets as a positive step towards victory. He underlined his gratuitous memoranda with heavy emphasis on his twenty-four years' military and civil experience, wisely not entering deeply into its nature. He made great play with his relationship, as uncle, to Thomas Lord Cochrane, the dashing but star-crossed young naval officer of growing repute, whom Napoleon respectfully dubbed 'le loup de mer' for his effective raids about the coasts of Spain. Cochrane-Johnstone was by this time a man who had a great need for any crumb of respectability to be found anywhere as food for his endlessly nefarious plans. These morsels he gleaned continuously, especially those that fell from the family table. But whatever else there is to be said of the man—and what tales there are—we cannot deprive him of his eminence as an arch-opportunist whose instinctive roguery sometimes served the public good almost as well as it was intended to fill the Cochrane-Johnstone purse. There is no stranger episode in the history of His Majesty's Spanish flock than the one in which this enigmatic man played his brief but central part. Nor can we even now do more than surmise on the details of his very questionable operations, though the main outline is at last clear. Nothing, however, is quite intelligible without the background of his career.

Life for Andrew James Cochrane had begun quietly enough as the youngest son of Thomas 8th Earl of Dundonald and Jane Stuart, later the Dowager-Countess of Dundonald who died in 1808—just as his Spanish adventure began. After six years' service in the Light Dragoons stationed in India, rising from Cornet to Captain, he returned to represent the Burghs of Stirling from 1791 to 1797, in the House of Commons. He assumed the additional surname of 'Johnstone' on his marriage to Georgiana, daughter of James 3rd Earl of Hopetoun. His first wife died in 1797 leaving him the irresponsible father of one daughter, Elizabeth. In the same year, gazetted a Colonel of the 79th Regiment of foot, or the Cameronian Volunteers, he was appointed Governor of Dominica. In January 1798 he was given the colonelcy of the 8th West India Regiment of foot. In April 1799 he was also made Brigadier of the Leeward Islands. Here at last in the seductive climate of the Caribbean his innate qualities came to life. His Dominican rule proved to be an extended exercise in extortion and vice. He became an adept profiteer in Negro slaves. A recent widower, he embellished his vice-regal office by keeping a harem. But before his return to England he had married a second time. Very soon, however, his second wife—a young French widow, Mme Godet of Martinique and the only daughter of the Governor of Guadaloupe—took steps to divorce him.

Finally, after six lurid years an indulgent Government ended his term of office for sustained acts of tyranny and suspended his commission. He and his Major, John Gordon, accused each other of peculation and both were court-martialled in 1804 and both found guilty of irregularities. He published a *Defense* in 1805 which found for him a champion in William Cobbett who used it as the basis for a slashing attack on the Duke of York relative to the sale of army commissions. Samuel Whitbread presented a petition to the House on his behalf without effect—after two hundred Members had been solicited but refused to support it. Then after a lavish campaign in bribery he and his brother, George Augustus, were both returned in the elections of May 1807 for the constituency of Grampound in Cornwall. His own election was declared void in March 1808 and he was unseated. By this time, however, he had returned to the Caribbean where his piratical instincts and his past experience led him unerringly to the main chance. Unabashed and blatant he battened again on the respectability of his family in the person now of his elder brother Sir Alexander Forrester Inglis Cochrane who was then Commander-in-Chief of the Leeward Islands station. Through his influence Cochrane-Johnstone, after the capture of the Danish islands of St. Croix, St. Thomas, and St. John, was made Agent for the Captors as far as the Navy was concerned. Here by a due process of bribery and other forms of corruption in the Vice-Admiralty Prize Court he obtained personal possession of estates and other property more usually considered the assets of the Crown. All this was going rather too far not only for the eighteenth-century ethic but even for the more relaxed code of the Caribbean in the eighteenth century. Andrew James was straining the flexibility of nepotism to its ultimate elastic limit. By 18 October 1808, Sir Alexander Cochrane, worthy Admiral of the Blue, was driven by these excesses of his youngest brother to write to his elder, the Honourable Basil:

I assure you, my Dear Basil, that I feel hurt, and vexed beyond measure, at the conduct of Andrew, who must have taken leave of his Senses, Had I conceived him capable of such behaviour to you, he never would have been appointed Agent for the Navy at l'Croix, but lest I should suffer from his imprudence, I enclose you a Blank Power to join a name to his, and I should suppose Mr Marryat would be a fit person. . . .[1]

There was fuel yet to feed the burning indignation of an elder brother whose trust had been betrayed and—worse it would seem, far worse—

whose professional integrity had been exposed in a bad light and whose career had been placed in jeopardy by a most naughty junior. The elder brother spoke—but he was many years late in his admonition—as he wrote to Andrew James on 25 October:

To crown all, you have been bringing up a highly improper address from Grampound, at a time, when it was your duty, as Agent for the Captors to ingratiate yourself as much as possible with His Majesty's Ministers.

Be advised, in all your transactions, to preserve your temper, and not add to the number of your Enemies, already too numerous, never act on the impulse of the moment, consult with those fit to give you advice; and do not consider them your Enemies, who merely differ from you in opinion. . . .[2]

A week later the incensed Admiral wrote again to the Honourable Basil making clear that he knew just what the irresponsible Andrew James had been doing:

The last of my letters was expressing my disapprobation of Andrews conduct who, contrary to my advice and his duty as an Agent, has been buying Estates at l'Croix, Gardens, Vessels, &c., all of which must have been done with the Captor's money, or his credit thereon—that he will never again be appointed by me in a similar situation [he may be sure] . . .[3]

But whatever his feelings so far, they were now to be tortured beyond bearing and the end came quickly as he wrote to the reprobate on 9 November:

Your letter of the 30th Sept[r] has not added to my comfort, By it, as well as others I have received, I am vexed to see you have not made up matters with your Brother Basil, I have also seen that *wicked address from Grampound*, and am *shocked* that a *Brother of mine*, should have countenanced it—Be studiously carefull of your reputation. Men are known by the Company they keep.

I am free to declare, that your Hostility to the King and Ministers, precludes me from appointing you as agent for the Navy in any future conquests, much as I have your Interest at heart, I will not connect their fortunes with one who has no bounds to his Emnities. . . .[4]

The ghost of the Grampound Election stalking the Caribbean was an unholy form of haunting ruinous to the nerves of the most upright of brothers but, when added to the scandals at Tortola, it was a nightmare of more than ordinary proportions. Immediate exorcism was performed. By a deed of revocation on 6 January 1809 Andrew Cochrane-Johnstone was removed by his brother and, in the month of February, Mr. Marryat was appointed alone to the office of Agent for the Navy Prize property in his stead. In a letter of 26 February 1809, to the Honourable Basil, a form of excommunication was pronounced by the Admiral:

If he will peruse with attention my last letters to him, he will see the true cause why I find fault with his conduct, for which he is really reprobated by both Army and Navy, whose interests have been sacrificed to his private resentments & violent proceedings. Having such just occasion to be displeased with his conduct, I have every right as the source whence he derived his authority to place the concerns of the Captors in other hands.

This letter I have no objection he should see, it will probably be the last communication we will have together and I shall ever sincerely regret, that my attachment to him as a Brother, induced me to repose in him the trust I did. . . .[5]

How much cause for regret the Admiral had for his misplaced trust is soon apparent when it is noted that all the extracts from these brotherly letters were gathered and set before Lord Castlereagh at home in Downing Street. They were prepared as a defence against 'an impression that he had encouraged his Brother the Hnble A. Cochrane Johnstone in the violence of his proceedings' and were assembled 'to shew that his proceedings were totally disapproved by the Honble Sir Alexander Cochrane and that he was in consequence removed from his office as private agent'. The malevolent genius who had created this situation seems to have been arrested but released on parole. Whereupon he escaped the immediate consequences of his crimes and lived to peculate another day as well as ultimately to realize a good profit from his misbegotten spoils at 'le Croix' and elsewhere.

We can, therefore, better appreciate the resilience of this indefatigable trickster as we find him now, scarcely two months after his ignominious dismissal at Tortola, diligently turning the distresses of the Spanish people to his own advantage from Seville.[6] His offer of one hundred muskets with bayonets which he proposed to obtain for the Supreme Junta as a spontaneously helpful gesture somehow developed into a firm contract for the supply of these weapons at a stipulated price of three guineas each. These he thoughtfully ordered without delay from Mr. Abram Atkins of Finsbury Square. They were duly manufactured in Birmingham for seventeen shillings apiece. Business in a modest way, it would seem, had begun again for the Honourable Andrew James Cochrane-Johnstone.

It is perhaps no surprise now to find that soon he was also working in Spain as an accredited agent of the British Treasury negotiating problems of credit and cash for the war with Napoleon. No doubt in this business the right hand of the Treasury knew not what the left hand of the Admiralty and the War Office had been doing, nor what the immediate past activities and attitudes of the honourable gentleman had been. It is perhaps even less surprising to observe the generous interpretation with which he approached his task. From muskets for the

Spanish patriots his mind moved easily to the thought of Merinos from
the Supreme Junta. In both directions there was clearly profit for
Cochrane-Johnstone thinly concealed now under a crust of specious
fervour for the national interest. All those measures which in his humble
opinion 'ought to be adopted in the present situation of the Affairs of
Spain' seemed providentially designed also to suit exactly the affairs of
the Honourable Andrew Cochrane-Johnstone. It was a happy accident,
he would have us believe, by which he heard that the Supreme Junta
might be disposed to sell the recently captured Negretti *cabaña*, and that
he became the purchaser. He may well have been engrossed also at the
time in securing licences for the export of Mexican and Peruvian silver
bullion. But clearly he had not overlooked the old Spanish proverb—
'Where the sheep's foot treads there the land turns to gold'.[7]

II

The last echoes of the battles and skirmishes between General
Cuesta and Marshal Victor had scarcely died away in the rocks and
gorges beyond Santa Ollala before this happy accident occurred and
the business somehow settled. Nearly eighteen years earlier an involved and protracted exercise in diplomacy had at length obtained
a mere forty-one sheep from the Negretti *cabaña* with all the courtesies
of *noblesse oblige*. Now the last remnants of the same vast flock, still
formidably large, had become a prize of war like the Paular *cabaña*,
after a brief and indecisive battle—the possession of an English adventurer and the King of England. Cochrane-Johnstone immediately began
his arrangements for realizing on his investment, probably with a wary
eye over his shoulder on the shadow of his past and another cast towards
new fields of adventure, counting the days and planning to move on as
quickly as could be devised—always the best tactics of the confidence-
man.

He wrote first on 3 May 1809 to Sir John Sinclair, then in his second
term of office as President of the Board of Agriculture, giving a circum-
stantial account of his acquisition:

I am sure that it will give you satisfaction to know that I have succeeded not
only in purchasing the finest Flock of Merino Sheep that ever existed in this
Country, but also in procuring permission from the Supreme Junta to
export them from Spain for England, a permission never granted before to
any Individual—this Flock consisting of above 12,000 was the property of
a Spanish Nobleman, who preferred following the fortunes of Bonaparte
instead of being loyal to his own country—this Flock was contiguous to the
Armies of General Victor and also of the Spanish General Questa—a Battle

was fought for this Flock lately, and it was seized upon by the Spaniards—
I heard by accident that probably the Supreme Junta might be disposed to
sell it, and in consequence of this information, I am happy to say that I
succeeded in becoming the Purchaser. . . .[8]

Then followed long instructions on ways and means—the procuring
of transports from the Navy through an application to Sir Arthur
Wellesley and by Sir John's own exertions as President of the Board of
Agriculture; problems of food and management for the sheep; their
public sale in England about the end of September; their consignment
to the care of Sir John Sinclair and William Cobbett; his own intention
to retain half of those that reached England as 'an entire Flock, on
purpose to preserve the Breed, from which Flock, a certain number
shall be annually sold of[f] to those Farmers who may want them from
our three Kingdoms'. But there was no mention here of any for the
King, only the triumphant note that he—and only he—had become the
purchaser and the fond hope 'that considering the great Sum of Money
which I have involved in this object for the good of my Country, and
the risque which I now run in getting them there, that Government will
not charge me for the freight'. This letter, he said, he was passing
through the headquarters of Sir Arthur Wellesley in Lisbon whence he
hoped to get approval for the whole project. There was, however, a
marked change of tone when finally on 9 May he clothed the enterprise
in patriotic platitudes and with his own brand of cheerful effrontery
left the matter with Sir John Sinclair:

I am sure that you will agree with me that it will be of the greatest importance to introduce into England as great a number as possible of the true
breed of the Merino sheep for improving the *wool*—if it is not done *now* it
will *never* happen again for these bloody wars have ruined many of the
Flocks and the French have driven many of them into France—
    I wrote to you the other day that I was endeavouring to purchase the
finest Flock of Merinos ever produced in Spain and that I was arranging
with the Supreme Junta to get leave to embark them for England—in this
I have succeeded—I have got 2000 of them without purchase *for the King*
(which I trust his Majesty will receive) and the remainder I have purchased.
This expense is however enormous and I have been obliged to undertake
it with others for the risque and expenses was too much for me. I saw
however the great advantage which would result to my Country from the
introduction of these sheep and therefore I have exerted my self on this
occasion. I think that considering the advantages which will accrue from
this measure it ought to entitle me to receive a Bounty p[r] head upon each
sheep from Government to ease me of the expenses. This I must leave to
your kind management and the sooner you set about it the better—you
never saw such fine Sheep—the wool is really superb— . . .[9]

Sinclair, so ready to organize other men, was for his part less ready to be organized himself—at all events not in this cavalier fashion. He was indeed quite prepared to pass the problem on to Sir Joseph Banks, or, at least that part of it which touched on the application for a bounty on the importation to be sought from the Board of Trade. But on this point Banks was obviously inclined to be deaf. He was in fact dutiful but not enthusiastic about the whole affair and made his attitude clear enough to Sinclair:

I am thankful that Mr C. Johnstone has put this Business into your hands I never interfere in the King's concerns unless I am prepared with H. M. Special Command & I have never volunteerd myself into any business which involves an Enormous Expence

during the many years I have been Labouring to introduce the Spanish Breed I found no difficulty in purchasing when I chose it at very cheap prices very fine wool'd Sheep. I always believd that Merino Sheep are much cheaper in Spain than most of our breeds are here.

My difficulty has been to induce farmers to adopt the breed & this obstacle is not yet surmounted, I have lately drawn [up] a Plan for Distributing Flocks of Merino Sheep into different Parts of the Kingdom under a general superintendence as is done in France,[10] but for doing this on a larger scale than is yet accomplished in France. One half of H. M. present Flock will be more than sufficient

Whether under these Circumstances it will be useful to introduce more Merino Sheep & whether it is possible to obtain better breeds than the Paular & Negretti which we at present possess I leave for others to determine. I think however I may venture an opinion that if we bring more Merino Sheep into England than can be Sold at Prices high enough to insure the intentions of the Purchaser to adopt the breed it will do no good

It is noteworthy that at this stage no one in England seemed to know that the sheep which were causing such general speculation and bother were in truth the coveted Negrettis. It was not a point expressly stated by Cochrane-Johnstone in any of his letters. Banks, at least, might have reacted with more enthusiasm had he known. On the other hand, regardless of the sheep, his attitude might as easily have been guarded by some fore-knowledge of Cochrane-Johnstone himself. He might also have been influenced against the project by the person of the other agent chosen to manage the dispersal of the new stock.

III

It was on many counts unfortunate, in the summer of 1809, that Cochrane-Johnstone should have nominated William Cobbett as the medium through which these spoils of the Peninsular Campaign were to be sold. As the energetic farmer of Botley, yes—perhaps. As the contentious Editor of *Cobbett's Weekly Political Register*—no.

Cobbett the farmer was not in any degree acquainted with the Spanish Merino except by hearsay and by the sight of eight sheep he had but recently received from Spain. He was an amateur of amateurs with the breed. But, as Cobbett the Editor of the *Register*, his long-standing and well-earned unpopularity with the Government was about to culminate in the charge of sedition which he would shortly bring recklessly on his own head. The long shadow of Newgate Prison was already stretching towards him and the events that were to lead him there had already become entangled with the business of the sheep in the political columns of his weekly diatribe. Cobbett would soon be burdened with personal worries of his own, enough in themselves to distract any man's thoughts from the affairs of a distant friend—even one many times more worthy than Cochrane-Johnstone. But worthy or not, Cobbett in his forthright impulsive fashion had every intention apparently, at least in June 1809, of supporting the venture of the man whose cause in a very different matter he had espoused in 1805. It is strange that Cobbett should on two occasions have so freely given his aid and comfort to a man whose whole life was such a patent mess of dishonesty and moral squalor. Yet Cobbett, riding his hobby-horses, seldom paused in his onward rush to note what lay beneath his feet still less beneath the surface. To such a man the shady side of so practised a hypocrite as Cochrane-Johnstone would perhaps be no more than blinked at. The conviction by court martial of Cochrane-Johnstone in 1805 for the peculation of regimental funds seems not to have deterred Cobbett from rising to his support in attacking the system by which army commissions were sold. The manifold sins of the man in Seville were not perhaps more likely to deflect Cobbett now from assisting in the importation of such a publicly desirable asset as Spanish Merino sheep. So, just one week before he flung his challenge to the Government over the flogging of the Ely Militia mutineers, he broadcast to the world his plans for executing the task in which Cochrane-Johnstone, spinning his web from Andalusia, had entangled him. *Cobbett's Weekly Political Register* for Saturday, 24 June 1809, carried the following message:

Several noblemen and gentlemen have written to me, upon the subject of *Sheep*, which they have it appears, been informed are coming from Spain, and are to be placed under *my* care; and, as it may possibly be of public interest and utility I shall here state what will, I hope, be considered as a sufficient answer to all those who have honoured me with applications on the subject.—I am not *certain* that any sheep will be sent to my care; but I have good reason to suppose, that several thousands of the very finest sheep in Spain will be sent to England, and that I without any *property* in them whatever, but out of friendship for the owner, shall have in a great degree, the care and management of them, unless he himself should arrive in England [with] time enough to take the care upon himself.—If the flock, or any part of it, should be *sold* under my direction and controul, the sale will certainly be *by auction*: and, I beg leave to observe, by way of saving the trouble of application for *preference* that *no part of the property will be mine*, and that, of course, I shall not be able unless the owner be arrived, to give the smallest preference to anyone.—When the sheep arrive (if they do arrive), it is my intention to give due notice thereof, to every part of the Kingdom; that is to say, if intended for sale. . . .[11]

This public announcement in the *Register*, with the detailed proposals which it embodied for handling the sheep, had emerged from action by Sir John Sinclair, himself obedient also to the tune being called from Seville. This had been conveyed to Cobbett in a letter of 18 June:

By Letters which I have received from M.[r] Cochrane Johnston I find, that he has purchased a considerable number of Spanish Sheep which he proposes consigning to your care when they arrive in England. The transportation of them will be attended with great difficulty at this season of the year when they will be apt to become feverish from the heat of the weather, and when it is impossible to furnish them on shipboard with green food or a sufficient quantity of water. I suppose that M.[r] Cochrane Johnstone will have explained to you the manner in which they are coming over and the places where they are likely to land. In the interim I have done all that lay in my power by procuring directions from the Treasury to have them disembarked the instant they arrive. I am just setting out for Norfolk and thence to Scotland, so that it will be impossible for me to be of any further use in the matter; but I think it right to submit to your consideration the following hints.—

1. Would it not be advisable immediately to secure intelligent Shepherds to drive them from the Port where they are landed to your neighbourhood where it would be proper to have pastures secured for their reception—

2. It would be necessary also to make some arrangements with the Transport Board for their freight.—

3. As soon as they are sufficiently refreshed, it would be right to advertise their sale in the English Scotch and Irish Newspapers that the Sheep may fetch an adequate price and may fall into the hands of those who, from their zeal in the cause are the most likely to do them justice.

I shall be most anxious to hear that the Sheep have safely arrived and I trust that the importation will prove advantageous to the Agricultural and indeed to the Manufacturing interests of the Country.

I will trouble you to communicate this letter to M.[r] Cochrane Johnston when he arrives in England; and I remain . . .

N.B. Owen Wynne Esq.[re] of Henrietta Street Dublin and [John] Tharpe Esq.[re] of Chip[p]enham Park near Newmarket would be glad to know when the sale takes place as they propose being extensive Purchasers.[12]

With these helpful suggestions to the receptive Cobbett, Sir John washed his hands of the matter for the moment and departed for his duty call at the Holkham Sheep Shearing in his journey to the north. It was a departure that had something of the appearance of an escape. Cobbett was left alone to shoulder at least one of the world's burdens that he had not sought. He replied immediately to the itinerant President of the Board of Agriculture in a letter of 20 June:

In the name of Mr Johnstone who I am sure will be very grateful for the very kind attention you have paid to his interest relative to the sheep, I return you very sincere thanks for your letter of the 18th inst. covering a copy of a letter from yourself to the Secretary of the Treasury[13] and also copy of a letter from him to the Transport Board.[14] Your hints will be carefully attended to, and indeed I had already taken all the precautions you have had the goodness to recommend, excepting what relates to *seafreight*, with which I have nothing to do, as the sheep will be consigned to M^r [John] Tunno, who is a merchant of great eminence and a very particular friend of Colonel Johnstone's.

Among my neighbours in the north west of this county and other gentlemen whom I know in Dorsetshire and Wiltshire, I shall have plenty of pasturage provided; and as to shepherds I have five men of my own whom I can safely trust, to whom I shall add about fifteen or twenty more; the moment I hear of the arrival of the sheep, I will take care to give due notice of the time of sale. The whole nation ought to have plenty of notice. It is of great consequence the sheep should be well *distributed*. The two gentlemen who you have pointed out as probable purchasers will of course be particularly informed of the time of sale.

Will you be so good as [to] send me as nearly as you can an account of the *prices* of Spanish sheep. I will make a point of giving you the very earliest information of the arrival of the sheep or any part of them; and I am sure you will excuse me for troubling you for further advice if I should be at a loss how to act.

The eight sheep which I have received from Spain, and which arrived about a week ago are doing very well; their wool is dirty from their sea-passage, but they are beautiful creatures.

From what I have heard, Mr Johnstone's are of the first quality; and I must take care as far as I can to make them bring the very first price. Will you take the trouble, sir, to let me know whither I can go to *see* the greatest variety of Spanish sheep; and how I ought to set about finding the price? I have a very great desire to do the part of this business which falls to my share in the best manner possible. I beg leave to repeat my thanks for your obliging and valuable communications . . .

P.S. I shall be of course regulated by numbers in the order of march; but it appears to me that the north side of *Portsdown* is a very good resting place after the first movement from Portsmouth.

The down itself is not bad: if the number be not very large I should suppose that I can very well provide for them between Meon Stoke and King's Worthy inclusive, taking in a tract of about ten miles long, Winchester being not far from the centre.[15]

Thus spoke William Cobbett, farmer of Botley, willing to do his best for the sheep in the interests of a distant and by no means either respectable or reliable friend. Should the sale take place—and he manifestly had his private doubts whether any sheep would arrive to be sold—he intended that it should be at Winchester. On this basis he continued, as Editor of *Cobbett's Weekly Political Register*, to proclaim his fervour to the world in the matter of Spanish sheep and the scope of his arrangements for their reception and ultimate disposal:

It is expected that the sheep will be landed at Portsmouth; and a letter which I have received from SIR JOHN SINCLAIR, as President of the Board of Agriculture, informs me, that, in consequence of an application from him, the Treasury has given orders to the Commissioners of Customs, at the Out-Ports, and also to the Transport Board, to afford every facility to the safe and quick landing of the sheep. The season of the year is rather unfavourable. The heat, and the scarcity of water on board ship, will, I am afraid, prove fatal to a part, at least, of the flock; but at any rate, it is of great importance, that there should be no delay in the landing; and to prevent this, the Treasury appears to have taken the necessary precaution. I have provided as much, and perhaps more, pasture than will be necessary; but, it is possible, that I may not have provided half enough. I therefore take this opportunity of requesting any gentlemen, who may be able to accomodate me with good wholesome pasture, for a month or two, to be so good as to write to me upon the subject. And also to let me know, if they can *lend* me shepherds for a little while, in case I should be at a loss for such assistance. It is a *public* concern; and, I trust, the friends of agriculture in the neighbouring counties as well as in this, will gladly afford me all the aid in their power. Any where between SOBERTON across to WINCHESTER and on towards Stockbridge or Sutton; in short, any where within twenty miles of Botley, where there is good and wholesome sheep feed, may do for the purpose.[16]

The latter-day pirate of the Caribbean, by this time at sea again in search of other spoils, could have had no complaint about the quality of his representation before the general public by the pen of William Cobbett in the *Register* nor of its Editor's value as a front man for the sheep.

IV

The rustic seclusion of Botley was not the only quiet corner disturbed by the hopeful intriguer in Spain. Deep in the Board of Trade something also stirred. Banks, who had received from Sinclair on 25 May an extract from Cochrane-Johnstone's letter of 9 May with its impudent claim for a bounty, had duly brought this to the attention of the President of the Board of Trade. On 30 May from the 3rd Lord Bathurst there came the frosty reply:

I never heard of Mr Cochrane Johnston's speculations in Spanish sheep until I received your Letter. I can not believe he was authorised by Government, and, if he has obtained these Sheep for the King without any authority he is, in my opinion, very much to be blamed for his conduct instead of receiving any encouragement. I will endeavour to call upon you to-morrow.[17]

Within the next day or so the President of the Board of Trade was further embarrassed and confused by what seemed to be new accessions to the flocks of the realm as he sent a quick note of appeal to Banks about 1 June:

An Account is this Morning arrived of the Junta at Seville having offered 4000 Merino Sheep to the King, being part of the Prince of Peace's flock. Mr Friend has accepted them. What can be done with them? Are these the Sheep which Mr Cockrane Johnson [sic] takes the credit of having procured?[18]

To this there was no immediate answer. Rumours and reports were growing and spreading. Confusion was ripening fast. The sheep business was not popular in or near Whitehall. Least of all was it so at Downing Street where in the past six months the name of Cochrane-Johnstone had gained an unsavoury distinction all its own. The Secretary of State for War and the Colonies had more than one good reason to raise an emphatic protest. Castlereagh wrote vehemently on 3 June to Lieutenant-General Sir Arthur Wellesley:

. . . We are much disturbed by Cochrane Johnstone's impudence in sending for transports to send his sheep home to Cobbett, who is the consignee in his speculation; they will be dismantled as troopships and detained God knows how long. I have written to the Admiralty forbidding their being detained on any account. . . .[19]

A week later the point of crisis seemed to have come. The President of the Royal Society came forward with truly alarming information. The veto of the Secretary of State for War and the Colonies apparently had been too late. On 10 June Banks wrote to Lord Bathurst:

The die is thrown & H.M. Ministers must abide by the hazard of the Cast; 12000 Merino Sheep are embarked on Board Transports in the Service of Government under the Sanction of the Admiral on the Station & will arrive possibly in a week; probably in a fortnight; & certainly in the course of the present month of June.

The animals are addressed by a Letter scarce amounting to a consignment to Sir John Sinclair P.B.A., & Mr Cobbett, the political writer. If they accept the office all will be well: if they decline it, Government, who must clear

350   HIS MAJESTY'S SPANISH FLOCK

their Transports of the Sheep in order that they may return to their Station, will have the pasturage to provide for the whole flock, which alone at the rate of $-/6^d$ a week a head, will incur an expence of £300 a week, besides the cost of Shepherds, medecines, &c., &c., &c., nor is it easy to guess where pasturage can be found at this season, when all Pastures are over stocked with animals intended to be spread over the [fields], after the meadows, now all shut up, have been cut, & the hay carried off.

If provision is not made the animals will die on board the vessels & in the Streets; & a clamor will be raised against the inhumanity of suffering them to starve, & the impolicy of neglecting animals so valuable & so much wanted at present.

What can be done? . . .

Left at this point, as Cameron abbreviated it, the letter has the echo of a despairing cry.[20] Banks, however, was making a rhetorical repetition of Lord Bathurst's query of some days before—'What can be done with them?'—and then proceeded to propound his own suggestions should Sinclair and Cobbett not 'accept the office'.

Notices may be sent to Sir John Sinclair and his Colleagues acquainting them that the Flock will very shortly arrive, & requesting them to know whether they will undertake the charge allotted to them by C[ochrane] J[ohnston]; as, in that case, the Transports will be ordered to such places as is most convenient to their arrangements. They may be told that the Freight in the Transports will be given up & that they will be charged with nothing but the cost of fitting up the vessels, putting on board & ordering the Shepherds, wages &c., & such extra charges.

In case they refuse, applications may be made to the Prince, to know whether H.R.H. will allow them to be put upon Dartmoor till the hay is cut & pasture can be obtained. M[r] Tyrwhit is probably on the spot.

If this will not do, they must be fed with hay in some of the waste parts of the Lines of P[ortsmouth] or P[lymouth] if they arrive before provision can be made for them.

The King's 2000 must be taken care of. Pastures may probably be obtained for them on the South Downs till autumn, as it will be right to do the best that can be done; or, on emergency of the nature of the present, may not these Sheep be given away by Flocks of 50 or 25 each, the persons who receive them, however, paying the cost & charge of Government for Freight, &c., &c., &c., probably £2 or 3 a head.

M[r] Cockrane the rich man lately returned from India may be asked if he will take charge of the Flock: it will not be losing concern, as the wool alone cannot be worth less when shorn than 2 or 3£ a sheep.[21]

By this time it is clear that Banks had received fairly specific information about this phantom flock from Spain—probably through Mr. John Barrow, Second Secretary to the Admiralty. From the beginning there was much confusion and doubt about the numbers involved and the questions were not easily answered from the jaunty letters dashed off at Seville. There was agreement, however, that the total seemed to be about twelve thousand. But the situation had changed since 3 May when Cochrane-Johnstone exultantly had proclaimed himself the purchaser of the whole *cabana*. In his letter of 9 May to Sinclair he had already retreated from this position of solitary commercial triumph. The first rapture of the opportunist profiteer was dying away as it was doubtless made clear to him that the Spanish people had their own views. The confiscated sheep of the renegade nobility still had a purpose to serve for the Spanish cause in the same fashion as the Paular flock of the detested Godoy. Cash and credit for arms and supplies certainly had a pressing importance, immediate and material. But there was still the wide-reaching power of a neat gesture to a fellow-belligerent—the bread cast on the political waters of a new alliance. The Supreme Junta in Seville was not likely to waste this resource even in the present national extremity. So, again, we now see the offer of the Spanish sheep as a gift to the King of England. We may also fairly deduce that Cochrane-Johnstone flattered himself when he claimed that by his own efforts he had got '2000 of them without purchase for the King'. We may reasonably suppose also that he had astutely sensed the feeling of the Spanish patriots and was modifying his own hopes of easy gain. He is clearly treading the path of expediency as he invokes noble economic motives to support the dignity of his enterprise in this 'great National object'. It is under pressure, therefore, that the Cochrane-Johnstone stake in the flock diminishes inversely as his hypocrisy in the affair grows and as he magnifies his fealty to the King. Ten short days had altered much as, anxious to be gone, he wrote on 13 May to Sinclair:

I beg of you to go to the Treasury and get an order that I may have what Transports are necessary to send home the Flock of Merino Sheep which are for the King and me. This is a great National object, as great a one as driving the French out of Spain, & unless we get the Sheep embark'd with the utmost expedition, they will die for want of Pasture. The King has to thank me for getting 4000 of them for nothing; & I have got 8000 for paying for them [I] recommend to His Majesty to keep the Sheep as an entire Flock & not allow them to be mixed with others—by that means he will be enabled to supply England yearly with rams; & the pasture of the Sheep must be changed frequently as otherways the nature of the Wool will degenerate—on this subject of the mode of treatment I shall write you fully when I have time. Let the Instructions be sent to Admiral Berkely at Lisbon who has hundreds of Transports laying idle. I am willing to pay the hire of the Transports for carrying *my* sheep if demanded; but I hope, that, considering what I have effected with the Supreme Junta on this subject it will not be demanded— Pray write to M.ʳ Duff, our Consul General at Cadiz, on this subject, who will communicate what you settle to my Agent there, as I leave this [country] to embark for Mexico. Not a moment must be lost by you to get the order from the Treasury. I hope that Admiral Berkeley will comply with my request before it arrives; but, for fear he does not, get the order sent immediately by every possible despatch.[22]

With this peremptory valediction and its undertones of nervousness Cochrane-Johnstone about ten days later departed for Vera Cruz on H.M. frigate *Undaunted*—leaving his dealings with the Golden Fleece of Spain, for the time being, to tamper with the silver hoards of Mexico. Whitehall and William Cobbett were left as strange and unlikely partners to resolve the problem of the sheep. As to numbers and destination it now remained only for the Press to misreport a few salient details and the confusion for posterity was complete:

Twelve thousand more Merino Sheep are ready to be shipped in Spain for this country. *Eight thousand* of them are a present to the King; and *four thousand* are the private property of Mr. Cochrane Johnson, who is waiting with great anxiety at Cadiz for vessels to ship them for England.[23]

But this highly professional wicked uncle was certainly not in Cadiz, however anxious he may have been about vessels to ship them to England. In the month of June 1809 he was amusing himself by making life very difficult for his nephew Captain Thomas Lord Cochrane of H.M. frigate *Ethalion* as well as for Captain Thomas James Maling of the *Undaunted*, on a few small matters of smuggling and currency.

V

Somewhere in the dispatches and memoranda for 1809 of Vice-Admiral George Berkeley and Lieutenant-General Sir Arthur Wellesley lie the decisions which probably determined the ultimate future of the twelve thousand sheep unseasonably grazing in the now hot Andalusian sun along the parching slopes between Gibraltar and Cadiz. Another part of the story must lie somewhere in forgotten boxes of the War Office. Castlereagh, the amateur strategist of Whitehall, could rise in wrathful opposition to the irresponsible use of his precious transports with every justice.[24] Castlereagh, the frequent target of Cobbett's political gun-fire could with some reason feel most unwilling to connive at any scheme in which the farmer of Botley was engaged—however patriotic. The Viscount was even now wounded and bleeding afresh, stung by the grapeshot charge from the muzzle of the *Register* of 1 July on the flogging of the Local Militia mutineers at Ely.[25] Castlereagh, the Secretary of State for War and the Colonies could hardly ignore the highly irregular military career and colonial maladministration of the gentleman issuing his orders from Seville—still less with his memories freshened by the same gentleman's recent exploits at Tortola as Navy Agent. The coalition of Cobbett and Cochrane-Johnstone in any enterprise, however noble its intentions on the surface, at just that moment in Downing Street must have worn all the appearance of a devilish invention. Castlereagh's repudiating orders and those of Lord Mulgrave from the Admiralty at his request must have reached Lisbon in time to take full effect in preventing the use of naval transports at least for that part of the princely but inconvenient flock of twelve thousand which Cochrane-Johnstone could claim as his own. They did not apparently apply to prevent the embarkation from Cadiz, however, of the first two thousand Merino sheep originally and specifically destined by a grateful Supreme Junta for His Majesty King George III of England.

About 15 July 1809, Mr. John Barrow of the Admiralty reported the arrival of transports at Portsmouth with sheep from Spain on board. On Monday, 17 July, Banks sent this news with the original note of advice from John Barrow to Richard Snart who received it that evening at Marsh Gate Farm.[26] Snart had been preparing to meet Henry Lacocke the following morning, Tuesday, 18 July, to select the sheep for the Royal sale which the King himself that year had ordained should be held on 26 July.[27] Instead Snart now thought it incumbent to be at Windsor very early on the Tuesday morning in case the King should have any commands to give in the matter of the new arrivals, assuming they were indeed for the Royal flock. On Wednesday, 19 July, he returned to Marsh Gate and that evening confirmed in a letter to Banks that George Canning had sent notice from the Foreign Office to Windsor Castle that morning confirming the fact that the sheep at Portsmouth were certainly those intended for His Majesty. Apart from the impending sale, however, Snart was busy with the summer problems of the harvest on the Royal farms and neither he nor Richard Stanford could easily be spared to go so far afield as to Portsmouth. The King, therefore, had given orders for the naval transports to come to Deptford. By this plan it was calculated that though a few more might perhaps die by the additional delay in disembarking them, more would be saved by the shorter journey on the road. Besides, the diversion would 'make a wonderful difference in the Expence'.[28]

On Thursday, 20 July, Snart, therefore, went early to Deptford to make the best arrangements possible for their landing and to provide grass for them near the docks should it not prove advisable from their general state to move them on to St. James's Park on the day of their arrival. The sheep, however, did not sail from Portsmouth until the evening of Wednesday, 26 July, the very day of the sixth public auction in the field near the Pagoda at Kew. Richard Snart received word of this on Saturday morning, 29 July, and also that they were daily expected in the Thames. Whereupon he immediately set out from Marsh Gate to meet them. Then at some time about the end of the month or in the first days of August 1809 the 'new' Negrettis from Cadiz, refugees and prizes of the Peninsular War, joined the 'old' Negrettis from Santander, the diplomatic 'Treasure of infinite value' that had now been the ornament of His Majesty's farms for eighteen eventful and frustrating years under the watchful shepherding of Sir Joseph Banks. And, as the sheep passed along the Thames to this tryst at Richmond, one wonders whether Castlereagh was taunted by the bleatings of the flock as it marched within ear-shot of the Horse Guards and Downing Street to its first stage on the grazing of St. James's Park.

No record is available of the number which actually survived the journey to pass under the hand and care of Richard Stanford. On 2 November, he noted as new Negrettis—twelve hundred and ninety ewes, two hundred and ninety lambs, six wethers, and twenty-nine rams, or sixteen hundred and fifteen head in all. On 2 December he noted—twelve hundred and seventy ewes, five hundred lambs, and six wethers, or seventeen hundred and seventy-six head. But it is at this period impossible any longer to keep a reasonable trace of the numbers in the flock. Certainly many fewer than the original two thousand shipped from Cadiz remained three months after their landing in England. From the evidence of former mortality rates it would be generous to suggest that eighteen hundred at most landed alive at Deptford to reach Kew. It is not likely that the losses would be any less than among the Paular importations of the previous year, trans-shipped from the north of Spain by a shorter route in the cooler autumn months. At all events, by November 1809, only about thirteen hundred adult ewes of each *cabana* seemed to have survived. Certainly Stanford only kept the record of what sheep were at Kew and Richmond and in these latter years of hectic arrivals and departures many details are hard to trace.

The new Negrettis were, on all the evidence so far, the last important group of sheep known to have been directly added from Spain to His Majesty's Merino flock in England. There were certainly other sheep accepted in the King's name by the Diplomatic and the Consular Corps and by the Commissaries of the Army at different times apart from the irregular episode of Cochrane-Johnstone. These have given rise to many confusing and irreconcilable accounts of the numbers actually added to the King's possessions of the Spanish Merino. It seems now, however, that we can accept as fact at least two Spanish gifts—the two thousand Paulars of 1808 and the two thousand Negrettis of 1809 from the Junta of the Asturias and the Supreme Junta respectively. We know now that this number of sheep from each of these two famous *cabanas* were actually sent from Spain for the King. We can accept also that, broadly, about eighteen hundred of each survived to land at Portsmouth and at Deptford, to dwindle within a few months by a further five hundred to something about thirteen hundred in each case. Most other reported gifts to His Majesty or alleged purchases on his behalf in Spain belong mainly to the intricate and often obscure dealings of the consuls, the commissaries, the merchants, and all the free-lance opportunists, not unlike Cochrane-Johnstone, vying with the French of the same ilk for the confiscated property and prizes as they fell to each side in the various campaigns.[29] Many more Spanish sheep came to Great Britain as a direct result of this war-time commerce, but few, if any, to join His Majesty's Spanish flock as gifts in the same fashion as the new Negrettis. As assets in Spain itself the Spanish Merinos were of great value to the Government in meeting the local costs of the war, so that many were sold for the best prices they would bring on the Peninsula. This left the problems of transport and shipping in the hands of the speculative buyers and their agents. Thereby no embarrassing situations were evoked such as that created by Cochrane-Johnstone with his importunate demands on the transports of the Royal Navy.

VI

There was, however, no end to the ingenuity of Andrew James Cochrane-Johnstone in creating embarrassing situations. In this he was ceaselessly active, losing no opportunity for turning almost any predicament in which he found himself to some dubious form of monetary advantage. As he sailed away south-west from Cadiz on the favourable winds of June any niggling doubts about the transports for his Negretti sheep were probably soothed by the thought of the order on the Spanish Royal Treasury at Vera Cruz which he carried in his baggage—the rewarding price of his contract for the supply of muskets to the Supreme Junta at Seville. As a diversion from sheep he had begun the first moves of a small exercise in smuggling by brow-beating Captain Maling of the *Undaunted* into accepting '4 small Bales of Cloathing to be landed at Barbados for my people in Dominica'.[30] To this Maling reluctantly agreed considering it 'rather contrary to the rules of service'. On which ship these were carried is not clear but, after the arrival of the *Ethalion* at Vera Cruz on 9 July, Maling, as the senior captain, wrote firmly to Cochrane-Johnstone:

... At this moment there are some Bales, I understand on board the *Ethalion* which if not entered at the custom house might endanger the ship; and at any rate is so contrary to the usage in British Men or War that I have to recommend their being landed immediately. ...[31]

Now whether these were the original four bales or not it is pretty clear that Maling was sure they had no right to be on one of H.M. frigates at Vera Cruz when he had only agreed—and with many misgivings—to a shipment to the Windward Islands. Martinique, their port of call there, was now far behind. This seems to have been the beginning of a long and very acrimonious dispute between Maling and Cochrane-Johnstone which interfered with the essential purpose of the latter's business at Vera Cruz, namely, to secure silver bullion for the British Government.

We need not attempt to follow the inner mysteries of the quarrel here. It is sufficient to note the upshot as it appears in a letter from Captain Thomas Lord Cochrane of the *Ethalion* giving a long account to his father, the 9th Earl of Dundonald, including this significant comment:

... I really think my uncle has been very wrong in the latter part of this business—there could be no possible excuse for his not putting the money on board of me [i.e. the *Ethalion*]; what excuse he will make to government, I cannot tell—it is carrying pique rather too far to deprive Gov.^t of the sum of 3 or 4 millions of Dollars because there is difference of opinion between him and Maling—he also interfered in other things which he certainly had nothing whatever to do with. . . .[32]

But in the end—somehow—the British Government seems to have acquired its three million silver dollars through the negotiations of Cochrane-Johnstone who thereby achieved the distinction of being the most successful of the Treasury agents in this pursuit.[33] There is also more than a little to suggest that the Government might have got even more had Cochrane-Johnstone cared to reveal the extent of his own dealings. There was certainly some little bother over the landing of silver bullion in England when he reached home at last about the end of December 1809 or early in January 1810.

But whatever profit there was for him in Mexican silver—and there seemed to be much—he lost no time in returning to his exploitation of the Golden Fleece of Spain in the bale or on the hoof. Apart from his concern in the remnants of the Negretti flock he had, before leaving Spain in May, invested heavily in purchases of wool from the shearings which would then be in progress under unusual conditions. His letter of 18 January 1810, from London to his agent in Cadiz, Mr. Patrick Wiseman, illuminates the character and methods of Cochrane-Johnstone at work:

You must allow me to express [myself] rather disappointed at finding no accounts or Papers waiting my return in this Country from you, by which I might be able to estimate the existing state of the account between us—perhaps this may in some measure have originated from an expectation that I should return to Cadiz from South America—By a letter my friend Mr John Tunno received from you yesterday dated 8th December, I believe you had further forwarded to Cadiz on my account 392 Bags of Wool making in all 1790 Bags; out of this quantity there are 165 Bags under the mark NE, which of course were shorn from my own Flock, so that the total quantity of purchased Wools which you have forwarded is 1625 Bags.—Estimating the prices of these 1625 Bags, at the same rates, as some of the purchases were effected at previous to my leaving Spain, and adding thereto an ample allowance for the washing, Packing &c. of them, as well as of the 165 Bags shorn from my own Flock, I estimate that you may in all have expended about £95, or £97,000, which of course leaves a very large Balance in my favour still in your hands—Now, under this impression, I feel in some degree uneasy at your saying in your letter to Mr Tunno, when speaking of the 392 Bags of Wool last forwarded, 'with these the Shipments of this year are concluded'.—it does strike me My good Sir, that as I deposited with you the actual Money so many Months ago, there has been ample time for you to invest and ship the whole off ere this—however as it would be uncandid in me to prejudge this matter, it is only right that I should wait your explanation—In the meantime as you are aware I have accounts to settle in Spain, I have enclosed to our mutual worthy friend James Duff Esquire a Power of Attorney authorising him to come to a settlement with you for me, and to receive from you the Balance of the appropriation of which I have given directions—The statement of Accounts will be very simple—just credit me for the Money I gave you, and per Contra debit me for the cost and expenses on the 1790 Bags of Wool; then the Balance as it may appear is to be paid over to Mr Duff, who will give you a receipt for it—I have not the least doubt that the whole of your statement will be found perfectly correct, but as a matter of regularity, it will be necessary that I examine them, and therefore I request you will immediately hasten on Copies of them under cover to my friend Mr John Tunno, where if they prove all right, as I am persuaded they will, I shall instantly forward you a Release in full.

Our worthy friend Father Eagan is the Bearer of this letter, and will inform you of the great exertions which I have made about the arms—altho the permission has been refused me, still however the discussion has had the happy effect of compelling our Government to send out more arms, and as there will soon be a change of our Ministry, I shall then be enabled to send the Supreme Junta as many arms as they want, for it is well known what are the sentiments of Lords Greville and Grey, the principal leaders of the opposition —I refer you to Cobbett's Newspaper for an account of this business—I have already purchased a considerable quantity of Arms, which will I Trust allowed to be sent for the payment of the Sheep. Pray remember me most be kindly to Mrs Wiseman and her Daughter and in the hopes of seeing you soon Believe me to be . . .[34]

Before the end of the year Cochrane-Johnstone was established at Lisbon, hovering there about the Commissary-General's office which had become a sort of clearing house on the Peninsula as the sheep trade with Spanish Merinos rose to a climax in the year 1811. He had, presumably, done well enough with his exchange of muskets for Merinos during the summer—the weapons made in Birmingham for seventeen shillings apiece and sold at a contract price to the Spaniards for three guineas each, so it is said. But there still remained the problem of selling the sheep themselves. There were only two courses possible— either to ship them to the British Isles somewhere or across the Atlantic to the United States. For Cochrane-Johnstone the British market had doubtless by now much less appeal or security than the American. A fresh untilled field was understandably more attractive and here was one that the plough had just entered.

The Honourable William Jarvis, United States Consul at Lisbon in the closing months of his residence in Portugal had, in 1809, initiated one of the first shipments of Merinos to Boston (or a near-by port) where they arrived early in April 1810.[35] These were said to be from the Escorial *cabana*. During the spring and summer of that year there was a small scattering of importations along the eastern sea-board of the United States, but the main stream was only at full flood between September 1810 and July 1811. Into this Merino exodus Cochrane-Johnstone flung his bleating assets as fast as he could charter ships, arrange credit, or secure consignees. The full tale of his disposal of the sheep which he claimed as his own in Spain cannot be told on the evidence we have. But we can at least gain some insight into the last stages of his Negretti speculation and the fate of some part of the flock which never did reach England—that for which Cobbett's, Sinclair's, and Banks's arrangements were all in vain. Whatever the sorry spectacle of the English losses among the Negrettis it is more than matched by the horrors of the transatlantic death-ships.

From Lisbon on 13 December 1810, Cochrane-Johnstone wrote to Messrs. John Murray and Sons announcing that he had dispatched no less than eight vessels with sheep consigned to them at New York. He himself proposed to embark for that city in a few days on board another chartered Portuguese vessel, the *Lord Wellington*, at that moment ready to sail from the Tagus with five hundred and seventy-three sheep from the Guadaloupe *cabana* on board. He also enclosed a bill of lading for a hundred and sixty bags of 'fine Leonesa Wool shorn this year from the Escurial Flock' which he had shipped to them by the *Hibernia*. He hoped also that they would, by the time of his arrival, have been able to purchase the twenty-five thousand barrels of fine American flour 'in the cheapest places' for shipment to Lisbon as he had directed in his letter to their Mr. William Ogden. Then he added,

I think it necessary to apprise you that having discovered that this Portuguese Ship which I have chartered, was the *Carmelite* formerly of New York, and that she had broke your embargo Laws, which prevents her returning to America, I have been under the grievous necessity of going with her on this account to Bermuda, where I shall be guided by information which I may obtain there of the real state of your laws in this respect; and I must beg of you to write to me there by the quickest possible conveyance, and to send some Hay for these sheep to Bermuda if possible, and the vessel which carries the Hay may bring back Sheep—I beg that you will have the goodness to give me your advice what to do with the Sheep there, and if you could either make a bargain for the delivery of them there, or put me in the way of embarking them on reasonable terms for your Coast—all the Sheep on board the *Lord Wellington* are of the celebrated Flock of Guadaloupe.

Trusting to [be] hearing from you at Bermuda in the manner the most expeditious, either by sending a vessel from New York, or Norfolk, or some other nearer Port, I remain . . . N.B. In all the vessels in which the Sheep have been sent, you will of course make the Captains produce the Skins of the different Sheep which may die, not only to prove the deaths but also on account of the Skins which are valuable for the Wool.[36]

But whatever he may have gleaned elsewhere among the aftermaths of the Peninsular War on land and sea there was to be no profit for Andrew James Cochrane-Johnstone in this affair. The whole American speculation was to wither away slowly and, it must be supposed, very painfully to a gambler whose luck had now run out. The relentless attrition of the Cochrane-Johnstone assets and the total failure of his trading expectations was recorded in letter after letter from New York to Lisbon—for somehow, in the end, he had not sailed on the *Lord Wellington* to the United States nor even to Bermuda. Though we can have little sympathy with Cochrane-Johnstone in his monetary losses or in whatever degree he suffered otherwise, we can assuredly grieve for the wastage and the suffering among the animals that were the victims in this and in many other similar speculations. He was, no doubt, a most reprehensible character but the train of disasters which shattered his particular venture cannot be viewed as a peculiar judgement justly administered. Nearly all who probed the Peninsular pie in search of mercantile gain by the same means at this period were afflicted in much the same sad way. The details may have varied but the stories were as cruel and often as calamitous.

The first reports were ominous. Writing on 9 January 1811, Messrs. John Murray and Sons registered the arrivals of the ships *Eliza* and *Four Sisters* and the brig *General Putnam* with their heavy toll of dead and dying sheep:

. . . they have got a very inveterate disease among them, which appears to be incurable and we are afraid there will not be as many survive as will pay the Freight—it is a most unfortunate speculation of yours and they could not have arrived here in a worse season it is now the depth of winter and when we have the severest cold weather—it is a pity that they were shipped before February or March so as to arrive here in the Spring most of the Fall importations have been attacked with the same disorder that prevails among yours and many have died.—The price of sheep is far below your expectation. they were sold in October and November from $50 to $100 & as there are a vast number here for Sale we apprehend they will be considerably lower in the Spring. We will do all in our power to preserve them and dispose of them to the best advantage for your account.

And then, on 10 January, they added an ominous postscript,

We shall have to advance upwards of $25,000 Freight on the animals which at this time is a most grievous thing as money is extremely scarce and the pressure immense. This shipment of yours has been a most inconvenient thing as relates to us and will we fear terminate very unfortunately for you. We conversed yesterday with some persons from the country who purchased some of the Sheep last Summer, they do not much approve of them. they are very subject to the Scab and it is difficult to cure them. All yours have the Scab and it will cost a considerable Sum to cure them besides reimbursing other expenses which will amount to considerable. Hay is now selling at 12/- p. cwt.[37]

On 28 January Messrs. John Murray and Sons chronicled the arrival of the last four vessels—the ship *Ann*, brig *Liberty*, ship *Belisarius*, and the ship *Asia*—and enhanced the long tale of death, pestilence, and mercantile depression.

... the destructive disease still prevails amongst them, and numbers of them have died and are dying every day, notwithstanding all our care and attention to prevent it, we are apprehensive there will not be a sufficient number survive to pay the freight, we purpose selling them in March, that being a season when the Farmers can come in from the Country without interfering with putting in their Spring Crops, It is impossible for us to execute your order for Flour, in the first place there is not one third of the quantity in our City, and in the second there is so great distress for money that Bills will not sell at any price. 25000 Barrels of Flour would cost upwards of $250,000 and it would be impossible to raise that amount on Bills in many Months, the times are so critical that we are induced to draw in our business, as much as possible and we do not intend to enter into any shipments of any description. The number of failures here and the pressure for money is beyond example great, we shall have to pay near $20000 freight to these Vessels that have arrived, which is a very heavy Sum at the present time, when Bills cannot be Sold, there are only about 700 Sheep now alive and many of them are diseased, the wool you mention you intend to Ship has not arrived, we fear you will sustain a very heavy loss by this speculation, as the price here is very much reduced, the last sales were from $40 to $50 the disorders these Sheep are subject to in this Country has deterred many of our farmers from buyin them . . . [P.S.] Wool has been sold here at $2 p^r lb. but considerable quantities have been imported latterly, which will no doubt reduce the price, at present there is no Sale.[38]

A week or so later there was a brief ray of light as the report came through of the arrival in New York of the *Hibernia* with her hundred and sixty bags of Escorial wool even though there were poor prospects of its immediate sale. With it, however, also came sobering news of the *Lord Wellington*, otherwise the proscribed *Carmelite*, on which had sailed Mr. Andrew Smith as Cochrane-Johnstone's agent with the Guadaloupe sheep. More footnotes were added to the long chapter of disasters. Disease had also broken out among the sheep on this vessel, a hundred had been lost at sea, and Smith—himself unwell with a liver complaint—had been induced to put into Madeira in search of green food for the survivors.[39] Here the stock were unshipped and here they stayed and died while Smith recovered and other ships were sought to carry them on to America—for Cochrane-Johnstone had been unequivocally warned by William Ogden again,

. . . If the *Carmelite* comes here [New York] she will certainly be seized our Government grants no indulgences in those Cases—A Foreigner may obtain permission to hold property in this State, but it altogether depends upon the will and favour of our Legislature. . . .[40]

Then, too, there was 'the unwarrantable infamy of the British Consul' at Madeira 'who would not clear them out on a British Vessel', all adding to the losses of the sheep '& the unavoidable expenses of keeping them during the Winter'. The expense, however, had by Smith's own confession been reduced to a pittance during March and April as he had got Government ground with sufficient pasture for three hundred head and a shepherd withal. As Andrew Smith sailed for New York by the brig *Fanny Roberts* on 30 April 1811, recovered of his liver disease, he left behind sixty Merinos 'all fat and plump under the charge of Mr. G. C. Smith' his friend and correspondent in Madeira. He reported also that of the hundred and fifty sheep which had been shipped from Madeira by the schooner *Chelsea* only ninety-two had been landed at New York.[41] With this last desolate note in the long gloomy sequence what comfort could there be for Cochrane-Johnstone to have the continued assurance of indefatigable zeal for his interest from his 'affect.^e & most faithfully devoted Servant'? And what did the master make of his servant's closing prayer—'May the God of Mercy bless you'? But by now Cochrane-Johnstone must have been immune to life's ironies. In the end, after two years of speculation in the Spanish sheep and wool trade, there was not much evidence of the Divine blessing. Indeed, there was very little evidence of anything. The forecast of Messrs. John Murray and Sons had been a true one down to the last profitless shipment. Of the two thousand seven hundred and twelve Spanish sheep which he had sent on nine ships across the Atlantic in the winter of 1810–11 Cochrane-Johnstone had, in the spring of 1811, probably no more than seven hundred and fifty alive and available for sale in the United States—and even of these many were sick and still dying. Most were infected with scab. The prices which in 1810 had ranged above $100 had in April 1811 fallen far below $50—if the sheep were saleable at all. His wool could not be sold—but at least that was durable and could be stored. The sheep on the other hand had to be cosseted—fed, watered, husbanded, and above all cured of the sheep pox and the scab. The celestial mercy had ordained no profit here— and no back freight, either, of twenty-five thousand barrels of flour as a compensating fiddle in the general racket of army supplies on the Peninsula.

In the estimated round figure of twenty-six thousand Spanish Merinos which were shipped to the United States in the frantic trading rush of 1810 and 1811 those of Cochrane-Johnstone clearly formed one of the largest single speculations. It was exceeded only by that of William Jarvis who shipped about three thousand eight hundred and fifty. Together these two men organized the export of about one-quarter of all the sheep that left Spain for the United States at this time. But the losses amongst those of Cochrane-Johnstone were undoubtedly some of the greatest. Whereas the general mortality on board, during the thirty to forty day passage, was usually about twenty-five to thirty-five per cent of those shipped, Cochrane-Johnstone lost more than half at sea and at least one-fifth very soon after landing. The loss among Jarvis's sheep were of the more usual order. At most no more than about nineteen thousand Spanish Merinos survived the voyages to reach the American coast in the speculative years of 1810 and 1811. The further wastage soon after landing was considerable and it is doubtful if many more than fifteen thousand survived to become useful foundations of the early American flocks. To these Cochrane-Johnstone may have contributed in the end just five per cent—from which he gained nothing.

Whatever the United States of America or His Britannic Majesty may have owed to the inspired opportunism and self-aggrandizement of Andrew James Cochrane-Johnstone; whatever he himself gained or lost in his purple progress through life, it is likely that he cared little about the disappointments, embarrassments, or disasters that beset his friends and relatives whom he variously entangled in his sleazy intrigues and in his interminable quarrels. A cunning exploiter of men and events to the end he returned to the House of Commons as Member for Grampound when his brother George Augustus accepted the Chiltern Hundreds in July 1812. He was returned again at the General Election in October that year. Then finally as the principal in a financial conspiracy in February 1814 which very successfully speculated on the Stock Exchange when false rumours of Bonaparte's death were circulated he was tried in June and found guilty. He loudly protested his innocence in the House and in the Press, threatening prosecutions for defamation of character. His unwitting nephew, Captain Thomas Lord Cochrane had been skilfully involved, was arraigned on the same charges, could not prove his innocence, and was sentenced to two years' imprisonment. His career of such promise with the British Navy was ended. But his wicked uncle, knowing where the truth lay, slipped secretly from the country before sentence was passed on him and escaped a retribution long overdue. In July 1814 Cochrane was formally expelled from the House of Commons and thereafter skulked in the shadows of history, discreetly but ignominiously obscure.

VII

We hear no more about Cochrane-Johnstone's sheep speculation as such in England. All 'the noted agriculturalists' and devoted 'readers of Cobbets Register' whom Banks suggested might be waiting for these sheep to arrive in 1809 to be sold in large numbers at lower prices than at the King's auction—all these were, from that source at least, to remain disappointed men. Even His Majesty's consignment had not been really expected for, as Banks had noted at the time:

... it was by a mistake I am told that the Transports were allowed to take on board those that are now arrived and which are the Kings, how shipping can be obtained for Johnstons Sheep I do not guess ...[42]

But there is some evidence that more of the Negretti *cabana* did in fact reach England by various means after 1809. In September 1809 Banks was seriously concerned about the remaining two thousand Negrettis for the King which were still in Spain:

... What the Event will be I cannot guess I fear the applications that deserve attention will be very numerous & I dread the Loss likely to happen to the next importation when the Ewes will be so much more forward with Lamb The Sheep are at Seville & I shall request that the Transports which are to bring them home after having landed Troops at Gibraltar may take them in at St Lucar instead of at Cadiz which saves the Driving of near 100 miles ...[43]

However, the exigencies of war no doubt intervened for the following summer this portion of the Negretti flock seems still to have been in Spain, increased in number by the lambs which were now nearly six months old. Of these we have a further view, apparently, as Banks writes again to Lord Spencer rather more optimistically:

. . . I have some pleasure in telling your Lordship that the main Flock of merinos now 3000 at least in number have not yet Fallen into the hands of the French, a bill of £600 was paid at the Treasury a few days ago for their keep, if the fortune of war favours us but a little in that Quarter & the engines of Pestilence are likely to labor in our Cause in a very short time, we shall yet Receive our Promisd Supply, & I shall be enabled I Trust to put your Lordships Flock upon a more respectable Footing The value of merinos increases daily in the Public estimation . . .[44]

Then, approximately at the same time that Cochrane-Johnstone's own sheep of the same flock were sailing west across the Atlantic, diseased and dying, some consignments of the King's portion were evidently reaching England and their dispersal being mediated by Sir Joseph Banks. This seemed to follow broadly the plan he had proposed in the first pressing days of the emergency in June 1809. A suggestion of this is contained in the wording of a printed facsimile of Banks's handwriting, evidently prepared as a circular request to all those who were receiving the imported sheep and dated 12 February 1811. The opening paragraph is clear:

The arrival of a Cargo of His Majesties Merino Sheep & the expectation that others will soon follow renders it necessary for me to Collect by a Rate on the Sheep already deliverd, the amount of the money advanced to me by the Treasury for Defraying the Charges of their importation and management . . .[45]

And then the following day in a note to Lord Spencer, correcting a small mistake in the account, he implies that the influx of sheep is continuing and that the business of distribution is in good heart:

. . . I feel myself now less Fettered than I was when the former distribution took Place & of course I have hopes of being able to Restore your Lordships Flock to its original State if not to better it I have just Receivd a Flock from Spain but they are all but 5 Rams others I hope will follow . . .[46]

It is not possible here to disentangle the ultimate fate and dispersal of the Negretti *cabana*. The evidence has still to be found and adequately sifted. At present the impression remains that, of the original twelve thousand so joyously heralded by Cochrane-Johnstone in May 1809, he himself may finally have sent out of Spain from this flock not much more than the two thousand odd animals to the United States of which about six hundred only were alive in February 1811. Sir Charles Stewart, the British Adjutant-General in Portugal at this time, is reputed to have bought and sent out of the country to England no less than six thousand Negrettis except for about a hundred which the United States Consul William Jarvis had bought from him.[47] If to these figures we add the four thousand which the Supreme Junta are said to have presented to the King of England, then a total of twelve thousand is attained. This assumes, however, that the sheep sent out of Spain by Sir Charles Stewart had probably been bought from Cochrane-Johnstone—who had in May 1809 already confessed that the finance of the whole flock was beyond him—and that they are not to be confused with those sent to England on the King's account. If this indeed proves to be so then it would seem that Great Britain had received the greater part of the remaining sheep of the Negretti *cabana* by the end of 1811—approximately ten thousand—but not as Cochrane-Johnstone property. With the two thousand Paulars and the numerous other shipments of Escurials, Portagos, and other *cabanas* from Spain to the British Isles it is possible that Great Britain as a whole received not many less as survivors of the Spanish Merinos shipped abroad than did the United States—about fifteen thousand. Of these nearly one-quarter were gifts from Spain to His Britannic Majesty.

VIII

And what, now, of the Editor of *Cobbett's Weekly Political Register*, twice a partisan in the Cochrane-Johnstone camp and so recently the putative consignee and publicity agent for the Negrettis in June 1809? He had in fact been carried away by his enthusiasms—but not for sheep, great as these had seemed to be—and had been deposited in a quiet place of reflection. On Saturday, 24 June 1809, Cobbett had proclaimed in the *Register* the impending descent of the Spanish sheep threatening to spread like a locust swarm on the over-crowded summer pastures of the southern counties. In the next issue on Saturday, 1 July, his 'Summary of Politics' carried his outburst against the flogging of the Local Militia mutineers at Ely, directed largely at Lord Castlereagh. The veto on the use of naval transports for the sheep effectively scotched Cochrane-Johnstone's schemes for an auction sale.[48] Cobbett was, therefore, free to contemplate the charge of sedition which his political attack had conjured up to hang above him like a threatening storm-cloud for a whole year. On 15 June 1810, it burst over his head as he was tried, and on Friday, 13 July, it swept him into the State Prison at Newgate under a sentence of two years. And here, oddly enough, in this academic seclusion, the thoughts of 'Cobbett the political writer' turned again to the subject of sheep and wool.

This was no mere piece of escapist dilettantism after the political turmoils of the previous year. It was at one with a theme which he had pursued in its wider implications two or three years earlier still. He knew well that ever since the American War of Independence the United States had been almost entirely dependent on imported woollen goods from Great Britain. Recalling the impoverished flocks of his own American days and labouring under the conviction that nothing less than grass fields, downs, and turnip fields would suffice for the profitable keeping of sheep he had seen no future for the United States in that branch of husbandry. Writing at an earlier stage in the recurrent disputes with America he had been emphatic that the Americans never could do without wool from other countries for want of winter herbage and turnip fields which they could not have because of the deep snows when these were most wanted. Then he had read the French work of C.-P. Lasteyrie—*Histoire de l'Introduction des Moutons à Laine fine d'Espagne dans les divers États de l'Europe et au Cap de Bonne-Espérance*— and had found this limited notion to be wrong. He was quick to note from this that, in Saxony and Silesia, flocks of sheep could be kept for whole winters year after year in houses and yards on various forms of stored fodder, sometimes for as long as five or six months. He was especially impressed that under this treatment the Merino race of sheep succeeded as well as others. It was decisive, in his view, to find that the very finest wool known to the English manufacturer was now coming from Saxony—forty-six years after the Spanish sheep had been introduced there—and that these flocks not only lived in such confinement but increased and produced most wonderfully. Perceiving all this he could not fail to revise his views. Now he did not doubt that the American States could multiply sheep to any extent by the same means. He was thus fully convinced by the arguments and evidence of the Frenchman that if the Americans did not speedily become independent of other countries in the matter of wool and woollens it would be entirely their own fault.

It was with a mind so quickened by the arguments from France, therefore, that Cobbett eventually saw and read the first American edition of the original *Treatise on Sheep* ... by the Honourable Robert R. Livingston.[49] Laid before the New York Society for the Promotion of Useful Arts it had been adjudged 'eminently calculated to diffuse general information as to the best mode of raising and managing the Merino Breed of Sheep'. Its public utility to the United States at that critical economic point in its history was recognized and its printing authorized by 'Resolutions of the Two Houses of the Legislature of the State of

New York' on 7 March 1809. To Cobbett this treatise contained all the proof he needed that now 'the increase of sheep and of the manufacture of wool are become objects of great public interest in America'. The vision of an America shortly able to supply herself not only with wool but also with woollen cloth now rose before his eyes. To him it was a vicarious joy to see this future unfold from the war-time measures against the commerce of the United States by the governments of England and France—'wholly unconscious, that they were, in this case, acting under the guidance of the genius of freedom'.

This is a great event. It is a great change in the affairs of nations. The Americans, who, until now, have been obliged to look to *England* chiefly for coats, made of wool that came from Spain; *ten millions* of people who got the principal articles of their wearing apparel in this round-about way, will now grow these articles upon their own lands, and will keep at home, for the feeding of cloth-makers, those articles of food, which they used to raise in order to pay England and Spain for manufacturing and for wool. The intelligent reader will be at no loss to perceive how great must be the advantage of this change to the American States; a change which that country owes to the folly and tyranny of other governments'.[50]

These ideas had no doubt all been further stimulated during his brief and abortive exercise in the affair of the Spanish flock that never came. As a prospective owner of a flock of Merinos and as the farmer of Botley he had immersed himself in what literature of the breed he could collect. Livingston's treatise he had found 'full of curious matter'. Artlessly, as an amateur, he confessed that it had the pleasing effect of bringing him 'as it were, *into a country*, which we have only *heard of* before'. He evidently found it, also, good bedside reading for a political prisoner. It opened the way to a sublimation of his thwarted demagogy and released his editorial energies again:

But, that which most strongly recommended it to me, and which induced me to re-publish it, was, that it completely settled the very important question, namely; *whether the American State: could dispense with European Wool and Woollens*; a question of very great interest to the world in general, and to England in particular.[51]

And so, while Cochrane-Johnstone, no longer high-minded about the good of his own country, from the mouth of the Tagus watched his material assets waste into nothingness on the waters of the Atlantic, Cobbett was creating his own form of political capital from behind the bars of Newgate. On Wednesday, 3 April 1811, he completed his editorial preface in the State Prison and launched *An Essay on Sheep* ... as the first English edition of Chancellor Livingston's American treatise. Repressed but not silenced he had poured into it a generous measure of his own rich brew of political comment and invective. Looking out from his cell—almost as though he were thinking of Cochrane-Johnstone —the world disgusted him: 'all is a scene of wrangling, rapacity, violence, insolence, deceit, bribery, perjury, filth, and disease'. But to any right-thinking man it was a pleasure to see so large and increasing a country as America become independent of others and free of 'a great, monopolising, combining, speculating, taxing, loan-jobbing commerce! hostile to everything that is patriotic, liberal and just!' And in this spate of indignation were embedded the words that must serve here as a final salutary comment on the whole chaos of those years:

But, this change, favourable as I hope it may prove, to the interests of man-kind in general, could not have been so rapidly produced, had it not been for the actual invasion of Spain by the Emperor Napoleon, who, without in-tending it, perhaps, has by this invasion, scattered the inestimable flocks of Spain over the face of the earth. Not the Spanish monarchy only, but the Spanish nation, has he *broken up*, dispersing its goods and chattels to all who were in a condition to take them away. Its pictures and its plate and its jewels, all its moveables, are, long ago, divided amongst its invaders; its flocks have been driven out, shipped off, or devoured; its houses, after having been pillaged, have, in no small proportion, been levelled with the ground: and, the ground itself is all that seems to have the security of remaining. Yet amidst all this ruin, amidst this general wreck of society, it is much to be questioned, whether the great mass of the people in Spain are not as well, and even better off, than they formerly were; for, what interest had *they* in the flocks which composed the riches of their country? What knew they of those flocks but in as much as they were a *scourge* to themselves? The exclusive property of the privileged order, not only was it impossible for the culti-vator of the land to obtain any share in the *benefit* arising from these flocks, but he was *compelled* to assist, without payment, in their support, by throwing open his fields and his garden to be devoured by them in their periodical journeys from one part of the country to the other! With this fact before him, what man, who is not either a tyrant or willing slave, can regret that these flocks have been dispersed? And, I think, it must be peculiarly gratifying to the American farmer, to see raised in his own fields and fashioned under his own happy roof, that coat, by his former mode of obtaining which he used to enrich and abet the owner of those flocks whose ravages insured hunger as well as nakedness to the miserable peasant of Spain.[52]

This was a picture swept in with the strong primary colours so typical of the Cobbett palette. But it is not entirely unfair as an Impressionist glance at the intricate contours of the Spanish scene as it was—especially as it might have been seen from the distant eminence and the gloom of Newgate Prison.

CHAPTER XIII

The Twilight Years, 1810–1820

I

NATURE did not smile on the birthday of His Majesty's Spanish flock and but seldom in its progress through the after years. The 4th of April 1788 when the King first viewed the small nucleus of his 'most national project' at Kew with Sir Joseph Banks was unpropitious and climatically unkind—a day of cold winds and flurries of snow in the pattern of those backward springs which so plagued the farmers of Britain in the last decades of the eighteenth century. Conceived in the depressed years after the loss of the American colonies the flock was born into the fleeting economic spring of the short peace with France before the Revolution set the world rocking. Its infancy and adolescence were spent in a world wholly out of joint—Man at odds with Man, and Nature with Humanity. The current of political affairs and the strange movement of the seasons each directly affected the rise and progress of the Royal flock in its own way. But there were also the complex interactions between the state of the weather and the state of the nation to confound the issues. Seldom in the history of Great Britain has a whole generation lived in a balance so precarious between the survival of the country and the destructive potential of foreign Powers—an equipoise then so much at the mercy of the weather and the subsequent character of the harvests. For twenty-five years in that long Anglo-French struggle the favours of the elements were capriciously bestowed—not so capriciously, however, that it was beyond the wit of either country to bend these circumstances to suit their strategy.

As early as 1792 Britain had sought to relieve her own wants from a poor harvest by large purchases of foreign corn. In doing so she sought also to embarrass France—whose crop that year was worse—by securing more than she needed from the Continent and storing it unobtrusively in bond.[1] The same tactics were more sharply elaborated in the disastrous harvest year of 1795. Wheat imports rose to a new peak as British agents bought heavily in the Baltic ports and the Government compelled all neutral ships with grain for France as far as possible to sell their cargoes profitably in British ports. Here, as before, the double purpose was relief to Britain and distress to France where, again, the harvest and the scarcity were worse. The turn of the century was distinguished by the two successive bad harvests of 1799 and 1800 with the unprecedented importations of continental wheat which ensued in spite of the strong efforts of the Directory to coerce neutral vessels against trading with Britain. The shadow of the new economic warfare was now clearly cast across the Channel. The upward sweep of Britain's export trade was checked. For the next ten years the balance of trade—favourable, though wildly fluctuating—tended rather to decline. The brief easement of the Peace of Amiens was no more than the false economic dawn of the new century for Great Britain.

The emergence of the First Consul in his new guise as the Emperor Napoleon brought the imminent threat of invasion in 1804 and the lowest point of Britain's export trade until the crisis year of 1811–12. With the Battle of Trafalgar came the turning-point which secured the sea routes and the vital colonial trade for Britain to offset the crippling effectiveness of the French Customs' net surrounding Europe. The balance of advantages was close indeed and mutually exhausting. The thrust of the Napoleonic Decrees and the counter-thrust of the House of Commons Orders-in-Council kept the economic issues in approximate equilibrium. The French blockade defied England to survive without the continental market, particularly for her textiles and her iron manufactures. Great Britain conversely challenged France to exist without goods of English manufacture. Baltic timber but especially French corn were trumps in Napoleon's hand and so, to a degree, was Spanish wool could he but draw it from the pack. For Britain in this complicated play the key cards were, after 1805, the cotton imports, the textile exports of the Atlantic trade routes, and the universal call for her woollen and iron products—the first fruits of her industrial inventiveness and progress. But it was the elementary and age-old question of food—the classic problem of res frumentarii—which, for both sides, determined the will and the means to wage war. The shadow of famine and the menace of explosive bread riots exacerbated the Revolution in France and was never far from the minds of Englishmen at home in the wars that followed. Napoleon more than once held the fate of the United Kingdom in his writing hand on the issue of the corn supplies of Europe when a stroke of his pen could have denied them to his enemy across the Channel. But the fatal decree was never written. Britain survived—but only, it would seem, by the quirk of one man's strategic concepts. Blockade and counter-blockade were never absolute. Napoleon needed, among much else, English cloth and leather for his vast armies. Even more he needed ready money. If this were English gold so much the better. In his view a depleted English Treasury was a victory for France. His economic blockade—his

Continental System—was never closer to final success than when, after a sequence of bad harvests from 1808, the calamitous season of 1811 brought Britain to the edge of famine. A completely ruthless logic would have denied French corn to English stomachs and—as we see it now—an English capitulation might well have followed. But reason on certain premises, not ruthlessness, had dictated otherwise. The defeat of England by financial attrition and the swelling of his own revenues with the gold reserves of his enemy was the theory that Napoleon chose to follow. He authorized the export of corn to England, with the payment of an export duty, on a scale that eclipsed all former operations of the kind. The financial strain on Britain was enormous and bankruptcy stalked freely through the land. But starvation was averted and England lived to prove Napoleon wrong. Throughout the French Wars from 1793 British agriculture had been unequal to the worst crises of food supply and the country had survived essentially on the strength of its commercial credit, its colonial trade, and the expanding American markets—the lost colonies that had become such good customers.

In the twenty-four years of the Royal Spanish flock's existence from 1788 to 1811 there had been only four harvest seasons considered bounteous—1791, 1796, 1798, and 1801. The six years of 1793, 1797, 1802, 1803, 1805, and 1806 were of average productivity. The remainder were poor, bad, or disastrous. In the same period there had been less than six years of peace—or rather, of surcease from war—the uneasy last few years from 1788 to February 1793 while France writhed under the Revolution, and one year of strange relief after the Treaty of Amiens. Then, finally, the years which should, in a saner world, have witnessed the fulfilment of the Royal hopes for the Spanish flock and a ripe measure of national enrichment—the seven years of the public sales from 1804 to 1810—this was the period when the whole world suffered under the dislocating strains of a deliberately imposed economic warfare for the first time.

These twenty-four years were also a period of metamorphosis in the British wool trade. After a century of slow change from a nearly self-sufficient state in the wool supply the country in 1788 was on the point of discovering the secret of its future in the need for Spanish wool. The onset of war made the quest more urgent and the price of Spanish wool rose steadily until the opening of the Peninsular Campaign made the lesson brilliantly clear. Prices reached values unknown before to mark the crisis years of 1809–11 with figures that were to remain memorable and unexcelled for nearly a century and a half thereafter. It was at this period of climax in the nation's affairs that the evening twilight of His Majesty's Spanish flock began.

II

The competitive intensity of the economic struggle between France and Great Britain, especially in the dramatic years of the war with the First Empire, tends to conceal the rise and fall of rival plans for disseminating the Spanish Merino on a national scale. By comparison with the overt cut-and-thrust of the Decrees and the Orders-in-Council there is nothing—or very little—immediately to attract the eye of the historian to the administrative events in which the Spanish fine-wool sheep was a crucial element. For at least fifty years France was unquestionably in advance of Britain in her knowledge and exploitation of the Spanish fine-wool stock—from the first tentative but well-conceived steps taken by Daubenton at Alfort and Montbard under the stimulus of Trudaine in 1766. The prime incentive was the simple aim to rid France of bondage to a monopolistic control by Spain of a raw material which was clearly increasing its place as an essential article of world trade and manufacture. Nearly twenty years later—and for the same inescapable reasons—England, in the person of Sir Joseph Banks, had espoused the same economic philosophy, derived very directly from the French savant and, with his actual assistance, had put it on a practical footing at Spring Grove in 1785.

The mantle of Daubenton had already fallen on the shoulders of Alexandre-Henri Tessier in the matter of Spanish sheep when, in 1786, these two savants advised the Count d'Angivillier, Superintendent of the Royal domain of Rambouillet, to request Louis XVI to seek an importation of fine-wool sheep from his uncle, Carlos III of Spain. On 12 October 1786, the Royal flock of Spanish Merinos was established at Rambouillet by the arrival of three hundred and eighteen ewes, forty-one rams, and seven *mansos* drawn from ten of the best *cabanas* in Spain.[2]

The mantle of Daubenton had also, in a sense, fallen on the shoulders of Sir Joseph Banks when, on or about 15 January 1788, there arrived at Kew Green five rams, thirty-seven ewes, and six young lambs from Montbard, Tour d'Aigues, and Alfort, the first fine-wool Spanish-type sheep to form the foundation of the Royal flock of George III at Windsor and Richmond. Thereafter Banks was the directive brain in all things touching the study and exploitation of the Spanish Merino in Great Britain as the former Abbé, Tessier, was in France. In 1788 both these eminent agricultural savants bore much the same relation to their respective Royal masters—that of scientific confidant and friend—but in just five years there was no longer a King of France and revolution and war had changed the relations of the two countries. Scientific collaboration between the savants of England and of France, though not broken entirely, was immeasurably complicated. Banks and Tessier were now set on separate paths unequivocally as ardent competitors in their countries' interests for the commercial growth of the Spanish Merinos and their Golden Fleeces.

At this early stage the advantage of time and situation was with France. Britain in any case could do little more than nibble at the Spanish flocks by smuggling and covert diplomacy. France always had these too at her disposal made easier by propinquity and a shared border along the Pyrenees breached by well-trodden contraband trails. France also had the Bourbon ties of the Blood Royal aiding her access to the sequestered *cabanas* of Leon and Segovia, the *élite* of the Spanish flocks—and by this she had profited greatly in the select foundations of the Rambouillet stud. Once war had been declared again in 1793 the precarious access of Britain to the Spanish flocks—mainly through the valleys of the Tagus and the Douro—was broken by the increased hazards to the mercantile marine.[3] For France, too, at this point there was little profit in the sheep trade as the Spanish hostilities made the Pyrenees border a battleground. Then came the Treaty of Basle on 22 June 1795 when Tessier with shrewd foresight managed to establish therein a secret Article on Spanish sheep. From this clause France secured the right to no less than one thousand rams and four thousand ewes of the Spanish fine-wool race.[4] Of these, however, very few more than one thousand in all had been obtained by 1800 through the agency of François-Hilaire Gilbert—the whole process hampered and delayed by Spanish reluctance under duress.[5] From among these came the second accession to the *ci-devant* Royal flock at Rambouillet, less to be admired perhaps but true Spanish fine-wool sheep for all that. Though the final gains from the Treaty were far less than Tessier may have hoped, France in total secured at this one stroke nearly eight times more true Spanish sheep than Britain had by then been able to acquire by any means from Spain itself before 1800.

By one means or another during these bitter years Banks kept a close watch on the progress of the French development and use of the Spanish sheep. Never was he more effective in his role as His Majesty's 'Ministre des Affaires Philosophiques'.[6] It is a measure of the efficiency of his vigil that, within a few weeks of its appearance in the *Moniteur* of 24 May 1800, he incorporated the substance of an advertisement for the sale of Spanish fine-wool sheep from the flock at Rambouillet into the body of his own quickly revised 'A Project for Extending the Breed ...'. He deftly twisted the French advertisement to his own purpose as he soberly pointed the moral:

... As those who have the care of his Majesty's Spanish flock may naturally be supposed partial to the project of introducing super-fine wool into these kingdoms, it has been thought proper to annex the following notice, in order to shew the opinion held of a similar undertaking in a neighbouring country, where individuals, however they have mistaken their political interest, are rather remarkable for pursuing and thoroughly weighing their own personal advantage, in all their private undertakings, and for sagacity in seizing all opportunities of improving by publick establishments, the resources of their nation . . .[7]

And what had the *Moniteur* to announce that had so caught the interest of Sir Joseph? No less than the sale of two hundred and twenty-five rams and ewes of the finest-woolled Spanish breed from the national flock of Rambouillet; of 2000 pounds of superfine wool, being the clip of 1800 from the national flock; and of 1300 pounds of wool from the Spanish cross-breds kept at the Ménagerie of Versailles. These figures were formidable enough as a token of the growing strength of the French enterprise, but there was menace in the notice which followed under the signature of Lucien Bonaparte as Minister of the Interior.

From the earliest years of the French Royal flock ewes and rams had been available for distribution as gifts by the King, until the year 1789 changed the course of history. Public auctions had been established in 1793. By such means, by private sale, and by gift more than fifteen hundred rams and ewes had been dispersed from Rambouillet in the fourteen years from 1786 to 1799—more than a hundred a year. Over the same period His Majesty's Spanish flock at Windsor and Kew had disposed of just two hundred and fifty-four rams and ewes, many not truly of the Spanish breed and virtually none from the *élite cabanas* of the Leonese studs, such as the French national flock could certainly claim. The full measure of this contrast could not have been known to Banks in just those terms but perhaps none but he in England at this stage could better weigh the import of such words as these from the French Minister:

. . . The weight of their fleeces is from six to twelve pounds each and those of the rams are sometimes heavier.

Sheep of the ordinary coarse-woolled breeds, when crossed by a Spanish ram, produce fleeces double in weight, and far more valuable than those of their dams; and if this cross is carefully continued by supplying rams of the pure Spanish blood, the wool of the third or fourth generation is scarcely distinguishable from the original Spanish wool.

These mixed breeds are more easily maintained, and can be fattened at as small an expense as the ordinary breeds of the country.

No speculation whatever offers advantages so certain, and so considerable, to those who embark in it, as that of the improvement of wool, by the introduction of rams and ewes of the true Spanish race among the flocks of France, whether the sheep are purchased at Rambouillet or elsewhere. In this business, however, it is of the greatest importance to secure the Spanish breed unmixed, and the utmost precaution on that head should be used, as the avarice of proprietors may tempt them to substitute the crossed breeds instead of the pure one to the great disappointment of the purchaser.

The amelioration of wool at Rambouillet has made so great a progress that in a circle from twenty-four to thirty-six miles in diameter, the manu-facturers purchase thirty-five thousand pounds of wool, improved by two, three, or even four crosses. Those who wish to accelerate the amelioration of their flocks by introducing into them ewes of this improved sort may find abundance to be purchased in that neighbourhood at reasonable rates.[8]

Such confident words from France were not news to Banks but they crystallized and confirmed all his fears. It was not chance, then, or a sudden whim that had caused him to prepare his thoughts on 10 April 1800 and to draft a notice to this effect:

Spanish Rams of the pure Merino blood will be Shewn in Their wool on the —th day of May next at Smallbury Green for Particulars Enquire of A Young Esqre Sec to the B[oard] of agriculture at the house of the Board in Sackville Street who will provide such persons as chuse to attend with Tickets specifying the Terms on which they will be Let or Sold & the Place where they will be Exhibited . . .

This unused draft further made clear the trend of Banks's thinking in these first months of the new century by whose close they would have been vindicated:

. . . as the motive for disposing of these Sheep is a desire to Promote Experi-ments for the improvement of the Clothing wools of this Kingdom by Crossing the best Clothing wool breeds with them, The Prices will be Calculated according to the Probable amount of the Profit to be obtaind, derivd from experiments which have been Tried & have provd successfull . . .[9]

The show and sale of Spanish sheep at Smallbury Green never took place, but the eighth public sale of such stock at Rambouillet certainly occurred and Banks carefully noted the prices obtained. His notes grew finally into the full text of 'A Project . . .' before the summer was far advanced when its publication drew towards him the few bright spirits who shared his percipience and confidence in what was already an established commercial fact across the Channel. But four more years were to elapse before the first public sales of Spanish sheep took place at Kew, eleven years after the first in France. This interval is a rough measure of the extent to which Britain lagged in the tussle for fine-wool self-sufficiency, while the prices realized at the auction of Spanish sheep at Rambouillet in 1800 have an interesting and clear relevance to the values established by Banks for the private sales from Windsor and Kew during the years 1800–3.[10]

Medium Price of a Ram	—	80 Franks	..	..	3^l	6^s 5^d
do. do. of an Ewe	—	68 do.	..	..	2^l	16^s 5^d
Highest Price of [a] Ram	—	120 do.	..	..	5^l	0 0
Lowest do. do.	—	60 do.	..	..	2^l	10^s 0
Highest Price of an Ewe	—	103 do.	..	..	4^l	5^s 10^d
Lowest do. do.	—	50 do.	..	..	2^l	1^s 5^d

There is little doubt that in establishing the price of 5 guineas (later 6 guineas) for a Spanish ram and 2 guineas for a Spanish ewe, as the private contract price to the patriots of the 'Project', Banks had the precedent of the Rambouillet sales clearly in view. His own more elaborate calculations, based mainly on the expected gains in fleece weight and quality in the Spanish cross, set the values for letting somewhat higher. For a ram he judged £16 a reasonable value for use in cross-breeding, but this he thought '... must vary as the Qualities of the Rams are more or Less Perfect'. On the other hand he intended,

... The Finest Rams to be set aside for those who intend to /breed/ keep Ram Lambs of these the Price must be arbitrary according to the Fancy of the Letter as is done in similar Cases from £25 to 50 Guineas ...
... Cull Ewes to be bespoke for those who mean to try the pure Blood at 5 guineas Each ...[11]

The plan for letting rams from the Royal flock at this stage never evolved. Surplus stock was sold outright and the hiring of rams at prices far beyond those nominated here by Banks were left as the prerogative of Lord Somerville and other free-lances.

Step by step the little English stud of Spanish Merinos traced out its history under the guidance of the President of the Royal Society, treading assiduously in the beaten path made by its rival, hastening a little as each year passed but not greatly closing the lead which France had established so long ago.

Then, after fifteen years of conflict, the war which had in a day effectively closed the frontiers and coasts of Spain to England on 1 February 1793 with equal speed had, by the Spanish Insurrection on 2 May 1808, opened the gates of the Peninsula again. In October 1808 His Majesty King George III of Great Britain and his devoted subjects were the richer by more than fifteen hundred Spanish Merinos of the Paular *cabana*, safe in the parks of Richmond and Kew. After years of frustration, under the slow torture of observing the progress of the French as their Merino flocks moved from strength to strength, Sir Joseph Banks was at last able to see the image of hope in the same field for his country. He moved forward quickly in the matter and by April 1809 the 3rd Earl Bathurst, President of the Board of Trade, had on his desk a well-drafted plan from the President of the Royal Society. Here at last was the apotheosis of His Majesty's 'patriotic plan'—'A Project for the Establishment of Merino Flocks in various parts of the Kingdom under the immediate superintendence and control of the committee of the Privy Council for Trade'.[12] He called it 'a slight sketch' and it remained a dream unfulfilled, but it was another positive step forward —and a somewhat novel one—in the evolution of British thought on the breeding of commercial livestock. It frankly acknowledged a debt to the clear-sighted rationalism of the Frenchman, Tessier, once his guest and, in spite of the war, still his correspondent—in fact, to the man through whom in one way or another Banks had managed to follow the course of French plans for the Merino as one member of the Institut National to another. But what the Imperial autocracy of Napoleon could do, working from the Socialist foundations of the First Republic, was not so easily performed under the more democratic monarchy of George III. The new 'Project'—even had there been no interference from other causes—was perhaps altogether too far beyond the capacity of individualist British breeders then or even now to contemplate with equanimity or enthusiasm. It may even have transcended the imaginitive virtuosity of Whitehall. The Board of Agriculture itself was, after all, finding life precarious and the British public by no means convinced of its claims to survival. What argument could there be, then, for invoking a piece of French planning as a pattern for action in propagating—save the mark!—a foreign breed of sheep?

Banks had noted in his outward-ranging curiosity that by now all the nations of Europe had acknowledged the great value of Merino wool by taking measures as speedily as possible to increase the growth of it in their respective countries. A recent and impressive example had been the action of the Emperor of Russia who had established a flock of Merino sheep at Odessa and had advertised to his subjects that they were now available for sale on generous terms and that a book would 'shortly be circulated gratis throughout the Russian Empire, giving an account of the best method of managing these sheep and of improving by their Cross, the Native Russian Breeds'. But again Banks repeated the substance of his prodding words of nine years ago:

... The French, a people acknowledged to be awake to their Public and to their private interests and not to be deficient in that kind of sagacity which teaches men to improve both the one and the other, have made the business of introducing the Merino breed into all parts of France a branch of the Home department of their Government, this gives an energy and activity to the establishment and will certainly accelerate materially the attainment of the great object of the institution that of supplying their manufacturers of Cloth, with fine wool the growth of their own country . . .[13]

Then he noted the character of the Merino studs under the general inspection of Tessier as Commissary-in-Charge which had been recorded in the *Almanack Imperial* for the year 1808 fearing that, even within the past year, it had been enlarged from the seven centres then established. Something of the same nature was much wanted, he thought, in Britain—'the adoption of it is very likely to do credit to the Minister with whom it originates'—to promote with certainty and speed 'the much desird object of rendering the Country independent of all others for that most valuable raw material fine wool'. To give a proper degree of consequence to the new establishment it should be under the immediate guidance and control of the Government and considered as a branch of one of the public offices—for example, the Committee of the Privy Council for Trade, as that to which it seemed naturally to belong. His dispositions for the staffing of the establishment were well cal-culated to reach the heart of all right-minded civil servants:

. . . *Controller* of the Merino Department, without Salary if he is one of the Committee of Privy Council for Trade, the nomination to the President.
Superintendent of Merino Flocks, with a Salary of £400 a year till the Flocks amount to more than ten and £20 a year for each additional Flock. To be nominated by the Controller with the consent of the President.
Clerks to the Controller with proper salaries to keep Books of all kinds and copy letters.
An Office with two Rooms in the Treasury Chambers at Whitehall to depend on the Office for Trade in the articles of necessary woman and messenger.
Managers of Flocks, these to be chosen among Country Gentlemen skilled in Agriculture and desirous of engaging in this Patriotic pursuit. To be appointed by the Controller with the consent of the President . . .[14]

Though basically the same as the French organization it was a neatly tailored piece of administrative surgery—the attempted graft of a piece of foreign tissue into the quivering flesh of Whitehall. But it suffered the common fate of such attempts. The immune response of the body politic prevented its acceptance and this excellent plan was sloughed away to survive only as a withered specimen in long-forgotten files in some dusty cabinet. The ghosts of the ideas still remain, however, and prompt our speculations on the might-have-been.

Each flock was to have consisted of fifty ewes and, at first, of ten rams, eight of which were to be let to the best bidder during the first year to offset as far as possible the charges of the office. The sheep were to be agisted at a price sufficient for their keep but not to leave a profit to the manager. This was estimated at about 13s. per head per annum or 3d. per head per week. A shepherd was to be allowed to each flock and a wool stapler was to attend at each shearing time and occasionally when wanted. The Controller was to superintend the office and administration but in addition was to see that proper notification was inserted in the London and provincial papers respecting the true value of the breed and all matters likely to afford real inducements to its adoption—a true task of agricultural education and extension. The Superintendent was to visit each flock at least four times a year and more often if necessary under the orders of the Controller. The Manager, to whose charge each flock was committed, had all the customary management from day to day of the flock and its breeding in consultation with the appointed Inspector, and to select and mate the rams and ewes—'but in all cases of a difference of opinion between a Manager and the Inspector the Manager to controll . . .'. No person was to be a manager who had Merinos of his own.

It was estimated that to initiate such an establishment an advance of £1000 or rather more would be needed to pay salaries and contingencies in the first year. Thereafter it was considered that if properly conducted the office must produce almost enough revenue to balance its expenses, even if liberal rewards were given, as was intended, to shepherds whose flocks improved in value. In ten years, it was presumed, the breed should have been sufficiently established to want no more public interference.

Where were the sheep to be found on which such a comprehensive plan could be based? Presumably these were none other than that windfall of the war, the new Paular flock so recently acquired. But here, perhaps, lay the final limiting reason why the scheme died unborn. His Majesty's consent had still to come but over His Majesty's mind an all-obliterating shadow was already cast to set a final veto on all decisions of the kind. Meanwhile His Majesty's loyal servant was at liberty to put the case in words that may at least stand as a record of faith and of hope deferred:

. . . If His Majesties consent can be obtain'd to spare from his Flock 500 Ewes and one hundred Rams which will leave at Kew 900 Ewes and 78 Rams besides all the Lambs of the Season, in fact as Many Merino Sheep as his Majesties Shepherds are able properly to take care of, the business may be begun on a proper scale, if more than ten Managers of a proper description present themselves application may be made to the King for further supplies. The Sheep to continue always the property of the King, the Flocks to be intitled the Royal Merino Flocks in order that the People may be kept in remembrance that the original introduction of the breed was entirely owing to the foresight the intelligence and the patriotism of their venerable and beloved Monarch, and every part of the establishment to be always at His Majesties disposal whenever His Majesty shall chuse to honor it with his Royal attention to its concerns or his most acceptable interference in the management of its affairs.[15]

The English plan was foredoomed never to be set in motion. The French plan was sweeping forward to success. Already there were ten Imperial Merino studs well distributed strategically throughout France of which those at Rambouillet and Malmaison were the central *élite*. For the three years 1807–9 their total cost of operation per annum had been comparatively modest:

1807	..	..	.. 43,600 francs	..	..	..	ca. £1900
1808	..	..	.. 48,356 do.	..	..	..	ca. £2100
1809	..	..	.. 42,000 do.	..	..	..	ca. £1820

For this annual outlay a total of about two thousand six hundred breeding ewes in the Imperial stud flocks were yielding about twelve hundred Merino rams each year for the general amelioration of the thirty-seven million sheep of France. Of these about thirty-two million were the common-woolled native breeds, five million were improved by crosses with the Merino, and two hundred thousand were pure Merinos originally from Spain, of which eighty thousand were breeding ewes. Against these figures, which Banks eventually saw clearly set out in the 'Report of the Minister of the Interior' for March 1811, his own plan was quite overshadowed.[16] But at the time of his proposal to the President of the Board of Trade in 1809 he flattered himself that it was greater than anything France had to oppose it. His illusions were soon dispelled.

If there were no other point in the French Minister's report to Napoleon the statement alone that eighty thousand pure Merino ewes were already established in France must have shocked Sir Joseph, long prepared though he was for such hard facts. Britain in 1811 probably had no more than one-tenth of this number of mature Merino ewes. But his plan of 1809—though it employed the full resources of breeding stock available for use then—was utterly lost in comparison with the new French proposals.

Montalivet, as Minister of the Interior, had carefully studied the industrial needs of France for fine wool taking, as his standard of excellence, the 1·5 million kilogrammes which were imported from the Leonese and Segovian piles of Spain. This was his measure of the principal burden that he intended France should discard. This and all that followed was certainly assessed by the industrious Tessier as Inspector-General of the Government Flocks. As such we may accept the picture as reasonable. From it we may glean some measure of the scope of the French fine-wool manufacture and trade statistics about 1811:

					million kg.
Consumption of fine and superfine wool	..	..	..	..	11·2
Production of fine and superfine wool	..	..	..	..	5·0
Importation of fine and superfine wool	..	..	..	..	
From *Spain*—Leonesa etc.		..	..	1·5	
Sorian etc.		..	..	1·6	
From *Germany* ..	..	..	..	2·1	
From *other countries*	..	..	..	1·1	
Total importation..		..	..		6·2

Montalivet supposed that the 4·8 million kilogrammes of second-quality fine wool from the Sorian piles of Spain, from Germany, and other countries, would easily be supplied in time by the fourth and fifth crosses of the Spanish breed on the appropriate native French stock, assuming a gain of 1 kilogramme in average weight from the cross. To achieve this result France would need some 4·5 million such animals but to make it safe he thought 5·4 million a better objective.

The crucial goal was, however, to increase the pure Merinos of the Leonese and Segovian standard. To produce 1·5 million kilogrammes of washed wool supposed 3·75 million kilogrammes in the grease. Reckoning the mean fleece weight in the yolk at 4 kilogrammes it appeared that France would have to do little more than quadruple the two hundred thousand pure Merinos already within her borders. In the final analysis the Minister thought they should aim to have constantly three million breeding ewes of the improved crosses beyond the number then in France. To serve these there should be ninety thousand pure Merino rams of the first quality and that these should be produced from a pure Merino breeding flock of about seven hundred and ten thousand similar ewes.

To attain this ambitious goal in the course of fourteen years—such was the measure in 1811 of French confidence in the future under Napoleon—it was intended to establish a national nucleus of twenty thousand pure Merino breeding ewes, adding the necessary number by importation from Spain to those of the ten existing Imperial studs and twelve new establishments to be formed immediately. From this foundation the pure Merino breed was to reach its target of at least eight hundred thousand. The twenty Imperial farms were also annually to furnish four to five thousand Merinos, male and female, towards improving the national flocks and would supply directly to commerce some 40 thousand kilogrammes of superfine wool. They would also have the additional utility of serving as models of instruction.

The grand operation of cross-breeding was to be conducted by establishing *dépôts*, each of about a hundred and fifty to two hundred and fifty pure Merino rams, strategically distributed in the sub-prefectures throughout the country under the supervision of the Sub-Prefects who would order their distribution to the principal landed proprietors and breeders appropriate to the plan. In each department there would be an Inspector of these *dépôts*, who apart from supervising the whole breeding plan would also have adequate veterinary training to recognize and control contagious disease, such as foot-rot and scab, and to prescribe for and treat other ailments. Above these there would be four Inspectors-General responsible to the Minister of the Interior. Over a period of seven years from forty in the first year the number of these *dépôts* was to increase annually until a total of five hundred and twenty-nine had been established throughout France. But even this impressive number was much below the figure of one thousand which Napoleon himself had it in mind to establish. The Minister drew the Emperor's attention to the point that

... if imperious circumstances have obliged me to ask a longer time in order to attain the end desired, the sum to be employed is, nevertheless, many millions [of francs] below that which you, Sire, had destined for the purpose. I must add that the desirable end in view will be accelerated in proportion to the number of Leonesa sheep, which can be immediately or successively imported from Spain. If, as I trust, in consequence of your Majesty's orders, the importation should shortly be considerable, the calculations, above made, will all be altered, to the more immediate attainment of our end.[17]

He then proceeded to assess, as the Emperor had commanded him, the advantages to France arising from the measures that had been planned. First, there would be the substitution 6·8 million improved or naturalized sheep for that number of the common sheep. Second, from this alone France could expect to gain about 32·3 million francs from the enhanced quality of her home-grown wools. Third, in the hands of the skilful French manufacturers French fine wools would acquire a new value and in proportion to their increase would enlarge the export of cloths and stuffs which, about 1810, returned already 22·7 million francs. Fourth and last, if the imported Spanish wool were valued on an average at 12 francs per kilogramme and the imported German and other wools from mixed breeds at 7 francs per kilogramme then France by her self-sufficiency would be relieved from paying 57 million francs per annum to foreign nations.

These were arguments dear to the heart of Napoleon. He had no cause to hesitate in reaching for his pen to sign at the Palace of the Tuileries on 8 March 1811 the decree already prepared for him on

'Measures Relative to the Improvement of Sheep', assigning a sum of 600 thousand francs per annum '. . . till the system of amelioration shall be fully attained'.[18] The Imperial decree was reinforced by a notable contribution from the savant to whom more than any other at that time France owed her active and intelligent exploitation of the Spanish Merino, since the death of Daubenton in 1800. A.-H. Tessier, the colleague and disciple of Daubenton, Inspector-General of the Government studs and of the *dépôts* of Merino rams, had been called upon by the Minister of the Interior, Montalivet, to rewrite and modernize the classic *Instructions pour Les Bergers*... by his old master, the last two editions of which (1797, 1799) had been distributed free by the Government and were no longer available. From this appeared the first edition of the new and authoritative *Instruction sur Les Bêtes à Laine, et particulièrement sur La Race des Mérinos*, quickly followed by the second enlarged addition in 1811. In this text was to be found a distillation of all that was known about the Merino and its breeding in health and disease to that date—a complete background in fact for the operation of the Imperial decree to meet whose prime purpose it was most effectively designed.[19] It revived the dictum of Virgil as the rallying motto of the new régime in French sheep breeding—'Continuoque greges villis lege millibus albos'[20]—freely translated by Tessier as 'Choisissez toujours pour vos troupeaux des animaux dont la laine soit trés-fine'—and France rallied to its inspiration.

What, by contrast, had Britain to oppose to all this Gallic *ésprit* and *élan*? There was a document in some unconsidered file at the Board of Trade in Whitehall perhaps. There was a savant at Soho Square, immobilized with years of gout. There was an almost democratic monarch at Windsor Castle, mourning his lost Amelia, cut off for ever from affairs of State, his farms, his friends, and the last traces of his sanity. There was the House of Lords and the farming aristocracy of England and all the noble army of improving landlords, temporal and spiritual. There were the gentlemen-farmers of comfortable means, the tenant-farmers, and the yeomanry. There was the House of Commons replete with 'all the good sense of England'. There was the West Country and all those gentlemen 'daily enriched by commerce' within and without the wool trade. There was the imminent threat of hunger in the midst of apparent plenty. There was bankruptcy and ruin in epidemic profusion. There was not much pleasure at all in the vision of the immediate future. As for Spanish Merinos there were the skinny wrecks driven from beneath French sabres and salvaged from the stinking holds of transports and merchantmen out of Lisbon and Cadiz. There were the partly restored relics of the Paulars from Gijon and the new Negrettis of the Cochrane-Johnston episode, overcrowding the grazings of Richmond Park and distracting Richard Stanford. There was, finally, the slender nucleus of the old Negrettis, still ornamenting His Majesty's farms at Windsor and Kew with their far-flung but small circle of staunch adherents. There were all these things—but there was not, and could not be, any instrument so decisive as an Imperial decree to mobilize and arrange these elements into a pattern of order and purpose. There was, however, the curious endless groping of the British public slowly feeling for a touchstone to charm some compromise to the surface of chaos. If this often goes no further than to produce a committee, it may, if the stars be right, conjure a new society into life. The Imperial decree was not consciously answered by the formation of the Merino Society. There was a certain coincidence in their horoscopes. But to the gentlemen who gathered at the Freemason's Tavern on 4 March 1811 the Imperial decree of 8 March had all the stimulating properties of a galvanic battery.

III

The month of November 1810 was darkened for Sir Joseph Banks by the final madness of his friend and King. This was the onset of twilight for the Spanish flock beside the Thames and for the Merinos of Britain. But it was the beginning of a new phase in their history marked by a short letter from Charles Henry Hunt to Banks, hastily covering a copy of his letter of 2 October 1810 to *The Farmers' Journal* in defence of the Merino cause against an attack from among the breeders of the South Downs:

At the same time y. I feel how much I ought to condole with you on the loss of your Friend & on the present unhappy State of his Majesty our great Merino Patron, I should be ashamed to trouble you with the enclosed trifling Effort of mine to check as far as I can the unfair attacks made upon us if I did [not] conceive it might amuse you at a leisure moment to find that notwithstanding all the discouraging circumstances we have lately met with some of us are still awake to the Interest of the good cause; towards which I cannot doubt but we shall always have the Honor of your countenance & the Benefit of your Support . . .[21]

Here, presumably, is one of our first tangible pieces of evidence on the genesis of the Merino Society in a hasty letter from the man who three days later on 10 November 1810, with John Tharpe of Chippenham Park in Cambridgeshire, signed the circular letter covering the draft advertisement with the ninety-one names subscribed thereto

. . . conceiving it would be highly advantageous to the Merino cause, to have an Annual Meeting in London of Gentlemen, who have interested themselves in the introduction of the Spanish Breed of Sheep, and its

Plate IX

Sir,

In consequence of the intimation which you have obligingly given me by Sir George Paul, that it was probable that the King would graciously please to receive specimens of cloth and kerseymere made from the wool of my sheep; I shall send them to you the beginning of next week; and I beg that you would use your own pleasure as to the time and manner of presenting them. In the same parcel I shall inclose specimens of my sheep and lambs wool of last season.

I am sorry that it is not in my power to answer the systematical queries contained in the paper transmitted to me by Sir George Paul. Those queries extend themselves only to two or three years. My experiments have gone farther as to time, and have been conducted in a somewhat different manner.

In the inquiries which have been made on this subject, it has generally been proposed to improve at once the carcase and the fleece; or at least to preserve the symmetry and size of the former, while means were employed to increase the value of the latter. These certainly ought to be our ultimate objects; but I much doubt whether they can be immediately attained together, if we mean to improve the fleece by an admixture of Spanish blood: For as the form of the Spanish Rams imported into this country is not that which accords with the present opinion of beauty, it is evident that this form will be communicated to their progeny; and it is reasonable to suppose that it will be most prevalent in those of their young which most resemble them in the fineness of their fleeces. This influence on the carcase has actually taken place; and in such a degree, as to make the common farmers extremely averse to the introduction of the Spanish breed into their flocks.

The question then which occurred to me was whether by repeated successive crossings with Spanish Rams we could not so far increase the value of the wool as to make the improvement more than counterbalance the deterioration of the carcase. This end I have endeavoured to attain in the quickest manner I have been able; and I have now gone so far as to have sheep which are five sixths Spanish.

When I have carried the improvement of the wool as far as I can, although I shall then try to mend the carcase. This may be

May 3 — 27

Dr. Caleb Hillier Parry, F.R.S., to Sir Joseph Banks, P.R.S., concerning his approach to the improvement of sheep by the Spanish Merino cross, 26 April 1800.

Plate X

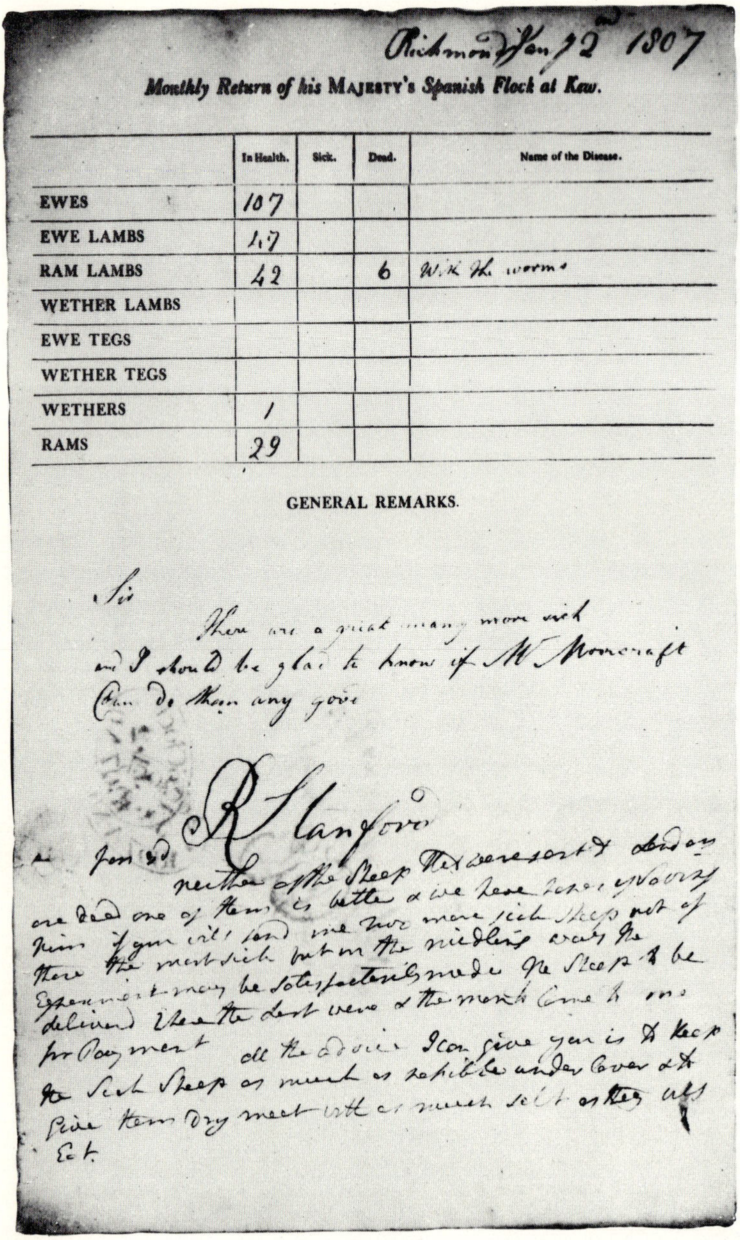

Monthly Return of his MAJESTY's Spanish Flock at Kew.

	In Health.	Sick.	Dead.	Name of the Disease.
EWES	107			
EWE LAMBS	17			
RAM LAMBS	42		6	With the worms
WETHER LAMBS				
EWE TEGS				
WETHER TEGS				
WETHERS	1			
RAMS	29			

GENERAL REMARKS.

Monthly return of His Majesty's Spanish flock at Kew, signed by Richard Stanford, 2 January 1807, with draft reply by Sir Joseph Banks, P.R.S., 3 January 1807.

different Crosses into these Kingdoms; and considering that the — day of March next, being the day previous to Lord Somerville's Annual Spring Meeting, would be a very fair and convenient day for that purpose, do hereby agree to meet at the Free-mason's Tavern at 3 o'clock on that day, for the purpose of communicating to each other the result of our experiments, our success, and our opinions generally on the subject; and to adopt such resolutions, &c., for future meetings, as may be thought advisable, and afterwards to dine together.[22]

The first list of those who supported this new stage in the evolution of the British Merino was a representative but not an exhaustive consensus of its breeders and supporters. It was an adequate beginning, however, and it had the full support and knowledge of Sir Joseph Banks whose name it contained. The text of the covering circular was probably the work of Hunt and Tharpe to whom, indeed, the first initiative seems to have belonged. Their words convey the circumstances of the breed at that time clearly enough:

. . . We have no doubt but it must have occurred to you, that an Institution of this kind becomes, at this time, expedient, from the operation of particular causes, (which in themselves prove the intrinsic value of the Merino Breed of Sheep) rather than from the futile, though active, calumnies of its avowed enemies, or the prejudices and ignorance of others: those which have lately most affected our object, are chiefly, the large importations from Spain; the miserable condition of the Sheep when offered for sale; the injudicious manner in which they are treated by speculating proprietors and their consignees; and the depreciation of Wool in general, from circumstances too obvious to repeat. All these causes have diminished, for a time, the value of Merino Sheep; but they are evils which, in themselves, bring their cure; and their duration must be short. If we do not swerve from the patriotic object of our pursuit, or suffer our ardour to abate, our point will be established, and our downs and heaths will be covered with the finest Wools of Spain; and, by the skill and attention of the British Farmer, the price of the raw material, both in War and Peace, will be insured at a reasonable, and therefore just, standard, for the benefit of our Manufactures. . . .[23]

Then on 7 February 1811 a further circular letter signed by Hunt and Tharpe fixed the '4th day of March next . . . for the Meeting of those Gentlemen who have signified their disposition to form a Society, for carrying into effect his Majesty's most gracious and most provident endeavour, to introduce and establish the Merino Breed of Sheep in the United Kingdom'.[24] Apart from receiving communications of interest and value concerning the results of '. . . Experiments on the Merino Breed of Sheep, and their different Crosses' it was proposed also to consider what further steps it would be necessary to take to support 'this great national object' by furnishing information to the public at large and to consider also 'the propriety of offering Premiums for fine wool, on good carcases, and such other productions as may be thought more likely to promote the grand object in view'. Sir Joseph Banks was to be present and 'should his health permit, will be prevailed upon to take the Chair'.

There was, one would think, never any doubt that Sir Joseph would take the Chair at this meeting unless his physical handicaps on the occasion were past all bearing. Here at last after thirty years of devotion to the sheep and wool interest of the kingdom was a public recognition, at a critical moment, of the part he had played and, indeed, could still play in shaping the economic history of his country. Tharpe and Hunt had consulted him closely at all stages in their preparations. Sir Joseph had clearly given them the benefit of all his experience in the management of such affairs and he had, moreover, prepared his own draft notes for the occasion and the course of the meeting in more than one form. If the series of motions which they represent did not all find a place in the available record of the Society as it finally emerged, they clearly mark an important stage in its evolution, being the seeds from which it grew. Two of Banks's draft proposals have a relevance to us here. In one version—probably the later of the two extant—his second motion was to be:

That the Society be Entitled The Anglo-Merino Society & that its business be to Extend to the utmost Limits of the British /Isles/ Empire the manifold benefits Conferrd on the Landed & the manufacturing interests of the united Kingdom by His Majesties benevolent wisdom & foresight in importing the pure Merino breed of Sheep from Spain in the year 1788.[25]

As the Society did not publish its 'Aims and Objects' but only its 'Rules and Orders' and its 'Premiums' we have as yet no means of judging how far this large intention found acceptance in the body of the Society. The 'Journal of Transactions' kept by the Secretary must be found before we can know how this was received on the day of the inaugural meeting, or if, in fact, it was submitted. But at least we glimpse here, however fleetingly, something of the vision which Banks had of the future that could unfold for 'the Merino breed of Sheep from Spain' no less than we can discern his own judgement of the historic origins of the whole protracted enterprise. To give point and finality to his backward glance on the Society's debt to the past there were the unequivocal terms of his seventh and eighth motions:

That the — day of — be considerd by the Society as a Festival held in Commemoration of the Success of H.M. first Endeavours to import merino Sheep from Spain which was Compleated by the arrival of the sheep at Kew on the 4th of april 1788

That all members in London or its neighbourhood be Summond on that day & if permission Can be obtained to Proceed to view H.M. Merino Flock & afterwards to dine together at Such Place as The President Shall appoint[26]

These were undoubtedly drawn up under the influence of a personal sorrow, a strong sentimental feeling towards the man with whom he had been so long and so closely associated in this visionary but haunted project. The declaration of the Regency at Carlton House on 5 February 1811 was a definitive end to a long partnership between the King and his scientific commoner on a matter of the widest public interest and advantage. It was not less incisive—and not less tragic—than the knife which had on 21 January 1793 separated the French King from Daubenton and Tessier in an enterprise conceived in the same fashion and pursued as steadfastly in the national interests of France. The inauguration of the Merino Society at the Freemason's Tavern in Great Queen Street on 4 March 1811 will serve no less to mark the day when in a sense the Royal task was done and the burden of the future was finally shouldered by the men who in one way or another would successfully foster the central idea of His Majesty's Spanish flock and conserve, by direct means and otherwise, the germ-plasm of the stock which composed it. The Society had a brief career but a more significant place in the history of its period than its critics would accord. It effectively formed a bridge across the uncertain and crisis-riddled years before and after Waterloo from 1810 to 1820 when the whole pattern of British sheep breeding and the wool trade was reshaping to the new industrial order. By its existence at this stage in the history of the Commonwealth it certainly ensured the survival of sufficient Spanish Merinos in Britain itself to serve the later colonial flocks of Australia and New Zealand in no small measure. Of wider but more subtle value it formed a channel of ideas, both of theory and of practice, through which the accumulated experience of Spain, of France, of Germany, of Britain, could be transmitted to that next generation in whose hands the present shape of the Commonwealth wool trade became established. Therefore, it was entirely right that its first and only President for the years of its existence should have been Sir Joseph Banks—no other man had laboured with more devotion or clearer insight to ensure such a future. The Society was a logical end, under the quaint patterns of British thought, to all the sequence of Projects that had gone before. The Imperial decree in its own time was no doubt also a suitable end to the long train of events ordered at intervals for fifty years or more by sapient French statesmen. But of the two men who strove so well as scientists in the service of agriculture only Tessier would live long enough to glimpse an impression of the new world they had made possible and to witness a peaceful fusion of their separate endeavours in the flocks of the southern hemisphere.[27]

Meanwhile the Society was born into a less tranquil world, and it is significant that in the discussion of the first meeting Viscount Castlereagh took an active part in framing various regulations 'for increasing this valuable race of animals; a measure which is become particularly important, from the great exertions in the same pursuit made by our wily and inveterate foe'.[28] It did not require the long report of the French Minister of the Interior in the *Moniteur* of 15 March to rally the noblemen and gentlemen of England, Scotland, Wales, and Ireland. The list of the original ninety-one signatories was quickly enlarged in number, respectability, and as a representative sample of British agriculture and commerce. Before the year was out the Society claimed three hundred and twelve members; had established committees in thirty-eight counties of England and Wales with representation in Scotland and Ireland; and through its Secretary, Benjamin Thompson of Redhill Lodge, Nottingham, translated the significant State paper in the *Moniteur*; had printed this in its first report with its Rules and Orders and the Premiums for its first show of sheep and fleeces to be exhibited in Goswell Street on Wednesday, 6 March 1812. It was blessed and sent on its way by the *Agricultural Magazine* which had taken fright at the *Moniteur* revelations:

... It is, therefore, a matter of the utmost importance that Great Britain should, as far as possible, guard her manufactures against the machinations of a designing enemy, by growing within her own shores the supply of her own wants; and experience having proved the practicability of doing this without any diminution in the quantity and quality of the mutton, we heartily wish success to the patriotic body which is associated to promote so praiseworthy and desirable an object.[29]

The *First Report of the Merino Society* ... was dated 15 April 1811 by the Secretary. It made a special feature of the State paper and the Imperial decree of 8 March, under orders from the President and the Superintending Committee, for the better education of the British public in 'the views of our subtle and inveterate enemy, respecting the growth of superfine wool in France'.

... The adage, *Fas est ab hoste doceri*, was never more applicable than on the present occasion; and it may be reasonably hoped, that the measures adopted in France will stimulate the breeders of the United Kingdom to render this country, as soon as possible, independent of foreign powers for a supply of superfine wool.[30]

This note of urgency sounded like a tocsin insistently from all quarters but there were other manifestations to underline the peculiarities of Merino sheep as strategic raw material.

IV

Sir Joseph had been installed just one month in the Presidential Chair of the Merino Society when he was visited by two gentlemen on a strange mission. On 5 April 1811 he received from them in person a letter from Benjamin Hobhouse as a form of introduction and invoking his interest on their behalf:

... It is in your character as President of the New Merino Society that you are to hear & judge of a proposal to be made to you by them. If I should meet you to day [4 April] (for I understand you will not see the Gentlemen until to-morrow) I will explain to you what in a very short interview I have been able to collect as to the proposal. I write in great haste . . .[31]

They carried also for his inspection the letter by which John Hiley Addington, Secretary to the Treasury, had in the first place brought them to the notice of Hobhouse in their quest for an interview with Banks himself. Addington as a Somerset man had long known the Englishman, Frederick Lenox Sandwell, as a respectable merchant of Bristol trading with Spain, a country in which he had spent much time. With Sandwell was a Spanish merchant friend on whose behalf was sought the interview with Sir Joseph 'to submit some Proposition to Him on the subject of Merinos'.[32] The Spaniard was Don Manuel Ynclan of the Principality of Asturias, a patriot merchant grieving over the chaos of his country scarcely less than the dislocation of his trade.

Don Manuel put his case on the laudable grounds of his sorrow as a Spaniard that so many of his countrymen could not join the armies of his nation for want of suitable arms. He thought himself obliged as a true patriot to employ all his means to relieve this need. He knew no other quarter to which he could appeal but through Banks 'to the generosity & to the just & equitable sentiments of the Government of his Brittanic Majesty'. His merchant house was, it appeared, the owner by the fortunes of war of certain flocks of 'Merinos of the first quality Leonesa Transhumante'. These were 'from the well known Piles of the Conde Fernando Nunes, of the Duke de Bejar & of the Royal Monastery of Escurial'.[33] Don Manuel now wished to make these invaluable assets secure from the continual threat of the common enemy and to bring them to Britain. This action, however, the Spanish Government had opposed. He, therefore, knew no other way to obviate this difficulty and at the same time to prove 'his ardent patriotism' than the course presented now. These then were the five propositions of Don Manuel Ynclan:

1 : That the Government in Consideration of his having already imported to this Kingdom on the 12 Sepr last 431 Merinos of his own property will permit him to export 6000 Stand of Arms of divers classes which he will select to send to Cadiz or Coruna in a Vessel appointed by this Government

2 : That a formal License shall be granted to him for the exportation of small Arms for the same destination after his having introduced into these Realms whatever quantity of Merinos, in proportion to the total value they may produce, & besides this contract or formal promise which he must exhibit to the Spanish Government he expects to be recommended by this in order to obtain the License from the others.

3 : The quality of the above mentioned Flocks may be ascertained as there are still 140 unsold near Bristol, being part of the 431 he introduced in the Kingdom in Sepr last & the other part is in the possession of Wm Tinker Esqr of Littleton House, West Lavington, Wilts where H.M. or any one deputed by the Government may examine the quality.

4 : If the Government wish to treat for the Merinos which Manuel Ynclan has near Bristol, either in exchange for small Arms or Money, he will have the preference.

5 : Don Manuel Ynclan is also ready to treat with the Government or any one appointed for the purpose, for the Merinos he wishes to export from Spain on the most reasonable terms, if the above License is granted to him.[34]

Banks was impressed and sympathetic but none the less he referred to his friend in so many other Spanish problems, José Mendoza y Rios, for some form of verification of Don Manuel's character. On 7 April he received this in writing to the effect that Mendoza y Rios had seen two respectable gentlemen from Asturias who confirmed the bona fides of Don Manuel Ynclan as a merchant of good reputation established at Aviles near Gijon and at several other places in the province.[35] Through Sandwell, Don Manuel on 17 April also sent Banks drawings of two of his Merinos 'by the Mail coach which puts [in] at the Swan with two Necks, Lad Lane' as an earnest of the existence of the sheep.[36] But for all the formidable support which Banks was able to afford the five propositions of Don Manuel there was, in this exercise at least, a greater than he in the corridors of power—one whose steely will was paramount on Peninsular affairs in the matter of arms, great or small, Merinos notwithstanding.

Lord Arthur Wellesley refused to countenance any proposal that smacked of a free-lance traffic in fire-arms to the Spaniards, however immaculate the credentials of Don Manuel. There were many less commendable opportunists as well as right-minded patriots at work in this fertile commerce and no sure way to tell one from the other. In any case Lord Arthur may well have recalled vividly the reprehensible antics of Andrew Cochrane-Johnstone with Merinos and the arms trade—an incident not yet entirely closed at the Horse Guards. Manuel Ynclan almost certainly spoke in some measure for his Government when he reiterated his claim and his hopes to Sir Joseph, 'persuaded that the British Government are desirous to supply my nation with what they want' and that Lord Wellesley had misunderstood the spirit and essence of his propositions, particularly the meaning which seemed to have become attached to the expression 'Traffic' in fire-arms. Don Manuel proposed no more than that for Merinos or for money, he would purchase arms which he would deliver to the Spaniards at the same prices and without profit, the licences being open to the inspection of the Spanish Government.

. . . If in consideration of these truths I obtain of the British Government the Licence it will be easy to calculate the benefit which may result to this Nation by the Introduction of Merinos. . . .[37]

There was no one to whom such a point could have appealed more than Banks, regardless of his new role as President of the Merino Society. It is certain that Don Manuel could have had no complaint that his case was not well presented by Sir Joseph. But, for once, the driving pen racing over the sheets at Soho Square found the point of its eloquence blunted and turned. Banks recognized the obstacle for what it was and recoiled from any further attack. Sandwell, in passing over the trans- lation of Ynclan's last repetition of the case to Sir Joseph, still hoped 'that you will do the best in your power to get the consent of Lord Wellesley, to one or other of the propositions, if that can be done without prejudice to the Policy of Government'.[38] There was, however, nothing but a final resignation from the field in Banks's frank acknow- ledgement of a defeat he seldom suffered:

I met with so decided a Repulse when I applied to Lord W[ellesley] on Don Manuels account as to Preclude in my judgment all hope of a change of opinion, The word Traffic seems to interpret differently from my meaning I meant that Government declind to permit any person whatever to become concernd in Supplying arms to Spain but themselves this is because they mean to supply all that our manufacturers can produce beyond our public wants for other purposes and are aware that a competition in the purchase from the manufacturers would tend either to Raise the Price or Reduce the Quality of the article rather than to increase the Quantity.
     Whether this or any other is the Reason of the Refusal I have met with seems to be of little importance. it was of a nature which in my opinion

precluded all hope of its being changed under any Representation I am able
to make I hope therefore Don Ynclan will excuse me for declining to renew
the Request [in] which I have no kind of hopes of being able to obtain any
than the same refusal I have already met with[39]

If Lord Arthur was adamant so now was Sir Joseph also. The little propositions of Don Manuel Ynclan had run their short course with the
President of the Merino Society probably as far as anyone could have
prepared a path for them in the circumstances of that year.

V

In July 1811 Richard Snart had discovered for himself that the King
was no longer accessible to consultation on the affairs of His Spanish
flock.[40] The Regency had been established for five months but there
was still the lingering hope that His Majesty was not so lost to this world
that all contact with his servants, both high and low, was past. This was
a year of uncertainty, a dismal interregnum of day to day decisions in
His Majesty's affairs. By general agreement on the advice of Sir Joseph
Banks the public sale of 1811 was first postponed and then abandoned.
After the resounding success of the sheep sale of 1810 and the soaring
prices of Spanish and, to a less degree, of home-grown fine wools in the
years 1809-10 everything seemed to have collapsed. The demand for
imported Spanish wool still remained high and the price reflected this
but it was no longer spectacular. In all else the market was disastrous.
Home-grown wool was at its lowest level for ten years. As for the
British Merino there had been nothing less than an almost total eclipse
of apparent interest. After the spectacle of 1810 it was an unbelievable
anti-climax. Snart recorded only one application for sheep from the
Royal flock by July 1811. He had also found the public and private
accounts of this extraordinary decline in the value of Merinos confirmed in his own experience in at least one instance. There were only
four bidders in October for some of John Maitland's pure Merinos at
Sadler's Repository—the ewes selling for a mere 25s. to 2 guineas each
and the rams for little more. One Paular ram which had been bought
for £42 from the King brought only 3 guineas at this sale.[41] Whereas
imported Spanish Leonese wool was still selling at 8s. to 9s. per pound
for the best qualities Snart had been offered as little as 3s. 6d. for His
Majesty's brook-washed clip though this had improved to 5s. for some
of the best. With a proper allowance for the difference in the clean
yield of the two kinds this was not in fact so far, if at all, below a fair
value. Snart, however, was not well informed on the character and
trends of the Spanish wool trade. He was content, therefore, to let
Banks sustain the burden of decision in this and related matters.

But Banks himself seems to have been loath to put himself forward as more than a sympathetic adviser at this distressing period and then only when his views were actually sought. But in relation to the King's flock his position was too well established for him to remain long undisturbed. It was not, however, until 16 March 1812 that something more than his opinion was called for by the Commissioners of His Majesty's Real and Personal Estate.[42] Snart had evidently no relish for being 'under the Necessity of acting from [his] own judgment' in 'the very unpleasant Situation' with which he was now involved. He had clearly in the intervening months by degrees deputed the major decisions concerning the flock to Banks—or as many of them as he could persuade the Commissioners should be dealt with in that way. Snart was almost certainly a very willing vehicle when he carried a long letter to Soho Square from the Commissioners presenting the state of the Spanish flock and asking for help in reducing the situation to order.[43] It was quite clear now that the King would never again be a partner in the daily affairs of the Spanish sheep—although Banks, like every one else, paid lip-service to the notion of possible recovery. This was the position as Richard Snart had reported it to the Commissioners on 14 March:

Merino Rams	..	..	..	..	..	..	..	500
D.° Ewes and Tegs	..	..	..	..	..	..	..	2190
D.° Lambs	..	..	..	..	..	..	..	600
Wethers and Ram Stags of different Sorts			..	..	..	..	360
Ryeland Ewes &c.	..	..	..	..	..	..	..	540
								4190

About 600 more Merino Lambs and 400 Ryeland Lambs are expected to be yeaned this Season—
  Of the above Sheep
218 are in Windsor Home Park
300 at His Majesty's Shrubs Hill Farm
440 Ryelands at General Fitzroy's Land in Northamptonshire
265 in Richmond Park
1047 in Richmond and Kew Gardens & Marsh Gate
1920 on Turnips bought at Ewell, Ashford, Teddington, and Ham.

4190

The Sheep are collectively considered in very fair store order—
  As the Number of Rams is so much greater than can be wanted for Use and Sale, it is presumed it might be advisable to castrate about 300 of the most

inferior and likewise all the Ram Lambs except about 100—which will leave a sufficient Number for future Selection both for use and Sale[44]

In submitting this statement to Sir Joseph the Commissioners delivered themselves of a suitable preamble:

. . . We are induced from the Knowledge which we have obtained of the Interest which you have taken in this Branch of His Majesty's Property, and of the Manner in which You have from time to time been concerned in the Administration and Disposal of it, under His Majesty's authority, to transmit to You a copy of this Statement and to submit for Your consideration the suggestions which are offered by M[r] Snart in regard to the Castration of a large Proportion of the inferior Rams.

We are confident that You will forgive our having recourse upon this Occasion to Your superior Judgement, and that You will not be surprized that We should feel desirous that such Orders as We may think it for the Advantage of His Majesty's Property to issue in regard to His Flocks should be sanctioned by Your respectable Opinion which We further request You will do us the favor of communicating in writing by the bearer M[r] [Richard] Snart whom we have directed to wait upon You in order that He may afford You every Information which You shall require upon this subject. . . .[45]

Replying to this last inclusive call on his services to a Sovereign who could no longer be the companion of his summer days and whom he had never failed at any time, Sir Joseph prepared a statement of some length but eminently constructive. As one of the last documents of any significance that he would produce on the management of the Spanish flock and as a good sketch of the background to these closing scenes it is worth presenting in full. Of the two partners in this long enterprise the President of the Royal Society and of the Merino Society, though physically crippled, was yet active and clear in mind and as vigorous in decision as he remained almost until his death. The Commissioners of His Majesty's Personal and Real Estate received full measure of advice and easement in their immediate worries concerning the flock:

I feel highly gratified by the Compliment you have paid me in consulting me on the subject of the M[erino] Flocks /which afforded one of the most Favorite amusements to our Reverd [King]. I feel [it] an high h[onour] with gratitude scarce to be expressed/ to be instrumental in the most remote degree in forming an arrangement which I Still must hope will ere long be Superintended by the Person whom we all must wish to have restord to us is a matter of /high gratification/ great Pleasure to me & I beg you Gentlemen to be assurd that nothing on my Part shall ever be wanting in a Prompt & diligent obedience to every Command you shall honor me with on this subject.

The whole State of our Merino Concerns has so very materially alterd itself since the last sight of our Royal Master that a Policy very different from that which was pursued Two years ago becomes absolutely necessary Merino sheep were then selling at £50 a head now they are scarce worth a Mutton price & as there are from 4 to 6000 importd sheep now in the Country which cannot be sold even on Low terms & the maintenance of which becomes every day more & more burthensome to the owners I do not see at present any hopes we can have of being able to dispose of any breeding sheep of that kind at any Rate whatever

under these Circumstances I can have no doubt in advising the Sale of the whole of the Hereford Sheep as they are a Saleable Commodity and I think also that the Merino Ram Stags & wethers which are merely mutton should also be sold These Sales when Effected will Relieve you of 900 sheep

I have also no doubt of the Propriety of [castrating] 300 out of the 500 Rams saving of course always the best Sheep and of not keeping above 100 of the Ram Lambs the castrated Sheep always to be sold Of[f] as soon as purchasers can be found which by degrees Reduce the flock still more but tho it will Leave as Large a Stock of Rams as can be wanted the keep of the Flock will still be so considerable as to create great difficulty in providing Pasture for them.

I must conclude that when Gen[eral] Fitzroy Considers a very Little he will withdraw his wish to have the Kings Sheep removd from his Land exactly at that period most inconvenient to the owners & most Profitable to the General The Earth scarce begins to be productive on the first of April but the Sheep who have paid Rent for the Barren Part of the Year appear to have Fair claim to the Productive Part which must follow after, they have not yet Lam[be]d they cannot therefore with safety be removd nor can they be sold on any Reasonable terms till the Lambs by their sides are able to attend them on their Removal I do not think myself that they ought to be brought to market till May & I am confident the General cannot wish to have them removd till they are in a proper State to be disposd of

On a Supposition that the Ryelands the Castrated Sheep and the Culls of which there will be Several when the sheep are markd in the Spring are sold & cleard away still a Number of Sheep will remain when the Lambs have all fallen more than can be provided on the land that has hitherto been destind for the Merino Flock in that Case it appears to me the best Policy to Reduce materially the Sheep usd upon the Farms in the Great Park which are Saleable Stock & Let the Pasture in the Great Park where these Sheep usd to be kept be occupied by the Remaining Merinos this if I judge Right will give Room enough & maintain the Merinos for the present year for the next we may I think look forward with a well founded hope that these valuable animals will have Regaind a Considerable Part of their Real value so that Sales may be had on terms not disadvantageous to the general interests of Farming[46]

The Commissioners acknowledged this letter on 23 March, thanked Sir Joseph for his 'Zeal and Readiness' to advise on the subject, and promised every attention in their power to his instructions. Richard Snart was given 'such General Instructions as We have considered advisable under the present Circumstances' and was directed to consult with Banks in regard to the sales and in carrying into effect the general policy he had suggested.

Six months later there still remained the problem of the accumulated stock of wool from the various flocks augmented by that from the shearing of 1812. On this matter Snart finally sought offers from Messrs. Martin and Oakley, wool staplers of Bermondsey, on 2 September after a long series of unfruitful efforts to dispose of the swollen clip with reasonable profit and security of payment. On 3 September this is what Richard Snart received from Bermondsey:

Pursuant to our engagement of yesterday, we now make you the following propositions for the purchase of His Majesty's Wool & we trust they will be deemed fair & liberal—viz—

1—The Nigrete & Paular flocks, at Marsh Gate & Windsor at four shillings & nine Pence per Pound
2^d the Rams of Ditto at four shillings & three Pence
3   the Merino Cross at three shillings & six Pence
4   the Lambs Wool at two shillings & six Pence
5   the Ryelands with liberty to throw out the coarse fleeces at Two shillings & six Pence
or
6   Ditto coarse & fine together at Two shillings to allow 1 lb in a score for the great waste &c. in it

The Payment as follows—viz, one third of its Amount in Cash at the scale, the remainder in 4 months afterw^{ds} guaranteed by one or two houses of the first consequence & respectability in the City of London.

It is presumed that no house would make a purchase of this magnitude, unless there was some prospect of profitting by it, and that allowance will be made for the precarious & uncertain state of our Wollen Manufactures.

It is computed there is 60,000 Bags of Spanish and Portugal Wools in the Kingdom at this time, our markets are glutted with it. Of these Wools there are two very large Sales coming on about the middle of this monthe—Mr Thos. Martin [for] one & that must be sold with out reserve ab^t 600 Bags—the other 800—

From these causes 'tis fair to infer, that our native fine Wools must feel some depression, Our offer therefore must appear liberal to you[47]

The substance of this situation with a copy of Messrs. Martin and Oakley's proposal was sent by William Taylor, one of the three Commissioners, to Banks on 9 September, noting that the stock of wool in hand was 'now so considerable as to have become an Article of much Inconvenience in more than one respect'. He proceeded:

... As You were so good as to say that You would allow us to resort to the Benefit of Your Advice upon these Occasions I shall feel infinitely obliged to You for an early Opinion as to the Expediency & Propriety of closing with this Proposal. I beg leave to add that Mr Snart has been engaged in repeated Negociations for the Sale of His Majesty's Wool and that He has received various Proposals for the Purchase of certain Portions of it, but that He has either been disappointed in the Results of these Negociations, or that the Proposals have offered so little Security in regard to Payment that it has been impossible to admit any other than that which I have the honor to enclose. I have further to observe that His Endeavours to dispose of the Wool at the Wool Fairs have proved ineffectual ... P.S. We are in hopes of making some arrangement for the Reception of a large Proportion of His Majesty's Merino flocks upon reasonable Terms. It will however occur to You that the Number of Rams is excessive and, as matters now stand, that the retaining such a Number is unnecessary & highly inconvenient; We should therefore wish to be favored with Your Opinion whether some Steps should not be taken for disposing of a Proportion of them either by advertised Sales, or by offering them privately for Sale at a Price sufficiently reasonable to induce Persons to purchase them.[48]

It is not easy to be sure how much wool had accumulated during this painful time of change. Since 1810 it is probable that none or very little of the Spanish Merino wool had been sold and that this was cluttering the barns and stores of the Marsh Gate Farm at Kew and odd rooms in some of the Lodges at Windsor. Assuming then that there was now a total of three years' wool on hand in September 1812 the few figures available permit an estimate of the quantities in very round terms:

Class of Sheep	Estd. Number of Fleeces (1810,+1811, +1812)	Approx. Total Weight of Washed wool (lb.)	Approx. Gross Value (£)
Ewes and Ewe Tegs (Paular, new and old Negretti)	5,500	20,000	4,750
Rams, Stags, Wethers (Paular, new and old Negretti)	900	4,000	850
Lambs (Paular, new and old Negretti)	2,700	2,000	250
Approximate totals:	9,100	26,000	5,850

This would have amounted in all roughly to a hundred and thirty bags of the Spanish size or about a hundred and ten English packs. In this estimate—and it can only be an inspired guess—we have a general picture of the material basis of the transactions on which Sir Joseph tendered this advice:

in the present State of the Wool market I have no dificulty in advising you to accept of the offer that has been made to you of Clearing away the growing

Stock of H M Wools which are now in hand I am always inclind especialy in agricultural Concerns to accept a timely price for my Produce Except in the Case of very Excessive depreciation /in the present Case/ You have kept back till a Price which in my Judgement is not a bad one has been offerd & the Security for Payment appears to me unexceptionable

When the wool Trade was Steady I was usd to think 4/6 a Pound for H.M. Merino wools washd in the Sheeps back a very Sufficient Price & in Fact it was as high as that of the best imported wools making allowance for Charge of washing & waste & I think by the Prices I see Quoted that the Price of 4/9 will not allow an exhorbitant Profit to the buyer at present I do not See in my own Judgement any Reason to expect a Rise in these wools. The war with America diminishes our Exports and as Spain & Portugal Can Send their wools to no other than the British market we are Sure of being somewhat over-supplied with them

in the Case of the Ryeland I advise you to Consider the Proposal When I had the honor of managing H M Flocks The Ryelands [were] Coarser every year if this is the Case the Inclosd Proposal [by Messrs. Martin and Oakley] of Selling the whole at 2/ [per pound] will be the most advisable in case of the buyer being allowd to throw out Fleeces as Coarse ones at his Pleasure he will not be Sparing in the Exercise of this privilege in the hope of Purchasing on the Spot those he has thrown out at an inferior Price & I by no means advise you to accede to the last proposal of Deducting 5 Per Cent for Great waste as I know of no Greater waste these Fleeces will be Subject to than other Lots of Old Wool.

Respecting the Rams I know not how to advise you the Pressure on the market made by the imprudent importations of Commissioners &c. is by no means Removd if 5 Guineas a head Could be procurd I should not advise you to Refuse it but I fear that no such price Small as it appears to be Can at present be obtained[49]

All this was excellent good sense. As such it was recognized by the Commissioners and on this basis the troublesome accumulation of frozen capital was effectively liquidated. From the Spanish wool alone the Royal accounts were enriched by about £5850, of which the produce of the old Negretti stock may be reckoned at about £450 or one-thirteenth, at the rate of £150 for each of the three years. This would represent a return of nearly 18s. per head among the adult sheep for the fleece wool. Though not unreasonable the value of 4s. 9d. per pound was equivalent to 6s. 6d. for wool in the Spanish state. As such it was almost 2s. below the current levels for prime Leonese, but as an average figure for the whole clip of the unsorted wool it was as Sir Joseph had judged it—a timely and acceptable price.

The urgent problem of the wool clip had been solved. There remained the more obstinate matter of the sheep themselves. On this it is difficult to know at present just what did happen, or exactly when the sheep were sold. There is no doubt, however, that by June 1813 the greater part of the Paular and the new Negretti acquisitions remaining from the wind-fall importations of 1808 and 1809 had been disposed of by an advertised sale—or were dead. His Majesty's Spanish flock had thus been restored to its pristine and essential nucleus—the old Negretti flock, descendants of the classic importation of 1791, small in number as it had always been but still the indubitable product of Banksian selection and breeding, the diminutive 'Treasure of infinite value'.

The last sheep return of Richard Stanford available to us set the numbers of the Royal Spanish flock on 4 January 1813 as follows:

> 680 Paular Ewes
> 738 New Negrete
> 143 Old Negrete
> 100 Rams
> 30 Weathers
> 670 [Ewe] Tegs
> 420 Lambs[50]

Here is a grand total of two thousand seven hundred and eighty-one Spanish Merinos of all ages and sexes. According to George Thomas Bucke who, with John Tharpe and several others of the Merino Society, was one of the principal buyers of His Majesty's sheep at this large disposal, 'about 3000' were advertised for sale by the auctioneer about two months before it took place.[51] However, he is emphatic that no more than seventeen hundred were in fact brought under the hammer, that these were in a disgraceful state from general bad management and starvation over the winter from which nearly one-half had died. He said there was not a good lamb in the whole flock as it was offered for sale in March or April 1813 and that so badly had the ewes been shepherded that they were suspected of being 'rotten', an idea that deterred many from buying who might otherwise have been large purchasers. In his view the prices were high '. . . considering the dread-ful state of poverty and neglect under which His Majesty's sheep laboured' at the time. Bucke cited, as an example of what had happened, the eight hundred Merinos which had been sent to the King's Shrubs Hill Farm to be wintered, from whence emerged about a fortnight before the actual auction no more than a hundred and twenty emaciated survivors—'as though designed to assist the efforts of prejudice' against the breed. Bucke was also inclined to impugn the integrity of the King's shepherds in this matter. The skins of the dead sheep he said were given to one shepherd and those of the dead lambs to another—'thus was premium offered for the destruction of the animals'. He also said that it was an undoubted fact that during the time they were at Kew—in the Gardens and on the Marsh Gate Farm—'a man was constantly employed in wheeling away the dead carcasses, to the number of 100 a day!'[52]

There is no doubt that the losses of that last overcrowded winter of the big flock were great and severe. Whether there was culpable negligence among the shepherds or wilful pilfering by them is not easily determined now. The sheep that survived the winter were certainly a poor spectacle and no ornament to His Majesty's farms. At least part of the trouble may have been an inattention to that part of Banks's instructions which counselled sales of other stock to leave room for the Merinos. In any case there seems to have been in the reports the usual streak of exaggeration and ignorance of the real situation. On the whole Richard Stanford's figures were reasonably sound, but if not always wholly beyond reproach they were the only official figures to which anyone could refer, then or now. As such they were the ones used by Banks and others—with whatever mental reservations that seemed appropriate. If then we deduct the probable numbers of the old Negretti flock—for these were not sold—from Stanford's last return to Banks of 4 January 1813 there is left a figure of about twenty-five hundred for the Paular and the new Negretti rams, ewes, and ewe tegs. If of these only seventeen hundred survived to the sale in the early spring then about one-third were lost that winter. This is appreciably less than one-half, the proportion which Bucke suggests was nearer the mark, but it is not at all admirable.

The prices were as depressing as the appearance of the sheep. The ewes, including those with lambs at foot as couples, brought about £4 each—a sad contrast to the leaping values of 1810 when £35 10s. 10d. was the female average. One ram at least brought £43 although it is unlikely that many sold outside the range of £6 to £8. But if the Merino sale was poor the return from the Ryelands was catastrophic—at 10s. per head! Even worse were the seven Southdown ewes, without lambs, which sold for just on 8s. each, at the same sale. Beside these values the Spanish Merinos were pearls of great price. No details, however, remain for us to assess the result more closely. It would seem none the less that the remnants of these old prizes-of-war and their offspring added perhaps about £6000 to £7000 to the Royal exchequer.

The last seven years of His Majesty's Spanish flock from 1813 until the death of its Royal owner are obscure but apparently uneventful. The period is, however, entirely the story of the old Negretti flock once more—'the small Merino flock' as it had become during the Regency, under the surveillance of the Commissioners of His Majesty's Real and Personal Estate, and the immediate management of the new Bailiff, John Engalle. Sir Joseph was still there, as ever, for consultation and guidance when the occasion required. His dedication to his 'hobby'

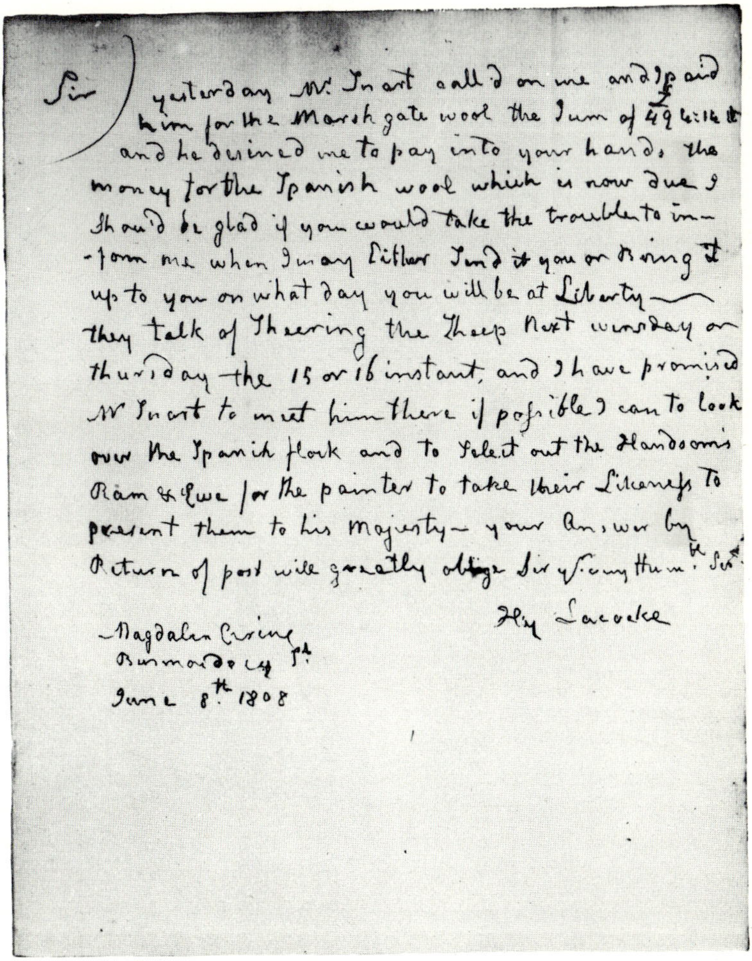

Plate XI

Henry Lacocke to Sir Joseph Banks, P.R.S., 8 June 1808.

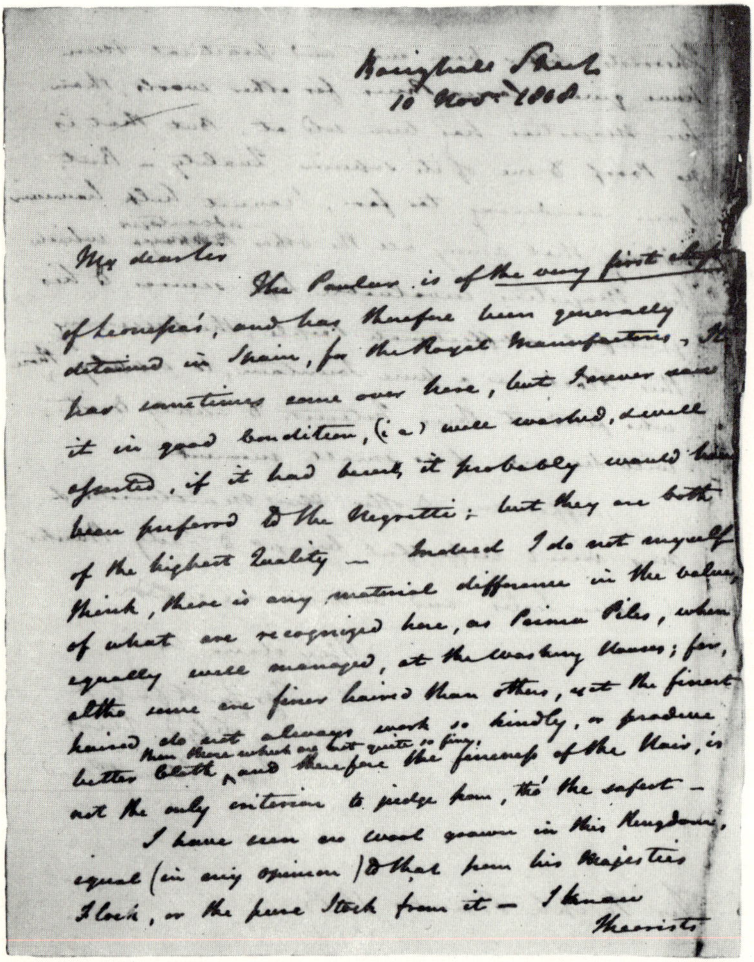

Plate XII

John Maitland to Sir Joseph Banks, P.R.S., 10 November 1808.

and 'the principal amusement' of an old blind friend with whom he could no longer speak was not less than it had been for the past twenty-five years and more. We can perceive this only in glimpses—such, for example, as in 1818. Banks was in his seventy-fifth year when on 25 August returning to Spring Grove from dining with a friend Sir A. Macdonald, he and his wife and sister were overturned by a drunken coachman.[53] All three were elderly and heavy people. They lay helpless for half an hour at the bottom of the upturned coach before they could be lifted out. They were to all appearances more shaken than seriously hurt. Yet this incident in its way was the first harbinger of the final change. A month later Sarah Sophia, his devoted sister and industrious amanuensis in so many things, was dead after 'a slight indisposition'. In the convalescent pause after the accident and in the week before his sister's death he received on 23 September a brief letter from William Taylor, busy at Kew about the King's personal affairs during the last illness of the Queen. This is evidently typical of many other small passages and in it we have one of the few surviving vignettes of the Spanish flock itself in the deepening twilight of its Royal day.

I beg to enclose our Bailiff's Letter respecting the Merinos but he has not explained what He meant by change of Keep altho I particularly desired Him to do so. I forgot to tell You when I had the pleasure of seeing You Yesterday that We had sold our Merino Wool about a Month ago for 4/1^{d} pr pnd taking in the Lambs Wool at that price. We have sold all our Culled Ewes (broken mouthed excepted) at £4 each, but from want of keep and the consequent impossibility of Fattening them, the whethers [sic], shorn, did not produce more than 23/ each. Still the small Merino flock, including Wool, has returned this Year about £530, the South Down, allowing for Numbers, little more than half.

The Queen has been more easy & comfortable this day than She was Yesterday.[54]

Here effectively ends our contact with the enterprise of the Spanish Merinos of His Majesty King George III of England under the stewardship of Sir Joseph Banks, Baronet, P.R.S. For both these men the time ahead was now short. For the flock itself as a Royal ornament the span of days was not much longer. To the end it continued as it had been from the beginning—a small flock. The crowded years of the Peninsular War from 1808 to 1813 with its sudden accessions from the shattered Paular and Negretti cabanas did not disturb the continuity of the generations from the original stock of the importation from Santander in 1791. These alone were the sheep that were in truth His Majesty's Spanish flock. These alone formed the original small nucleus on which was exercised for the first time and, in the main, continuously for almost one human generation—about seven sheep generations—the particular selective theories and prejudices of British sheep breeders with the Spanish Merino. At the end in 1820 they probably numbered somewhere between a hundred and a hundred and fifty breeding ewes, a total flock ranging from about two hundred and fifty to three hundred and fifty in all. This was larger than it had in fact been when, up to the onset of the Regency, it was the prime source of Spanish Merino breeding stock for Great Britain. For twenty years from 1791 to 1811 the breeding ewe flock averaged no more than eighty head and the whole flock about two hundred—a resource so slender as to be almost ridiculous but, in the right hands, powerful enough. This, however, was the deceptively ordinary and even ugly little flock that in the end proved the truth of the 1st Lord Auckland's *obiter dictum* tossed lightly on the desk of Sir Joseph Banks just one week before the sheep themselves reached Windsor:

... I think it possible that our Flock may prove a Treasure of infinite value to His Majesty's good old Island of Great Britain. ... [55]

The casual prophecy so well to be fulfilled may justly serve as an epitaph to the first Merino stud in British hands.

VI

The year 1820 ended the long reign of George III. It was the end also of an enterprise and of a sustained partnership between two men of the eighteenth century who in the long autumn of their lives prepared together a rich heritage for a new world of industry in the nineteenth. To the society which mourned them at their passing this was not evident. To the generations that have succeeded them their contributions have been by no means clear. Neither the King who was a farmer by inclination nor the knight who was a rich landowner by birth and a scientist by instinct have been fully recognized as the colleagues they were in a long study whose results influence us yet. In the history of agriculture there have been few collaborations in themselves as long, as happy, or as profitable to the society which it was intended to benefit. In the history of animal breeding there seems to be none with which to compare it. As an episode in the growth of science as a servant of the nation, however, it is not unique. It is merely an early and most significant British example with a special relevance in the field of agricultural research. No such thoughts, however, found their place in the encomiums, the *éloges*, or any of the obituaries of these men in that year—and little to the point since.

The King died on 28 January 1820. There was universal mourning and a funeral on a scale never seen before for an English king—for a man who had at last found release from ten years of deep personal distress, blindness, and insanity, but who, long before these afflictions had borne him down, had also become for many of his subjects something more than a symbolic 'Shepherd of his People'.

Sir Joseph died on 19 June 1820. For him there was no public mourning, his funeral was unostentatious, his burial-place for long forgotten. He was no less mourned in the international world of science, to which he assuredly belonged, than was his King within the nation. Many years of physical pain had laid heavy hands upon him but he died, as few men have, still rich in the possession of a vigorous mind active in public affairs almost to the last—secure, also, in the knowledge that, though his physical senses were failing him, he was valued for himself. On 13 May 1820 he was told by Francis Brothers, Secretary of the Merino Society:

... I beg to state that the Society by a unanimous vote was pleased to reelect you as President for the ensuing Year and to offer you their best thanks for your valuable support and assistance. . . .[56]

This was his tenth successive year in that office. Within a week had come the generous refusal of the Royal Society to accept his resignation from the same position among the *élite* of his scientific peers by the unanimous resolution of the Council of 18 May 1820:

The Council do with one voice express their most cordial wishes that the President should not withdraw from the Chair which he has filled so ably and so honourably during a period of forty-two years.[57]

But one month later, at Spring Grove, both Societies had lost their President and, in the evolution of British science—certainly in that of agriculture at least—an age had passed. Arthur Young, blind for a decade, had died but two months earlier. Lord Somerville had been dead scarcely eight months. The King, their patron and supporter, lost to them all for years was buried at last. Within the next two years the 1st Earl Sheffield and Caleb Hillier Parry would have gone. So also would the Board of Agriculture—but its originator Sir John Sinclair, of all that talking, writing, perambulating small group which so moulded the thoughts of their fellow-countrymen by word and deed in agricultural pursuits, for nearly forty years, he alone would survive— writing and rewriting, condensing and codifying for another fifteen years. The heritage of their work, the boundless dynamism of the eighteenth century, had by then passed safely into the hands of a younger and no less vigorous generation.

The King rests at Windsor Castle and Sir Joseph Banks within the precincts of the parish church at Heston. The Royal farmer of

Berkshire and Surrey and the experimentalist of Spring Grove in Middlesex remain, each of them, still close by the scenes where once they met so often in the long days of summer to order the affairs of the Spanish sheep grazing along the valley of the Thames—'the Treasure of infinite value' left by them as a legacy to an unformed and distant Commonwealth and to a future of wealth still untold.

CHAPTER XIV

The Legacy, 1788–1962

I

In the long rambling process of detection and the tedious reconstruction from scattered fragments of the life history of the Royal Merinos of England it is possible to forget that, in the international chess-game which determined their movements, these silent pawns were in fact living four-footed animals of some general biological interest. For centuries the Spanish Merino—and its near relatives elsewhere in the Mediterranean region—had been known intimately as an individual sheep and as a flock, small or large, only to those remote few humans[1] who, as shepherds and their immediate masters, tended them by day and night in ceaseless wanderings from pasture to pasture on the distant mountains, hills, and plains which formed their traditional habitat. It was its ancient virtue as a breed that it could convert the rough grasses and miscellaneous herbage of semi-arid terrain, otherwise inhospitable or unproductive, into a fibre of cherished fineness for sophisticated textile purposes in the centres of civilization. The Spanish fleece had become both famous and necessary in the wool markets of the Western world during the Renaissance, but was seen and handled inside Spain only by a few merchants in its native state. Even this condition was soon transformed and no sure guide remained to the character of the original covering of the animals that had grown it. The Spanish practice of sorting and washing the shorn fleece before export presented the international wool trade with a commodity which was commendably clean—free on the whole from the ordure and secretions of the animal and from the dust and vegetable debris gathered in its migrations during the year. The great packs that moved north from the *esquileos* and *lavaderos* of Central Spain in the mule trains to Burgos and on to the Biscayan ports contained a material, therefore, which left few clues to the outward appearance of the animal from whose pelt it had emerged. In its heyday the animal itself was safely screened from the curiosity of the world by its very remoteness from the ordinary paths of all but the more adventurous travellers. Its segregation was made even more secure by the legal locks set by the Spaniards which for so long prevented its export abroad. In these circumstances we need not wonder that the Spanish Merino was ill understood as a domestic sheep by all European nations for so long. They could only peer from a distance across the ragged peaks of the Pyrenees and the Cantabrian ranges and guess at the reality behind. The sheep itself rested for centuries in the hands of illiterate men who saw almost nothing of the outside world beyond their camp-fires, responsible to distant owners who had little interest in them as people and less in revealing the truth about the animal whose fleece was so readily converted into ducats and doubloons to support their superior estate.[2] The chance commentary of an occasional traveller's tale was often the only—and the much-quoted and mis-quoted—source of any information whatever. The few accounts that strayed into circulation were fragmentary, unsatisfying, and mostly offhand. It is significant that a single letter from an Irishman, 'long resident in Spain' and writing in 1764 as one naturalist to another in England, should for more than half a century have been almost the only document in English available to those few who wished to know more.[3] Plagiarized and mutilated it haunts the slim literature on the subject— almost to the third and fourth generation. Of those who sought to penetrate the Iberian mysteries of the Merino with something more than scholarly detachment the Frenchman, Louis-Jean-Marie Daubenton, has a clear priority in the eighteenth century as the most influential experimentalist—as the first systematic breeder of the Spanish Merino for a national purpose with some scientific claims. This in no way denies the historical priority of the Swede, Jonas Alstroemer, as the first to establish in a European country outside Spain a viable and effective commercial population of improved fine-wool sheep derived from the Spanish Merino. Influenced by these two examples, but mostly by that of the French Sir Joseph Banks began for Great Britain what Alstroemer had done sixty years earlier for Sweden, and Daubenton twenty years before for France. It is to Banks then that we must first look if we are to understand the nature of the legacy bequeathed by His Majesty's Spanish flock.

II

Whatever else there is to be said—and there is much—there can be little doubt now that it was Sir Joseph Banks who placed the Spanish Merino and the essential knowledge of its breeding, management, and productive attributes at the industrial disposal of Great Britain. No single man did more to probe the intricate question of how to supply the British wool manufactories with the salient raw material on which their growth in the nineteenth century and their present strength in international commerce would depend. There were certainly few important aspects of wool growth and end use which his restless curiosity did not explore during the earlier years—that important transition period we now call the Industrial Revolution when, in the textile industries, the cottage was evolving into the factory, steam-power was displacing water, when the spindle and the one-thread wheel were slowly giving way to the advances of the water-frame, the spinning jenny, and the mule. It was Banks who almost alone for many years bore the burden of taking some form of continuous effective action—as distinct from the more capricious outpourings of voluble publicists such as Arthur Young and Sir John Sinclair—on the subject of the fine-wool supply at a critical period and on the means of closing the gap between that and the ever-rising and ever-more selective demand. His commitment to the task certainly arose from his first concern as a Lincolnshire gentleman of means among the growers of long wool hard hit by the war-induced depression in that commodity during the crisis years of 1778–83. From this personal entanglement it was a short step to his engagement in the more comprehensive national problem. For the rest of his life he worked quietly but with all the relentless energy of his powerful nature towards a solution of this vital question as he saw it. His vision was comprehensive. Based firmly on the knowledge and experience of a great landowner with an unusually wide practical command of the minutiae of British agriculture, it was enriched and enlightened by his unique position as President of the Royal Society. Here he remained for forty-two years until the end of his life at the cross-roads of intellectual power facing the dawn of the new age of Science in the service of Industry. Here he remained for so long also an anomalous and misunderstood figure—a new form of biological thinker presiding at the inmost council of the natural philosophers, both the eminent and the dilettante, but which comprehended within its circle the cream of the scientific minds of Great Britain devoted then, as now, rather more to shaping the future of mathematics and astronomy, of chemistry and physics, than of the sciences arising from the study of the earth itself and the plants and animals spread across its surface. A clear and broad rather than perhaps an original or profound thinker Banks was almost inevitably that odd man out—the intellectual man of action. The very range and mixture of his personal qualities and daily interests undoubtedly meant that he was an enigma to his contemporaries no less than he has remained to his posterity within and without the ivory towers of the scientist and the historian. Few men can have enjoyed the friendship or shared the interests of quite such an extensive sample of their contemporaries more than Banks. From the dwellings of his dusky friends in distant 'Otahite' as a slightly brash but most gifted young man to the more secluded dignity of the Presidential Chair at Somerset House in the maturity of his years, the face and personality of Banks had cast its own indefinable spell on his associates the world over. A welcome guest everywhere, a pleasant host, a generous and unswerving friend and colleague, a lively and at times hilarious companion among the intimates of his own circle, there were in him still deep reserves which few ever quite tapped. Not many knew the wide extent over which his pen ranged as it moved incessantly across the papers in the study and the bedroom at Soho Square and Spring Grove or in the orderly quiet of the great farm office at Revesby Abbey. No one really knew much about the long hours—too often excruciatingly painful hours, days, and months—wherein his thoughts and instructions, his questions and answers, were put on paper and sent round the world in an unceasing stream, fertilizing the minds, stimulating and guiding the actions of men in a boundless search for knowledge of Nature and her products useful to humanity. Some saw only the man of wealth, enjoyed his patronage but envied him his state. Some saw and knew only the authoritative President of the Royal Society and the breakfasts and soirées at Soho Square without ever achieving the intimacy and freedom of the bookshelves and the collections behind the *salon* wherein was revealed the true depth and extent of his knowledge and experience. Some saw in this only the superficial trappings of the wealthy patron who found these things an end in themselves. Of such a mind was Sir Humphry Davy who surely has left us the most warped and superficial estimate of the man to whom he owed more than he cared to reveal and whom he was content evidently to damn with faint praise:

He [Banks] was a good-humoured and liberal man, free and various in conversational power, a tolerable botanist, and generally acquainted with Natural History. He had not much reading, and no profound information. He was always ready to promote the objects of men and science, but he required to be regarded as a patron, and readily swallowed gross flattery. When he gave anecdotes of his voyages, he was very entertaining and unaffected. A courtier in character, he was a warm friend to a good King. In his relations to the Royal Society he was too personal, and made his house a circle too like a Court.[4]

The more acidulous imputations of this subtle mixture of truth and rather less than half-truth are against the evidence. Banks was no courtier though he had many friends at Court. He was truly 'a warm friend to a good King', but it was essentially as one man to another sharing a field of common interests and those plainly enough of a practical and useful kind. As to the atmosphere of his social functions this was so far from itself suggesting a Court that we have ample support from many men for the truth of Sir William Edward Parry's judgement and experience that they were 'not like those of fashionable life, but given from a real desire to do everything which could in the smallest degree, tend to the advancement of every branch of science'.[5] It may, therefore, be as well to balance the bleak strictures of Humphry Davy with another estimate more in line with the impression that emerges from long and close study of the man at work:

His manners are polite and urbane; his conversation rich in information, frank, engaging, unaffected, without levity, yet endowed with sufficient vivacity. It may have been, in mistake, supposed by some that he was merely a naturalist and a virtuoso. No error was ever farther from the truth. He possesses information upon almost every different subject within the range of art or nature. On most occasions he exercises the discriminating and inventive powers of an original vigorous mind: his knowledge is not that of facts merely, or of technical terms and complex abstractions alone, but of science in its elementary principles and of Nature in her happiest form.[6]

It is more truly in this guise that we find the man who, once he had ceased to be the fortunate youth and the romantic young explorer, became by degrees the first Minister of Science, unpaid, and unrecognized except in a jovial aside by Lord Auckland when he dubbed him His Majesty's 'Ministre des Affaires Philosophiques'. Here, also, we find something nearer the man who among other manifestations was a prototype of the modern agricultural scientist, a function which was almost explicitly acknowledged as such in his own lifetime:

The institution of the Board of Agriculture has had its utility greatly increased by means of the counsels of the President of the Royal Society. In his attentions to the improvement of the breeds of our sheep and other domestic animals,—to the drainage of the fens of Lincolnshire, in which his estates chiefly lie, to the amelioration of gardening and husbandry, as well as of the implements employed in them,—he had given many signal and happy instances of that scientific patriotism, which has long been the best benefactor of our country.[7]

Into this phase of his life's work clearly fits the creation and supervision of His Majesty's flock of Spanish Merinos and all that flowed from it.

His relation to the enterprise was comprehensive. From Banks emanated the germ of the idea caught from across the Channel and transmitted after incubation at Spring Grove to the receptive tissues of 'H.M. Mind'. From this point on he shouldered the task of execution. There was first the planning of ways and means, both the strategy and the tactics. Out of this arose the long and intricate exchanges through the by-ways of Whitehall and the City, the foreign correspondence with the savants of France, the merchants of the British factories on the Iberian Peninsula, and the gentlemen of His Majesty's Diplomatic and Consular Corps. Then came the problems of the mercantile marine at sea and ashore and the placation of the Lords Commissioners of His Majesty's Customs. There were the tricky problems of finance and the long series of prompt disbursements from his own pocket to cover the running expenses of the protracted negotiations—on his private theory that 'short accounts make long friends'. There were the long and often detailed arrangements to be made for the actual transport and well-being of the Spanish sheep themselves. There was in this alone a formidable mass of paper work—drafting, calculating, and accounting—all of which Banks managed in his own hand among a conflicting mass of many other interests and responsibilities, private and public.

With the sheep established at Windsor and then later more extensively at Kew and Richmond there entered another factor commanding the time and attention of Sir Joseph. This was the development of a system of management in the Royal parks and gardens through the agency of men whom he could not command under the aegis of a King to whom he was bound to defer. Into this situation he had to inject what he knew of the management and needs of this strange and foreign breed of sheep and somehow to cajole an acceptance of it within the Royal precincts by an unconvinced if not, at times, a hostile staff. Banks may not have been a courtier but he had extensive gifts as a diplomat and these alone carried him forward on this unpromising path. To execute the plan under these conditions required a large measure of his personal time and physical presence at particular operations. For seventeen years at least from 1788 he was an assiduous manager closely in touch with the animals themselves most of which he seems to have seen and handled himself on many occasions until gout and its sequels crippled and confined him. The summer months especially saw him out and about the King's farms and gardens among the sheep from early June to late August until the time came for his regular autumn pilgrimage to Revesby Abbey and to the affairs of his own land and its flocks. In this period each year his major task was to witness the shearing of each ram and ewe, to record his observations, to classify and discard, to select the animals for gift and sale, and to arrange the matings for the autumn. There was also the matter of the accumulated wool clip, its examination and weighing fleece by fleece, its packing and dispatch to the staplers and the clothiers. There were few things that he did not do in a practical way himself at some time with the flock—and the King often with him—even to the opening and examination of sheep post-mortem. He asked nothing that he could not or would not attempt himself. He was up betimes and out late in this as in any other business that required long hours and early rising[8]—wherein he so often found the King's servants wanting. He delegated much—especially later to Henry Lacocke and Richard Stanford in these manual tasks—but he delighted in every chance of close and direct observations of the sheep themselves and their fleeces in the manner and tradition of all good and successful breeders of livestock. There were limits, however, to the fulfilment of his fondest hopes as a breeder of Spanish sheep for the King. These were set by the very complexities of the loose liaison with the Royal estates under which he worked. Banks had few moments of real satisfaction in the results he achieved with the King's flock but, though these fell short of his aims, it is doubtful if under the circumstances many men could have done more than he.

Casting aside his role as a practical breeder and husbandman of Spanish sheep on his return to the *sanctum sanctorum* of Soho Square during the winter and spring he became the interpreter and exponent of the lessons he had himself learned at first hand with the animals themselves. This he prosecuted through his reports to the King and his correspondence to all who sought information. There were also the occasions of his own breakfasts and soirées to say nothing of the more spectacular events each year at Woburn and Holkham and Sadler's Repository for the verbal exchanges that made these social gatherings so highly effective as a medium of technical education and scientific stimulus. His presence at the wool fairs, especially that at Lewes and later his patronage of those at Hounslow[9] and Dorchester,[10] were an important part of the pattern he developed for spreading his knowledge and inspiration in agricultural affairs. There were in fact few activities of note concerning the agricultural well-being of the kingdom which Banks did not support in a constructive and enthusiastic manner. Outside the Royal Society which had the prior claim there were few interests stronger than his agricultural pursuits. His figure was a familiar one wherever livestock were gathered for display, for competition, or any form of educational purpose. His opinion as an agriculturist and animal breeder was respected as much as it was in his more recognized capacity as President of the Royal Society, and therefore as a leader in the realms of natural philosophy.

As such a person he himself was the embodiment of a union of science and practice, of theory and of applied common sense. He stood astride the gulf which in a less enlightened period seems at times to yawn between the two. He could as easily discuss with authority the prices of wool and the merits of individual fleeces with Henry Lacocke as he could consider the theory and use of the eriometer with Thomas Young[11] or apply one of Dollond's eye-micrometers to the measurement of the wool fibre himself.[12] He was at home among the sheep in the farmyard and the field and with the wool piles in the barn and the store. After long years of association with John Maitland and the clothiers of the West Country in processing trials with the Spanish fleece, his own and the King's—pure and crossed—he was wise in his understanding of the relations between the raw material and the qualities of the finished fabric. His foreign and his home correspondence was an efficient system which kept him abreast of the economic place of Spanish fine wool and of the state of Great Britain's competitors for security and self-sufficiency in that commodity. For a generation he was almost single-handed an intelligence centre and source of reference on all things pertaining to the sheep and wool supplies of Great Britain. The writers and publicists, organizers and enthusiasts, improvers and scientists— James Anderson, Arthur Young, Sir John Sinclair, Lord Sheffield, Caleb Hillier Parry, Lord Somerville, Francis Duke of Bedford, Thomas William Coke, Robert Bakewell—these and many more all deferred in various ways to the judgement and knowledge of Sir Joseph Banks in matters touching the agriculture and rural economy of the country and its European neighbours. His was an opinion often sought, too seldom explicitly acknowledged, too often deeply buried in the intricacies of a free-running correspondence on so many other themes—or lost in the generous exchange of his conversation on in-numerable occasions, social, casual, and scientific.

Banks himself left the nineteenth century a legacy of general know-ledge laboriously won and, in the main, shrewdly distilled from more than forty years' intimate contact with the problems of wool produc-tion and commercial use. He foreshadowed a pattern of scientific research and administration for national and public ends—and for the benefit of agriculture as much as any other branch of the country's economy. However, in his particular concern with the daily affairs of the King's sheep he combined his experience as a Lincolnshire land-owner and as a savant in natural history to evolve a form of practice in sheep breeding and the disposal of the fine-wool products of the Spanish Merino which would be followed in its essentials for almost a century. In this he translated and modified the traditional Spanish methods to meet contemporary methods in British agriculture and commerce. This compromise would in turn be inherited as the founda-tion of early colonial husbandry in Australia by men who were them-selves the associates of Banks or of those who worked with him or under his influence. This extended even to the daily details of flock manage-ment and the virtues and failings of the Spanish Merino during the process of selection and breeding. From the application of the very practical abilities of Sir Joseph Banks in the pursuit of his 'favorite hobby' would emerge the broad shape of the colonial and later of the Commonwealth wool trade as we know it now. This view, however, will not be clear without a glance at the legacy in its material form as the sheep itself and the fleece it once grew.

III

The animal first known to Banks and his contemporaries as the Spanish fine-woolled sheep, and only later as the Spanish Merino, was in general a small sheep—smaller than the English Southdown of the period—but extremely variable in size as in most other features. Rams at maturity appear to have ranged in live weight from less than 100 pounds to more than 150 pounds; the ewes from below 60 pounds to above 100 pounds.[13] The rams were characteristically horned, as they are now, but most *cabanas* in Spain produced an appreciable incidence of polled or hornless animals. The ewes were also typically polled but the incidence of horned ewes was sufficiently notable.[14] Every country during the eighteenth century that received Spanish fine-woolled sheep in any number could record some polled sheep among the stock received, especially if the numbers were large. That the character for hornlessness was widely dispersed among the flocks of the Peninsula is suggested by the early appearance of polled animals among those bred from small and miscellaneous lots gathered from diverse sources as in the case of the first stock collected by Banks to establish the Royal flock. With these there were several polled or very small-horned rams noted before 1791 among those bred from smuggled stock. Then among the Negretti stock which, after 1791, became the foundation of the Royal enterprise as it lasted for the next thirty years, polled or nearly hornless sheep appeared so soon and in such sufficient numbers that Banks was able from an early stage to indulge a preference for hornlessness and to select accordingly. As a result this character was quickly transferred to other flocks stemming from the Royal stock, of which that of George Tollet was an important example in following the lead set by Banks and in passing it on.

The sheep that were landed from the foetid holds or from the pens on the sea-washed decks of the small merchant ships docked in the Thames or elsewhere usually carried the insignia of the various old Spanish customs. The rams had their horns cut short leaving a stump of about six to eight inches after a crude, often sanguinary operation with a mallet and chisel. Both rams and ewes were fire-branded on the side of the face with the distinctive mark of the *cabana*. Their ears were variously slit, notched, or trimmed as an additional identification. In many cases there would be a large and distinctive pitch-brand in particular positions on the body as well. The tails of both sexes were always cut short—an operation performed with a razor on the young lamb—leaving about four to six inches from the butt.

Apart from the horns, which the British breeders mostly at first allowed to grow untouched to their full impressive length, the

outward appearance of the Spanish fine-woolled sheep was an affront to
the insular eye which by now was becoming accommodated rather to
well-rounded tubs of tallow. It was otherwise myopic about many
traditional oddities of its own fields and mountains. The body archi-
tecture of the Spanish sheep in its first years in Britain certainly left
much room for improvement even by the most modest standards of
any country interested more in fat meat than in wool or milk. Some
of this distressing insufficiency was transitory—the consequence inevitable among animals that had been born into a life of ceaseless
movement in a warm to hot climate grazing over pastures adequate for
subsistence in such conditions but certainly not for fattening or rapid
growth. Added to this there was the period of starvation often almost
to the point of death during the sea passage from Spain. These animal
wrecks—living certainly but often only just alive—that were landed in
the Pool of London or elsewhere too often were the only representatives
of this foreign breed seen by British eyes. Harrowing descriptions of
these freaks on their first entry tended to become the accepted image
among the agriculturists of the day, for it was many years before sufficient animals had been bred under suitable conditions away from the
seclusion of Windsor or Kew—in the privacy of the Royal parks and
gardens—for a more balanced impression to become established. The
eye of prejudice tended to be the master of the eye of faith, and the
latter often suffered from astigmatism. The impressed environmental
effects of a tough start in life were not, however, easily disentangled
from the inherent genetic pattern with which it had begun. There is
not much evidence to show that the Spaniards were concerned with
anything much beyond maintaining in their fine-woolled flocks the
general character of a fleece to which their foreign clients had become
accustomed and an ability to survive under the migratory pastoralism
to which on the whole they had allowed themselves to become en-
slaved. The Spanish breeder was not concerned with the mutton attributes of his fine-woolled flocks. If he was then his aim was quite
dissimilar to that of his British counterpart—as was the whole pattern
and rationale of his sheep husbandry. Fat meat was no more the choice
of the Spanish palate then than it is now. The genetic selection of the
Spanish Merino in Spain appears never to have given much weight to
the beauty of its body form up to the period of its exodus into the world
outside the Peninsula. However, in one degree or another sufficient
animals of reasonably seductive proportions and design to attract an
English eye could be found among the *cabanas* if a search with such
intentions were made. Lord Somerville evidently established this point
to his own and others' satisfaction. But even among the scarecrows of
the first few Spanish haphazardly selected animals composing the contra-

band and the diplomatic stock there were individuals giving hope of a better generation yet to come if British standards of selection could be applied to qualities of carcass. Arthur Young has recorded for us a glimpse of this when he visited the Royal flock in June 1793. He notes:

. . . I was pleased to find several of the sheep very tolerably *shut in the twist*, as a Sussex man expresses it; without the thin shank and shambling walk of legs that cross for want of fullness in the thigh to keep them asunder; common faults in many Spanish sheep. Another circumstance is the superiority of the sheep bred in England, in point of carcass, to those that came from Spain.[15]

On these points Young could speak with some authority for he had seen a little of the Spanish flocks—not the best or the most typical, however—during his travels through northern Spain in 1787. His impressions are well supplemented by those of two solid English breeders whose names are not otherwise unknown. A year previously John Boys of Betshanger in Kent and John Ellman of Glynde in Sussex had together toured the Midlands and the south-eastern counties in a characteristic 'rural ride' of the period. Boys had minuted the impressions of them both on 24 July 1792:

Arrive at Windsor;—call upon M^r [John] Robinson, his Majesty's steward of the little park, who very obligingly shews us His Majesty's Spanish flock, dairy &c.—The rams, many of them, much superior to M^r [Arthur] Young's Don; their fleeces very thick and fine; the size of the carcase rather less than the South Down, but by no means so well shaped, being very narrow in the chine, and thick about the throat with large horns. If these defects could be remedied, this kind of sheep would certainly be a very great acquisition to this country, provided that the superior quality of the wool could be retained; but *quere*—Will not such rich pastures as these sheep live upon soon change the quality of the wool?—The ewe flock seems much handsomer than the rams, having very good chines; fine necks; and being without horns; most of them very well made little ewes, and in fine order; their fleeces wonderfully thick and fine. . . .[16]

Boys and Ellman not long before had seen Arthur Young's much-hymned Spanish ram 'Don'. They had commented on his 'very pretty little carcase', but had demurred at his 'immense horns' and his 'throat like a southern hound', feeling that any improvement in English wool to be had from such an animal could only be at 'the expence of spoiling the carcase' and but little gained 'for the horns and coarser parts about the throat, will doubtless require great part of the food taken in at the mouth of the animal for their nourishment, which will be a great loss, those parts being merely offal'.[17] Out of the mouths of the experts

rolled such fallacies as these to influence the minds of those who tamely
followed with half-shut eyes. Snap judgements from the saddle have
led many a stockman astray in the bush. This has been the weakness of
so many 'rural rides'. The Spanish Merino could not so easily be
properly assessed. It was necessary to dismount and part the fleece—to
focus a little more closely on what lay within.

The exterior appearance of the fine-woolled sheep from Spain was a
gross departure from the norm as it was understood by the sheep
breeders of Europe as well as of Great Britain. Wherever it eventually
found a home outside Spain there was a long preliminary period of
confusion and misconception before the truth emerged and the breed
was accepted for what it was and used appropriately. Sometimes this
moment of enlightenment never came and the fine-woolled anomaly
among sheep failed to find a niche in the haunts of its pre-established
competitors. In a sense it was its own worst enemy—an ugly duckling
from the start. The by-products of these first facile misconceptions of
the breed are not the least part of the legacy bequeathed to us by His
Majesty's Spanish flock.

'These ill-looking animals, whose fine and costly wool forms a dirty
crust full of cracks round their bodies', as a contemporary observer
found them on their winter pastures in Estremadura about 1800[18]—
this was the prevailing first impact of the Spanish Merino at that early
period in its emancipation. This also was how Arthur Young saw his
own ram 'Don'—'the colour to the eye very dark, dirty, and even
blackish arising from the superior degree of closeness'. When to this
unlovely sight are added those 'thickenings' about the throat,

... The second property to be noted in this breed ... a tendency to throatiness, a pendulous skin under the throat, which is generally deemed a bad
quality in this country, and the very reverse in Spain, where it is much
esteemed, because it is supposed to denote a tendency both to wool and to a
heavy fleece ...[19]

it becomes finally clear how far the Spanish Merino deviated from the
ideal of a British breed of sheep then and always. The skin folds about
the neck and to varying degrees about the body elsewhere in the early
Spanish Merino do not seem on the whole ever to have appeared as
those exaggerated convolutions which emerged under a more specific
and powerful selection about a century later. But the skin folds were
there, damped in their expression no doubt by the limiting effect of the
arduous Spanish environment and husbandry and elsewhere outside
Spain by the inhibitions of European and British breeders who as a
whole positively disliked the character. Lord Somerville was definite
on this point:

. . . By drafting the most faulty ewes, and a due attention to the rams, the throatiness, and the sinking, or hollowness in the neck, which usually accompanies it, can be got rid of; so that, in a few years, it is probable few traces of them will be found.[20]

Scarcely less attractive to British eyes was 'the large tuft of wool which covers the head',[21] tending also to mark off the Spanish breed as a race apart. Yet Arthur Young was percipient on this as on other details as we have seen when he first viewed the King's Spanish flock on its home ground in June 1793:

It was with singular satisfaction I viewed his Majesty's flock of Spanish sheep at Windsor and Kew. They form a noble experiment, that will ascertain, to conviction, the quality of wool that may be produced in this climate. There are some among them woolled to an extraordinary degree; quite owl-headed in wool; with such a profusion in the forehead, and under the throat and so thickly covered in every part of the body, that the weight of Spanish fleeces will surprize no person that views them on the sheep's backs.[22]

But this solid profusion was not appreciated by the English shearers groaning a few days after this pronouncement as they struggled to remove the fleece, spending more than twenty-five minutes on each sheep according to the average calculated from Sir Joseph Banks's watch.[23] This feature, too, did not endear the Spanish sheep to British agriculturists. About fifteen sheep a day per man was the Spanish rate and this English performance was not much faster, if at all.[24]

Apart from the external appearance of blackness due to the concentrated waxy secretion impregnated with dirt from the surroundings, there were animals who were certainly black in every sense.[25] Although such sheep occurred in all the Spanish *cabanas* and were discarded or culled therefrom because their fleeces were unwanted in the export markets, their wool was still sold in Spain at almost the same price as the white. It was consumed in the local manufacture of habits for the priests and monks and for the clothing of the citizens themselves. There seems not to have been a very stringent attitude against the breeding of such stock and whole black flocks of fine-woolled sheep are still found on the Peninsula. Although there was a general preference for rams and ewes without any trace of colour about their fleeces, black, pied, and spotted animals were sights familiar enough at every lambing season throughout the *cabanas*. Among the small colony of Spanish sheep in the King's possession at Windsor and Kew as early as 1791 there had appeared three black lambs among about sixty-six born that year. They were shorn in 1792 and seem, in common with others that appeared in later years, to have been taken to Revesby Abbey where Sir Joseph 'had

the Whim of keeping a Flock of Black Merinos of pure blood'.[26]
Several were still there in 1809 when he confessed this to Benjamin
Thompson. He found that he could obtain white lambs from such a
black flock and these, when they appeared, he gave to Phillip Gell a
near neighbour of his at the Overton estate in Derbyshire.[27] On more
than one occasion it would seem that anything up to five per cent of all
lambs born in particular years may have been sufficiently black to have
been noted as such in the Royal flock. Apart from these more extreme
cases of inherited pigmentation there was always a considerable incidence of sheep of both sexes with black, red, or rusty spots about the
face, the head, and the legs. This feature was repeatedly noted by Banks
in his annual review of the rams—'black spot on one Ear', 'lips spotted
with black & red black', 'black spots over both Eyes', 'Spotty legs',
'Red spots on nose'—in such terms in some years these were typical
comments on almost every animal.[28]

One of the most revealing details related to this matter of coloured
sheep in the Royal flock is a note by Banks in June 1793, after the
arrival of the Negretti sheep and their first lambs to a mating in England.
Of thirty-four ram lambs born that spring he ordered twelve to be
'Gilt' or castrated as having 'coarse or colord wool' though he found
later that, as to the 'Spotty Lambs', this order was not obeyed.[29] He
stated in this connexion unequivocally that 'many Lambs that are red
as a Fox when dropd will become White in time'—an observation
innocent and plain enough but fraught with clues to a later generation
engrossed with the interplay of genes and the segregation of particular
fleece characters among Merinos forty bleating generations thence and
thirteen thousand miles away. It serves also to focus our attention more
closely on the fleece itself and the nature of the Spanish wool that could
so powerfully engage the attention of a King and a President of the
Royal Society.

IV

During their visit to Windsor on 24 July 1792, when they viewed
His Majesty's incipient Spanish flock, John Boys and John Ellman were
privileged to examine the clip of 1792 as it lay spread on the floor of a
room at the Lodge. This was where Sir Joseph had left it in three piles
to dry on 9 June after a wet shearing. They were among the very few
who ever saw His Majesty's wool at this early stage. It was a singularly
favourable and fortunate chance for these two inquiring laymen that
they should be able to see it also as Banks had separated it—first, the
'Santanders' or the original Negretti importation of 1791; second, the
original 'contraband' lot; and third, the 'Windsor-bred'—and just one
week before Sir Joseph himself returned to put it into packs. Here it

finally lay for more than two years before it was sent in the spring of 1795 with the clips of 1793 and 1794 to George Hawker of Dudbridge for manufacture. Their words on the occasion are few but they are enough to fix a first impression of the Spanish fleece as it appeared then —a novelty to the English eye especially when grown on an English pasture.

View his Majesty's growth of wool from the Spanish flock, which we examine with attention; find it much finer than any we ever saw, and longer than we had any idea of; a great quantity of oil in it, which makes the fleece very heavy, even to the weight seemingly of 6 lb. or 7 lb. each [fleece].[30]

This, let it be recalled, was largely wool from the first shearing of the old Negretti flock in England and the one which had evoked the comment of the shearers on the extreme greasiness of the fleeces 'which cannot be washd out by cold water'.[31] The following year in June 1793 Arthur Young saw substantially the same flock before it was shorn and added his own brief but pointed comment from which much also may be inferred:

... The length of fibre in some of the fleeces is very great for such fine wools; but I examined it particularly to see if such fleeces appeared coarse in proportion to their length, which I could not observe; however this is a point to be ascertained only by the manufacturer. . . .[32]

These are some of the earliest recorded impressions on which we can build any notion of how the Spanish fleece appeared to the British agriculturist or breeder and of the questions it raised with him. To Ellman, for example, as a breeder of Southdowns, it was much finer than he had ever supposed a fleece could be. There immediately occurred to him the query—'Will not such rich pastures as these sheep live upon soon change the quality of the wool?' To Arthur Young, as an agricultural journalist and part-time farmer, educated by his association with Banks in the fight against the Wool Bill a few years earlier, the length of the fibre seemed too long for the prevailing notions of what a fine wool should be. He saw this extra length as an evil arising from rich pasture and a humid climate and conceived that this defect would be easily remedied on short pasturage and shorter food.

In essence these men simply repeated questions and ideas that had endlessly before and that endlessly since have tended to bedevil the upward and outward progress of the Spanish fine-woolled sheep to its present place in the sheep and wool industries of the world. Herein implied are all the seemingly immortal questions rising Phoenix-like from the ashes of the previous generation of breeders and agriculturists. Seven such generations have passed and still the old arguments and fallacies are resurrected, moaning wraith-like about the conference halls and committee rooms or wherever it is supposed that scientific truth is now to be found. But what little do we know of the character of the Spanish Merino fleece which the eighteenth century, through the agency of His Majesty's Spanish flock under the supervision of Sir Joseph Banks, passed to the British breeders of the twentieth century?

The impressions are legion but the facts are few. There are not many succinct statements but this will serve as a short text for discussion and as fair a summary as may be found:

... The wool of the Merino sheep is uncommonly fine, and weighs upon an average about three pounds and a half per fleece. The best Merino fleeces have a dark brown tinge on their surface, almost amounting to black, which is formed by dust adhering to the greasy, yolky properties of its pile; and the contrast between it and the rich white colour within, as well as the rosy hue of the skin ... surprize at first sight[33]

First, let us consider the fleece weight. In spite of discouraging appearances there is a reasonably good agreement about this—at least as to the general figure which emerges from direct statements and from various types of crude estimation. Adequate data in terms of weights and numbers with other qualifying circumstances were not a distinctive product of the eighteenth or earlier centuries. However, the weight of fleece in its natural (i.e. unwashed) greasy state produced by the average Spanish adult fine-woolled ewe seems to have been close to 5 pounds, and for the ram about 8 pounds. As in the case of the live weight of these animals there was an ample range about such values. Ewes for example might well grow as much as 8 pounds or 9 pounds and rams 12 pounds to 16 pounds in individual cases,[34] but for whole flocks and larger populations the average figures tend to apply with great consistency. These, however, were not the figures of daily commerce, for the characteristic practice was that of washing the shorn fleece in Spain before the material entered the ordinary channels of trade for export. Elsewhere in Europe and in Great Britain the unshorn fleece was washed on the sheep's back just before shearing. Whereas there was some form of standard practice at the *lavaderos* in Spain there was little among the growers of wool in the matter of sheep washing. At the *lavaderos* hot water and something close to the final method of commercial scouring was applied. Among the growers outside Spain the method ranged from a quick crude dunking in the cold water of some near-by flowing stream to the more elaborate approach of a soapy lather in tubs of warm water. The former was more typical of the English system whereas the latter was to be found more often among the farms of Saxony and Sweden. It followed from these practices that the state of the fine-woolled fleece entering the textile industries of Western Europe came to vary greatly. Hence the unit by which the productivity of the sheep itself could be roughly measured—the quantity of fleece per head— might range from that of a nearly clean-scoured weight as in the figures of Spain and Saxony, through intermediate values for the brook-washed products of Britain or France, to the much more rare figures derived from the untouched fleece itself. If, as is convenient, we take the raw fleece weight of the eighteenth-century Spanish fine-woolled sheep to have been about 5 pounds then its brook-washed weight was approximately 3·5 pounds and its clean-scoured weight about 2·25 pounds. Depending on the circumstances in particular countries much variation about one or other of these three orders of value will be found. They are a conservative expression of the productivity of His Majesty's Spanish flock, while the figure of 1 kilogramme of clean wool per head (2·22 pounds) was the essential basis for many French calculations of the expected average output from ewes of the pure breed imported from Spain. It may be noted also that this figure is a very good approximation to the weight of fine wool in 1 yard of West Country English broadcloth. Under British conditions the loss on scouring was probably a little less than with the Spanish fine-wool fleece in the Spanish or French environments. The potential output of natural secretions from the skin to form the 'grease' or 'yolk' was no doubt similar, but the amount of circulating dust available to be bound into the extruded wax, which was certainly more copious than would be acceptable now, was much greater. Thus the yield of clean wool to be expected from a Spanish or some French-grown fleeces was as low as thirty to forty per cent. At Windsor and Kew the recovery was between forty-five and fifty per cent, probably nearer the higher figure.

The variation in the colour of the unwashed fleece of the early Spanish Merino as it appeared when the fleece was parted seems to have been considerable—as for every other feature of the breed. The 'rich white colour within' may have been more common among the British flocks of the Merino at a later period, but the consensus of evidence is that the typical trend in the colour was more to a golden or dingy yellow, certainly nearer cream than white. Verbal descriptions are perhaps unsafe for any firm generalization, but the few surviving specimens of the natural fleece of the period tend to support the notion that the yolk colour was far from white if due allowance is made for the discolouring effect of age.

The staple length of the Spanish fine-woolled fleece at the end of the eighteenth century appears to have been about $2\frac{1}{2}$ inches on the average, ranging mostly between 2 and 3 inches, for the twelve months' growth on the rough pastures of its native home. This was found to increase under the favourable grassland conditions of the Thames valley from Kew to Windsor and the staple length as a whole advanced nearer to an average of 3 inches. Short by modern standards for the best of fine wools this was enough, as we have seen, to cause Arthur Young some concern and it was a phenomenon calling for repeated explanation from Banks to his correspondents. Spanish wool was a clothing wool and was expected to remain suitably modest in its rate of growth accordingly. It did not, during the lifetime of His Majesty's Spanish flock, aspire to the role of a combing wool in itself, although Banks foresaw this possibility and experimented with suitable Merino × long-wool crosses to produce such a type. It was appreciated, of course, that the fine Spanish wool was able to grow continuously and that two or three years consecutive growth was enough to provide it with a combing length. The incentives to do this, however, were not sufficient. It remained for a later generation in the colonies to establish the virtues of a combing length in the descendants of the eighteenth-century Merino. This evolved only when the importance of an advance in fleece weight and clean yield came to transcend the earlier preoccupation with fineness of fibre and felting properties, attributes of significance to the fine broadcloth industry of the eighteenth and earlier centuries but less so to the emergent worsted manufactures which grew to dominate the markets of the nineteenth. Broadly, however, it was the fineness of the Spanish fleece that first fascinated and engaged the attention of all those concerned with the breed. The doubts and demands of the clothiers who manufactured the finest fabrics in the trade transmitted their effects to the breeders of the period in the same very direct fashion of today—through the price paid. The breeders responded as best they knew how. The situation, however, was invested with a dense fog of mystery and folk-lore.

At least two centuries of experience in commercial manufacture had established the Spanish Merino fleece as the doyen of textile fibres in Great Britain by 1788—at first with imported fine wool in the making of hat felts of high quality, then with the new Spanish medley cloth, and later the fine broadcloths and cassimeres of the West Country.[35] The intrinsic fineness of the best piles of the Leonese fleeces and their superiority to the best home-grown wools in Britain was no longer in doubt—nor was their importance to the evolving British wool trade. Speculation, rumour, and conjecture, however, grew and flourished about the perennial question: Was this fineness of fibre a particular product of the Spanish hinterland and its migratory flocks and impossible to reproduce elsewhere? How deeply entrenched was the notion that Spanish wool was the unique consequence of the migrations and the Peninsular climate is something we have already seen. What has not been so clear is just how fine and admirable this magic fibre really was.[36] We need not doubt that the best was very fine indeed though we may wonder how much was available. The remnants of finished cloth, of clothing, and the pattern-books do not readily help us here for these are the end-points after blending when the origins of the fibres have been lost. Few authentic specimens from identifiable fleeces still remain and where they do the appropriate measurements have not been made. Only tentative opinions can be formed even from the little direct evidence we have.

It seems probable that, although fine enough relative to its contemporaries in other breeds, the early Spanish Merino was on the average coarser than its nearest counterparts later in Saxony during the nineteenth and elsewhere as in Tasmania in the twentieth century. A sufficient number of specimens of the actual staple survive to confirm this impression, evident beyond much doubt to the discerning eye without the refined aid of micro-measurement. To establish a more exact evaluation, however, raises many difficult questions. It has been suggested that eighteenth-century Spanish fine wool was similar in fibre thickness to a modern Merino 60/64's quality to use the wool-trade term,[37] judging from actual surviving samples. It is always difficult at any time to know in such cases how representative the staples are, both of the fleece and the flock. If there was a bias, however, there seems to have been a human trend towards selecting the finest staples from the fleeces of the finest sheep, to keep and admire and to demonstrate the quality attained or attainable. If a modern eye has judged a specimen as 60/64's the truth may well be a little coarser rather than otherwise. Such a trend is certainly to be noticed in the selection of specimens on which attempts were made by Caleb Hillier Parry to obtain some objective measure of fibre thickness by optical means. Using an adaptation of the lamp-micrometer devised by William Herschel,[38] who suggested its use, Parry made the first published measurements of Spanish wool and contemporary English specimens available to us. If we can accept his calibration as accurate—and Parry was a careful man—then most of his values lie between those to be expected from qualities that would be assessed today as ranging from 60's to 70's. Allowing for his acknowledged selection of the specimens from the finer regions of the fleeces that he himself had sampled and the suspicion that those who sent him material tended to do the same we may well judge the bulk of the Spanish fine wool to have been rather coarser than this.

There is, however, one feature apart from the sheer fineness of the fibres that remains as an impression of the pristine Spanish staple. Whatever the beauties of the selected Raffinos or equivalent sorts may have been the Terceros seems to have contained what would be now regarded as an unacceptable amount of coarse and hairy wool. This defect, overtly described or otherwise implied, repeatedly appears in the early references to the Spanish Merino during its transition from the isolation of the Peninsula to the flocks of Western Europe and Great Britain. Of this there were many examples in the account of the first importations by Sir Joseph Banks and throughout the history of the early years of the Royal Merinos. There is ample evidence on the point from the first son of 'Monsieur Ram' from Montbard onwards. How often, for example, did Banks note such observations as these?—'his Pole grown hairy'; 'Kempy front very long wool'; 'kempy face'; 'hairy legs'; 'Spotted Legs & Cats hairs'; 'kemp on his skirt'.[39] It is only necessary to glance briefly at the staples kept from the first Spanish ram lamb to arrive from Spain itself under 'the Bilbao plan' on 28 June 1788 to appreciate the force of these comments. More significant still is the staple recording the fleece of Ram No. 15, one of the four original Negretti rams to arrive in 1791, mated to the flock for five consecutive years from 1792 to 1796, stamping his characters more widely on the flock than any other single ram in its history. His genes alone might almost be enough to account for the 'hairy Poles' and 'Kempy fronts' of so many of the rams dispersed through Britain in those early years of genetic exploration with the breed. In the same context, also, how significant are those coarse-coated lambs 'red as a Fox when dropd' which became white in time? Collectively taken all the evidence leads us to a very qualified vision of the beauties of the Spanish Merino fleece as it came under the hopeful gaze of British breeders at the end of the eighteenth century. As a 'Treasure of infinite value' it was more to be compared with a rough and uncut diamond than with a scintillating gem dazzling the eye of the beholder.

V

Here, then, is the essence of the material legacy passed down from His Majesty's Spanish flock to the sheep populations and their breeders in a modern Commonwealth—a small, unlovely, but incredibly resilient animal bearing a short, not over-fine but truly golden fleece on its moderately wrinkled pelt—and somewhere, locked in the nuclei of its germ cells, an imprinted message waiting to be read by those who were yet to release its true potential. If the animal itself was small in stature, modest in productivity, and imperfect in many of its qualities, the sample which the Royal flock and its off-shoots represented from among the five millions—more or less—of the parent Spanish population was on the face of it almost negligible. Among the European nations which over a century cozened, stole, or plundered Spanish fine-wool sheep from the *élite cabanas* of Spain itself, Britain acquired the least in number and, as a sample, the most limited in the range of qualities represented. Where France and Germany—even Denmark—had secured stock from not less than six of the principal Leonese *cabanas* to be counted in hundreds rather than in tens, Britain by contrast depended heavily for the first twenty years on a mere forty original breeding sheep from one only —the Negretti. Of the other sheep acquired, among the hundred and ninety-two received from 1788 to 1792 most were stolen goods snatched in the dark, as it were, from sources unknown or hard to verify. The few from France were, in a sense, second-hand material whose origins had been mixed or lost. A twist in the fortune of war belatedly added the unexpected accretions of the Paular and later of a large portion of the Negretti *cabana* in 1808–9. These were followed by indeterminate numbers to other ownerships of stock from the Escorial, Infantado, Portago, Montarco, and perhaps some few other *cabanas* as speculative adventures with the aftermath of the Peninsular Campaign. But by the time these had arrived in the crisis years of the Napoleonic Wars the main task of establishing a viable nucleus of Spanish Merinos in Great Britain from the Royal flock had almost been accomplished. This had been done with the tenuously small numbers of Negrettis and their miscellaneous predecessors patiently acquired by the back-room labours of the President of the Royal Society. From this nucleus had also been budded in 1804 the tiny colony of Negretti rams and ewes which had sailed with John Macarthur in the *Argo* to the settlement in New South Wales. Even with these few added the sum of undeniable Spanish Merino genes in that distant Colony during its first quarter-century was to be less probably than one-eighth of those which formed the foundation of the Royal flock itself during its first five years. Yet, in both cases, these were just enough to set in motion the evolution of new patterns of wool production and trade from which the present Commonwealth economy would so largely grow.

At the end of the seventeenth century Britain imported probably less than 0·5 million pound of Spanish fine wool for all purposes. This slowly grew during the eighteenth century until just before the American War of Independence it was in the vicinity of 2 million pounds weight. Soon after the Treaty of Versailles during the ten years of peace that intervened before the war began with Revolutionary France this figure leaped to the order of 4 million pounds. It further advanced in spite of the war to almost 8 million pounds until the Napoleonic Decrees exerted their economic effects and impeded further intakes from Spain. From the year 1800 may conveniently be dated the beginning of Britain's unwilling emancipation from bondage to Spanish fine wool as almost her sole foreign import of this commodity. Her demand for this ingredient among the textile fibres at her disposal had increased at least sixteenfold during the previous century. Banks had foreseen at least fifteen years earlier that what was so abundantly clear to the trade and the nation in 1800 was inevitable if England was to maintain her place in that international wool trade. His piece of 'business in a Philosophical way', with William Eden in 1787, had marked the effective beginning of his attempts on a national scale to forestall the crisis of supply. Now that the story is nearly told, it is worth recalling the few significant words he wrote:

I have sometimes turnd my Thoughts towards the subject of wool & lamenting that we in England [who] are so Famous for that article were under the necessity of drawing our supplies For the finer Manufactures from Spain I have attended much to the Flock managd in Burgundy at the Royal expence by M. Daubenton & have hitherto procurd all that has been publishd on the subject with any appearance of authenticity . . .[40]

After centuries of self-sufficiency in her wool supplies the economic situation of Britain had so far changed and was so rapidly evolving that, to percipient and thoughtful minds, some constructive action was needed. Against the background of the period it was a rational step to meet this by enhancing the volume of home-grown fine wool. No more effective and rapid means to this end existed than to secure the Spanish fine-woolled sheep itself. Sweden had been successful. The Electorate of Saxony was well forward to the same goal. France, the mercantile competitor of fearsome size, had been moving steadily and by the application of scientific thought towards a solution of the same problem. The pace of progress was increasing and the Spanish flock of His Britannic Majesty was founded as an enterprise to help redress a balance that had begun to swing against English woollen manufactures. In its immediate aims it never finally succeeded. Britain herself never closed a gap that her own technological skills was making wider and more obvious every year. Against the current of agricultural change on her own soil and against a great national inertia compounded of prejudice and ignorance the Spanish breed was established in Great Britain and survived there in authentic flocks for another century in a numerical strength at least as evident as half her own cherished native breeds today. When Banks and his King died and the Royal flock passed into other hands Britain was almost equally dependent on Spain and Saxony and only negligibly on her own or her colonial fine-wool supplies. For a quarter of a century thereafter Saxony would be her mainstay and Spain would have almost completely passed out of her trade in this material to a point less than the Spanish contribution at the end of the seventeenth century. But at this stage the legacy of the Spanish Merino itself and the heritage of ideas and experience which His Majesty's Spanish flock had accumulated in the thirty-two years of its Royal ownership—all these would have passed into the hands which in the end fulfilled the grand design, in principle though not in the detail which Sir Joseph Banks intended. Recast in a somewhat different mould the colonial flocks of Australasia had become in function the Spanish Merino of the southern hemisphere. By 1850 they outnumbered the remote parent stock on the Iberian Peninsula. In various ways their character had been changed—in subtle details rather than very dramatically in outward form. The process had been half a century in the making but, in the end, the British colonies had rendered the mother country free from its long continental dependence for the finer wool supplies and the ultimate goal of the President of the Royal Society, stated in the year of the Australian Colony's birth, had been attained. To both enterprises—the Colony and the colonial wool trade—no other single man had contributed more. It was a vision of which he had but a distant glimpse before he died, but he lived long enough to see the precepts and the example of the Royal flock carried forward and improved by another generation of breeders building on the foundations he had so firmly laid.

VI

Australia alone today depastures probably more than twenty times as many sheep called Merinos as ever Spain contained among her migratory flocks at the height of their development several centuries ago. In one form or another—for there are now many derived types— the modern world possesses in all at least twice this number or, very broadly, about two hundred million. Spain itself still retains Merino flocks near the traditional number—about five million—and these are perhaps not greatly different in size, in general appearance, and in gross productivity from the Spanish Merino known to Banks and his contemporaries. Very close they may be but identical they certainly are not. Though there is much in the husbandry of the travelling sheep of Spain and of those which, though fine woolled, do not travel and also in the general pastoral life of the Peninsula to remind us most forcibly of the eighteenth-century pattern much has changed. The flocks themselves, especially the *élite cabañas*, were shattered by the six years' cataclysm of the Peninsular War. Much of the breed's peculiar merit was sullied by unrecorded crossing with other stock in the confusion of war and its aftermath. Many flocks were affected in some degree. The Spanish Merino was bereft of many of its best genes judged according to the lights of the period. As a breed, however, it could not be deprived by this means alone of that inherent store of variation with which the selective breeder works. It appears slowly to have adapted itself to an age in which the attributes of a combing wool of moderately fine fibre have taken precedence over the old carding or clothing types more suited to the technology of what we may roughly term the 'broadcloth régime'. The Spanish Merino is still recognizably a Merino by any standards—though much more by eighteenth-century than by twentieth-century criteria. For all the vicissitudes of life in Spain during and since the Napoleonic Wars, however, it is there more than in any other place that we may still see some semblance of the stock from which the present Merino-type population of the world has sprung. What now of the men who grasped the opportunity which His Majesty's Spanish flock had prepared for British breeders with this ancient stock in the fashion we have seen and in whose footsteps have followed those who now produce nearly two-thirds of the apparel wool annually consumed today?

VII

As an augury for the future of the Spanish Merino in a very peaceful new world, one well-aimed pistol-shot fired at Parramatta, New South Wales, on Monday, 14 September 1801, at one o'clock in the afternoon may seem a curious portent. It would seem to be odder still in this imbroglio that the name of Sir Joseph Banks should have been involved in the correspondence which was one reason for the duel between Captain John Macarthur and Lieutenant-Colonel William Patterson, F.R.S. Yet it was this small affair of honour arising out of the strange society and its always unpredictable complications in the Colony at Port Jackson which brought Captain Macarthur under arrest to London just before Christmas 1802 to face a court martial at his own request. This unpromising overture, nevertheless, served to introduce into the near vicinity of the King's Spanish flock the man who would more effectively than any other carry the sheep and the essential inspiration from Windsor and Kew to a first unshakeable hold on the edge of the second-last continent. This is no place to explore all the intricate mysteries which during the year 1803 transformed Captain Macarthur the turbulent spirit of the New South Wales Corps into Mr. John Macarthur the industrious petitioner and the visionary of a new world of wool growing. It is enough here to record that this reincarnation occurred and that he became unquestionably the first colonial pupil to absorb and use all the accumulated experience which Banks, with John Maitland, Henry Lacocke, Richard Stanford, and many others had assembled from fifteen years' direct experience not only with the Spanish breed but with the problems of the fine-wool supply and the struggle to be free from Spain itself in this regard. If there were nothing else to revive what seems to have been his flagging and uncertain interest, how delighted John Macarthur must have been to receive at first hand soon after his arrival those stimulating few words of Henry Lacocke, formulated as a report more than a year before, with the other details concerning his own wool grown at Elizabeth Farm. In particular there was that pregnant sentence about the fleece of the ram lamb, the son of the ewe from Colonel Robert Jacob Gordon's flock at the Cape:

Nearly as good as the King's Spanish wool at Oatlands; quite free from hair and of an excellent quality; worth 5s. per pound; and could the Colony produce such kind of wools, it would be a great acquisition to our Manufactory in England.[41]

Were these in fact the magic words that finally sealed his interest and so largely determined the course of his life? Could this have been the moment when the future became clear? It was two and a half years since he had sent away those eight fleeces through Lieutenant-Governor King by H.M.S. *Buffalo* 'for the Inspection and Opinion of Sir Joseph Banks, President of the Royal Society' in July 1800. Scarcely two months later he had been firmly declaring his intention of leaving the Colony, disposing of his assets, and offering his farms and livestock to the Government for the comfortable sum of £4000.[42] Many things had happened since that particular moment, including the fortunate duel. He had, in fact, increased his farming and other livestock assets suddenly to become the largest owner of sheep in the Colony after the duel and shortly before his departure under arrest—but he certainly could not have seen that illuminating report by Henry Lacocke before December 1802. The *Communication respecting the Breed of Sheep in the Colony* had been dispatched on board H.M.S. *Glatton*, under the command of Captain James Colnett, only in late September 1802, three months before his arrival in London and long after his departure from Sydney. Macarthur could have had no inkling, therefore, until he reached London what Sir Joseph Banks or anyone else thought of his wool from Parramatta. It is clear, however, that he was not entirely unprepared for the future. He had come bearing other specimens of more recent growth from his flock and these evidently fully endorsed the favourable impression created by the fleeces that had come by the *Buffalo*.

From the beginning his relations with Henry Lacocke and John Maitland seem to have been close and confiding—with the former as an expert valuer of the fleece and now a practised exponent of the art of classing or selecting Spanish sheep; with the latter as one businessman to another. It was evidently the attentive ear of John Maitland which first heard the beguiling story from John Macarthur of how a bright future could open out for English capital invested in the growing of Spanish fine wool in New South Wales now that it had been shown so convincingly in the Elizabeth Farm fleeces valued by Henry Lacocke as almost the equal of the rams' wool from the Royal flock itself—with which, incidentally, few were better acquainted than Maitland himself, Sir Joseph Banks's oldest confidant in matters touching the properties and supplies of Spanish wool. As such John Maitland appears to have been the ready and frequent means of contact with Banks and also the willing channel through which an exchange of ideas ebbed and flowed concerning the New South Wales 'adventure'. At the same time it was a fortunate circumstance that during the period 1802–4 a Select Committee of the House of Commons was hearing evidence on the petitions of merchants and manufacturers from the County of York and the town of Halifax and from the Counties of Somerset, Wiltshire, and Gloucestershire on the troubles of the industry and the Wool Bill of 1803. The influx of these petitioners to London at intervals inevitably brought them into contact with John Maitland. John Macarthur soon had ample occasion to display his wares well calculated to 'excite the particular attention of the merchants and principal English manufacturers' anxious about future supplies now that war with the French had been resumed. By 26 July 1803 Macarthur's *Statement of the improvements and Progress of the Breed of Fine-woolled Sheep in New South Wales* had been prepared for Mr. Under-Secretary John Sullivan. On 21 September William Fawkener, Clerk to the Privy Council, submitted to Sir Joseph Banks as a member of that special body this document supported now by memorials from the woollen manufacturers of Yorkshire and elsewhere in the kingdom, seeking an opinion on the subject of the new Antipodean vision.[43]

The next day brought that carefully qualified reply fearing 'that the Captain has been too sanguine in his wishes to give a favorable representation of that Country' and its luxurious pastures 'fitted for the pasturage of Sheep'.[44] Banks expressed his personal doubts but continued as a responsible adviser:

. . . From what I have stated above you will easily perceive that I am not inclined to advise their Lordships to commend any Special encouragement to be given at present either by grants of land or the sending out of Shepherds, to a prospect which as yet is a mere theoretical Speculation, unsupported by any decisive evidence in its favor, & of the success of which I confess I entertain no manner of hope. It will in my opinion be time enough for government to interfere when the industry of individuals has grown & sent home a few tons at least of their wool, & thus ascertained the price at which it can be afforded at our market, & its comparative value on Manufacture when compared with real Spanish wool; & there is no doubt, that, if the

Trade proves nearly as profitable as Capt. McArthur expects it to be, we shall soon obtain some supply of wool & compleat information on the subject.

In the mean time, their Lordships may, if they see fitting examine such persons now in London as have been in N.S. Wales on the subject, & order Letters to be written to the governor, requiring from him the best information he shall be able to procure in the Colony, relative to the nature of the luxuriant pastures described by Capt. McArthur & their fitness in their natural state for the Pasturage of fine wooled sheep . . .[45]

These last vital words after the phrase 'a mere theoretical Speculation . . .' have not been given their due weight as evidence of Banks's considered opinion nor as the advice which effectively directed subsequent events—especially that critical sequence of happenings in England and in Australia during the next two years. Again we need not pursue the intricacies of this situation here—tempting though it is at this moment to shed some light on issues that have too long been clouded and confused. It will suffice if we note—and note with emphasis—that Banks was the focal point to and from whom passed all the significant exchanges with the hopeful merchant-adventurers who wished to develop the Colony as additional security against the economic threat of the French in the fine-wool supplies on the one hand, and on the other with a hard-pressed Government at one of the lowest ebbs in the tides of a long war. Closely involved at all levels in these negotiations was the small band of enthusiasts whom in various ways Banks had gathered into the orbit of His Majesty's Spanish flock and had inspired and in some cases virtually trained for the day when Great Britain would be able to break free from the Spanish enslavement in the provision of her most critical textile fibre.

Into this prepared situation John Macarthur had fortuitously entered in person for a reason that had more to do with fire-arms than fine wool. He was in some ways the same sort of adventuring opportunist as Andrew Cochrane-Johnstone. Both men might, as it were, have been born under the same star—was it perchance under Mars in the sign of Aries the Ram?—in 1767. Each in his own way was a powerful factor in dispersing the genes of the Spanish Merino into continents ripe to receive them. Each appeared at the scene of his most effective exploits in this mercantile chess-game as embattled knights by a characteristic side-ways leap into the dispute. But each did so for his own more personal reasons in a situation where a little overt patriotism judiciously invoked went a very long way. There the similarity ends for Macarthur displayed, from the moment of his commitment to the cause, a constructive persistence from which—whatever his private motives at the beginning—both the nation and his posterity were to profit almost beyond measure. On the great study table in Soho Square Banks

recorded his inner feelings about the matter as it stood in March 1804
—a characteristic but unpublicized footnote memorandum to himself
in the course of a correspondence whose publicized fragments have
tended to create quite other impressions:

a number of Respectable merchants of London and other parts appear much
inclind to associate under the advice of Capt Macarthur of his majesties
N.S. Wales Rangers and the opinion of Capt Waterhouse of H.M. navy
for the purpose of cultivating on a large scale The breed of Fine wool'd
Sheep in H.M. Colony of N. South Wales & it seems very probable that if
due encouragement is given to the undertaking that a Capital of £10,000
at the Least will be raisd by Subscription for this Patriotic Purpose
The Success of this Enterprise will manifestly be an advantage of no
inconsiderable importance to the manufacturing interest of this Kingdom
& Even in the Event of its Failure much benefit must arise to the infant
Colony by the money that will be Sent there for the purpose of trying the
Experiment . . .[46]

Step by step the situation moved forward along the paths sketched
out in the spider-scrawl of Sir Joseph Banks. By 4 May 1804 John
Macarthur (no longer a captain in 'his majesties N.S. Wales Rangers')
had completed his *Memorial . . . To the Right Honourable the Lords of the
Committee of His Majesty's most Honourable Privy Council appointed for the
Consideration of the Matters of Trade and Foreign Plantations.*[47] The Lords
of the Committee duly sat in the Council Chamber in Whitehall taking
evidence as they saw fitting from 'such persons now in London as
have been in N.S. Wales' and from others on this and related subjects,
according to the recommendation of Banks nine months before. On 14
July 1804 Sir Stephen Cottrell, Clerk to the Privy Council, sent the
considered opinion of their Lordships to Edward Cooke, Under-
Secretary of State for War and the Colonies, in terms which again
reflected the broad character of the original advice from Soho Square.
The opinion entertained 'no doubt that it is well deserving the attention
of His Majesty's Government to encourage the produce of fine wool
in the colony of New South Wales'; it 'observed that a conditional
grant of lands of a reasonable extent may be perhaps with safety granted
to Mr. McArthur for the pasturage of sheep only, or to other persons,
provided a power be reserved in such grant to resume the same at any
future period . . . '; on the other hand their Lordships conceived that,

. . . without more knowledge than they now possess of the nature and state
of the colony, and without full communication with the Governor of the
settlement, inconvenience might arise from recommending an unconditional
grant of lands to Mr. McArthur, or to a joint company, or to any individual,
as such grant might retard or prevent the other inhabitants of New South

Wales from turning their attention to the growth and improvement of fine wool, or perhaps in other respects counteract the improvement of the colony. . . .[48]

In what followed from this point there was a great deal more logic and a great deal less personal drama than historians have disclosed or have been prepared to admit—or indeed than they may have known. On 15 August 1804 at the first public sales of His Majesty's Spanish sheep, John Macarthur was a prominent figure, airing weighty opinions already on fine-woolled sheep in the Colony and buying boldly no less than ten out of the forty-four sheep offered for auction that day—seven young rams and three old ewes.[49] On 5 October Lord Camden applied to the Lord Commissioners of the Treasury on his behalf for their easement through the embargo legislation preventing their export:

Mr. McArthur, who is possessed of a very large flock of sheep in New South Wales, and whose attention during a long residence in that country has been particularly turned to the improvement of the fleeces of his sheep, in which he has made very great progress, is now about to return thither for the purpose of still further prosecuting this object, which has been deemed by His Majesty's Privy Council of so great importance to the manufactures of this Kingdom as to induce them to recommend that a tract of land should be granted to Mr. McArthur for the pastures of his flocks.

With this in view, Mr. McArthur has procured in this country, and proposes to take out with him, seven rams and two ewes of the Spanish race, and has applied to me for a dispensation for that purpose. I am therefore to desire that your Lordships will receive His Majesty's pleasure for issuing such directions as may be necessary thereupon.[50]

On 31 October Lord Camden also wrote the necessary directive to Governor King concerning the land grant saying, among other things,

. . . I am commanded by His Majesty to desire that you will have a proper grant of lands, fit for the pasture of sheep, conveyed to the said John McArthur Esq., in perpetuity, with the usual reserve of quit rent to the Crown, containing not less than five thousand acres.

Mr. McArthur has represented that the lands he wishes to be conveyed to him for this purpose are situated near Mount Taurus, as being peculiarly adapted for sheep; and I therefore am to express my wishes that he may be accomodated in this situation. . . .[51]

On 29 November 1804 John Macarthur sailed from Portsmouth in the whaler *Argo*, as part-owner with his new-found partners, Messrs. Hullett Brothers,[52] of whom one had been his dummy at the Royal auction in the purchase of two of the three old Spanish ewes—one recently dead. The voyage was a classic one in many ways, but for us at this moment it was notable for the seven young rams and the two surviving old ewes from the King's flock which it carried, of whom one ram and one ewe were to die on the passage. On 7 June 1805 after a voyage via Rio de Janiero the *Argo* was entered inwards at Sydney Harbour. Of the sheep one more ram died soon after landing so that in the end only five survived to reach Elizabeth Farm at Parramatta of those that had set out from Revesby Abbey in Lincolnshire for Kew with old John Moor the drover on 18 July scarcely eleven months before. Of the ewes from the breeding flock only one remained.

Then on 27 July 1805 in Sydney there appeared the General Order under the signature of Governor King declaring:

The Governor having received a Despatch from the Honourable Earl Camden, His Majesty's Principal Secretary of State for the Colonies, dated Oct. 30, 1804, Requiring the fullest Information being transmitted for the Lords Committee of the Privy Council for Trade and Plantations, Respecting the Increase and Improvement of the Breeds of Sheep with Growth and Improvement of Wool raised in this Territory; His Lordship having also in the strongest manner recommended a general attention being paid to that important national object . . .[53]

So the list of nine questions was sent on its way among 'the Officers and other Persons who have bred or possess Flocks of Sheep'—the first questionnaire designed to investigate the state of Australia's flocks, but by no means the last—ably drafted at His Excellency's request by John Macarthur and the Reverend Samuel Marsden in a most unusual collaboration. And, to make the instance more modern, in order that 'the Quality of the different Fleeces may be clearly ascertained' His Excellency 'requested M^r· [Edward] Wood, the Professional Gentleman who came in the *Argo* and two other Gentlemen experienced in that kind of Stock and Wool to inspect the Fleeces of the different Flocks'. With this official injunction the first field survey of Australian livestock was launched—and again the two experienced gentlemen seem to have been intended as John Macarthur and the Reverend Samuel Marsden. In the event this examination of 'the different fleeces on the sheep's backs' was 'very accurately done' by the practical parson and Edward Wood, who must be reckoned the first sheep classer in Australia pursuing the tradition originally established in 1796 by old Henry Lacocke under the tutelage of Sir Joseph Banks himself. Thus by 10 October His Excellency the Governor was able to send His Lordship the Minister of State for War and the Colonies[54] a full and particular report fulfilling the conditions of inquiry which Banks had set out in his letter to William Fawkener just over two years before.[55]

Then, two days later, John Macarthur returned 'from an excursion into the woods'. Here he had been for five days seeking an alternative area of five thousand acres to those he had nominated in London and to which Governor King had demurred as being in the centre of his cherished 'Cow Pastures' where grazed those wild cattle which had been so much the concern of 'Government' since the day in 1795 when their existence had been reported to Governor John Hunter.[56] Macarthur reported:

> . . . I made choice at first of a tract in the vicinity of Prospect Hill, but I afterwards discovered it to be within the boundary of the Orphan Ground. Except that, I have not seen any unappropriated range of 5,000 acres that contains 500 acres of dry pasture on which I would think it safe to feed sheep. . . .[57]

Where now were those 'Tracts of Land adapted for Pasture' which in his *Memorial* . . . to the Lords of the Committee he had declared to be 'so boundless that no assignable limitation can be set to the number of fine woolled Sheep which may be raised in that Country'?[58] There was clearly not so much in sight when it came to the point as he had led the Committee to expect—or his fellow-speculators of the 'Company to Encourage the Increase of Fine woolled sheep in New South Wales'. The informed caution of Banks, it seemed, was reasonable on this matter of 'luxuriant pastures of the natural growth of [New] South Wales at all fitted for the pasturage of Sheep'. It was a matter on which he did well in counselling the Government to seek further before succumbing to the blandishments of a young stranger noted perhaps more for the steadiness of his firing arm than for his judgement of grazing land at that stage in his career. Banks was right in defining 'the Natural grass of the Country' if not wholly so as 'tall, coarse, reedy' at least as 'very different from the short sweet mountain grass of Europe, upon which sheep thrive to the best advantage'.[59] His fear 'that the Captain has been too sanguine in his wishes to give a favorable representation of that Country' was a judicious caution from one who was not so ignorant of botany and of grazing pastures as to be easily beguiled by the first enthusiast to paint a rosy picture. Even on the 'Cow Pastures', the choicest natural grazing evidently then known in the County of Cumberland, Time has since indeed proved that Banks was not far wrong when he suggested:

> . . . that it will be found, on enquiry, that Sheep do not prosper well there, unless on Lands that have been cleared & prepared for their reception with some labor & expence . . .

Yet on 13 October 1805 Governor King finally conceded the argument to Macarthur and ordered the convict Assistant-Surveyor, James Meehan[60] 'to proceed to the hut at the Nepean and trace the course of that river to the southward as far as or a little beyond Mount Taurus'. In that vicinity he was to measure, with due regard to other circumstances, the five thousand acres for John Macarthur as Governor King had been directed by Lord Camden from London.

From this day then it might be said that the Spanish sheep from His Majesty's flock in principle entered their own particular inheritance. For the remote descendants of those five rams and one old ewe—'the *Argo* lot' as they were known to Macarthur's sons William and James in whose hands they fulfilled their promise—may still be seen among the 'Cow Pastures' near Mount Taurus, somewhat changed as are the original Spanish Merinos from their forebears but still very recognizably the distant scions of His Majesty's Spanish flock in the image they create to the mind's eye from the direct and indirect evidence at our disposal.

In the event, then, Captain John Macarthur found the pastures suitable for extensive sheep grazing when he came to seek them much more limited than he doubtless in good faith had supposed. But even before he returned to make this sobering discovery, one of the three men who was to release the Colony from this very real confinement was himself already groping towards the same goal by his interest in the sheep of the King's flock. It was in fact the account of the very sale at which John Macarthur had bought his sheep that caught the eye of the Sussex farmer Gregory Blaxland, who forthwith wrote to Banks:

I take the liberty of writing to request you to procure me one or two Spanish Ram Lambs & as many old Ewes. observing an Account of the sale of some of them in the papers first raised my curiosity to see them. They appear to me the most profitable stock I ever saw if the wool fetches as much per pound as the Shepherd informed me it did. if I can procure some before next sale by using the rams this autumn I hope soon to get a flock of three hundred exactly like the original breed by first crossing them with the Dorset sheep which they greatly resemble. I am informd they first went to Spain from that county. I intend them for my Farm in Sussex.[61]

This was a gesture beyond Banks's power to make at that moment and regretfully he so informed Blaxland. He hoped, however, that Blaxland would be able to suit himself at the next sale and would 'Execute without further delay the Extensive Plan you have laid out for the improvement of the Dorsetshire breed'.[62] But for Gregory Blaxland at some time within the next six months his vision of the future changed from 'Extensive Plans' to reform the Dorsetshire breed in Sussex to one of emigration to New South Wales in the wake of John Macarthur— with Spanish sheep of his own, in spite of his disappointment over stock from the King's stud. The news of Macarthur's success in finding a way through the sheep embargo by a Treasury order for their export had not been slow in making its point. A new world of possibilities was opening to those with the imagination, the courage, and the drive to grasp them. John Blaxland was prepared to fit out his younger brother and later to join him on a venture to the new Colony from which neither would return. Eight years later Gregory would lead the way across the mountain barrier that for a generation had cramped and encompassed the settlement on the unprofitable shales, sandstone, and podsolized clays of the narrow coastal strip where in a fickle climate it struggled to exist. Across the Blue Mountains lay the future of the Spanish Merino in numbers and in a form beyond the dreams of Banks or Macarthur and of the man who, at a single stroke, was to open that future.[63] On 24 April 1805 Gregory Blaxland was so far committed that he was seeking a further dispensation from Edward Cooke, Under-Secretary of State for War and the Colonies, for additional Spanish sheep:

I shall esteem it an additional favour if you will allow me to take out twelve Spanish sheep instead of four. By Lord Somerville's assistance all difficulty, I am in hopes, will be removed respecting their being exported. He is fearful that if I take out so few that I shall not succeed in getting the breed out safe; and I am willing to leave sufficient things behind which I intended to take with me to make room for the provision of water for the extra sheep in the fifteen tons allowed me. The sheep will do on deck, and I find on enquiry, as the ship is not began, that room can be made for them.[64]

So, under the encouragement and advice of Sir Joseph Banks, the Blaxland brothers built two ships in association with the firm of Hullett Brothers—first the *William Pitt* and then *The Brothers*—and within two years were both established with their farming assets close to the western limits of the Colony if not in the shadow of the mountains at least in their rain shadow at Penrith and at Luddenham. Whether Gregory, who sailed first in the *William Pitt* on 1 September 1805, carried with him four or twelve or any Spanish sheep at all remains to be shown. If none reached Sydney under his care it was not for lack of an intention or a will to do so. This is another small mystery which Time has yet to solve for us.

VIII

It is the beginning of a new task to pursue from this point on all the ramifications of thought and action derived from the small nucleus of the King's sheep by the Thames. In the field of animal breeding this has almost the same forbidding aspect as that of attempting to trace the influence of the partnership between the King and Banks radiating out to the limits of plant geography from the Exotic Garden at Kew and the *hortus siccus* of Soho Square. Created modestly in the Royal seclusion of the Little Park at Windsor Castle, emerging a little nearer to the public gaze at Marsh Gate Farm, the Old Deer Park, and the gardens of Richmond and Kew, the Spanish flock became an effective focal centre of public interest only after the printed report of 1800 appeared in *The Philosophical Magazine* as 'A Project for Extending the Breed of Fine Wooled Spanish Sheep, now in the possession of his Majesty . . .'. From this date there was less conjecture and a great deal more profitable curiosity about the purpose and function of the Spanish flock in the quickening embryo of the new world of industry which was reshaping the towns and the fields of Great Britain. The Spanish flock of His Majesty King George III of England was, as it were, the foetal heart in the differentiating structure of the Commonwealth sheep and wool industries and 1800 was the year when it first began to beat. Responsive to the rhythm and the activating flow of nutrient ideas pulsating steadily from Windsor and Soho, Kew and Spring Grove, feeble but continuous movement in the several parts of the complex body were soon to be seen, reflex rather than conscious but indubitably the signs of a new life.

The original small flock of the old Negrettis itself lived on to become a respectable centenarian among the Merino studs of the Commonwealth in the hands of Messrs. T. B. Sturgeon and Sons somewhat nearer the mouth of the Thames at South Ockenden Hall near Grays in Essex. As such it continued until 1895 to transmit its genes to distant parts for the Sturgeon sheep were much sought in their day until the infant studs of the Australian mainland and of Tasmania grew to maturity and cut the apron-strings.

The first colonial stud of any consequence under the Macarthurs of Camden Park drew a small infusion of Spanish Merino blood from the King's flock to compound with a dose of similar size, in which the disproportions of the rams and ewes were complementary, from the Spanish or mainly Spanish stock of the tiny flock of Colonel Robert Jacob Gordon in South Africa at Cape Town. More perhaps than for its foundation sheep the Camden flock perhaps drew on the circle of men who had grown about the King's flock for its knowledge of sheep husbandry and of the handling of a fine-wool clip in the new century of the wool trade.

Scarcely less significant to the future of the wool trade was the English flock of Thomas Henty of West Tarring in Sussex derived largely if not entirely from the King's sheep in one way or another. When these were first obtained cannot be said with finality. There is no record of Henty buying direct from the Royal flock before the large public sale of 1809 when he bought not an old Negretti but one of the new Paular rams, a full-mouthed animal for £36 10s.[65] In the long and meticulous records of Sir Joseph Banks up to 1811 no other sheep appears against his name. However, his long and close association with the 3rd Earl of Egremont who received two rams (Nos. 38 and 75) selected by the King himself in 1794[66] makes it likely that Henty derived this breed from Petworth as he did so many other blood stock of various kinds. The Earl of Egremont received in 1797 one of the largest and most important gifts of sheep from the King—two rams (No. 15, the most important of the original Negretti sires, and No. 83) and no less than twenty ewes. From such a beginning the Earl soon had stock to disperse and, though it has yet to be proved, there is none more likely than Thomas Henty to have profited by this store of Spanish Merino sheep of undoubted authenticity. From thence we may for the present assume came many of the forebears of the sheep dispersed from the farm at West Tarring until its last remnants were carried to Tasmania to be finally the pioneers of the true Merinos in Victoria at Portland Bay at the end of 1834. But before this from 1826 on there had been a succession of exports to New South Wales and Tasmania to say nothing of the Colony at the Swan River in the west during 1829.

From the Paular stock which Henty bought at the sale of 1809 came also those five sheep which the Reverend Samuel Marsden received from the King in the same year on which he was duly congratulated:

. . . I rejoice heartily in the success of your Merinos: the gift was worthy of the royal donor, and cannot fail to be of nearly as much value to the colony as to your self. What would I not have given to have been with you at their very unexpected arrival at Spithead, after all the plans we had thought of to accomplish so important a point. I have written to Sir Joseph Banks upon this subject, and shall have a long conversation with him up[on] it when next I see him. By cross breeds from these there can be no doubt that your wool, already so fine, will rival if not surpass the best wools in the world; and the soil and climate are so propitious.[67]

Of a similar character was the inception of the flock of Charles Callis Western—'Squire' Western the bachelor of Felix Hall and later the 1st Baron Western—another gift of the King's on the recommendation of Banks from the Paular *cabana*.[68] This was founded on a breeding flock of thirty ewes selected at Portsmouth by the ships' sides in 1808 and with which Western undertook, at the acknowledged stimulus of Sir Joseph Banks, to improve the mutton qualities of the Spanish breed.[69] Through this stock, again, many head during the nineteenth-century rise of the colonial flocks contributed their mite to that source of imported wool for British machines.

It is abundantly clear that by the time the King's mind had finally receded from the affairs of his Spanish flock the original purpose had been served. After 1810 not only was the breed firmly established in British hands and numerically invulnerable as a solid base for the future, but the essential ideas from which it had been born were now also in safe-keeping with those men who were destined to mould the final shape both of the sheep and the trade we know today. From the beginning of the Regency it is more profitable to trace the history of the Anglo-Merino and to analyse the meaning of this confusing term through the activities of that small body of men who on 4 March 1811 in London at the Freemason's Tavern banded themselves under the authoritative leadership of Sir Joseph Banks as the Merino Society—in which one in five among its members had derived his stock directly from the Royal Merinos of His Majesty King George III. By this means was the fine-wool sheep of old Spain husbanded across that interval of years at the cross-roads of modern commerce when Western Europe ceased to be self-sufficient in its wool supplies and until, as for the last century, it became the vast consumer on which depends so largely the economy of the southern hemisphere today. In this cosmic transition His Majesty's Spanish flock was a small but vital element.

APPENDIX

TABLE I

ANALYSIS OF THE SHEEP IMPORTATIONS ON HIS MAJESTY'S ACCOUNT, 1788–92

Date	Number Rams	Ewes	Ship	Captain	Remarks
1788					
—	5	39	*Union* packet	Captain Sutton	*France* via Calais. Per Broussonet and Daubenton
4 Mar.	1	2	*Betsy*	Captain Michael Firth	*Spain* via Lisbon. Per Thomas March and Co.
28 June	1	—	—	—	*Spain* via Bilbao. Per Evan Nepean.
	7+	41 = 48			
1789					
26 June	1	3	*Hope*	Captain Hopkins	*Spain* via Oporto. Per Evan Nepean.
26 Nov.	1	2	—	—	*Spain* via Bilbao. Per Evan Nepean.
30 Dec.	1	2	—	—	*Spain* via Bilbao. Per Evan Nepean.
	3+	7 = 10			
1790					
6 May	—	3	*Juno*	Captain George Kennedy	*Spain* via Lisbon, Per Thomas March and Co. 5 ewes and 3 lambs embarked; 3 ewes only arrived.
[24] July	8	16	*Betsy*	Captain Michael Firth	*Spain* via Lisbon. Per Thomas March and Co. 30 sheep embarked; 6 ewes died at sea.
	8+	19 = 27			

TABLE I—*continued*

ANALYSIS OF THE SHEEP IMPORTATIONS ON HIS MAJESTY'S ACCOUNT, 1788–92—*continued*

Date	Number Rams	Ewes	Ship	Captain	Remarks
1791					
— Feb.	—	6	*Speedy*	Captain William Messer	*Spain* via Lisbon. Per Thomas March and Co.
21 Mar.	1	13	*Jemima*	Captain Anderson	*Spain* via Lisbon. Per Thomas March and Co. 1 ram and 19 ewes embarked; 6 ewes died at sea.
14 Oct.	4	36	*King George*	Captain John Burnell	*Spain* via Santander. Per Lord Auckland and Anthony Merry
	5+	55= 60			
1792					
— Aug.	—	26	*Jemima*	Captain Anderson	*Spain* via Lisbon. Per Thomas March and Co.
— Oct.	4	17	*Jemima*	Captain Anderson	*Spain* via Lisbon. Per Thomas March and Co. via London to Hanover.★
	4+	43= 47			
TOTAL	27+	165=192			

★ Excluded from Table II; not imported to England permanently.

TABLE II

SUMMARY OF THE SHEEP IMPORTATIONS ON HIS MAJESTY'S ACCOUNT, 1788–92

Origin	Breed and Number				Agency
	Real Spanish		*Métis Spanish*		
	Rams	Ewes	Rams	Ewes	
1. *'Daubenton's Flock'*					
Montbard	3	12	—	10	L.-J.-M. Daubenton
Tour d'Aigue, Provence	—	—	2	12	and
École Royale Vétérinaire,					P.-M.-A. Broussonet
Paris	—	—	—	5	
	—	—	—	—	
	3	12	2	27	
	—	—	—	—	
2. *'The Bilbao Plan'*					
Bilbao	3	4	—	—	Evan Nepean, Henry
Oporto	1	3	—	—	Hinckley, William Warre
	—	—	—	—	
	4	7	—	—	
	—	—	—	—	
3. *'The Lisbon plan'*					
Lisbon	10	66	—	—	Thomas March and Co.
	—	—	—	—	
	10	66	—	—	
	—	—	—	—	
4. *'Lord Auckland's undertaking'*					
Santander	4	36	—	—	William Eden 1st Lord
	—	—	—	—	Auckland, Anthony
	4	36	—	—	Merry
	—	—	—	—	
	21	121	2	27	

142   29

171

TABLE III

ANALYSIS OF THE COMPOSITION OF HIS MAJESTY'S SPANISH FLOCK, 1788–1811

| | Males | | | | Females | | | | Approx. No. of Lambs Born per cent Ewes Mated |
| | Rams | | Wethers | | Ewes | | | | |
YEAR	Adult and Tegs	Lambs	Adult and Tegs	Lambs	Adult	Tegs	Lambs	TOTAL	
1788	4	—	—	—	14	—	—	18	—
1789	7	2	—	—	12	—	3	24	—
1790	10	—	—	—	38	—	4	52	—
1791	12	11	—	20	88	—	25	156	66
1792	19	28	5	—	87	—	24	163	60
1793	36	34	5	11	95	18	42	241	92
1794	34	30	16	18	107	40	48	293	90
1795	44	26	27	20	102	40	48	307	92
1796	18	20	47	14	90	35	33	257	75
1797	22	16	47	—	67	23	22	197	57
1798	15	17	25	—	52	6	22	137	75
1799	16	22	23	—	57	21	19	158	72
1800	16	20	23	—	76	21	25	181	59
1801	15	35	11	—	73	21	25	180	82
1802	19	26	—	—	75	25	30	175	75
1803	15	33	—	—	80	25	26	179	74
1804	36	33	—	—	89	22	47	227	90
1805	42	40	20	—	88	42	41	273	92
1806	45	48	38	—	95	37	47	310	100
1807	29	45	19	—	107	43	43	286	82
1808	24	49	29	—	116	38	53	309	88
1809	23	45	4	—	122	51	55	300	78
1810	25	[54]	6	—	128	53	[58]	321	88
1811	25	[44]	6	—	122	53	[48]	298	76

TABLE IV

THE GENERAL STATISTICS FOR
HIS MAJESTY'S SPANISH FLOCK, 1792–1811

	Rams	Ewes	Total
Born into the flock	658	672	1330
Disposal by gift or sale	348	487	835
Loss by natural mortality	310	185	495

Average Flock Composition
(at or about shearing in June)

Rams—adults and tegs	26
Rams—lambs	28
Ewes—breeding	80
Ewes—tegs	32
Ewes—lambs	34
Total	200
Ewes put to the ram	80
Lambs reared to shearing time	64
Annual disposal by sale or gift	40
Annual loss by natural mortality	24
Annual total loss to the flock	64

TABLE V

ANALYSIS OF THE DISPERSAL OF SHEEP FROM HIS MAJESTY'S SPANISH FLOCK, 1791–1810

YEAR	Sheep Presented by His Majesty		Sheep Sold by Private Contract		Sheep Sold by Public Auction		Total Number of Sheep Disposals per annum		
	Rams	Ewes	Rams	Ewes	Rams	Ewes	Rams	Ewes	Both Sexes
1791	8	—	—	—	—	—	8	—	8
1792	12	—	—	—	—	—	12	—	12
1793	19	—	—	—	—	—	19	—	19
1794	18	—	—	—	—	—	18	—	18
1795	23	61	—	—	—	—	23	61	84
1796	11	46	—	—	—	—	11	46	57
1797	7	40	—	—	—	—	7	40	47
1798	3	7	—	—	—	—	3	7	10
1799	4	—	—	—	—	—	4	—	4
1800	—	—	8	10	—	—	8	10	18
1801	—	—	11	17	—	—	11	17	28
1802	—	—	6	15	—	—	6	15	21
1803	—	—	13	3	—	—	13	3	16
1804	—	—	—	—	30	14	30	14	44
1805	—	—	—	6	17	21	17	27	44
1806	—	—	1	2	31	20	32	22	54
1807	—	—	—	—	16	26	16	26	42
1808	—	—	—	—	17	25	17	25	42
1809	—	—	18	43	40	60	58	103	161
1810	—	—	2	1	33	70	35	71	106
1811	—	—	—	—	—	—	—	—	—
TOTAL	105	154	59	97	184	236	348	487	835

TABLE VI

SUMMARY OF THE DISPERSAL OF SHEEP FROM HIS MAJESTY'S SPANISH FLOCK, 1788–1810

Mode of Distribution	Number of Recipients (Individuals and Societies)	Number of Sheep Distributed		
		Rams	Ewes	Total
1791–1799 Royal Gifts	43	105	154	259
1800–1803 Private Contract	36	38	45	83
1804–1810 Public Auction	118	184	236	420
1805–1810 Private Contract	24	21	52	73
1791–1810 Grand Total	221	348	487	835

TABLE VII

SUMMARY OF THE RETURNS FROM THE SHEEP SOLD BY PUBLIC AUCTION FROM HIS MAJESTY'S SPANISH FLOCK, 1804–10

	Number Sold		Average Price Per Head		Total Sum
YEAR	Rams	Ewes	Rams	Ewes	Rams and Ewes
			£ s. d.	£ s. d.	£ s. d.
1804	30	14	19 4 0	8 15 6	697 7 6
1805	17	21	34 14 2	24 3 0	1148 14 0
1806	31	20	17 4 0	12 7 0	470 18 6
1807	16	26	24 15 6	20 3 1	920 6 0
1808	17	25	33 10 2	24 17 8	1191 15 0
1809	40	60	48 18 7	34 0 4	3998 8 0
1810	33	70	65 6 8	35 10 10	4714 10 0
TOTAL	184	236	— — —	— — —	13141 19 0

TABLE VIII

SUMMARY OF THE SHEEP BOUGHT BY JOHN MACARTHUR AT THE FIRST PUBLIC AUCTION SALE OF HIS MAJESTY'S SPANISH FLOCK, 1804

Lot	Sex	Age	Price	Fleece Weights—lb.		
			£ s. d.	Greasy†	Washed	Clean†
1.	Ram	Shearling	6 15 0	4·72	3·25	2·26
6.	Ram	Shearling	11 0 0	—	—	—
11.	Ram	Shearling	15 15 0	5·45	3·75	2·62
13.	Ram	Shearling	16 16 0	4·72	3·25	2·26
15.	Ram	Shearling	23 2 0	6·89	4·75	3·30
22.	Ram	Shearling	22 1 0	6·15	4·25	2·96
30.	Ram	4-toothed	28 7 0	9·42	6·50	4·52
33.	Ewe	Aged	8 8 0*	—	—	—
41.	Ewe	Aged	11 11 0	—	—	—
45.	Ewe	Aged	6 6 0*	—	—	—
		TOTAL SUM	£150 1 0			

* Bought by Hullett as dummy for John Macarthur.
† Estimated from washed weights by an arbitrary figure derived from the values found with the Royal flock.

TABLE IX

ANALYSIS OF THE WOOL PRODUCTION OF THE BREEDING EWES OF HIS MAJESTY'S SPANISH FLOCK, 1798–1804

YEAR	Number Shorn	Clip Weight Washed lb.	Clip Weight Scoured lb.	Clip Yield per cent	Fleece Weight Clean lb.	Fleece Weight Washed lb.	Fleece Weight Greasy lb.	Fleece Yield per cent
1798	89	295	203	69·0	2·28	3·32	4·98	45·8
1799	109	346	254	73·5	2·32	3·17	4·75	48·8
1800	100	398	294	73·8	2·94	3·98	5·97	48·3
1801	108	397	285	72·0	2·64	3·68	5·53	47·8
1802	96	352	256	72·7	2·67	3·67	5·51	47·7
1803	92	305	223	73·0	2·42	3·32	4·98	48·6
1804	105	418	303	72·3	2·88	3·98	5·97	48·2

TABLE X

ANALYSIS OF THE WOOL CLIP VALUE OF THE BREEDING EWES OF HIS MAJESTY'S SPANISH FLOCK, 1798–1804

YEAR	Number Shorn	Value of Clip £ s. d.	Value per Fleece £ s. d.	Value per pound Clean d.	Value per pound Washed d.	Value per pound Greasy d.
1798	89	47 8 9	0 10 7	56·7	38·3	25·5
1799	109	63 14 6	0 10 8	55·2	40·4	26·9
1800	100	65 11 0	0 13 1	53·4	39·5	26·3
1801	108	72 1 9	0 13 4	63·0	43·5	29·0
1802	96	69 8 0	0 14 6	65·2	47·5	31·6
1803	92	72 15 3	0 15 10	78·4	57·3	38·2
1804	105	94 1 0	0 17 10	74·5	53·8	35·8

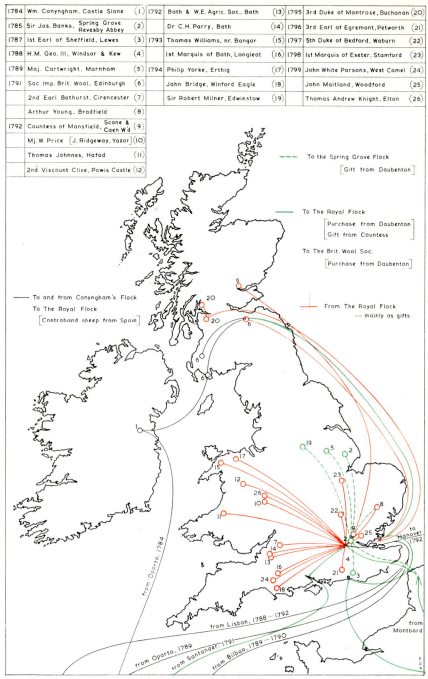

1784	Wm. Conyngham, Castle Slane	(1)	1792	Bath & W.E. Agric. Soc., Bath	(13)	1795	3rd Duke of Montrose, Buchanan	(20)
1785	Sir Jos. Banks, Spring Grove Revesby Abbey	(2)		Dr C.H. Parry, Bath	(14)	1796	3rd Earl of Egremont, Petworth	(21)
1787	1st Earl of Sheffield, Lewes	(3)	1793	Thomas Williams, nr. Bangor	(15)	1797	5th Duke of Bedford, Woburn	(22)
1788	H.M. Geo. III, Windsor & Kew	(4)		1st Marquis of Bath, Longleat	(16)	1798	1st Marquis of Exeter, Stamford	(23)
1789	Maj. Cartwright, Marnham	(5)	1794	Philip Yorke, Erthig	(17)	1799	John White Parsons, West Camel	(24)
1791	Soc. Imp. Brit. Wool, Edinburgh	(6)		John Bridge, Winford Eagle	(18)		John Maitland, Woodford	(25)
	2nd Earl Bathurst, Cirencester	(7)		Sir Robert Milner, Edwinstow	(19)		Thomas Andrew Knight, Elton	(26)
	Arthur Young, Bradfield	(8)						
1792	Countess of Mansfield, Scone & Caen W'd	(9)						
	Mj. W. Price [J. Ridgeway, Yazor]	(10)						
	Thomas Johnnes, Hafod	(11)						
	2nd Viscount Clive, Powis Castle	(12)						

Figure 1   The entry into Great Britain of Spanish Merinos and their dispersal from 1788 to 1799.

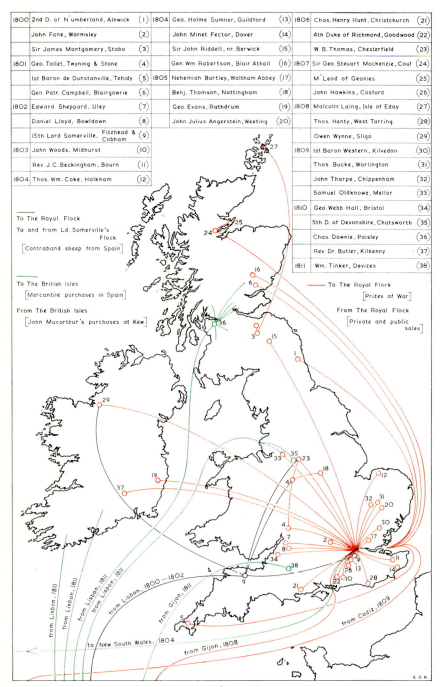

1800	2nd D. of N'umberland, Alnwick	(1)	1804	Geo. Holme Sumner, Guildford	(13)	1806	Chas. Henry Hunt, Christchurch	(21)
	John Fane, Wormsley	(2)		John Minet Fector, Dover	(14)		4th Duke of Richmond, Goodwood	(22)
	Sir James Montgomery, Stobo	(3)		Sir John Riddell, nr. Berwick	(15)		W. B. Thomas, Chesterfield	(23)
1801	Geo. Tollet, Twyning & Stone	(4)		Gen. Wm. Robertson, Blair Atholl	(16)	1807	Sir Geo. Steuart Mackenzie, Coul	(24)
	1st Baron de Dunstanville, Tehidy	(5)	1805	Nehemiah Bartley, Waltham Abbey	(17)		M'Leod of Geanies	(25)
	Gen. Patr. Campbell, Blairgowrie	(6)		Benj. Thomson, Nottingham	(18)		John Hawkins, Cosford	(26)
1802	Edward Sheppard, Uley	(7)		Geo. Evans, Rathdrum	(19)	1808	Malcolm Laing, Isle of Eday	(27)
	Daniel Lloyd, Bowldown	(8)		John Julius Angerstein, Weeting	(20)		Thos. Henty, West Tarring	(28)
	15th Lord Somerville, Fitzhead & Cobham	(9)					Owen Wynne, Sligo	(29)
1803	John Woods, Midhurst	(10)				1809	1st Baron Western, Kilvedon	(30)
	Rev. J. C. Beckingham, Bourn	(11)					Thos. Bucke, Worlington	(31)
1804	Thos. Wm. Coke, Holkham	(12)					John Tharpe, Chippenham	(32)
							Samuel Oldknowe, Mellor	(33)
						1810	Geo. Webb Hall, Bristol	(34)
							5th D. of Devonshire, Chatsworth	(35)
							Chas. Downie, Paisley	(36)
							Rev. Dr. Butler, Kilkenny	(37)
						1811	Wm. Tinker, Devizes	(38)

To The Royal Flock

To and from Ld. Somerville's Flock

[Contraband sheep from Spain]

To The British Isles

[Mercantile purchases in Spain]

From The British Isles

[John Macarthur's purchases at Kew]

To The Royal Flock

[Prizes of War]

From The Royal Flock

[Private and public sales]

Figure 2   The entry into Great Britain of Spanish Merinos and their dispersal from 1800 to 1811.

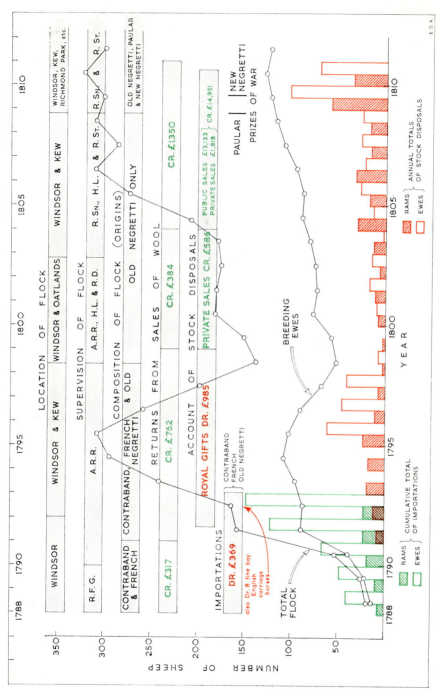

Figure 3   A general summary of the affairs of His Majesty's Spanish flock from 1788 to 1811.

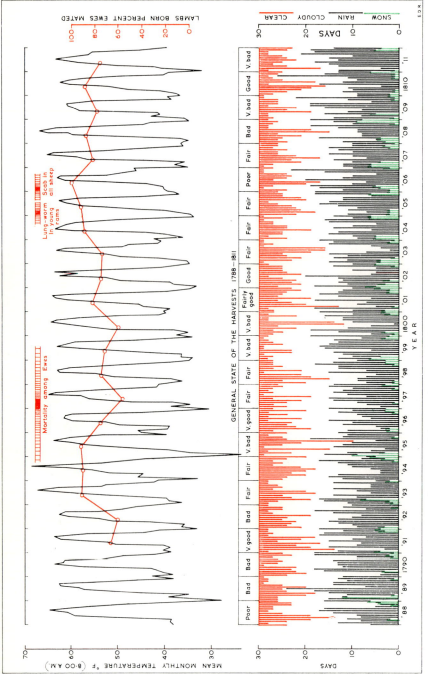

Figure 4   The general pattern of the weather recorded at Sion House by Thomas Hoy from 1788 to 1811.

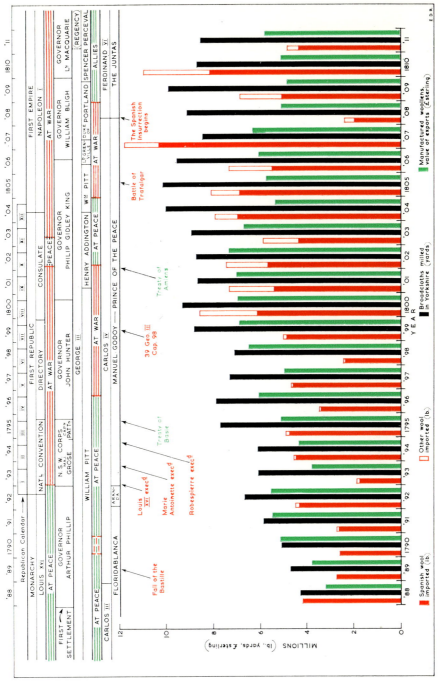

Figure 5   The political background and the trends in the wool trade from 1788 to 1811.

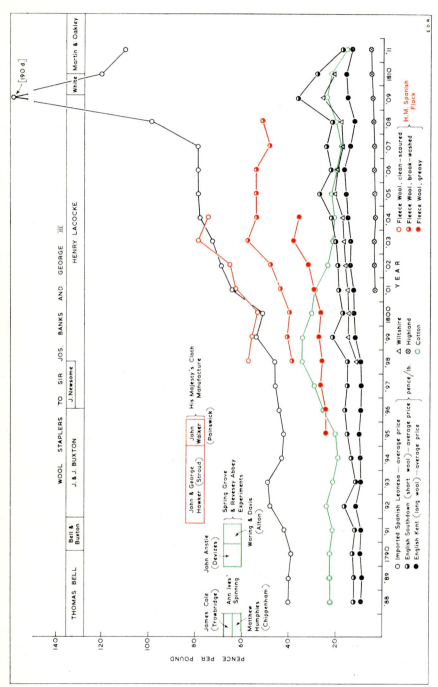

Figure 6 The relative levels and general trend of wool prices from 1788 to 1811.

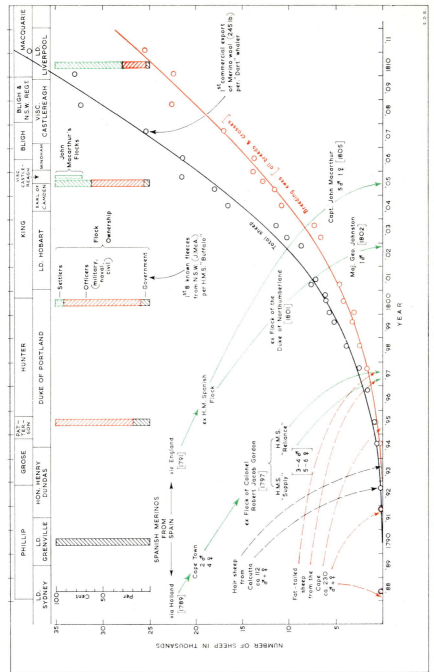

Figure 7   The entry of sheep into Australia and the sheep population growth from 1788 to 1811.

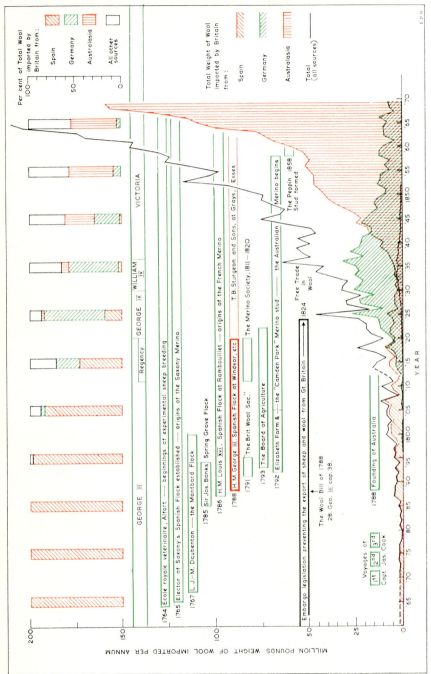

Figure 8   A century of growth and development in sheep breeding and the British Wool Trade from 1760 to 1860.

TABLE XI

SUMMARY OF THE CLEAN WOOL YIELDS TO BE EXPECTED FROM VARIOUS MODES OF WASHING

Category of Fleece	Treatment	Yield after complete commercial scouring Clean Wool per cent	Waste per cent
1. Spanish fleeces (Raffinos)	Washed by the merchant after shearing and sorting—hot water	88	12
2. Spanish fleeces (average)	Washed by the merchant after shearing and sorting—hot water	85	15
3. Saxony fleeces (average)	Washed by the grower on the sheep's back—warm water	80	20
4. English fleeces (average)	Washed by the grower on the sheep's back—cold water	75	25
5. English fleeces (average)	Unwashed	60	40
6. Spanish fleeces (His Majesty's Spanish flock)	Unwashed	48	52
7. Spanish fleeces (average)	Unwashed	45	55

(Nos. 1, 3, 4, 5, and 7, after Bakewell (1808); Nos. 2 and 6, after Banks (1800–4).)

TABLE XII

THE GENERAL BALANCE SHEET FOR
HIS MAJESTY'S SPANISH FLOCK, 1788–1811

	Credit £	Debit £
1. Initial Cost of Importations: 1788–92		369*
2. Value of Royal Gifts: 1792–9		985
3. Estimated Cost of Maintenance: 1788–1811 (24 Years at about £120 per annum)		2880
4. Returns from Sales of Wool and Cloth: 1788–1811 (estimated 1806–11)	2812	
5. Returns from Private Treaty Sales of Rams and Ewes: 1800–3	586	
6. Returns from Public Auction Sales of Rams and Ewes: 1804–10	6007	
7. Credit Balance on the Operation of the Flock: 1788–1811†		5171
	£9405	£9405

* Debit also the value of '8 fine bay English carriage Horses' at, say, £50 each=£400.
† This is based on the assumed operation of the 'small' or 'old Negretti' flock only.

TABLE XIII

THE SPINNING OF ANNE IVES, 1787–9

Date	Type of Wool	Hanks/lb.	Yards/lb.	Miles/lb.
1787				
March	Lincoln wether	137	76,800	43·6
November	Lincoln × Spanish tup	186	104,000	59·1
1788				
January	Spanish tup	256	143,000	81·4
June	Spanish tup	280	156,000	89·1
1789				
September	Spanish tup	292	163,000	92·8

TABLE XIV

COMPARATIVE SPINNING PERFORMANCES
OF THE EIGHTEENTH CENTURY

	Hanks/lb.	Yards/lb.	Miles/lb.
Spinning in the schools (Norwich)	24	13,440	7·6
Superfine spinning (Norwich)	70	39,200	22·3
Mary Powley (1754)	150	85,000	48·2
Ann Ives (1789)	292	163,000	92·8
Cotton (Douglas's Mills, 1789) (hanks=840 yards)	190	159,700	90·7
Cotton (finest Indian spinning) (hanks=560 yards)	363	203,000	115·3

TABLE XV
ANALYSIS OF HIS MAJESTY'S EXPERIMENTAL CLOTH MANUFACTURE, 1792–3

Cloth No. and Colour	Wool Sort	Weight of each Sort Washed lb.	Scoured lb.	Clean Wool per cent	Length of Broad-cloth yards	Clean Wool per yard Broad-cloth lb.
1 Scarlet	Spanish R	83·0	44·0	53·0	21·00	2·09
	(=imported Spanish second R; 'very good stout cloth')					
2 Scarlet	Spanish F	80·5	48·0	59·7	23·00	2·09
	(=imported Spanish second F; 'very good neat cloth, not stout')					
3 Blue	Spanish T	52·5	30·0	57·2	13·50	2·22
	(=best Shropshire; 'good stout cloth')					
	Total =	**222·0**	**122·0**	**55·0**	**57·50**	**2·12**
4 Scarlet	French prime	42·0	29·0	69·0	12·75	2·28
	(=rather superior to imported Spanish first R; 'very good the best cloth')					
5 Blue	French second and third	41·5 / 27·0	29·0 / 18·0	68·6	22·25	2·11
	(=nearly as fine as the best Herefordshire; 'very good stout cloth')					
	Total =	**110·5**	**76·0**	**68·8**	**35·00**	**2·17**
6 Scarlet Blue (double-dyed)	Spanish × Hereford Head (abb) Second (warp)	64·0	44·0	68·8	18·25	2·41
	(=best Southdown; '5 Bracks full of black blotches, bad scarlet; not fit to use')					
7 Blue	Spanish × Hereford Head (abb) Second (warp)	41·0	28·0	68·3	15·00	1·87
	(=best Southdown; 'good stout Cloth coarse and high')					
	Total =	**105·0**	**72·0**	**68·5**	**33·25**	**2·15**

TABLE XVI
SUMMARY OF HIS MAJESTY'S EXPERIMENTAL CLOTH MANUFACTURE, 1792–3

Flock and No. of Sheep	Weight of Each Clip Washed lb.	Scoured lb.	Clean Yield per cent	Mean Fleece Weight Washed lb.	Scoured lb.	Yards of Broadcloth Total yards	Per Sheep yards
True Spanish (=64)	222·0	122·0	55·0	3·47	1·91	57·50	0·90
French (=36)	110·5	76·0	68·8	3·07	2·11	35·00	0·98
Spanish × Hereford (=32)	105·0	72·0	68·5	3·28	2·22	33·25	0·95
Total (=132)	437·5	270·0	61·7	3·31	2·04	125·75	0·94

TABLE XVII

DR. C. H. PARRY'S MEASUREMENTS OF FIBRE THICKNESS ON SAMPLES FROM IMPORTED SPANISH PILES, c. 1806

Pile	Tip	Middle	Base	Mean	Remarks
Lastiria	22·2	20·9	17·2	20·1	From Edward Sheppard of Uley, ex. imported pile of 1803–6.
Coronet [=Escurial]	20·8	20·8	19·9	20·5	From the best imported piles of c. 1796–7.
Negretti	21·6	21·6	20·8	21·4	
Alva	23·4	20·6	20·7	21·6	From Sir Samuel Wathen, from imported pile of 1803–6.
Imperial	22·7	24·2	20·2	22·4	From a Wool merchant of Bristol, 1805, per William Matthews, Secretary of Bath and West of England Society.

*1 micron = 1/25,400 inch.

TABLE XVIII

DR. C. H. PARRY'S MEASUREMENTS OF FIBRE THICKNESS ON FLEECE SPECIMENS OF VARIOUS SPANISH MERINO STOCK, c. 1806

Breed	Tip	Middle	Base	Mean	Remarks
Spanish Merino Ram	22·1	20·6	19·0	20·6	Full mouthed.
Saxon Merino Ram	20·8	21·3	21·2	21·1	Per Mr. Gordon Grey.
Rambouillet Merino Ram (ex. Charles Pictet's flock)	21·4	20·6	21·6	21·3	Per Mr. William Poole. Considered by Charles Pictet the finest specimen he had seen.
Negrette Ram Marquis of Bath	25·5	26·0	20·9	24·2	Full-mouthed sire of No. 1 below. Ex. His Majesty's Spanish flock.
Pure Anglo-Negrette Ram	25·0	24·9	22·1	24·0	Six-tooth.
King's Merino Ewe	19·5	21·2	17·8	19·5	Ex. His Majesty's Spanish flock.
Rambouillet Ewe	23·8	22·4	20·6	22·3	Collected by Dr. Charles Parry from Professor Chabert of the Veterinary School, Maisons Charenton, 1802.

TABLE XIX

DR. C. H. PARRY'S MEASUREMENTS OF FIBRE THICKNESS ON SHEEP OF HIS OWN FLOCK AND OF SOME OTHER BREEDS, *c.* 1806

Breed	Tip	Middle	Base	Mean	Remarks
		Diameter in microns			
Merino × Ryeland					
Ram No. 1	23·0	21·4	19·4	21·2	Full mouthed, son of M. of B. Negrette ram, 4th cross.
No. 25	22·3	19·5	18·4	19·9	Shearling
No. 89	22·7	21·0	17·7	20·4	Shearling, sire of No. 1 ex. 4th cross ewes (inbred 4th cross).
No. 93	24·6	20·6	20·1	21·8	Shearling
No. 95	25·1	23·4	20·4	23·0	Shearling
No. 100	24·5	23·2	22·2	23·2	Shearling
No. 101	24·4	23·2	19·4	22·3	Shearling
No. 109	26·9	21·6	18·3	21·8	Shearling
No. 111	23·1	21·9	19·8	21·7	Shearling
Ewe No. 1	20·6	17·7	17·3	18·5	⎱ Flock of Dr. C. H.
No. 5	24·2	19·8	16·7	20·2	⎰ Parry, 4th Cross.
Ram Knott	25·4	24·5	21·2	23·7	
Ryeland Ram	26·8	26·9	23·4	25·7	
Charenton Ram (Merino)	24·3	27·4	23·3	25·4	Collected by Dr. Charles Parry in 1802 from Professor Chabert.
Ryeland Ewe	24·3	21·2	22·2	22·6	⎱ To Dr. C. H. Parry 'from relative & friend
Southdown Ewe (ex John Ellman's flock)	24·8	22·3	21·7	22·9	⎰ professionally acquainted with wool'.
Cape Ewe 4th cross (ex Van Reenan flock, Cape Town)	29·8	25·5	26·2	27·1	Per Sir George Yonge, October 1805.
Wiltshire Ewe	30·8	35·2	28·9	31·5	

454 HIS MAJESTY'S SPANISH FLOCK

TABLE XX

SUMMARY OF THE NEGRETTI SHEEP SHIPPED BY ANDREW COCHRANE-JOHNSTONE TO THE UNITED STATES OF AMERICA ON HIS OWN ACCOUNT, 1810–11

| Ship | Captain | Number of Sheep | |
		Shipped at Lisbon (December 1810)	Landed at New York (January 1811)
General Putnam	Captain Laborquet	200	110+ 3 lambs
Eliza	Captain Lane	305	145+ 5 lambs
Four Sisters	Captain Williams	300	107+ 5 lambs
General Colburn	Captain Prince	314	107+ 9 lambs
The Eliza Ann	Captain Mix	300	55+ 5 lambs
The Asia	Captain McReay	280	87+ 5 lambs
The Belisarius	Captain Morgan	270	185+ 2 lambs
The Liberty	Captain Russell	180	161+ 8 lambs
		2149	957+42

Of which, on 21 February 1811, there remained alive, 621 sheep only including 43 sick.

BIBLIOGRAPHY

ORIGINAL MANUSCRIPTS, STATUTES, OFFICIAL DOCUMENTS, RECORDS, REPORTS AND
PARLIAMENTARY PAPERS, PERIODICALS, NEWSPAPERS PRINTED BOOKS, AND PAMPHLETS
CONSULTED DURING THE PREPARATION OF THIS WORK.

The sources of reference cited here are selected to include those most relevant to the subject or its immediate background. All have been consulted but no attempt has been made to separate the most important from those used in a more or less cursory fashion. The lettered numbers in the manuscript references are those of the libraries or collections to which they belong except in the case of the microfilm copies of the Banks Papers in the Sutro Library, San Francisco. Here the author has initiated and used a personal system for the purpose of this work which may or may not be adopted as official. No means of direct cross-reference is at present available to the code used in the Sutro Library itself, but no difficulty exists in identifying any particular document in the bound series of microfilm prints at present lodged in the Department of Botany, British Museum (Natural History). These volumes were developed from the original four microfilms made available by courtesy of the California State Library to the author in 1955 and 1957. Printed by an arrangement with the Trustees of the British Museum in 1958 they have been arranged in four series, Nos. I–IV, each series being one microfilm. The subdivision into volumes was established by the author according to the marked sections of each film indicating the order in which the original bundles were photographed. Each folio in each volume is equal to one frame of the film and follows the sequence of the papers in the original bundles and folders in the Sutro Collection. The use made of these papers here is the first for systematic research and it was therefore necessary to establish a convenient code. The method is easily capable of extension to other papers in the collection.

A reference such as BM(SC), II, **8**, 44–51, reads, in effect, British Museum, Sutro microfilm copies, series II=film 2, volume **8**, folios= frames 44–51.

The titles of printed books and pamphlets are not always given in full, but certain selected early volumes have the full form presented as an informative though, at times, tedious, summary of the contents of value in bibliography.

MANUSCRIPT COLLECTIONS

The Sutro Library, San Francisco, California
    The Banks Sheep and Wool Papers
The Mitchell Library, Sydney, New South Wales
    The Banks Papers
    The Macarthur Papers
    The Marsden Papers
    The King Papers
The British Museum (Natural History), South Kensington, London
    The Banks Papers in the Dawson Turner Copies
The British Museum, Bloomsbury, London
    The Additional Manuscripts
The National Library of Scotland, Edinburgh
    The Liston Papers
    The Cochrane Papers

The Library of the Meteorological Office
    The Weather Diaries of Thomas Hoy, 1771–1822
Private collections
    The Bathurst Papers
    The Althorp Papers
    The Dawson Manuscript Collection

BRITISH PARLIAMENTARY PAPERS

Report of the Committee to whom the Petition of the Several Persons, whose names are thereunto subscribed, being concerned in the Woollen Trade and Manufactories, within the Counties of Somerset, Wilts., and Gloucester was referred, London, 1803. This includes the evidence of Edward Sheppard, Daniel Lloyd, Abraham Lloyd Edridge, Thomas Joyce, George Wansey, John Maitland, and others concerned in the experimental cloth manufacture arising from the King's and other flocks of Merinos and Anglo-Merinos in the early years.

Report from the Select Committee on the Petition of Merchants and Manufacturers concerned in the Woollen Manufacture in the County of York and Town of Halifax, London, 1803.

Report from the Select Committee on the Petitions of the Manufacturers of Woollen Cloth in the County of York, London, 1803.

Report from the Committee appointed to consider of the State of the Woollen Manufacture of England, and to Report their Observations thereupon to the House; and to whom the several Petitions, relating to the Woollen Manufacture, were referred, London, 1806. An important document presenting a comprehensive picture of the social and economic state of the wool industry of England in the first years of the nineteenth century.

Report from the Select Committee of the House of Lords, appointed to take into Consideration the State of the British Wool Trade, and to Report to the House; together with the Minutes of Evidence taken before the said Committee, and an Appendix and Index Thereto, London, 1828. A document no less important than that of the Committee of the House of Commons for 1806 with which a profitable comparison may be made for the relative states of the industry and of trade during and after the wars with France, 1793–1815.

HISTORICAL RECORDS AND GENERAL WORKS OF REFERENCE

Historical Manuscripts Commission Reports.
Historical Records of Australia, series I, vols. I–XVII; series III, vols. I–IV; series IV, vol. I.
Historical Records of New South Wales, vols. I–VII.
Bibliography of Australia.
Dictionary of National Biography.
Nouvelle Biographia Générale.
Biographie Universelle.
Dictionary of American Biography.
The Australian Encyclopedia.
Burke's Peerage, Baronetage, and Knightage.
Complete Peerage of England, Scotland, Ireland, Great Britain, and the United Kingdom. Extant, Extinct, and Dormant.

CONTEMPORARY NEWSPAPERS AND PERIODICALS
(a) Newspapers

Stamford Mercury
Cambridge Chronicle
The Morning Chronicle
County Chronicle

London Chronicle
St. James' Chronicle
The Morning Herald
Herald News
General Advertiser
The British Press
London Courant
Edinburgh Evening Courant
Edinburgh Oracle
Caledonian Mercury
Sydney Gazette

(b) Periodicals

Philosophical Transactions of the Royal Society
Transactions of the Society for the Encouragement of Arts, Manufactures and Commerce
Journal de Physique
The PhilosophicalMagazine
Annual Register
Gentleman's Magazine
Annals of Agriculture
Letters and Papers of the Bath and West of England Society
Agricultural Magazine
The Farmer's Magazine
Communications to the Board of Agriculture
Cobbett's Weekly Political Register

PRINTED BOOKS, PAMPHLETS, AND ARTICLES BEFORE 1830

[ANONYMOUS], Report of the Committee of the Highland Society of Scotland on the Subject of Shetland Wool. With an Appendix containing some Papers, drawn up by Sir John Sinclair and Dr. [James] Anderson in reference to the Said Report, Edinburgh, 1790.

[ANONYMOUS], The Windsor Guide, containing a Description of the Town and Castle . . . , Windsor, 1792.

[ANONYMOUS], An Answer to Lord Somerville's address to the Board of Agriculture, on the subject of sheep and wool . . . , Gloucester, 1799.

[ANONYMOUS], The Compendious Gazetteer, or Pocket Companion to the Royal Palaces . . . , Windsor, 1801.

[ANONYMOUS], On the Name and Origin of the Merino Breed of Sheep, London, 1811.

AIKIN, JOHN, Annals of the Reign of King George the Third; from its commencement in the year 1760 to the General Peace in the year 1815, London, 1816.

ALSTROEMER, CLAS, 'Discours sur la race des Brébis à laine fine', Journal de Physique, tome I (Janvier 1772), 441–56; (Fevrier 1772), 534–59.

ANDERSON, ADAM, An Historical and Chronological Deduction of the Origin of Commerce, London, 1787–9.

ANDERSON, JAMES, Observations on the Means of exciting a Spirit of National Industry, Edinburgh, 1777.

ANDERSON, JAMES, Essays relating to Agriculture and Rural Affairs, vol. II, Edinburgh, 1784.

AN EXPERIENCED BREEDER [HUNT, C. H.], A Practical Treatise on the Merino and Anglo-Merino Breeds of Sheep; in which The Advantages to the Farmer and Grazier, peculiar to these Breeds, are clearly demonstrated, London, 1809.

BAKEWELL, ROBERT, *Observations on the Influence of Soil and Climate upon Wool; from which is deduced A Certain and Easy Method of Improving the Quality of English Clothing Wools, and Preserving the Health of Sheep after shearing: an inquiry into the structure, growth, and formation of wool and hair; and remarks on the means by which the Spanish breed of sheep may be made to preserve the best qualities of its fleece unchanged in different climates. With occasional notes and remarks by the Right Hon. Lord Somerville*, London, 1808.

[BANKS, SIR JOSEPH], *The Propriety of Allowing a Qualified Exportation of Wool, Discussed Historically. To which is added an Appendix, containing a Table, which shows the value of the Woollen Goods of every kind that were entered for Exportation at the Custom House from 1697 to 1780 inclusive, as well as the Prices of Wool in England during that period*, 1782.

[BANKS, SIR JOSEPH], 'A Project for Extending the Breed of Fine Wooled Spanish Sheep, now in the possession of his Majesty, into all parts of Great Britain, where the Growth of Fine Cloathing Wools is found to be profitable', *The Philosophical Magazine* (first series), VII (June–September 1800), 350–5.

BANKS, SIR JOSEPH, 'Some Circumstances relative to Merino Sheep, chiefly collected from the Spanish Shepherds, who attended those of the Flock of Paular, lately presented to His Majesty by the Government of Spain; with Particulars respecting that great National Acquisition; and also respecting the Sheep of the Flock of Negrete, imported from Spain by His Majesty, in the year 1791', *The Philosophical Magazine*, XXXIII (1809), 239–48, 287–90, also CBA, VI (1809), 268–86.

BARTLEY, NEHEMIAH, *A Series of Letters on the National Importance, as well as the Individual Benefit, of Extending the Growth of Fine Clothing Wool, by Interbreeding with Spanish Rams and British Ewes. Occasionally addressed to the Editor of the Agricultural Magazine, interspersed with Cursory Remarks on the Superiority of the Smaller Breeds of Animals; the Culture of the Potato; and of the Mangold Wurzell Plant as winter and spring food for Cattle . . .* , Bath, 1804.

BARTLEY, NEHEMIAH, *Essays on Extending the Growth of Fine Clothing Wool by interbreeding with Spanish Rams and British Ewes . . .* , London, 1807.

BOURGOING, J.-F., *Tableau De l'Espagne Moderne . . .* , Paris, 1807; London, 1808.

[BOWLES, WILLIAM], 'Account of the Sheep and Sheep Walks of Spain in a Letter from a Gentleman in Spain to Mr. Peter Collinson, F.R.S.', *The Annual Register, or a View of the History, Politicks, and Literature for the Year 1764*, Natural History, 77–89, London, 1765.

BOWLES, WILLIAM, *A Treatise on the Merino Sheep and the Fine Wools of Spain*, London, 1811.

[BUCKE, THOMAS GEORGE, Secretary], *The Second Report of The Merino Society. Established 4th March, 1811*, London, 1812.

[BUCKE, THOMAS GEORGE, Secretary], *The Third Report of The Merino Society. Established 4th March, 1811*, London, 1813.

CARLIER, ABBÉ CLAUDE, *Considerations sur les moyens de rétablir en France les bonnes éspèces des bêtes-à-laine*, Paris, 1762.

CARLIER, ABBÉ CLAUDE, *Traite des bêtes-à-laine, ou methode d'elever, et de gouverner le troupeau au champs et à la bergerie: ouvrage pratique, suivi du denombrement et de la description des principales éspèces de bêtes-à-laine, dont on fait commerce en France: avec un état des différentes qualités de laine, et de usages auxquels servant dans les manufactures*, Paris, 1770.

CARLIER, ABBÉ CLAUDE, 'Observations historiques concernant le régime, la nature et l'état actuel des troupeaux de Bêtes à laine transhumantes d'Espagne', *Journal de Physique*, tome XXIV (Mars 1784), 177–87.

CARLIER, ABBÉ CLAUDE, 'Observations historiques sur l'état ancien et l'état actuel des troupeaux, et des laines d'Angleterre', *Journal de Physique*, tome XXIV (Avril 1784), 271–80.

CARLIER, ABBÉ CLAUDE, *Remarques sur l'Instruction de M. Daubenton, pour les bergers et pour les propriétaires des troupeaux*, Paris, 1785.

CARLIER, ABBÉ CLAUDE, *Remarques sur l'Instruction de M. Daubenton, pour les bergers et pour les propriétaires des troupeaux*, Paris, 1787.

CLERK [afterwards CLERK-MAXWELL], SIR GEORGE, *Observations on The Method of Growing Wool in Scotland and Proposals for improving the quality of our Wool. In Two Letters to the Commissioners and Trustees for Improving Fishing and Manufactures in Scotland*, Edinburgh, 1755.

CULLEY, GEORGE, *Observations on Livestock; containing Hints for Choosing and Improving the Best Breeds of the most useful kinds of Domestic Animals*, London, 1807.

DAUBENTON, L.-J.-M., *Instructions pour Les Bergers et pour Les Propriétaires des Troupeaux*, Paris, 1782.

DAUBENTON, L.-J.-M., *Instructions pour Les Bergers et pour Les Propriétaires des Troupeaux; avec d'autres Ouvrages sur les Moutons et sur les Laines*, fourth edition, ed. J. B. Huzard, Paris, 1810.

DILLON, [SIR] JOHN TALBOT, *Travels through Spain with a view to illustrate The Natural History and Physical Geography of that Kingdom, in a Series of Letters . . .*, London, 1782.

FAREY, JOHN [SEN.], *General View of the Agriculture of Derbyshire*, vol. III, London, 1817.

FAUJAS DE SAINT-FOND, BARTHELEMI, *Travels in England, Scotland, and the Hebrides . . .*, London, 1799.

FINK —, [Treatise on the *Rearing of Sheep in Germany, and the Improvement of Coarse Wool*—in German], Halle, 1799.

FOOT, PETER, *General View of the Agriculture of the County of Middlesex, with Observations on the Means of their Improvement*, London, 1794.

GODOLPHIN, SIR WILLIAM, *Hispana Illustrata: or the maxims of the Spanish Court from . . . 1667 to . . . 1678 laid open in Letters to the Lord Arlington from the Earl of Sandwich, the Earl of Sunderland and Sir Wm. Godolphin during their Embassies in Spain . . . also a treatise by my Lord Sandwich, concerning the advantages of a nearer union with that Crown, and another by Sir Wm. Godolphin about the Woolls of Spain*, England, 1703.

HALL, GEORGE WEBB, 'Essay on the Growth and Management of Merino Wool in the United Kingdom of Great Britain and Ireland', *The Second Report of The Merino Society . . .*, London, 1812, pp. 35–65.

HASTFER, F. W. [Baron], *Instruction sur la manière d'élever et de perfectionner des bêtes-à-laine*, Paris, 1756.

HENDERSON, ANDREW, *The Practical Grazier; or A Treatise on the Proper Selection and Management of Livestock; with Cures and Preventives for the most prevalent Disorders that attend them: likewise a proper system of management pointed out, for Grazing Farms of Different Soils, in Various Climates and Situations, containing several modes of improving waste lands, draining, and irrigating; with useful hints to the Landlord and Practical Grazier*, Edinburgh, 1826.

HERNANDEZ DE VARGAS, F., *Memoria sobre el origin y antiguedad de la Lana Merina*, Madrid, 1814.

HOGG, JAMES [THE ETTRICK SHEPHERD], *The Shepherd's Guide: being a Practical Treatise on The Diseases of Sheep, their Causes and the best Means of Preventing them; with Observations on the most suitable Farm-Stocking for the various Climates of this Country*, Edinburgh, London, 1807.

HOLROYD, JOHN BAKER [LORD SHEFFIELD], *Observations on the Commerce of the American States with Europe and the West Indies; including the several articles of Import and Export; and on the Tendency of a Bill now depending in Parliament*, London, 1783.

HOLROYD, JOHN BAKER [LORD SHEFFIELD], *Observations on the Objections made to the Export of Wool from Great Britain to Ireland*, London, 1800.

[HORNE, THOMAS HARTWELL], *A Treatise on the Choice, Buying, and General Management of Livestock; comprising Delineations and Descriptions of the Principal Breeds of Black Cattle, Sheep, Swine, Horses, Shepherds' Dogs, Asses, Mules, Poultry, Rabbits and Bees,/Together with An Appendix on the Improvement of British Wool, and on The Destruction of Vermin Infesting Farmyard, &c., &c.*, London, 1807.

[HORNE, THOMAS HARTWELL], *The Complete Grazier; or Farmer's and Cattle Breeder's and Dealer's Assistant, etc. etc. . . . With an Introductory View of the Different Breeds of Neat Cattle, Sheep, Horses, and Swine; The Present State of the Wool Trade, and the Improvement of British Wool, etc. etc.*, London, 1839.

HUISH, ROBERT, *Memoirs of George the Third or The Public and Private Life of His Late Most Excellent and Most Gracious Majesty, George the Third*, London, 1821.

HUMPHREYS, DAVID, 'Some Accounts of the Spanish Sheep', *Papers on Agriculture, Consisting of Communications made to the Massachusetts Society for Promoting Agriculture*, pp. 79–84, Boston, 1803.

[HUNT, JOHN], *Agricultural Memoirs; or, History of the Dishley System, in Answer to Sir John Sebright*, London, 1812.

HUNTER, A., *Georgical Essays, Volume IV*, York, 1803.

JOVELLANOS, GASPAR MELCHOR DE, *Memoir on the Advancement of Agriculture and Agrarian Laws. Addressed to the Supreme Council of Castile by the patriotic society of Madrid, and drawn up by one of its members*, London, 1809.

LABERGERIE, ROUGEIR, *Rapport fait à l'Assemble Nationale, au nom du comité d'Agriculture, sur l'amélioration des bêtes-à-laine le 24 Juillet, 1792, l'an 4 de la liberté, imprimé par ordre de l'Assemblé Nationale*, Paris, 1792.

LABORDE, ALEXANDRE DE, *A View of Spain; comprising A Descriptive Itinerary of Each Province, and a General Statistical Account of the Country; including its Population, Agriculture, Manufactures, Commerce and Finances; its Government, Civil and Ecclesiastical Establishments; the State of the Arts, Sciences, and Literature; its Manners, Customs, Natural History, etc.*, London, 1809.

LASTEYRIE, C.-P., *Traité sur Les Bêtes à Laine d'Espagne, leur éducation, leurs voyages, la tonte, le lavage, et le commerce des laines, les causes qui donnent la finesse aux laines; Auquel on a ajoute l'historique des voyages que font les moutons des Bouches-du-Rhône et ceux du royaume de Naples; l'origine, les succès, l'état actuel du troupeau de Rambouillet, et les moyens de propager et de conserver la race espagnole dans toute sa pureté* Paris, 1799.

LASTEYRIE, C.-P., *Histoire de l'Introduction des Moutons à Laine fine d'Espagne dans les divers États de l'Europe et au Cap de Bonne-Espérance*, Paris, 1802.

LASTEYRIE, C.-P., *Geschichte der Einfuhrung der feinwolligen Schafe in die verschiedenen europaischen Lander*, Leipsic, 1804–5.

LASTEYRIE, C.-P., *An Account of the Introduction of Merino Sheep into the Different States of Europe, and at the Cape of Good Hope . . . .*, London, 1810.

LAWRENCE, JOHN, *A General Treatise on Cattle, the Ox, the Sheep, and the Swine: comprehending their Breeding, Management, Improvement and Diseases*, London, 1805.

LIVINGSTON, ROBERT R., *An Essay on Sheep, intended chiefly to promote the Introduction and Propagation of Merinos in the United States of America, by proving, from actual Experiments, the great advantage thereof to Agriculture and Manufactures*, London, 1811.

LONGUET, C.-H., *Clôture productive . . . methode imitée de l'Anglais pour l'Education des bêtes-à-laine . . .*, Paris, 1791.

LUCCOCK, JOHN, *The Nature and Properties of Wool, illustrated: with a Description of the English Fleece*, Leeds, 1805.

LULLIN, C.-J.-M., *Observations sur les bêtes-à-laine, faites dans les environs de Génève pendant vingt ans*, Geneva, 1804.

MACKENZIE, SIR GEORGE STEUART, *A Treatise on the Diseases and Management of Sheep . . .*, Edinburgh, 1809.

MAITLAND, JOHN, *Observations on the Impolicy of Permitting the Exportation of British Wool, and of Preventing the Free Importation of Foreign Wool*, London, 1818.

MALCOLM, JAMES, *A Compendium of Modern Husbandry, principally written during a Survey of Surrey, Made at the desire of the Board of Agriculture; Illustrative also of the best practices in the neighbouring Counties, Kent, Sussex, etc. in which is comprised An Analysis of Manures Shewing their Chemical Contents and the proper application of them to Soils and Plants of all descriptions, also An Essay on Timber Exhibiting a view of the increasing scarcity of that important Article, with Hints on the Means of Counter-acting it; together with A Variety of Miscellaneous Subjects Peculiarly adapted to the present state of the Internal Economy of the Kingdom*, London, 1805.

MAVOR, WILLIAM, *General View of the Agriculture of Berkshire*, London, 1808.

MILLS, JOHN, *A Treatise on Cattle; Shewing the most approved Methods of Breeding, Rearing, and Fitting for Use, Horses, Asses, Mules, Horned Cattle, Sheep, Goats, and Swine; with Directions for The Proper Treatment of them in their several Disorders; To which is added A Dissertation on their Contagious Diseases. Carefully collected from the best Authorities, and interspersed with Remarks*, London, 1776.

NAISMITH, JOHN, *Observations on the different breeds of sheep, and the state of sheep farming in the southern districts of Scotland . . .*, Edinburgh, 1795.

PALLAS, PETER, *An Account of the Different Kinds of Sheep Found in the Russian Dominions and among the Tartar Hordes of Asia. To which is added Five Appendices tending to Illustrate The Natural and Economical History of Sheep and other Domestic Animals by James Anderson, L.L.D., F.R.S., F.A.S.S.*, Edinburgh, 1794.

PARKINSON, RICHARD, *Treatise on the Breeding and Management of Livestock; comprising Cattle, Sheep, Horses, Asses, Mules, Pigs, Deer, Goats, Rabbits, Poultry, Bees, Fish, etc. etc., in which the Principles and Proceedings of the New School of Breeders are Fully and Experimentally Discussed./To which are added Directions for making Butter and Cheese, curing Hams, pickling Pork and Tongues, preserving Eggs, etc. etc.,/with An Appendix containing Tables of Prices in the Live and Dead Markets, some extra-ordinary Sales of Cattle and Sheep, and other Particulars*, London, 1810.

PARRY, CALEB HILLIER, *Facts and Observations tending to shew the Practicability and Advantage, to the Individual and the Nation, of Producing in the British Isles Clothing Wool, equal to that of Spain: together with Some Hints towards the Management of Fine-Wooled Sheep*, Bath, 1800.

PARRY, CALEB HILLIER, 'An Essay on the Nature, Produce, Origin, and Extension of the Merino Breed of Sheep: to which is added a History of a Cross of that Breed with Ryeland Ewes; describing their Qualities and Produce, and a successful Method of managing them', *Communications to the Board of Agriculture*, vol. v, Part I, No. XVIII (1806), 337–541.

PARRY, CALEB HILLIER, 'On improved Sheep by the Spanish Mixture; their Wool and its Value in Superfine Cloth &c.' A letter to the Bath and West of England Society dated 10 December 1804. *Philosophical Magazine*, XXVII (1807), 239–46.

PARRY, CALEB HILLIER, *An Experimental Inquiry into the Nature, Cause, and Variation of the Arterial Pulse; and into Certain other Properties of the Larger Arteries, in Animals with Warm Blood*, Bath, 1816.

PETRI, BERNHARD, *Das Ganze der Schafzucht in hinsicht auf unser deutsches Klima, und der angrenzenden Lander, insbesondere von der Pflege, Wartung, unde den Eigenschaften der Merinos und ihre Wolle*, Wien, 1815.

PICTET, CHARLES, *Faits et Observations Concernant la Race des Merinos D'Espagne à Laine Superfines et les Croisemens*, Geneva, 1802.

REDHEAD, WILLIAM; LAING, ROBERT; AND MARSHALL, WILLIAM, *Observations on the Different Breeds of Sheep, and the State of Sheep Farming in Some of the Principal Counties in England. Drawn up from a Report transmitted to Sir John Sinclair, Baronet, Chairman of the Society for the Improvement of British Wool*, Edinburgh, 1792.

SEBRIGHT, SIR JOHN SAUNDERS, *The Art of Improving the Breeds of Domestic Animals. In a Letter addressed to The Right Hon. Sir Joseph Banks K.B.*, London, 1809.

SINCLAIR, SIR JOHN, *General Report of the Agricultural State, and Political Circumstances, of Scotland. Drawn up for the Consideration of the Board of Agriculture and Internal Improvement*, Edinburgh, London, 1814.

SINCLAIR, SIR JOHN, *Essays on Agriculture, Farming, Breeding and Fattening Cattle, and on Longevity, with the modern improvements in Utensils, Management of Land, etc.*, London, 1818.

SINCLAIR, SIR JOHN, *The Code of Agriculture; including Observations on Gardens, Orchards, Woods, and Plantations*, London, 1821.

SMITH, JOHN, *Chronicon Rusticum-Commerciale; or Memoirs of Wool, etc. being A Collection of History and Argument, concerning the Woollen Manufacture and Woollen Trade in General; particularly the Rise, Progress, Improvements, Declensions, Revolutions, and Respective Causes thereof (with a View of the different Prices of Wool, at certain distant Periods) in England; as given by a Succession of Writers, from ancient down to the present Times./Also An Account of the several Laws, from Time to Time made, and of many Schemes offered, for preventing the Exportation of Raw Wool; likewise of other Expedients for preserving, and promoting the Interest of the Kingdom, in that Commodity manufactured: With occasional Notes, Dissertations, and Reflections upon the Whole*, London, 1747.

SOMERVILLE, JOHN SOUTHEY [LORD], *Address to the Board of Agriculture, on the Subject of Sheep and Wool . . .*, London, 1799.

SOMERVILLE, JOHN SOUTHEY [LORD], *The System pursued by the Board of Agriculture, illustrated with Dissertations on Sheep and Wool, on the Poor and Poor-Laws, on Scarcity, on Implements of Husbandry . . .*, London, 1809.

SOMERVILLE, JOHN SOUTHEY [LORD], *Facts and Observations Relative to Sheep, Wool, Ploughs and Oxen; in which the Importance of Improving the Short-woolled Breeds of Sheep by a Mixture of the Merino Blood is demonstrated from actual Practice, together with some Remarks on the Advantages which have been derived to the Author's Flock from the Use of Salt . . .*, London, 1809.

SOUTHEY, THOMAS, *Observations Addressed to the Woolgrowers of Australia and Tasmania, respecting Improvements in the Breed of Sheep, preparing and assorting wools etc. and also the Introduction of other Laniferous animals suited to their Climates and Localities and recommended for their adoption*, London, 1830.

STUMPF, GEORG, *Versuch einer pragmatischen Geschichte der Schafereien in Spanien . . .*, Leipsic, 1785.

STUMPF, GEORG, *An Essay on the Practical History of Sheep in Spain and on the Spanish Sheep in Saxony, Anhalt-Dessau . . .*, Dublin, 1800.

SWINBURNE, H., *Travels through Spain in 1775 and 1776 . . .*, London, 1787.

TESSIER, ALEXANDRE-HENRI, *Instruction sur Les Bêtes à Laine, et particulièrement sur La Race des Mérinos. Contenant la manière de former de bons Troupeaux, de les multiplier et soigner convenablement en santé et an maladie*, Paris, 1811.

THOMPSON, BENJAMIN, *A Letter to the Most Noble the Marquis of Titchfield, President of the Newark Agricultural Society, on the Practicability and Importance of Introducing the Merino Breed of Sheep, extensively upon the Forest Farms of Nottinghamshire,* Nottingham, 1808.

[THOMPSON, BENJAMIN, Secretary], *First Report of The Merino Society, Established 4th March, 1811, Containing Lists of the Officers, Rules and Orders, Premiums and Certificates, To which are added, An Alphabetical List of all the Members, With the Places of their Residence, And an Account of the Plans, about to be adopted, for promoting the increase of Merino Sheep in France,* Nottingham, 1811.

TOOKE, THOMAS, *Thoughts and Details on the High and Low Prices of the Last Thirty Years,* Parts I–IV, London, 1823.

TOWNSEND, JOSEPH, *A Journey through Spain in the Years 1786 and 1787; with particular attention to the Agriculture, Manufactures, Commerce, Population, Taxes and Revenue of that Country; and Remarks in passing through a Part of France,* London, 1792.

TRIMMER, JOSHUA KIRBY, *Practical Observations on the Improvement of British Fine Wool and the National Advantages of the Arable System of Sheep Husbandry,* London, 1828.

TWISS, R., *Travels through Portugal and Spain in 1772 and 1773 . . . ,* London, 1775.

WAGNER, JOHANN PHILIPP, *Ueber Merinos-Schafzucht in Bezug auf die Erfordernisse der Wolle für ihre Anwendung,* Königsberg, 1828.

WESTERN, CHARLES CALLIS [LORD WESTERN[, *A Letter from Lord Western on the Management of his Flock of Merino Sheep, addressed to James Bischoff, Esq.,* London, 1842.

YOUNG, ARTHUR, *Travels during the Years 1787, 1788, and 1789, Undertaken more particularly with a View of ascertaining the Cultivation, Wealth, Resources, and National Prosperity of the Kingdom of France. To which is added The Register of a Tour into Spain,* Dublin, 1793.

YOUNG, ARTHUR, *General View of the Agriculture of the County of Lincoln . . . ,* London, 1799.

YOUNG, ARTHUR, *General View of the Agriculture of Sussex . . . ,* London, 1808.

YOUNG, ARTHUR, *General View of the Agriculture of Oxfordshire . . . ,* London, 1809.

ZAPATA, D. AND BALTAZAR, ANTONIO, *Noticia del origin y establecimiento increible de las Lanas Finas de Espana en el Extrangero por culpa muestro en no haber impedido major La Extraccion de Muestro Ganado Lanar Y un discurso sobre el origin del ganado lanar transhumante, el del Concejo de la Mesta, y Cabana Real,* Madrid, 1820.

PRINTED BOOKS, PAMPHLETS, AND ARTICLES SINCE 1830

AUSTIN, H. B., *The Merino, Past, Present and Probable,* Sydney, 1944.

BARRAL, JEAN-AUGUSTE, *Dictionnaire D'Agriculture,* Paris, 1889.

BASSETT, MARNIE, *The Hentys,* London, 1954.

BATH AND WELLS [BISHOP OF], *Journal and Correspondence of William Eden, Lord Auckland,* London, 1861-2.

BERTRAND, LOUIS AND PETRIE, SIR CHARLES, *The History of Spain,* London, 1934.

BETHAM-EDWARDS, M. (ed.), *The Autobiography of Arthur Young. With Selections from his Correspondence,* London, 1898.

BINDOFF, S. T.; MALCOLM SMITH, E. F.; AND WEBSTER, C. K. (eds.), *British Diplomatic Representatives 1789–1852,* London, 1934.

BISCHOFF, JAMES, *A Comprehensive History of the Woollen and Worsted Manufactures, and the Natural and Commercial History of Sheep, from the earliest records to the present period,* London, 1842.

BLACKLOCK, AMBROSE, *A Treatise on Sheep; with the best means for Their Improvement, General Management, and the Treatment of Their Diseases. With a Chapter on Wool, and a History of the Wool Trade. New Edition with an Additional Chapter on the Management of Sheep in Australia*, Glasgow, 1840.

BLADON, F. McKNO (ed.), *The Diaries of Colonel the Hon. Robert Fulke Greville, Equerry to His Majesty King George III*, London, 1930.

BONWICK, JAMES, *Romance of the Wool Trade*, London, 1887.

BOWDEN, PETER, 'Wool Supply and the Woollen Industry', *Economic History Review* (second series), IX (1956), 44–58.

BOWDEN, PETER J., *The Wool Trade in Tudor and Stuart England*, London, 1962.

BOWMAN, F. H., *The Structure of the Wool Fibre, in its relation to the Use of Wool for Technical Purposes; Illustrated with numerous Engravings and Coloured Plates*, Manchester, 1885.

BROUGHAM, HENRY [LORD], *Lives of men of letters and science who flourished in the time of George III*, London, 1845–6.

BROWN, GEORGE A., *Sheep Breeding in Australia, containing An Historical Sketch of the Merino Sheep; The Pedigrees of the Principal Stud Sheep in the Australian Colonies; and A Treatise on Breeding*, Melbourne, 1880.

BURFITT, CHARLES T., *History of the Founding of the Wool Industry of Australia*, Sydney, 1907.

CAMERON, H. C., *Sir Joseph Banks, K.B., P.R.S., The Autocrat of the Philosophers*, London, 1952.

CAMPBELL, W. S., 'From Colony to Commonwealth. A Short Account of the Rise and Progress of Agriculture in New South Wales, from the Foundation of the Colony, 26th January, 1788, to 1st January, 1901', *The Agricultural Gazette of New South Wales*, XII (1901), 1–113.

CARMEN, E. A.; HEATH, H. A.; AND MINTO, J., *Special Report on the History and Present Condition of the Sheep Industry of the United States*, Washington, 1892.

CHASTENET, JACQUES, *Godoy, Master of Spain*, London, 1953.

CLUNN, HAROLD P., *The Face of London*, London n.d., c. 1956.

COLEMAN, J., *The Sheep and Pigs of Great Britain*, London, 1870.

COLMEIRA, MANUEL, *Historia de la Economia Politica en España*, Madrid, 1863.

DARBY, H. C. (ed.), *An Historical Geography of England before 1800*, Cambridge, 1951.

DAWSON, WARREN R. (ed.), *The Banks Letters: A Calendar of the manuscript correspondence of Sir Joseph Banks preserved in the British Museum, The British Museum (Natural History) and other collections in Great Britain*, London, 1958.

DE BEER, SIR GAVIN, *The Sciences Were Never At War*, London, 1960.

DESAIVE, MAX, *Les Animaux Domestiques*, Liège, 1842.

DOBSON, AUSTIN (ed.), *Diary and Letters of Madame D'Arblay (1778–1840)*, London, 1904.

DUNHAM, A. L., *The Industrial Revolution in France, 1815–1848*, New York, 1955.

ELLIS, K. L., 'British Communications and Diplomacy in the Eighteenth Century', *Bulletin of the Institute of Historical Research*, XXXI (1958), 159–67.

ELLIS, M. H., *John Macarthur*, Sydney, 1955.

FORD, RICHARD, *Gatherings from Spain*, London, 1846.

FUSSELL, G. E. AND GOODMAN, CONSTANCE, 'Eighteenth Century traffic in Live-stock', *Economic History Review*, III (1935), 214–36.

GIBSON, W. H. AND SON, *The Scone Merinos*, Launceston, 1883.

GILL, CONRAD, 'Blackwell Hall Factors, 1795–1799', *Economic History Review* (second series), VI (1953–4), 268–81.

GRAHAM, JOHN RYRIE, *A Treatise on the Australian Merino*, 1870.

GRAHAME, E. MAXTONE, *The Beautiful Mrs. Grahame: and the Cathcart Circle*, London, 1927.

HALÉVY, ÉLIE, *A History of the English People in the Nineteenth Century. I. England in 1815*, London, 1961.

HAMILTON, ARCHIBALD, 'On Wool Supply', *Journal of the Statistical Society*, London, XXXIII (1870), 486–521.

HANDLEY, JAMES E., *Scottish Farming in the Eighteenth Century*, London, 1953.

HEATON, HERBERT, *The Yorkshire woollen and worsted industries*, Oxford, 1920.

HEATON, HERBERT, 'Benjamin Gott and the Industrial Revolution in Yorkshire', *Economic History Review*, III (1931–2), 45–66.

HELMAN, MAURICIO B., *Ovina Tecnia*, Buenos Aires, 1954.

HENDERSON, W. O., 'The Anglo-French commercial treaty of 1786', *Economic History Review* (second series), X (1957).

HERR, RICHARD, *The Eighteenth-Century Revolution in Spain*, Princeton, New Jersey, 1958.

HILLS, ALFRED, 'The Squire's Merinos', *Essex Farmers' Journal*, XVI (1938), 759–60.

HORN, D. B. (ed.), *British Diplomatic Representatives, 1689–1789*, London, 1932.

JAMES, JOHN, *History of the Worsted Manufacture in England, from the earliest times*, London, 1857.

KER, JILL, 'The Wool Industry in New South Wales, 1803–1830. I', *Bulletin of the Business Archives Council of Australia*, I (1961), 28–49.

KER, JILL, 'The Wool Industry in New South Wales, 1803–1830. II', *Business Archives and History*, II (1962), 18–54.

KLEIN, JULIUS, *The Mesta, A Study in Spanish Economic History, 1273–1836*, Harvard Economic Studies, XXI, Cambridge, Massachusetts, Harvard University Press, 1920.

LANGER, WILLIAM L. (ed.), *An Encyclopaedia of World History, Ancient, Mediaeval and Modern, Chronologically Arranged*, London, 1956.

LANGNAS, I. A., 'The Relations between Great Britain and the Spanish Colonies, 1808–1812', *Bulletin of the Institute of Historical Research*, XVI (1939), 195.

LEONARD, RUDOLPH, *Agrarpolitik und Agrarreform in Spanien unter Carl III*, Berlin, 1909.

LIPSON, EPHRAIM, *The History of the Woollen and Worsted Industries*, London, 1921.

LIPSON, EPHRAIM, *A Short History of Wool and its Manufacture (mainly in England)*, London, 1953.

LOEHR, RODNEY C., 'The influence of English Agriculture on American Agriculture', *Agricultural History*, XI (1937), 3–15.

LOUDEN, J. C., *An Encyclopaedia of Agriculture: comprising the Theory and Practice of the Valuation Transfer, Laying out, Improvement, and Management of Landed Property; and the Cultivation and Economy of the Animal and Vegetable Productions of Agriculture, including All the Latest Improvements; A General History of Agriculture in all Countries; and a Statistical View of its Present State, with suggestions for its future progress in the British Isles*, London, 1835.

LOW, DAVID, *On the Domesticated Animals of the British Islands: Comprehending The Natural and Economical History of Species and Varieties; The Description of The Properties of External Form; and Observations on The Principles and Practice of Breeding*, London, 1845.

LYONS, SIR HENRY, *The Royal Society, 1660–1940. A History of its Administration under its Charters*, Cambridge, 1944.

LYSAGHT, AVERIL, 'Some Eighteenth Century Bird Paintings in the Library of Sir Joseph Banks (1743–1820)', *Bulletin of the British Museum (Natural History)— Historical Series*, I, (London, 1959), 251–371, Plates 35–7.

MACAULAY, ROSE, *They Went to Portugal*, London, 1946.

MAIDEN, J. H., *Sir Joseph Banks, The 'Father of Australia'*, Sydney, 1909.

MALLINSON, CHARLES, *The Merino in South Africa*, Sydney, 1915.

MANTOUX, PAUL, *The Industrial Revolution in the Eighteenth Century*, London, 1961.

MARSHALL, J., *Digest of all the Accounts relating to the Population, Productions, Revenues, Financial Operations, Manufactures, Shipping, Colonies, Commerce, etc. etc., of the United Kingdom of Great Britain and Ireland, diffused through more than 600 volumes of Journals, Reports and Papers, presented to Parliament during the last Thirty five Years*, London, 1833.

MARSHALL, W. A. L., *A Century of London Weather*, London, 1952.

MARTIN, W. C. L., *On the Value and Diffusion of the Merino Breed. The Farmers' Library*, vol. II, Animal Economy, 51–73, London, 1852.

MCKEE, W. M., *South African Sheep and Wool*, Cape Town, 1913.

MCLACHLAN, JEAN O., *Trade and Peace with Old Spain, 1667–1750: a study of the influence of commerce on Anglo-Spanish diplomacy in the first half of the eighteenth century*, Cambridge, 1940.

MINCHINGTON, W. E., 'Agricultural Returns and the Government during the Napoleonic Wars', *Agricultural History Review*, I (1953), 29–43.

MITCHELL, B. R. (with DEANE, PHYLLIS), *Abstract of British Historical Statistics*, Cambridge, 1962.

MITCHISON, ROSALIND, 'The Old Board of Agriculture (1793–1822)', *English Historical Review* (January 1959), 41–69.

MITCHISON, ROSALIND, *Agricultural Sir John. The Life of Sir John Sinclair of Ulbster, 1754–1835*, London, 1962.

MORRELL, L. A., *The American Shepherd: being a History of the Sheep, with their Breeds, Management, and Diseases . . . With an Appendix, embracing upwards of Twenty Letters from Eminent Wool-Growers and Sheep Fatteners of Different States, Detailing their Respective Modes of Management*, New York, 1851.

MORRIS, J., 'The West of England woollen industry, 1750–1840', *Bulletin of the Institute of Historical Research*, XIII (1935), 106.

NEITZSCHUTZ, W. VON, *Studien zur Entwicklelungs-Geschichte des Schafes*, Danzig, 1873.

ONSLOW, S. MACARTHUR, *Some Early Records of the Macarthurs of Camden*, Sydney, 1914.

PARGELLIS, STANLEY AND MEDLEY, D. J. (eds.), *Bibliography of British History. The Eighteenth Century, 1714–1789*, Oxford, n.d.

PAWSON, CECIL H., *Robert Bakewell. Pioneer Livestock Breeder*, London, 1957.

PETRIE, SIR CHARLES, *George Canning*, London, 1946.

PLUMB, J. H., *The First Four Georges*, London, 1957.

PONTING, K. G., *A History of the West of England Cloth Industry*, London, 1957.

PROTHERO, ROWLAND E. [BARON ERNLE], *English Farming, Past and Present*, London, 1961.

PUGH, L. P., *From Farriery to Veterinary Medicine*, Cambridge, 1962.

RANDALL, HENRY S., *Fine Wool Sheep Husbandry. With an Appendix containing Valuable Statistics in reference to Wool Culture, Imports, Prices of Fine Wool from 1840 to August 1st, 1863, etc.*, New York, 1863.

SCOTT WATSON, J. A. AND HOBBS, MAY ELLIOT, *Great Farmers*, London, 1937.

SENKEL, WILLY, *Wollproduktion und Wollhandel im XIX Jarhundert mit besonderer Berucksichtigung Deutschlands*, Tübingen, 1901.

SHAW, THOMAS, *The Australian Merino, being a treatise upon Wool Growing in Australia*, Melbourne, 1849.

SMART, WILLIAM, *Economic Annals of the Nineteenth Century, 1801–20*, London, 1910.

SMITH, ADAM, *The Wealth of Nations* (fifth edition, 1789), London, 1961.

SMITH, EDWARD, *The Life of Sir Joseph Banks, President of the Royal Society with Some Notices of his Friends and Contemporaries*, London, 1911.

SOUTHEY, THOMAS, *The Rise, Progress and Present State of Colonial Sheep and Wools, continued from 1846, and comprising those of Australia, Van Diemen's Land, New Zealand, South Africa, China . . .*, London, 1851.

SPOTTEL, WALTHER AND TANZER, ERNST, 'Rassenanalytische Untersuchungen an Schafen unter besonderen Berucksichtigung von Haut und Haar', *Archiv fur Naturgeschichte*, Band 89, A. Heft 6 (1923), 1–242.

STIRLING, A. M. W., *Coke of Norfolk and his friends. The life of Thomas William Coke of Holkham, first Earl of Leicester*, London, 1908.

SUMMERSON, JOHN, *Georgian London*, London, 1945.

TAYLOR, R. R., 'The History of the Merino and the Development of Fine Wool Pure Merino Sheep in Tasmania', *The Tasmanian Journal of Agriculture* (August 1949), 149–57.

THE JONDARYAN WOOLSORTER, *A Treatise on Wool Growing and Merino Breeding*, Brisbane, 1868.

THIRSK, JOAN, *English Peasant Farming. The Agrarian History of Lincolnshire from Tudor to Recent Times*, London, 1957.

THOM, H. B., *Die Geskiedenis van die Skaapboerdery in Suid Afrika*, Amsterdam, 1936.

TROW-SMITH, ROBERT, *A History of British Livestock Husbandry, 1700–1900*, London, 1959.

WALLACE, ROBERT, *Farm Live Stock of Great Britain*, Edinburgh, 1923.

WATSON, J. STEPHEN, *The Reign of George III, 1760–1820*, Oxford, 1960.

WELLINGTON, 2ND DUKE OF (ed.), *Supplementary Despatches, Correspondence and Memoranda of Field Marshal, Arthur, Duke of Wellington, K.G.*, vol. VI, London, 1860.

WILKINS, GUY L., 'A Catalogue and Historical Account of the Banks Shell Collection', *Bulletin of the British Museum (Natural History), Historical Series*, I (London, 1955), 69–119, Plates 4–14.

WILSON, CHARLES, 'Cloth Production and International Competition in the Seventeenth Century', *Economic History Review* (second series), XIII (1960), 209–21.

WILSON, JOHN, 'On the Various Breeds of Sheep in Great Britain especially with reference to the Character and Value of their Wool', *Journal of the Royal Agricultural Society of England*, 1855, XVI (1).

WOOD, ALEXANDER, *Thomas Young, Natural Philosopher, 1773–1829*, Cambridge, 1954.

WOOL INDUSTRIES RESEARCH ASSOCIATION, *Wool Research, 1918–1948*. Volume 6, *Drawing and Spinning*, London and Bradford, 1949.

WRIGHT, C. W., *Wool-Growing and the Tariff*, Harvard Economic Studies, V, Cambridge, Massachusetts, 1910.

YOUATT, WILLIAM, *Sheep: Their Breeds, Management, and Diseases. To which is added The Mountain Shepherd's Manual*, London, 1837.

REFERENCE NOTES

ABBREVIATIONS

AA: *Annals of Agriculture*
AM: *Agricultural Magazine*
AR: *Annual Register*
BAO: Correspondence of Banks, Boulton, and Watt in the Birmingham Assay Office. Not numbered.
BM.A.MSS: The British Museum Additional Manuscripts. Quoted by number and folio.
BM(SC): The British Museum (Natural History), microfilm copies of the Banks Papers in the Sutro Library, San Francisco, California. Quoted by series (I–IV), volume (e.g. 1–22) and folio (e.g. 1–50). In the Department of Botany, B.M.(N.H.).
Bodleian: The Bodleian Library, Oxford.
CBA: *Communications to the Board of Agriculture*, vols. I–VII.
DTC: The British Museum (Natural History), copies of the correspondence of Sir Joseph Banks made for Dawson Turner, F.R.S., of Great Yarmouth in 1833–4 by his daughters. Quoted by volume (e.g. 1–xx) and folio (e.g. 1–100 etc.). In the Department of Botany, B.M.(N.H.).
GM. *Gentleman's Magazine.*
HRA: *Historical Records of Australia.* Quoted by series and volume.
HRNSW: *Historical Records of New South Wales.* Quoted by volumes.
Kew BC: The Library of the Royal Botanic Gardens Banks Collection.
LPBS: *Letters and Papers of the Bath and West of England Society.*
ML: The Mitchell Library, Sydney, New South Wales.
NLS: The National Library of Scotland, Edinburgh.
SAS: *The Statistical Account of Scotland 1790–8.* Quoted by volumes.
WPR: *Cobbett's Weekly Political Register.*

CHAPTER I: THE BACKGROUND, 1700–1800

1. Anderson, Adam, *An Historical and Chronological Deduction of the Origin of Commerce*, vols. I–IV (1787–9). The extensive tables in this work showing the import and export values from 1701 to 1785 for the countries of Western Europe give perhaps the best single picture of this relationship. However, these and all statistics referred to in this volume should be examined and checked against the data in the volume published since this work was finalized, viz., *Abstract of British Historical Statistics* by B. R. Mitchell with the collaboration of Phyllis Deane (1962). Nearly all the data used by the present author have been summarized and presented critically by Mitchell and Deane in their *Abstract* whose authority must be taken as paramount where discrepancies are found.

2. Perhaps the most authoritative study of the wool supplies of Great Britain up to the beginning of the eighteenth century is that by Bowden, Peter J., *The Wool Trade in Tudor and Stuart England* (London, 1962). The evolving place of Spanish fine wool in British manufacturing is made very clear.

3. For the purposes of approximate calculation the following contemporary currency values seem reasonable:
   1 doubloon or doblon=17 shillings and 4 pence sterling=4 pieces of eight.
   1 piece of eight=4 shillings and 4 pence sterling.
   1 real vellon=2·81d. sterling=34 maravedis=25 centimes.
   1 franc or livre tournois=11·24 pence sterling up to about 1726; =10·50 pence sterling approximately thereafter.
   3 livres=1 écu; 24 livres=1 louis.
   1 livre=20 sous; 1 sou=12 deniers=4 liards.

4. 'A Discourse by Sir William Godolphin touching the Wools of Spain.' Attached to a letter dated 24 December 1667 (O.S.) to Lord Arlington from Bilbao. See *Hispana Illustrata . . .*, London, 1703, 106–9.

5. According to Townsend, Joseph, *A Journey through Spain in the Years 1786 and 1787 . . .* (1792), the merchants reckoned the weight equivalents thus:

1 quintal=4 arrobas=93 pounds avoirdupois. Thus 1 arroba=23·2 pounds avoirdupois.
On the other hand Dillon, John Talbot, *Travels through Spain* . . . (1782) assesses the relative weight thus:
1 quintal=4 arrobas=97 pounds avoirdupois=100 pounds Spanish. Thus 1 arroba=24·25 pounds avoirdupois=25 pounds Spanish.

However, the common calculation for general purposes seems to have been:

1 arroba = 25 pounds approximately,
1 quintal=100 pounds approximately,
and 1 bag   =200 pounds approximately.

6. Cf. this chapter, note 4.

7. Young, Arthur, *The Farmer's Letters to the People of England* (1767), 22.

8. For the evolution of the industrial pattern in the eighteenth century it is difficult to pass the study of Mantoux, Paul, *The Industrial Revolution in the Eighteenth Century* (1961), supplemented by that of Halévy, Élie, *A History of the English People in the Nineteenth Century. I. England in 1815* (1961), for the transition to the nineteenth-century background.

9. 1st Earl of Sheffield, *Observations on the Commerce of the American States* . . . (1783), for a discussion of the situation arising out of William Pitt's 'bill for the provisional establishment and regulation of trade and intercourse between the subjects of Great Britain and those of the United States of America'.

10. Cf. Henry Lacocke to Sir Joseph Banks, 8 October 1799, BM(SC), II, **8**, 5-6, for the prices of these sorts in 1799; and Henry Lacocke to Sir Joseph Banks, 22 July 1800, *ibid.*, **5**, 39-40, for the prices in 1800.

CHAPTER II: THE FOREGROUND, 1782-1788

1. Henry Pacey to Sir Joseph Banks, 17 October 1781, BM(SC), III, **9**, 4-5.

2. Bischoff, James, *A Comprehensive History* . . . (London, 1842), I, 208.

3. *Ibid.*, 209.

4. *Cambridge Chronicle*, 19 January 1782.

5. Bischoff James, *A Comprehensive History* . . . (1842), I, 209-10.

6. Charles Chaplin to Sir Joseph Banks, 30 November 1781, BM(SC), III, **8**, 19-20.

7. Sir John Dalrymple to Sir Joseph Banks, 5 December 1781, *ibid.*, 47-8.

8. Benjamin Stephenson to Sir Joseph Banks, 12 December 1781, *ibid.*, **9**, 36-8.

9. Henry Pacey to Sir Joseph Banks, 16 January 1782, *ibid.*, 12-13.

10. Bischoff, James, *A Comprehensive History* . . . (1842), I, 219-23.

11. *Ibid.*, 223-5.

12. Charles Chaplin to Sir Joseph Banks, 15 December 1781, BM(SC), III, **8**, 21-3.

13. Sir Joseph Banks to Charles Chaplin, 18 December 1781, *ibid.*, 23-6.

14. Sir Joseph Banks to 7th Viscount Stormont, 5 January 1782, *ibid.*, **10**, 1.

15. Charles Hellstedt to Sir Joseph Banks, 26 February 1782, *ibid.*, **10**, 10-11.

16. Charles Hellstedt to Sir Joseph Banks, 25 January 1782, *ibid.*, 6-7.

17. Charles Hellstedt to Sir Joseph Banks, 18 January 1782, *ibid.*, 2-3.

18. Robert Barclay to Charles Hellstedt, 15 February 1782, *ibid.*, 16-17.

19. Charles Hellstedt to Sir Joseph Banks, see this chapter, note 15.

20. MS. documents in French and German of which several translations into English are written in Banks's hand, BM(SC), III, **10**, 24-48.

21. News-cutting, *Herald News*, 7 February 1782, *ibid.*, **11**, 28.

22. MS. translation from the German, correspondent unknown, to Banks's hand, *ibid.*, **10**, 38.

23. Sir Joseph Banks to Sir John Dalrymple, 31 January 1782, *ibid.*, **8**, 56-8.

24. Sir John Dalrymple to Sir Joseph Banks, 5 February 1782, *ibid.*, 64-5.

25. News-cutting, *Herald News*, 2 February 1782, *ibid.*, **11**, 26.

26. News-cutting, *Herald News*, 5 February 1782, *ibid.*, 25.

27. Printed circular, *Resolutions of the Committee of Owners and Occupiers of Lands in the County of Lincoln* . . . , *ibid.*, 18-20.

28. *The Morning Herald*, 20 January 1782.

29. Charles Chaplin to Sir Joseph Banks, 27 February 1782, BM(SC), III, **8**, 38-9.

30. Charles Chaplin to Sir Joseph Banks, 13 April [1782], *ibid.*, 40-1.

31. *Minutes of the Evidence taken at the Bar of the House of Commons upon the Second Reading of the Bill to explain, amend, and reduce into One Act of Parliament* . . . [*of 1788*], *ibid.*, IV, **7**, 7-22.

32. *Report from the Committee* [*of the House of Commons*] *appointed to Consider of the Illicit Exportation of Wool, Live Sheep, Worsted and Yarn* (1786), *ibid.*, 1-7.

33. Charles Chaplin to Sir Joseph Banks, 31 May 1786, *ibid.*, III, **1**, 28-9.

34. *Resolutions of the Lincolnshire Wool Meeting, 19 October, 1786*, *ibid.*, 16-18.

35. 'Copy of Petition and Agreement for a Subscription.' MS. list of subscribers and the sums of money promised by each. *Ibid.*, 20–2.

36. *Evidence adduced [by the Manufacturers] in support of the Wool Bill, July 1786.* With a critical preface this was printed at the expense of the Lincolnshire Wool Committee. The Bill in question was John Anstie's first Bill. *Ibid.*, IV, **6**, 2–5.

37. Pemberton Milnes to the Reverend Mr. [—] Beveridge, 14 October 1786, *ibid.*, III, **1**, 11–12.

38. Sir Joseph Banks to 1st Baron Hawkesbury, 17 June 1788, *ibid.*, IV, **5**, 8–9.

39. 1st Baron Hawkesbury to Sir Joseph Banks, 18 June 1788, *ibid.*, 10.

40. *A Bill, intituled An Act to explain, amend, and reduce into One Act of Parliament, several Laws now in being for preventing the Exportation of live Sheep, Rams, and Lambs, Wool, Woolfels, Mortlings, Shortlings, Yarn, and Worsted, Cruels, Coverlids, Waddings, and other Manufactures, or pretended Manufactures, made of Wool slightly wrought up, or otherwise put together, so as the same may be reduced to and made use of as Wool again, Mattresses, or Beds stuffed with combed Wool, or Wool fit for combing, Fullers Earth, Fulling Clay, and Tobacco-pipe Clay, from this Kingdom, and from the Isles of Jersey, Guernsey, Alderney, Sark, and Man, into Foreign Parts; and for rendering more effectual an Act passed in the Twenty-Third Year of the Reign of King Henry the Eighth, intituled, An Act for the Winding of Wool* (1788). When this was passed as the Act 28 Geo. III, c. 38, Banks's clause was section 14. *Ibid.*, 1–35.

CHAPTER III: THE SAVANTS, 1782–1794

1. Under the title *Ichthyologia sistens Piscium descriptiones et Icones decas prima*, London, 1782 and 1785.

2. Pierre-Auguste Broussonet to Sir Joseph Banks, 20 January 1783, BM.A.MSS., 8095, 124–5 et seq.

3. This was the paper 'Sur le premier Drap de Laine Superfine du cru de la France' by L.-J.-M. Daubenton. Pierre-Auguste Broussonet to Sir Joseph Banks, 22 April 1784, BM.A.MSS., 8095, 253–4.

4. Louis-Jean-Marie Daubenton to Pierre-Auguste Broussonet, 26 August 1784, *ibid.*, 260. Enclosed with Pierre-Auguste Broussonet to Sir Joseph Banks, 3 September 1784, *ibid.*, 261.

5. Pierre-Auguste Broussonet to Sir Joseph Banks, 23 August 1785, *ibid.*, 8096, 56–8.

6. Daubenton, L.-J.-M., *Instructions pour Les Bergers . . .* (1782), 282–301. This is the memoir read before the Académie Royale des Science, 9 April 1777.

7. Carlier, Abbé Claude, *Considerations sur les moyens de rétablir en France les bonnes éspèces des bêtes-à-laine*, Paris, 1762.

8. Cf. Chapter V, note 3.

9. Young, Arthur, *Travels in the Years 1787, 1788, and 1789 . . .*, I (1793), 140.

10. Young had met Broussonet very briefly for the first time on 27 May 1787 as he passed through Paris *en route* for the Pyrenees. *Ibid.*, 18.

11. *Ibid.*, 141.

12. *Ibid.*, 239.

13. Wichmann, Christian Auguste, *Catechismus des Schafzucht* (1795). Cited by Huzard, Jean-Baptiste, in the Preface to *Instructions pour Les Bergers . . .* (fourth edition, ed. J.-B. Huzard, 1810), xliv.

14. Pierre-Auguste Broussonet to Sir Joseph Banks, 16 June 1785, BM.A.MSS., 8096, 50–1.

15. John Sinclair to Sir Joseph Banks, 1 September 1785, *ibid.*, 33978, 27.

16. MS. notes, Spring Grove sheep account for 1786, BM(SC), I, **17**, 40.

17. The planet Uranus, discovered by Herschel in 1781.

18. William Herschel to Sir Joseph Banks, 26 August 1782, DTC, II, 172; also 22 November 1785, *ibid.*, IV, 169.

19. Faujas de Saint-Fond, Barthelemi, *Travels in England, Scotland, and the Hebrides . . .*, I (1799), 59–64.

20. MS. note by Banks: 'The two Spanish Fleeces of this year [1786] with the two of 1787 made two Coats of Superfine Broad Cloth which I wore & found as good as any made of Real Spanish wool Mr [Matthew] Humphries made the Cloth', BM(SC), I, **17**, 39.

21. MS. draft, *ibid.*, III, **5**, 27–41.

22. 1st Earl Sheffield to Sir Joseph Banks, 8 June 1787, *ibid.*, 41–3.

23. Adeane, J. H., *The Girlhood of Maria Josepha Holroyd . . .* (1896), 23.

24. Aunt 'Serena' was Sarah Holroyd.

25. Sunday, 2 August 1788.

26. Adeane, J. H., *The Girlhood of Maria Josepha Holroyd . . .* (1896), 29.

27. *Ibid.*, 17.

28. 'Sketch of a Chronological Account of the Introduction of Merino Sheep into the United Kingdom', BM(SC), II, **1**, 60–1.

29. MS. note by Banks, *ibid.*, I, **17**, 50.

30. *Ibid.*, 44.

31. *Ibid.*, 47.

32. 'Sketch of a Chronological Account . . .', *ibid.*, II, **1**, 60–1.

33. MS. note by Banks, *ibid.*, I, **17**, 48.

34. It is worthy of note that the washed fleece of this ewe weighed 5 pounds, equivalent roughly to 7 pounds in its natural state. The weight is interesting in view of the particular cross and what it suggests about the character of the Wiltshire fleece in 1792.

35. MS. note by Banks, BM(SC), I, **17**, 47. Cf. also *Catalogue of the Contents of the Museum of the Royal College of Surgeons in London* (Francis Warr, Red Lion Passage, London, 1831), Part III, *The Human and Comparative Osteology*, 150–1. Item 1036 is 'Horns of a Sheep. Merino variety Ovis Hispanicus, Linn.' Item 1037 is 'Skull and Horns of a Ram. Merino var. Ovis Hispanicus.' Items 1038 and 1039 have the same description. It is almost certain that John Hunter would have obtained these from Sir Joseph Banks. They may have included his own ram and others from the King's flock. After an investigation the author feels, with Miss Jessie Dobson the present Curator of the Museum, that these specimens were certainly lost with the greater part of the Hunterian osteology collection when the College was bombed during the last war.

36. Sir Joseph Banks to an unknown, 24 February 1795, BM(SC), I, **17**, 50.

37. Robert Liston to William Burton Conyngham, NLS, Liston Papers, 5539, ff. 11, 23–6, 107–16.

38. William Burton Conyngham to Sir Joseph Banks, 28 June 1788, BM(SC), II, **1**, 12–14.

39. H. S. Hole to Sir Joseph Banks, 7 August 1788, *ibid.*, 14–16.

40. William Burton Conyngham to Sir Joseph Banks, 13 July 1791, *ibid.*, 19–20.

41. Thomas Sibbert to Sir Joseph Banks, 15 June 1791, *ibid.*, 22–3.

42. Pierre-Auguste Broussonet to Sir Joseph Banks, 29 December 1785, BM.A.MSS., 8096, 232.

43. 'Preliminary Observations on the Origin of the Board of Agriculture and its Progress for Three Years after its Establishment. By The President of the Board [Sir John Sinclair]', 4 September 1796, CBA, I, iv–xiv.

44. Arthur Young always seems to have felt slightly aggrieved about the origin of the Board of Agriculture, claiming that he had the idea as far back as 1767. The fact remains that Sinclair brought it into being.

45. Pierre-Auguste Broussonet to Sir Joseph Banks, 24 October 1790, BM.A.MSS., 8097, 285–6.

46. 'Substance of a Conversation between Lord Daer and M. Broussonet respecting Spanish Sheep and Wool, at Paris, on 4th June 1791', *The Farmer's Magazine*, VI, August 1805, 302–3.

47. Lord Daer to Sir John Sinclair, 29 June 1791, *ibid.*, 301.

48. 'Transactions of the Society for the Improvement of British Wool from the date of its Institution on the 31st of January 1791 to the 31st of January 1792', MS. copy, BM(SC), I, **19**, 32–40.

49. This was the contemporary name for the Brighton of today.

50. Sir John Sinclair to Sir Joseph Banks, [— July 1791], BM.A.MSS., 33979, 107.

51. Sir Joseph Banks to Sir John Sinclair, 11 August 1791, BM(SC), II, **6**, 52.

52. Sir John Sinclair to Sir Joseph Banks, 5 August 1791, BM.A.MSS., 33979, 108.

53. Sir Joseph Banks to Sir John Sinclair, [— July 1791], *ibid.*, 107.

54. Cf. this chapter, note 48.

55. News-cutting, *Edinburgh Oracle*, 1 October 1791, BM(SC), II, **6**, 62.

56. A particular case is the correspondence of Antoine-Laurent Lavoisier, the great chemist, who was executed during the Reign of Terror on 8 May 1794. Letters to him from such men as Joseph Black, Joseph Priestley, Josiah Wedgwood, and many others were examined by a committee which, incidentally, included Fourcroy the chemist and the former associate of Pierre-Auguste Broussonet at Alfort. These documents were included among the pretexts for Lavoisier's death-sentence 'for conspiracy with the enemies of France against the people'. The correspondence has been published: Mackie, D., 'Antoine-Laurent Lavoisier', *Notes and Records of the Royal Society*, VII (1950), I.

57. Abbé Theodore-Augustin Mann to Sir Joseph Banks, 9 July 1787, BM(SC), III, **6**, 25; the document enclosed with this letter is entitled 'Remarks upon the Wool of the Low Countries', *ibid.*, 22–3.

58. Pierre-Auguste Broussonet to Sir Joseph Banks, [— April 1786], BM.A.MSS., 8096, 238.

59. Pierre-Auguste Broussonet to Sir Joseph Banks, 2 April 1787, BM(SC), III, **6**, 17–19.

60. William Davy to 1st Earl Sheffield, 7 June 1787, *ibid.*, **5**, 43–4.

61. Cf. this chapter, note 59.

62. Pierre-Auguste Broussonet to Sir Joseph Banks, 14 May 1787, BM.A.MSS., 8096, 398–9.

63. Pierre-Auguste Broussonet to Sir Joseph Banks, 4 June 1787, *ibid.*, 400.

64. MS. note by Banks, BM(SC), II, **5**, 25.

65. L.-D. Mouron was a correspondent of Arthur Young. In the evidence given by Young the

following year before the Bar of the House of Commons in relation to the Wool Bill of 1788 the information gathered for him by Mouron is much quoted. See BM(SC), IV, **7**, 8–13. The letter from Sir Joseph Banks to L.-D. Mouron on 18 December 1787 is not extant at the British Museum. The reply to it is: L.-D. Mouron to Sir Joseph Banks, 28 December 1787, BM.A.MSS., 8096, 479.

66. John Walcot to Daniel Braithwaite, 21 December 1787, *ibid.*, 33978, 166.
67. John Walcot to Sir Joseph Banks, 26 December 1787, *ibid.*, 167–8.
68. L.-D. Mouron to Sir Joseph Banks, 29 December 1787, *ibid.*, 8006, 480.
69. John Walcot to Sir Joseph Banks, 1 January 1788, *ibid.*, 33978, 94.
70. L.-D. Mouron to Sir Joseph Banks, 4 January 1788, *ibid.*, 173.
71. R. Thompson to Sir Joseph Banks, 6 January 1788, *ibid.*, 174.
72. Customs certificate, BM(SC), II, **1**, 58.
73. MS. account of Thomas Winstone's route and expenses, *ibid.*, 57.
74. MS. notes by Banks, *ibid.*, 59.
75. Bertier de Sauvigny to Sir Joseph Banks, 16 May 1788, *ibid.*, III, **6**, 34–6.
76. 'Instruction given to the Council [*sic*] against the Wool Bill [of 1788]', by Sir Joseph Banks, AA, IX (1788), 479–506.
77. MS. notes by Banks and accounts of expenses, BM(SC), II, **5**, 25.
78. Pierre-Auguste Broussonet to Sir Joseph Banks, 23 April 1789, BM.A.MSS., 8097, 142–3.
79. Sir Joseph Banks to Pierre-Auguste Broussonet, 1 May 1789. Private collection of Professor John Read of the University of St. Andrews, Scotland. Cited by Read, John, *Humour and Humanism in Chemistry* (London, 1947), 338: 'I shall remember you when I get a kangaroo, the ship which carries the curiosities destined for me is not yet arrived, but if it does it will bring one which is yours . . .'.
80. Pierre-Auguste Broussonet to Sir Joseph Banks, 29 July 1789, BM.A.MSS., 8097, 146–7.

CHAPTER IV: THE BRITISH FACTORIES, 1787–1792

1. 5 January 1787, Dobson, Austin (ed.), *Diary and Letters of Madame D'Arblay*, III, 157.
2. 16 January 1787, *ibid.*, 161.
3. Bladon, F. McKno (ed.), *The Diaries of Colonel the Hon. Robert Fulke Greville* . . . Addendum at the end of first diary headed: 'Importation of Merino Sheep'.
4. Greville had, nevertheless, travelled in Saxony and learned much by direct observation and inquiry.
5. On this particular topic. The King and Banks had been closely associated already for almost fifteen years in the development of the Royal Gardens at Kew—especially the Exotic Garden. We can reasonably assume that the subject of sheep and wool had during this period been much discussed between the King and Banks in various ways. For five years past Banks had been active in the long arguments over the wool legislation and in early 1787 was publicly in the thick of the last abortive attempts of the Lincolnshire Wool Committee to defeat the embargo machinery brought forward by the manufacturers in the House of Commons. At all stages over the years the King had shown the closest interest in the argument and this alone could have been a thriving subject for discussion with Banks.
6. The progress of these plans is illuminated by the series of seven questions sent by Banks to Sir Morton Frederick Eden (later 1st Baron Henley), the youngest brother of William Eden 1st Lord Auckland. Morton Eden was Envoy Extraordinary in Saxony from 1783 to 1789. On 12 March 1787 Banks apparently sent these questions to him:

'1. Are the Spanish Sheep as much esteemd now as they were at First or have they degenerated
2. Has it been Found more advantageous to keep the Spanish Breed Pure or to Mix it with the Sheep of the Country
3. Are any Particular precautions necessary in the management of the Spanish Breed & if so What are they
4. Are the Sheep of the Country housd in the winter
5. At What Price did the Wool of the Spanish Sheep Sell for when they First came over & at What price does it now Sell
6. At What price does the dearest wool of the Country Sell & at what price does the cheapest Small Specimens of as many Sorts of Spanish Mixd & Saxon wool as can easily be procurd with their values will be a most acceptible communication
7. are the Spanish Sheep so defended that it would be impossible to procure any or could a score be procurd for a hansome price & driven to a Place from whence they may be sent here'.
The matter was evidently well attended to by Morton Eden for in May 1788 Banks noted: 'a long & very sensible answer was received to this paper purporting that the wool had not sensibly degenerated I put it into H.M. hands who never returnd it'. But no sheep were got from this source. BM(SC), I, **18**, 28–9.

7. There are various stories and some historical evidence that sheep from Spain were, in earlier centuries, brought into England. Whether any of these, as is often implied, were to be considered as Spanish Merinos is a matter for much further research. For the present I am content to accept the statement of Banks to the Duke of Grafton: 'I have not however been able to Learn from either history or tradition that Merino sheep were ever imported into this Country till the arrival of those his Majesty now possesses', 19 August 1791, BM(SC), II, **6**, 51. However, the question is still an open one in my opinion.

8. Sir Joseph Banks to Robert Walpole, [n.d. ?1787], BM(SC), I, **21**, 33. This was noted by Banks as having been sent to Evan Nepean to be forwarded to Walpole at Lisbon in 1787. It may have been sent at or about the same time at the questionnaire to Morton Eden, i.e. March.

9. Sir Joseph Banks to Thomas March, [n.d. but before March 1788 and probably in 1787], *ibid.*, 34-5.

10. Collier to Evan Nepean, 9 June 1788, *ibid.*, 57.

11. Henry Hinckley to an unknown (almost certainly Collier of New Broad Street), 15 July 1787, *ibid.*, 55-6.

12. Sir Joseph Banks to His Majesty King George III, 10 August 1787, DTC, v, 205-6. The extract from Henry Hinckley's letter was enclosed.

13. *Ibid.*

14. His Majesty King George III to Sir Joseph Banks, 10 August 1787, *ibid.*, 207.

15. His Majesty King George III to Sir Joseph Banks, 29 November 1787, *ibid.*, 283.

16. Captain Michael Firth to Sir Joseph Banks, 4 March [1788], BM(SC), I, **21**, 35.

17. Sir Joseph Banks to Thomas March, 31 May 1788, *ibid.*, 36-8. It may be noted here that a brand 'something like an H' is recorded on a bill of lading against wool from the Munoz *cabana* consigned to Messrs. Maitland, Sterry and Nettleship from Bilbao, 26 November 1802. Sent under cover of a letter from John Maitland to Sir Joseph Banks, 6 August 1803, BM.A.MSS., 33981, 119; bill of lading, *ibid.*, 121.

18. MS. draft by Banks in 1811 proposing the formation of an 'Anglo-Merino Society', BM(SC), II, **10**, 32-3; cf. also The Weather Diaries of Thomas Hoy kept at Sion House from August 1782 to March 1822, for the weather on 4 April 1788 at Kew immediately across the river. The grazing grounds of the Spanish flock lay mostly within a radius of one mile from Sion House. The present weather records kept at Kew Observatory record values at a point just a half a mile south-south-west of where Thomas Hoy took his observations.

19. The cost of this first illicit importation was £8 9s. 4d. including the cost of the sheep. On the account Banks has noted:

'Gave him [Captain Michael Firth] by H.M. permission 20 guineas in discharge of this bill & for his care & assistance April 23 1788

The sheep cost in Spain five shillings each The man who procurd them chargd for his trouble & Journey of more than 200 miles [£]1 : 16 which was thought so reasonable that the merchant & Capt. Firth agreed to make him a present of another 36 sh. peice'. BM(SC), III, **5**, 25.

20. See this chapter, note 17.

21. Thomas March to Sir Joseph Banks, 18 August 1788, BM(SC), I, **21**, 38-9.

22. Sir Joseph Banks to His Majesty King George III, 16 September 1788, *ibid.*, 40.

23. Sir Joseph Banks to Thomas March, 30 September 1788, *ibid.*, 39-40.

24. Sir Joseph Banks to 1st Earl of Liverpool, [9 November 1788], BM.A.MSS., 38223, 250.

25. Dobson, Austin (ed.), *Diary and Letters of Madame D'Arblay*, IV, 117-19.

26. *Ibid.*, 184.

27. *Ibid.*, 187-96. The White House was also known as the Queen's Lodge, Kew House, Kew Palace, and Kew Lodge. Its site was near the Broad Walk a little south-south-west from Museum No. 3. The house at present known as Kew Palace was the so-called Dutch House, known first as the Royal Nursery and then as the Prince's House. It was the house 'over the way', i.e. it stood on the opposite side from the White House of the old public road to Kew Gardens.

28. Bladon, F. McKno (ed.), *The Diaries of Colonel the Hon. Robert Fulke Greville . . .* , 172-3.

29. *Ibid.*, 239. Cf. also Sir Joseph Banks to an unknown, 23 February 1789, GM, xc (ii), August 1820, 99.

30. Bladon, F. McKno (ed.), *The Diaries of Colonel the Hon. Robert Fulke Greville . . .* , 240.

31. Dobson, Austin (ed.), *Diaries and Letters of Madame D'Arblay*, IV, 264-72.

32. Sir Joseph Banks to Thomas March, 10 April 1789, BM(SC), I, **21**, 40.

33. Thomas March to Sir Joseph Banks, 11 July 1789, *ibid.*

34. Sir Joseph Banks to Thomas March, 31 July 1789, *ibid.*, 41.

35. Sir Joseph Banks to His Majesty King George III, 25 November 1789, *ibid.*, **18**, 23-4.

36. William Warre to John Lodge, 19 April 1788, *ibid.*, II, **5**, 5.

37. William Warre to John Lodge, 16 March 1789, *ibid.*, I, **21**, 62-3.

38. William Warre to John Lodge, 6 June 1789, *ibid.*, II, **5**, 1-2.

39. Evan Nepean to Sir Joseph Banks, 24 June 1789, *ibid.*, **4**, 59-60.

40. Evan Nepean to Sir Joseph Banks, 22 November 1789, BM.A.MSS., 33978, 273.
41. See this chapter, note 35.
42. Robert Fulke Greville to Sir Joseph Banks, [November 1789], BM.A.MSS., 33982, 301-2; DTC, vi, 183.
43. Thomas March to Sir Joseph Banks, 22 February 1790, BM(SC), I, 21, 42.
44. Thomas March to Sir Joseph Banks, 24 April 1790, ibid.
45. Sir Joseph Banks to Thomas March, 19 July [1790], ibid., 43.
46. John March to Sir Joseph Banks, 14 July 1790, ibid., 44.
47. Sir Joseph Banks to John March, [— July 1790], ibid., 45.
48. John March to Sir Joseph Banks, 5 February 1791, ibid., 46-7.
49. John March to Sir Joseph Banks, [—] March 1791, ibid., 47.
50. Sir Joseph Banks to John March, 20 August 1791, ibid., 49-50.
51. John March to Sir Joseph Banks, 12 November 1791, ibid., 53-4.
52. Sir Joseph Banks to John March, 17 April 1792, ibid., 54.
53. John March to Sir Joseph Banks, 9 June 1792, ibid., 15, 33-4.

Chapter V: THE DIPLOMATS, 1787-1792

1. The extract is from an item headed 'Anecdote of the Introduction of Merino Sheep into England' published in The Australasian, 15 September 1888. It was said to have been found among the papers of a Dr. Bland, dated Sydney, January 1834, by a writer who signed himself 'H' but was otherwise unknown.
2. Sir Joseph Banks to William Eden, 20 March 1787, BM.A.MSS., 34424, 187-8.
3. The pamphlet which Banks had sought and received from Eden was the paper by L.-J.-M. Daubenton, Observations sur la comparaison de la nouvelle laine superfine de France, avec le plus belle laine d'Espagne, dans la fabrication du drap, read before the Académie Royale des Sciences on 16 November 1785. An Addition à ces observations was read on 29 March 1786. The two papers were printed that same year 'à l'imprimerie royale' in octavo, with twenty-four pages and a title-sheet. They appeared also in the Memoires of the Académie for 1785 (pp. 454 and 459) this volume actually being printed in 1788. Both papers appear together in Instructions pour Les Bergers . . . (fourth edition, ed. J.-B. Huzard, 1810), 343-61.
4. Sir Joseph Banks to William Eden, 11 May 1787, BM.A.MSS., 34424, 427-8.
5. 'Statement relative to the Sheep received from Madrid in consequence of Ld. Auckland's undertaking', DTC, viii, 53; also MS. note by Banks, BM(SC), I, 5, 20.
6. This was signed by William Eden and the Count de Montmorin. It was an explanation of the Thirteenth Article of the Treaty of Peace signed at Versailles on 3 September 1783.
7. Nevertheless, Arthur Young was in France that summer on his third and last tour of that country—5 June 1789 to 30 January 1790—and dining in Paris within a fortnight of the fall of the Bastille.
8. He was proclaimed on 17 January 1789 and crowned on 28 September 1789.
9. Anthony Merry to William Eden, 22 June 1789, BM.A.MSS., 34429, 316-17.
10. Anthony Merry to William Eden, 16 July 1789, ibid., 359-60.
11. Sir Joseph Banks to His Majesty King George III, 25 November 1789, BM(SC), I, 18, 24.
12. Anthony Merry to Sir Joseph Banks, 1 May 1792, ibid., 20, 42-3.
13. Cf. this chapter, note 5.
14. Lord Auckland to Sir Joseph Banks, 3 April 1790, ibid., 5, 18.
15. Ellis, K. L., 'British Communications and Diplomacy in the Eighteenth Century', Bull. Inst. Hist. Res., xxxi (1958), 159-67.
16. Lord Auckland to Sir Joseph Banks, 14 September 1790, BM(SC), I, 5, 21-2.
17. Sir Joseph Banks to Lord Auckland, 17 December 1790, BM.A.MSS., 34434, 335-6.
18. Lord Auckland to Sir Joseph Banks, 29 December 1790, DTC, viii, 184.
19. Captain John Burnell to Sir Joseph Banks, 15 October 1791, BM(SC), I, 20, 11.
20. Sir Joseph Banks to Lord Auckland, 23 October 1791, ibid., 15.
21. Lord Auckland to Sir Joseph Banks, 28 October 1791, ibid., 5, 19-20.
22. William Seward to Sir Joseph Banks, 16 October 1791, ibid., 20, 16-17.
23. Anthony Merry to Sir Joseph Banks, 26 September 1791, ibid., 17-18.
24. Sir Joseph Banks to David Maclean, 23 October 1791, ibid., 14.
25. Sir Joseph Banks to the Commissioners of His Majesty's Customs, 23 October 1791, ibid., 15.
26. David Maclean to Sir Joseph Banks, 26 October 1791, ibid., 23.
27. Sir Joseph Banks to Captain John Burnell, 23 October 1791, ibid., 13-14.
28. Captain John Burnell to Sir Joseph Banks, 27 October 1791, ibid., 22-3.
29. Anthony Merry to Sir Joseph Banks, 17 October 1791, ibid., 30-1.
30. Bill of lading signed by Captain John Burnell, 7 October 1791, ibid., 12.

31. Captain John Burnell to Sir Joseph Banks, 26 October 1791, *ibid.*, 20–1.
32. See this chapter, note 28.
33. Captain John Burnell to Sir Joseph Banks, 29 October 1791, *ibid.*, 27.
34. William Seward to Sir Joseph Banks, 29 October 1791, *ibid.*, 25–6.
35. Sir Joseph Banks to David Maclean, 3 November [1791], *ibid.*, 24.
36. David Maclean to Sir Joseph Banks, 5 November 1791, *ibid.*, 27.
37. Sir Joseph Banks to William Smith, 11 November 1791, *ibid.*, 33–4.
38. William Smith and W. Pintott to Sir Joseph Banks, 12 November 1791, *ibid.*, 34–5.
39. MS. diary notes by Banks, *ibid.*, 36–7.
40. MS. account by William Whiteway and Thomas Zurd, 'The Expences of the Spanish Sheep in coming from Southampton', *ibid.*, 35.
41. Sir Joseph Banks to Ramsay Robinson, 15 November 1791, *ibid.*, 35.
42. Ramsay Robinson to Sir Joseph Banks, 16 November 1791, *ibid.*, 36.
43. MS. diary notes, see this chapter, note 39.
44. *Ibid.*
45. Lord Auckland to Sir Joseph Banks, 8 November 1791, DTC, VII, 271.
46. Anthony Merry to Lord Auckland, 17 October 1791, *ibid.*, 272–3. In the Dawson Turner Copies this letter is wrongly noted as having been addressed to Lord St. Helens, who was at the date of writing still in Spain with Merry. The context and the circumstances make it clear that it was addressed to Lord Auckland, continuing former correspondence on the same subject. It is certainly the enclosure referred to by Auckland in his letter of 8 November (cf. this chapter, note 45) and by this route it entered the correspondence files of Banks. Cf. also Banks's own references to the subject in his letter to Merry of 30 November 1791, BM(SC), I, **20**, 38–40.
47. It should be noted that Count Bernardo del Campo di Alange, as Spanish Minister Plenipotentiary at the Court of St. James's, had on 9 June 1789 given a notable fête in the gardens at Ranelagh to celebrate His Majesty's recovery. He was much in the social circle at Windsor apart from his diplomatic occasions. Of this we have another glimpse from Fanny Burney as she notes the month of June 1789: 'This month, till our journey to Weymouth took place, passed without mark or likelihood, save one little token of Spanish gallantry from the Marquis del Campo, who, when he came to Windsor, after reproving me very civilly for being absent from his fete [she had been suffering from facial neuritis], told me he had remembered me during the drawing of his lottery that night, and "had taken the liberty to bring me my prize", which was a blue enamel ring with a motto.

'Now, though this remembrance on such an evening was impossible, there was no refusing, without affronting him, the very good-humoured and polite pretence.' Dobson, Austin (ed.), *Diary and Letters of Madame D'Arblay*, IV, 289.
48. Anthony Merry to Lord Auckland, cf. this chapter, note 46.
49. *Ibid.*
50. MS. note by Banks, BM(SC), I, **20**, 33.
51. Sir Joseph Banks to Anthony Merry, 30 November 1791, *ibid.*, 38–40.
52. *Ibid.*
53. Sir Joseph Banks to James Bland Burgess, 2 December 1791, *ibid.*, 40.
54. James Bland Burgess to Sir Joseph Banks, 7 January 1792, *ibid.*, 41.
55. Sir Robert Murray Keith to James Bland Burgess, 24 December 1791, *ibid.*
56. Anthony Merry to Sir Joseph Banks, 1 May 1792, *ibid.*, 42–3.
57. Sir Joseph Banks to Anthony Merry, [— May 1792], *ibid.*, 44–5.
58. 'A Statement of Moneys Paid by Sir Jos: Banks on account of the King Principally on account of his Majesties Spanish Flock', *ibid.*, I, **14**, 47.
59. See this chapter, note 5.
60. *Edinburgh Evening Courant*, No. 11, 589, Thursday, 30 August 1792.
61. Sir Joseph Banks to His Majesty King George III, 6 August 1793 (fourth report), BM(SC), I, **16**, 8–13.
62. Ilminster, Earl of (ed.), *The Spanish Journal of Elizabeth Lady Holland* (1910), 322.

CHAPTER VI: THE FAITHFUL SHEPHERD, 1788–1811

1. Cf. Chapter IV, note 5.
2. Bladon, F. McKno (ed.), *The Diaries of Colonel the Hon. Robert Fulke Greville . . .* , 320–2.
3. Robert Fulke Greville to Sir Joseph Banks, [26 or 27] November 1789, BM.A.MSS., 33982, 301; DTC, VI, 183. See also Chapter IV, note 42.
4. MS. diary notes, BM(SC), I, **18**, 21.
5. MS. diary notes, *ibid.*, 32.
6. MS. diary notes, *ibid.*, 27.
7. *Ibid.*

8. MS. diary notes, *ibid.*, II, **6**, 54.

9. MS. diary notes, *ibid.*, 53.

10. *Ibid.*

11. MS. 'General Account', a copy of which was given to the King on 5 August 1791, *ibid.*, **5**, 28.

12. Sir Joseph Banks to John Robinson, 7 August 1791, *ibid.*, **6**, 45–6.

13. *Ibid.*

14. Ramsay Robinson to Sir Joseph Banks, 6 April 1792, *ibid.*, I, **17**, 8.

15. MS. diary notes, *ibid.*, **22**, 24.

16. Ramsay Robinson to Sir Joseph Banks, 28 May 1792, *ibid.*, **17**, 11.

17. MS. diary notes, *ibid.*, 9–10.

18. Under the heading 'Destinations Proposed by Sʳ Jos: Banks, for his Majesties Spare Rams', and dated 11 August 1792, *ibid.*, **16**, 19–20.

19. 'A Report of the State of His Majesty's Flock of Fine Wooled Spanish Sheep For the Year ending Michaelmas 1803', *ibid.*, II, **11**, 126–7.

20. Robert Fulke Greville to Sir Joseph Banks, 27 October 1794, *ibid.*, **2**, 50–1.

21. MS. diary notes, *ibid.*, I, **13**, 24.

22. MS. diary notes (review of rams), *ibid.*, II, **2**, 43–4.

23. MS. diary notes, *ibid*, I, **13**, 24–6.

24. Sir Joseph Banks to Robert Fulke Greville, 13 August [1796], *ibid.*, **17**, 27.

25. MS. diary notes, *ibid.*, **10**, 41–2.

26. MS. 'Report on the King's Flock of Merinos (with two Appendices)' by Banks, [1797]. DTC, x², 136–52. ' . . . The principal disease of the Flock was according to the Shepherd's account, the Scour, owing in his opinion to the coldness and dampness of the Spring; had Sir Joseph been apprised of the state of the Flock, which the feeble state of his health prevented him from visiting during the cold weather, it is more than probable many might have been sav'd, by giving them some slight shelter & a small proportion of bran mix'd with a few oats and a little salt to them that were diseased . . .' .

27. MS. notes, BM(SC), I, **19**, 47–8.

28. 'An account of the Expences of the King's Spanish Flock . . .' , *ibid.*, II, **7**, 21.

29. Robert Dickson to Sir Joseph Banks, 28 May 1798, *ibid.*, I, **19**, 51.

30. Sir Joseph Banks to Robert Dickson, 1 June 1798, *ibid.*

31. MS. diary notes, *ibid.*, **22**, 23.

32. *Ibid.*

33. The 'disease' was most probably a massive infestation by the large stomach worm of sheep (*Haemonchus contortus*).

34. The term 'goggles' may almost certainly be equated with 'scrapie'. There are many contemporary references to the condition but these two will serve to describe the condition and to set it in the context of the late eighteenth century. They also have a familiar modern ring: (1) ' . . . It is incumbent on me to take notice of a disorder peculiar to sheep, which is sometimes fatally experienced in this county [Dorset], called the Goggles; it attacks them at all ages, and no remedy is at present known for it; the first symptom is a violent itching, which is very soon succeeded by a dizziness in the head, staggering of gait, and a weakness in the back, as if the spinal marrow was affected, under which they languish a few weeks, and this disorder has been known to be fatal to the greatest part of a flock, and it is considered as the most calamitous circumstance, the sheep owners have to dread. . . .' Claridge, John, *General View of the Agriculture of Dorset . . .* (1793), 10.

(2) ' . . . As to the disorder called the *goggles*, which has operated more to bring the Wiltshire kind of sheep into discredit than all the other reasons put together, it being so dispersed through the flocks, and at the same time kept so secretly, that no breeder has, for some years past, known where to buy a ram, without running the risque of introducing the disorder into his flock. It does not clearly appear when this disorder was introduced into Wiltshire, nor is it certain that it is peculiar to this kind of sheep.

It was very little noticed in Wiltshire till about twenty five years ago [i.e. about 1770]; and yet it is certain that a disorder, though called by another name, was known in Lincolnshire upwards of forty years ago [i.e. about 1745] '. . . called the rickets or shaking . . . ; that it was communicated in the blood by the rams, and would frequently be in the blood twelve months or two years before it was perceivable; but that when once a sheep had this disorder, it never recovered.'

Perhaps the reason why this disorder has been of late chiefly known as the *Wiltshire disorder*, is that the greatest part of the Wiltshire sheep are sold off when lambs, with intent to be fattened before they are two years old; and if the goggles is in the blood, the pushing them with high keep at that age, will be sure to shew it.

Many thousands that have been sold, not only out of Wilts, but also out of Hants and Dorset, have shewn it; . . . However the disorder has been for a long time on the decline; and will if care be taken in selecting rams, probably soon wear out.' Davis, Thomas, *General View of the Agriculture of the County of Wilts* . . . (1794).

Yet at Mr. Anderdon's sale of half- to three-quarter-bred Spanish Merinos at Henlade near Taunton in June 1806 it was thought necessary to advertise them as 'Warranted free from Goggles.' BM(SC), I, **20**, 52.

35. 'Monthly Return of His Majesty's Sheep at Oatlands', 2 November 1798, *ibid.*, **19**, 56.

36. Sir Joseph Banks to Robert Dickson, [— November 1798], *ibid.*, 56 (recto) and *ibid.*, **20**, 1 (verso).

37. Robert Dickson to Sir Joseph Banks, 2 December 1798, *ibid.*, **20**, 1.

38. Sir Joseph Banks to Ramsay Robinson, 10 February 1799, *ibid.*, II, **7**, 47.

39. *Ibid.* [footnote].

40. MS. diary notes, *ibid.*, I, **22**, 22.

41. 'Expences of the Spanish Flock at Oatlands from The 29th of May 1798 to The 29th of May 1799', MS. account, *ibid.*, II, **7**, 30.

42. 'Account of the Proceeds from the wool of his majesties Spanish Flock', MS. notes, *ibid.*, **5**, 10.

43. MS. diary notes, *ibid.*, I, **22**, 22.

44. MS. diary notes, *ibid.*, 24.

45. MS. notes, *ibid.*, **20**, 49.

46. Sir Joseph Banks to Matthew Boulton, 26 June 1799, BAO (65).

47. Matthew Boulton to Sir Joseph Banks, 28 June 1799, *ibid.* (66).

48. Matthew Boulton to Sir Joseph Banks, 4 July 1799, *ibid.* (67).

49. Sir Joseph Banks to Matthew Boulton, 6 July 1799, *ibid.* (68).

50. MS. diary notes, BM(SC), I, **22**, 22.

51. Sir Joseph Banks to Matthew Boulton, 10 July 1799, BAO (69).

52. Matthew Boulton to Sir Joseph Banks, 14 July 1799, BM(SC), II, **7**, 44–5.

53. Sir Joseph Banks to Matthew Boulton, 17 July 1799, BAO (70).

54. Matthew Boulton to Sir Joseph Banks, 22 July 1799, BM(SC), II, **7**, 46.

55. News-cutting, paper unknown, *ibid.*, 55.

56. Sir Joseph Banks to Matthew Boulton, 2 August 1799, BAO (71).

57. MS. diary notes, BM(SC), I, **22**, 23.

58. MS. note, *ibid.*, II, **4**, 37.

59. William Cheshire to Sir Joseph Banks, 22 May 1800 (with account enclosed), *ibid.*, **5**, 48.

60. Sir Joseph Banks to Ramsay Robinson, 22 July 1801, *ibid.*, **4**, 44–5.

61. Ramsay Robinson to Sir Joseph Banks, 23 July 1801, *ibid.*, 45–6.

62. Sir Joseph Banks to Henry Lacocke, 11 August 1801, *ibid.*, 40.

63. Sir Joseph Banks to Ramsay Robinson, 14 August [1801], *ibid*, 39.

64. Henry Lacocke to Sir Joseph Banks, 6 October 1801, *ibid.*, I, **14**, 45–6.

65. Richard Snart to Sir Joseph Banks, 21 September 1802, *ibid.*, **13**, 6–7.

66. Sir Joseph Banks to Richard Snart, 26 September [1802], *ibid.*, 7.

67. Henry Lacocke to Sir Joseph Banks. 18 September 1802, *ibid.*, 9–10.

68. Cf. Henry Lacocke to Sir Joseph Banks, [— October 1802], *ibid.*, 8–9.

69. 'Monthly Return of His Majesty's Spanish Flock at Oatlands', 2 October 1802, *ibid.*, **15**, 13.

70. Cf. this chapter, note 68.

71. Henry Lacocke to Sir Joseph Banks, 20 October 1802, *ibid*, **13**, 14–15.

72. Richard Snart to Sir Joseph Banks, 25 October 1802, *ibid.*, 12–13.

73. Henry Lacocke to Sir Joseph Banks, 29 January 1803, BM(SC), I, **14**, 48.

74. 'Monthly Return of His Majesty's Spanish Flock at Kew', 1 November 1803, *ibid.*, 53.

75. Richard Snart to Sir Joseph Banks, 6 September 1803, *ibid.*, **18**, 57–8.

76. MS. account by Henry Lacocke, *ibid.*, 49–50.

77. *Survey of the Private Estates of His Late Majesty Geo. 3 situate at Richmond and Kew C⁰ Surrey by T. Chauvner and H. Rhodes, 1829*, P.R.O., ref. no. L.R.R.O. 1/1170, p. 7. The actual site of the cottage is probably now within the grounds of the Richmond Council School near Parkshot. In 1829 the occupier was still stated as being 'Richard Stanford who was Shepherd to His late Majesty and has lived here 34 years' (i.e. as far back as 1795). In the *Schedule of His late Majesty's Private Property in Lands & Houses, delivered to the Commissioners of Woods & Forests and Land Revenues in Obedience to the Commands contained in the King's Sign Manual Warrant, bearing the Date the 13th December 1820* (P.R.O., ref. no. L.R.R.O. 60/1252) it was described as 'The house standing on the Ground called the Shepherd's Cot, contains six rooms on the Ground Floor brick built and Slated, within a good kitchen garden well walled in. The garden includes a slip towards the South West which by Mʳ Richardson's plan [of 1771] would seem to have been a part of the Royal Gardens. . . . The fruit trees . . . were planted by the occupier. The house is greatly affected by Dry Rot.' The rent was £18. At the same time Richard Stanford was the

lessee of 'The Ha! Ha! Piece adjoining the South End of Kew Gardens'; in other words 'the field south of the Pagoda' or the present Richmond County Cricket Club ground. This area was described as 'only divided by a post and rail fence from Richmond Old Park', was 22¼ acres in extent and let to Stanford at £3 10s. per acre or £77 17s. 6d. per annum. It was further noted in connexion with this area: 'This Property lying near to Kew Gardens, the pasture land called the Ha Ha piece only intervening, it may be deemed advisable to retain at least controul over the same as will prevent the employment of it hereafter in any manner prejudicial to the enjoyment of the Royal Gardens &c.'

78. Richard Stanford to Sir Joseph Banks, 2 February 1805, BM(SC), I, **18**, 37.
79. Henry Lacocke to Sir Joseph Banks, 6 February 1805, *ibid.*, II, **1**, 3–4.
80. Footnote to above by Sir Joseph Banks, 4.
81. Richard Stanford to Sir Joseph Banks, 13 February 1805, *ibid.*, 1.
82. MS. notes by Sir Joseph Banks, *ibid.*, 5–7.
83. The scab mite, *Psoroptes communis* var. *ovis*. See also Chapter X.
84. Sir Joseph Banks to Richard Snart, 1 November [1805], BM(SC), I, **9**, 41.
85. Sir Joseph Banks to Richard Snart, 6 January 1806, *ibid.*, **10**, 5.
86. 'Monthly Return of His Majesty's Spanish Flock at Kew', 2 January 1806, *ibid.*, **20**, 53
87. Sir Joseph Banks to Richard Stanford, 26 November 1806, *ibid.*, **22**, 5.
88. Richard Snart to Sir Joseph Banks, 21 January 1807, *ibid.*, 6.
89. Richard Snart to Sir Joseph Banks, 17 March 1807, *ibid.*, 7.
90. Richard Stanford to Sir Joseph Banks, 2 March 1809, *ibid.*, II, **9**, 27.

CHAPTER VII: THE ROYAL FLEECE, 1788–1809

1. Daubenton, L.-J.-M., *Instructions pour Les Bergers* . . . (fourth edition, 1810), 328–42.
2. *Ibid.*, 343–61.
3. *Ibid.*, 357.
4. See Chapter V, note 3.
5. Spring Grove weigh bill MS., 6 June 1787, BM(SC), I, **17**, 40.
6. 'Account of Five Fleeces of Wool received from Sir Joseph Banks', July 1787, probably prepared by John Maitland, BM(SC), II, **1**, 35.
7. John Maitland to Sir Joseph Banks, 26 September 1787, *ibid.*, 36–7.
8. AA, x (1788), 217; cf. MS. note by Banks, BM(SC), II, **3**, 22.
9. James Cole's account of the Spanish ram hog shorn in 1787, MS., BM(SC), II, **1**, 40–1.
10. Matthew Humphreys to John Maitland, 16 September 1787, *ibid.*, 38.
11. Matthew Humphreys to John Maitland, [16 December 1787], *ibid.*, 42–3.
12. Matthew Humphreys to John Maitland, 17 December 1787, *ibid.*, 40.
13. Spring Grove weigh bill MS., 6 June 1786 (footnote by Banks), *ibid.*, I, **17**, 39.
14. Matthew Ives to Sir Joseph Banks, 7 March 1787, *ibid.*, II, **3**, 4.
15. The ancient distaff and spindle of England was often termed the 'Rock'. The reputation so long enjoyed by Norwich stuffs for fineness was due to the quality of the worsted yarn produced by the Rock spinners of Norfolk (see James, John, *History of the Worsted Manufacture in England* . . . (1857)). In this form of spinning the thread was drawn out from the end of a sliver of combed wool. The spindle was twirled by a dexterous movement of the right hand against the thigh and allowed to revolve suspended by the thread which gradually lengthened as the fibres were drafted from the sliver. The yarn already spun was wound round the shaft of the spindle and caught in the notch at the top. As each new length was spun the yarn was unhooked, wound on, caught in the notch again, and the spinning procedure repeated. Banks compared the spinning of Ann Ives directly with the cotton thread spun by the Hindu women to this effect: 'The Finest Spinning known is spun with the Rock at Dacca by Women who rub their Fingers when they spin with a kind of Clay Probably to absorb the perspiration Part of a Skein of this weighd 34$\frac{9}{10}$ grains its Length was 5 yards 7 inches & it consisted of 196 threads consequently its whole Length on a thread was 1018 yards & 7 inches this with a small allowance for fractions gives 29 yards to a grain 203,000 to a pound avoirdupois of 7000 grains that is 115 miles 2 furlongs & 60 yards or 362 hanks 3½ Lees at 7 Lees to the Hank. One of these Threads broke with a weight of 9 dwts another at 10 another at 11·13 grains & a fourth at 11·20 or 284 grains J^{no} Wilkins who gave me the thread says that the women who spin it alter the weight of their spindles as often as is necessary by adding to or diminishing a small piece of Clay stuck upon them.' BM(SC), II, **3**, 8–9, cf. this chapter, note 8.
16. MS. note by Banks, *ibid.*, BM(SC), II, **3**, 22.
17. Printed note, dated 1789 in MS., *ibid.*, 18, cf. Minutes of the Royal Society, 30 May 1754.
18. Ann Ives to Sir Joseph Banks, 10 December 1787, BM(SC), II, **3**, 21.
19. Ann Ives to Sir Joseph Banks, 14 January 1788, *ibid.*, 19.

20. MS. note by Ann Ives, [17 June 1788], *ibid.*, 22.

21. Ann Ives to Sir Joseph Banks, 17 June 1788, *ibid.*, 20–1.

22. Ann Ives to Sir Joseph Banks, 22 September 1789, *ibid.*, 17–18.

23. John Harvey to Sir Joseph Banks, 23 April 1792, *ibid.*, 15–16.

24. George Chalmers to Sir Joseph Banks, 18 November 1790, *ibid.*, **1**, 43–4.

25. John Anstie to George Chalmers, 1 December 1790, *ibid.*, 45.

26. Sir Joseph Banks to John Anstie, 7 December 1790, *ibid.*, 46.

27. The very greasy nature of the yolk of the fleece of the Spanish Merino and its relative insolubility in cold water under the usual conditions of sheep washing in England at that time was a continual source of error and confusion in appraising the shorn fleece among the wool staplers and clothiers. Anstie's comments here are good examples of these misunderstandings.

28. John Anstie to the Secretary of the Bath and West of England Society, [— December 1790], MS. extract, BM(SC), II, **1**, 49.

29. John Anstie to Sir Joseph Banks, 1 January 1791, *ibid.*, 48.

30. 'Information was received from John Anstie, Esq. that he is now manufacturing a quantity of the wool of South Down sheep, which have been fed upwards of two years on the Wiltshire Downs, and that from its fineness and peculiar quality, he is strongly of opinion, that race of sheep may be so much improved by crossing, especially with Spanish rams, as to possess nearly the properties and value of Spanish wool.' 'Account of the Annual Meeting of the Bath and West of England Society', 13 December 1791, AA, xvii, 1792, 402–3.

31. 'Sketch of a Chronological Account of the introduction of Merino Sheep into the United Kingdom', MS. note by Banks, BM(SC), II, **1**, 60–1.

32. MS. note by Banks, *ibid.*, I, **17**, 44.

33. MS. draft account by Banks of the Spring Grove and related operations from 1785, *ibid.*, **18**, 17–18; MS. copy, *ibid.*, 15–17; incorporated in Foot, Peter, *General View of the Agriculture of the County of Middlesex* . . . (1794), 60–4.

34. It is instructive to note the later comments of Lord Sheffield himself in which no reference to Banks or these early experiments is apparent: 'In consequence of his Majesty having imported Spanish sheep, I have been enabled to make several experiments in the breed of Spanish and the best Herefordshire and Southdown sheep, and I succeeded in respect to the quality of the wool. I found the wool of the Spanish breed, which had been nineteen years from Spain, and had been two years in my Park in Sussex, retained its quality so well that it appeared as perfect as the generality of samples I have seen from Spain; but as I could not get the intrinsic value, not even more than the South Down price, it could not answer to me to sacrifice the carcass, and to prejudice the shape of my flock, by mixing them with any other breed, far less by introducing the entire breed of Spain or of Herefordshire, which by the estimation of the county is not so good as the best South Down. Wool-staplers, however, have said, that the wool I shewed them was worth 3s. 6d. per pound (I do not mean the whole flock); but as it was not worth while to make it a principal object, I have never but twice received so much even as 2s. per pound for wool. The flock is of the best South Down kind I could breed. I find the wool does not become coarser in a park which is fed close; on the contrary it is of a softer and better quality than on the South Downs, the soil of which being chalk, is supposed to give it a certain harshness. I have during several years worn cloth made of wool grown in my Park and in respect to appearance it is not distinguishable from cloths made of Spanish wool: but wool-staplers will generally only afford the price they have been used to give for English wool; therefore it does not answer to a farmer to aim at any other than the fleece of the country.' Holroyd, John Baker, 1st Earl Sheffield, *Observations on the Objections made to the Export of Wool from Great Britain to Ireland* (1800), footnote, 53–4.

No short statement could summarize more completely all the attitudes and objections which then and now have tended to impede in principle and in practice a change of breed or a form of management—especially in relation to the balances sought between fleece weight, wool quality, and carcass. The same general problem has appeared in all countries at all times and is with us yet.

35. The Reverend Edmund Cartwright, inventor of the power-loom was born at Marnham, Nottinghamshire; elder brother of Major John Cartwright.

36. Cf. this chapter, note 31.

37. MS. note by Banks, BM(SC), I, **17**, 50.

38. MS. note by Banks, *ibid.*, **18**, 21.

39. *Ibid.*

40. MS. note by Banks, *ibid.*, 17. Such shifting sands are often trodden by the experimenter today.

41. Cf. this chapter, note 33.

42. John Wallace to Sir Joseph Banks, 18 January 1794, BM(SC), I, **18**, 19; cited also by Foot, Peter, see this chapter, note 33.

43. Cf. this chapter, note 31.
44. MS. note by Banks, BM(SC), I, **18**, 32.
45. *Ibid.*
46. MS. note by Banks, *ibid.*, II, **6**, 54.
47. Sir Joseph Banks to His Majesty King George III, 11 August 1792 (draft of first report), *ibid.*, I, **16**, 19–20.
48. MS. diary notes by Banks, *ibid.*, **18**, 27–8.
49. Sir Joseph Banks to John Hawker, 8 August 1791, *ibid.*, II, **6**, 56–7.
50. *Ibid.*
51. The French Royal family were arrested at Varennes on 23 June 1791.
52. Sir Joseph Banks to His Majesty King George III, 18 March 1793 (draft of the second report), BM(SC), I, **16**, 1–2.
53. Sir Joseph Banks to George Hawker, 9 April 1793, *ibid.*, 9–10.
54. 'Remarks on the Wool of the Spanish Breed . . .' by George Hawker, MS. copies, *ibid.*, 2–5.
55. George Hawker to Sir Joseph Banks, 30 April 1793, *ibid.*, 5–6.
56. [*Sic*] The matter of the sheep from France was negotiated in 1787 but the sheep were not actually landed in England at Dover until the night of 5 January 1788.
57. Sir Joseph Banks to His Majesty King George III, 6 August 1793 (draft of fourth report), BM(SC), I, **16**, 10–13.
58. MS. diary notes by Banks, *ibid.*, **13**, 24–6.
59. Sir Joseph Banks to George Hawker, 14 February 1795, *ibid.*, **10**, 8–9.
60. George Hawker to Sir Joseph Banks, 22 February 1795, *ibid.*, 9–10.
61. Sir Joseph Banks to George Hawker, 6 April 1795, *ibid.*, 11.
62. MS. notes, 'Proceeds from the Wool of His Majesties Spanish Flock', 13 April 1800, *ibid.*, II, **5**, 9–10.
63. John Buxton to Sir Joseph Banks, 5 August 1795, *ibid.*, I, **10**, 47.
64. MS. notes by Banks, *ibid.*, 5.
65. MS. note by John Buxton, 27 June 1799, *ibid.*, II, **7**, 29.
66. MS. account by John Walker to Messrs. J. and J. Buxton, 19 May 1797, *ibid.*, 25.
67. John Buxton to Sir Joseph Banks, 21 August 1797, *ibid.*, 23–4.
68. John Buxton to Sir Joseph Banks, 24 September 1798, *ibid.*, 27.
69. John Buxton to Sir Joseph Banks, 10 June 1799, *ibid.*, 22.
70. Sir Joseph Banks to John Buxton, 12 June 1799, *ibid.*
71. Cf. cost per yard of cloth manufactured by George Hawker in 1793 at 7s. 5d. per yard.
72. John Buxton to Sir Joseph Banks, 20 February 1797, BM(SC), II, **6**, 32–3.
73. MS. diary notes, *ibid.*, I, **10**, 41–2.
74. MS. diary notes, *ibid.*, II, **6**, 4–5.
75. Henry Lacocke to Sir Joseph Banks, 18 July 1798, *ibid.*, I, **19**, 42–3.
76. In the matter of punctuation Banks was impatient rather than careless or ignorant. His practice varied and could range from over-punctuation to none at all. The latter is, not unreasonably, more characteristic of his draft documents and notes. These form the bulk of the material cited in his work. It is to be noted, however, that there is seldom any doubt about his meaning. His sentence construction is generally adequate to convey the sense clearly without the aid of stops. In any case the use of punctuation among his contemporaries was as full of individual quirks—for example, Nelson.
77. Henry Lacocke to Sir Joseph Banks, 17 August 1798, BM(SC), I, **19**, 44.
78. Sir Joseph Banks to Henry Lacocke, 20 August 1798, *ibid.*, 45.
79. Henry Lacocke to Sir Joseph Banks, 17 April 1799, *ibid.*, II, **7**, 34–5.
80. MS. account, *ibid.*, **4**, 54.
81. Henry Lacocke to Sir Joseph Banks, 31 May 1799, *ibid.*, **7**, 37.
82. Sir Joseph Banks to Henry Lacocke, [31 May 1799], *ibid.*, 38.
83. Charles Fencock's MS. account, *ibid.*, **4**, 54.
84. MS. statement by Henry Lacocke to Sir Joseph Banks, 13 November 1799, *ibid.*, **7**, 31.
85. Henry Lacocke to Sir Joseph Banks, 8 October 1799, *ibid.*, **8**, 5–6.
86. MS. account by Henry Lacocke, *ibid.*, **7**, 34.
87. MS. diary notes, *ibid.*, **5**, 55.
88. Probably on 20 January 1800 when Henry Lacocke called to pay Banks for the King's Wiltshire wool and the R's of the Spanish clip of 1798 sold to Thomas Poole. MS. diary notes, *ibid.*
89. Henry Lacocke to Sir Joseph Banks, 15 February 1800, *ibid.*, 53.
90. MS. diary notes, *ibid.*, **5**, 56.
91. Draft MS. headed 'Spanish Rams', 10 April 1800, *ibid.*, **7**, 10–11.
92. Draft MS. headed 'A Project for Extending the breed of Spanish Sheep to such parts of the Island as may be most suitable to the Production of Fine Wool' (written probably about April 1800), *ibid.*, 11–12.

93. *Moniteur*, 24 May 1800.
94. *The Philosophical Magazine* (first series), VII (June–September 1800), 350–5; cf. also draft MS., BM(SC), II, **5**, 43–6.
95. MS. draft of deed by Banks, BM(SC), II, **5**, 49–50.
96. Henry Lacocke to Sir Joseph Banks, 27 May 1800, *ibid.*, 49.
97. Henry Lacocke to Sir Joseph Banks, 16 October 1800, *ibid.*, **4**, 47–8.
98. Henry Lacocke to Sir Joseph Banks, 22 October 1803, *ibid.*, I, **18**, 14.
99. Captain Henry Waterhouse to Sir Evan Nepean, 27 August 1800, HRNSW, IV, 119.
100. Henry Lacocke to Sir Joseph Banks, 10 December 1800, BM(SC), II, **4**, 34–5.
101. MS. account, *ibid.*, I, **5**, 32.
102. MS. diary notes, *ibid.*, II, **4**, 36.
103. Governor John Hunter to Sir Joseph Banks, 1 July 1801; also Captain William Kent to Sir Joseph Banks, 1 July 1801, HRNSW, IV, 427.
104. Acting-Governor Philip Gidley King to Sir Sir Joseph Banks, 28 September 1800, HRNSW, IV, 205.
105. MS. note by Henry Lacocke, BM(SC), I, **5**, 33. Both 12 Magdalen Street and 62 Bermondsey Street are now demolished. Their sites may, however, be identified close under the Southern Railway approaches to London Bridge Station, by which they are now separated. Portions of the original row of houses may still be seen in Magdalen Street from No. 14 onwards. No. 12 would now occupy the site on the corner of Bermondsey Street. Nos. 62 and 64 Bermondsey Street are now part of an open yard but Nos. 60 and 66 exist as business premises. Again the character of the Georgian street may still be assessed by the few remaining fronts.
106. 'Communication Respecting the Breed of Sheep in the Colony', *Sydney Gazette*, 26 March 1803. Cf. also HRA, series I, IV, 665; HRNSW, V, 80–1.
107. No. I was the 'Fleece of a Ewe imported from the Cape of Good Hope, said to be of the Spanish Breed' and No. II was the 'Fleece of a Ram of one-year old bred from No. I.' The ewe in this case was, therefore, one of the survivors of those few brought by Captain Henry Waterhouse in H.M.S. *Reliance* and by Lieutenant (later Captain) William Kent in H.M.S. *Supply* from Cape Town to Sydney in 1797. These had been purchased from the widow of Colonel Robert Jacob Gordon who had bred them from the original two rams and four ewes derived from Spain through the Dutch government in Holland. Of these 'Gordon' Merinos John Macarthur obtained an uncertain number—probably one or two rams and two or three ewes. John Macarthur said this of the original Gordon importation: 'The fine-Woolled Sheep imported here from the Cape of Good Hope in the Year 1797 were said to be of the Spanish Breed. The Excellence of the Fleece of these Sheep combined with the Consideration of their peculiar form, bears strong Evidence in favor of the Correctness of this Report, tho' it is impossible to say whether they originally Sprung from the best kind of Sheep that is bred in Spain.' (HRA, series I, v, 566–8.) Whatever their origin or quality it is sufficient to note here that the actual fleeces submitted to Henry Lacocke matched those of His Majesty's Spanish flock in 1800 very closely.
108. John Macarthur to Lord Pelham, 21 December 1802, HRNSW, IV, 919.
109. MS. note by Banks, BM(SC), I, **13**, 16–17.
110. Henry Lacocke to Sir Joseph Banks, 18 September 1802, *ibid.*, 9–10.
111. q.v. Chapter X, section VII; the events arising from Banks's private sale of three ewes to Thomas William Coke in 1805, the King's anger, and Sir Joseph's nominal resignation from the active supervision of the flock.
112. Sir Joseph Banks to Henry Lacocke, 11 August 1805, BM(SC), I, **22**, 11.
113. Henry Lacocke to Sir Joseph Banks, 20 December 1805, *ibid.*, **9**, 50.
114. Richard Snart to Sir Joseph Banks, 11 August 1806, *ibid.*, 52–3.
115. Richard Snart to Sir Joseph Banks, 17 July [1809], *ibid.*, II, **9**, 7–8.

CHAPTER VIII: THE KING'S GRACE, 1791–1799

1. Sir William Musgrave to Sir Joseph Banks, 1 January 1791, BM.A.MSS., 33979, 66.
2. MS. note by Banks, BM(SC), III, **6**, 44.
3. Sir Joseph Banks to 2nd Earl Bathurst, 7 August 1791, *ibid.*, 47–8.
4. Parry, C. H., 'An Essay on the Nature, Produce, Origin, and Extension of the Merino Breed of Sheep . . . ', CBA, v (1806), 434.
5. 2nd Earl Bathurst to Sir Joseph Banks, 10 August 1791, BM(SC), II, **6**, 47.
6. AA, XVI (1791), 480–607.
7. Sir Joseph Banks to Arthur Young, 7 August 1791, BM.A.MSS., 35127, 115–16.
8. AA, XVII (1792), 529–33.
9. *Ibid.* (plate).
10. MS. diary notes by Banks, BM(SC), II, **6**, 53.

11. Sir John Sinclair to Sir Joseph Banks, 3 September 1790, *ibid.*, I, **1**, 21–2. The paper submitted was the *Report of the Committee of the Highland Society of Scotland, to whom the subject of Shetland Wool was referred. With an Appendix, Containing some Papers, drawn up by Sir John Sinclair and Dr. [John] Anderson, in reference to the said report,* Edinburgh, 1790.

12. Sir Joseph Banks to Sir John Sinclair, 17 September 1790, BM(SC), I, **1**, 21–2.

13. Sir John Sinclair to Sir Joseph Banks (enclosure addressed to Lady Banks), 22 September 1790, *ibid.*, **2**, 18.

14. Sir Joseph Banks to Sir John Sinclair, 28 September 1790, *ibid.*, 17.

15. Sir Joseph Banks to Sir John Sinclair, 21 January 1791, *ibid.*, 21.

16. The resolutions to be put to this meeting were filed by Banks under the heading 'Sir John Sinclairs Plan of Establishing a Society in England on the Plan of his Scotts Society', *ibid.*, 15–17.

17. Invitation-card to the meeting circulated by Sir John Sinclair, 19 March 1791, *ibid.*, 19.

18. Sir Joseph Banks to Sir John Sinclair, 31 March 1791, *ibid.*, 19–20.

19. Sir John Sinclair to Sir Joseph Banks, 16 May 1791, *ibid.*, **2**, 18.

20. Sir Joseph Banks to Sir John Sinclair, 17 May 1791, *ibid.*, 19.

21. Sir Joseph Banks to John March, 17 April 1792, *ibid.*, **21**, 54. Anxiously waiting for news about some of the last sheep to be smuggled out of Spain through Lisbon, Banks wrote on this date to John March seeking assurance from that quarter that no misfortune would prevent him receiving the consignment. Among other things he voices one of the few sentiments of the kind to be found in his correspondence: 'A soci[ety] is established in Scotland which I think means to take from me the credit of having introduced a usefull improvt.' It is also one of the few cases in which he expresses openly his feelings that credit may be due to him in the matter of the introduction of Spanish sheep.

22. Sir Joseph Banks to Sir John Sinclair, 19 May 1791, *ibid.*, **2**, 23.

23. *Edinburgh Evening Courant*, No. 11, 410, Monday, 4 July 1791.

24. Sir Joseph Banks to the Rt. Hon. Henry Dundas, 11 August 1791, BM(SC), II, **6**, 52.

25. Ramsay Robinson to Sir Joseph Banks, 10 October 1791, *ibid.*, 42–3.

26. News-cutting, *Edinburgh Oracle*, 8 October 1791, *ibid.*, 22.

27. 'Account of a Flock of Sheep', AA, VII (31 July 1786), 1–16.

28. 'On Mr. Ducket's Mode of Cultivation', by Mr. Ralph Robinson of Windsor, *ibid.*, (1 January 1787), 65–71; 'Further Remarks on Mr. Ducket's Mode of Cultivation', by Mr. Ralph Robinson of Windsor, *ibid.*, (5 March 1787), 332–6.

29. AA, VII (31 July 1786), 16–20.

30. Sir Joseph Banks to 3rd Duke of Grafton, 7 August 1791, BM(SC), II, **6**, 51.

31. AA, XIX (1793), 441–98. The outcome of this is described by Arthur Young in his account of 'A Week in Norfolk' in that number.

32. 3rd Duke of Grafton to Sir Joseph Banks, 17 August 1791, BM(SC), II, **6**, 49–50.

33. Sir Joseph Banks to 3rd Duke of Grafton, 19 August 1791, *ibid.*, 51. Cf. Chapter IV, note 7.

34. 2nd Duke of Newcastle to Sir Joseph Banks, 11 August 1791, BM(SC), II, **6**, 47.

35. Sir George Yonge to Sir Joseph Banks, 18 April 1791, Kew BC, II, 40.

36. MS. note by Banks, *ibid.*, 45.

37. Banks was Secretary of the Dilletanti Society from 1778 to 1797.

38. Sir William Hamilton was Ambassador to the Court of Naples from 1764 to 1800.

39. Sir William Hamilton to Sir Joseph Banks, 4 July 1786, BM.A.MSS., 34048, 30; DTC, v, 37.

40. Emma Lady Hamilton to Sir Joseph Banks, 31 May 1797, DTC, x, 148–51.

41. Dobson, Austin (ed.), *Diary and Letters of Madame D'Arblay*, III, 361.

42. *Ibid.*, 385.

43. *Ibid.*, 481.

44. *Ibid.*, 357–8.

45. The matter was of passing interest to the public and evidently the subject of some speculation:

'EARLDOM OF MANSFIELD

The supposition that there will, on the death of the present venerable EARL OF MANSFIELD, be *two Earls* of that title, in virtue of the two patents now held by his Lordship, is not well grounded. To reconcile the seeming intricacy of the case, it is necessary to shew, that should the Earl die to-morrow, the circumstance of the two successions in question could not take place. The first patent (that of Earl Mansfield in Nottinghamshire) granted Oct. 31. 1776, is expressly limited, in default of issue male, to Louisa Viscountess Stormont, to whom it gives the dignity of Countess, and after her decease confers the title of Earl on her issue male.

The latter patent of 1792, creating him Earl of Mansfield in Middlesex, conveys that honour, on his demise, to *Lord Stormont himself*, who in that case becomes a British peer, and Earl of Mansfield; while his Lady, at the same time in virtue of the first patent, becomes a Peeress in her own right; and the two titles will be consolidated in their joint heir, Should indeed Lady Stormont die before she inherits the entailed honour, it might happen as surmised, and there would be two Earls of Mansfield both at once; but even should that event happen (which for the sake of the amiable Expectant, it is hoped will not be the case), the Minister could easily adjust the matter by having recourse to the rage for Marquis-making.' *Edinburgh Evening Courant*, No. 11, 588, Monday, 26 August 1792.

46. MS. diary notes by Banks, BM(SC), I, **17**, 10.

47. The copious mixture of skin secretions which is so distinctive a character of the Merino fleece is commonly referred to now as the 'yolk' or the 'grease'. The word 'nature' is used by Banks here to mean the same thing.

48. Sir Joseph Banks to Robert Fulke Greville, 13 August 1793, BM(SC), I, **15**, 24.

49. Bladon, F. McKno (ed.), *The Diaries of Colonel the Hon. Robert Fulke Greville*, 280

50. Robert Fulke Greville to Sir Joseph Banks, [—] July 1794, BM(SC), II, **2**, 46–7.

51. Robert Fulke Greville to Sir Joseph Banks, 12 August 1794, *ibid.*, 48–9.

52. Robespierre had in fact been executed on 28 July 1794.

53. The *Romney*, fifty guns, Captain the Honourable William Paget, captured the French ship *Sybille*, forty-five guns, off the island of Miconi in the Mediterranean on 17 July 1794.

54. Bladon, F. McKno (ed.), *The Diaries of Colonel the Hon. Robert Fulke Greville*, 280–1.

55. Robert Fulke Greville to Sir Joseph Banks, 24 August [1794], BM(SC), II, **2**, 52–3.

56. MS. diary notes, 18 June 1794, *ibid.*, 43–4.

57. Sir Joseph Banks to Ramsay Robinson, 7 January 1793, *ibid.*, I, **17**, 22.

58. MS. diary notes, 4 April 1795, *ibid.*, **22**, 24–6.

59. MS. diary notes, 19 July 1794, *ibid.*, **13**, 24–6.

60. SAS, XVIII, 73.

61. Dobson, Austin (ed.), *Diary and Letters of Madame D'Arblay*, II, 385.

62. *Ibid.*, 222.

63. MS. diary notes, 18 June 1796, BM(SC), I, **10**, 41–2.

64. Robert Fulke Greville to Sir Joseph Banks, [—] July 1794, *ibid.*, II, **2**, 46–7.

65. Robert Fulke Greville to Sir Joseph Banks, 16 January 1796, *ibid.*, I, **10**, 24.

66. The Weather Diaries of Thomas Hoy, 1771–1822. Cf. also Figure 4.

67. Josiah Ridgeway to Major William Price, 12 December 1795, BM(SC), I, **10**, 24–5.

68. MS. 'Account of Wool sold by Josiah Ridgway of Upperton Herefordshire to Mr Gale Everett of Heytesbury Wiltshire in the last seven Years commencing July 1793 and ending July 1799 being the Average produce of 325 Sheep'.

The average price per pound received as set out below for the whole clip may be compared with the values for other wools plotted for the same period in Figure 6.

Year	Price per pound
1793	18·3
1794	21·1
1795	26·4
1796	25·9
1797	24·0
1798	26·4
1799	24·6

Ibid., II, **4**, 50.

69. 'A Report of the State of His Majesty's Flock of Fine Wooled Spanish Sheep during the Years 1800 and 1801 . . . ', AM, IX (August 1803), 80–4.

70. Sir Joseph Banks to Robert Fulke Greville, 13 August 1800, BM(SC), II, **5**, 50–1.

71. Robert Fulke Greville to Sir Joseph Banks, 25 July 1792, *ibid.*, I, **17**, 15–16.

72. Thomas Johnes to Sir Joseph Banks, 25 July 1792, *ibid.*, 17–18.

73. MS. diary notes, 14 August 1792, *ibid.*, 20.

74. Sir Joseph Banks to Thomas Johnes, 11 August 1792, *ibid.*, 19–20.

75. Ramsay Robinson to Sir Joseph Banks, 12 January 1793, *ibid.*, 21–2.

76. Sir Joseph Banks to Robert Fulke Greville, 14 August 1792, *ibid.*, 2–3.

77. MS. 'Report on the King's Flock of Merinos (with two Appendices)' by Banks [1797], DTC, X², 136–52.

78. Philip Yorke to Robert Lely and Benjamin Handley, 6 November 1786, BM(SC), III, **1**, 30.

79. Thomas 2nd Baron Walsingham (1748–1818), Chairman of Committees of the House of Lords.

80. Philip Yorke to 2nd Baron Walsingham, [n.d.]. Cited by Robert Fulke Greville to Sir Joseph Banks, 3 September [1794], BM(SC), II, **2**, 60–1.

81. Philip Yorke to Sir Joseph Banks, 3 October 1794, *ibid.*, **3**, 1–2.

82. Philip Yorke to Sir Joseph Banks, 18 February 1798, *ibid.*, I, **17**, 34, enclosing a report by Yorke up to December 1797, *ibid.*, 32.

83. Philip Yorke to Sir Joseph Banks, 6 February 1799, *ibid.*, II, **11**, 68–70, with a note by Banks thereon about the mercers' valuations.
84. Sir Joseph Banks to Philip Yorke, 14 February 1799, *ibid.*, 70–1.
85. Philip Yorke to Sir Joseph Banks, 17 December 1799, *ibid.*, I, **6**, 22–3.
86. Father of Queen Victoria.
87. Bladon, F. McKno (ed.), *The Diaries of Colonel the Hon. Robert Fulke Greville*, 311–12.
88. *Ibid.*, 320–1.
89. John Bridge to Sir Joseph Banks, 24 December 1796, BM(SC), I, **10**, 39–40.
90. Sir Joseph Banks to John Bridge, 30 April 1799, *ibid.*, II, **7**, 42.
91. John Bridge to Sir Joseph Banks, 17 May 1800, *ibid.*, I, **6**, 27–8.
92. At the foot of Bridge's report Banks has written the following interesting comments: 'The Case of the ½ Spanish & ½ Leicester is different, because fine Combing wools are not wanted in the English market. These wools however were in July 1799 worth more than /15ᵈ a Pound to be cut into Clothing wools . . . ', *ibid.*, II, **4**, 51.
93. Sir Joseph Banks to John Bridge, 3 August 1800, *ibid.*, I, **6**, 29.
94. Henry Lacocke to Sir Joseph Banks, 23 February 1801, *ibid.*, **5**, 31.
95. John Bridge to Sir Joseph Banks, 15 October 1800, *ibid.*, 29–30.
96. The situation is summed up in the final paragraph of Robert Fulke Greville's letter to Sir Joseph Banks of 3 September 1794:
'. . . We seem to have had an escape at Portsmouth—Our negligence abᵗ. Strangers Emigre's &c. & thousands of French Prisoners in the Neighbourhood of our Docks tempts all kind[s] of desparate Enterprise against Them—I hope the loss of this one Ship will at least prove a good warning—I am sorry to hear that the French have got Sluys—'. *Ibid.*, II, **2**, 60–1.
97. Bladon, F. McKno (ed.), *The Diaries of Colonel the Hon. Robert Fulke Greville*, 350–1.
98. To the west of Ken Wood House today is The Spaniards Inn on Spaniards Road. Near by is also Spaniards Close. It is not straining credulity too far to suggest that these names may mark, in Greville's commonly used term for the Spanish Merinos, the grazing grounds of these sheep on Hampstead Heath.
99. Robert Fulke Greville to Sir Joseph Banks, 15 October 1794, BM(SC), II, **3**, 2.
100. Sir Joseph Banks to Robert Fulke Greville, 22 October 1794, *ibid.*, 3.
101. Robert Fulke Greville to Sir Joseph Banks, 15 October 1794, *ibid.*, 3.
102. Robert Fulke Greville to Sir Joseph Banks, 27 October 1794, *ibid.*, **2**, 51.
103. Sir Joseph Banks to 3rd Earl of Egremont, 29 July [1797], *ibid.*, **6**, 10–11.
104. 3rd Duke of Montrose to Sir Joseph Banks, 19 July 1795, *ibid.*, I, **3**, 8–9.
105. Sir Joseph Banks to 3rd Duke of Montrose, 18 July 1795, *ibid.*, 10–11.
106. 3rd Duke of Montrose to Sir Joseph Banks, 23 July 1795, *ibid.*, 12–13.
107. Archibald Edmonstone [or Edminstone or Edmondston] to [—] Menzies, *ibid.*, 14–15.
108. The actual specimen still exists. It is filed with the original papers beside this document by Edmonstone (see this chapter, note 107).
109. *Transactions of the Society for the Improvement of British Wool . . . to the 31st January 1792*, BM(SC), I, **19**, 32–40.
110. Cf. The Weather Diaries of Thomas Hoy, 1771–1822 and Figure 4.
111. SAS, XVIII, 571.
112. Sir Joseph Banks to 3rd Duke of Montrose, 1 August 1795, BM(SC), I, **3**, 15–16.
113. Sir Joseph Banks to 3rd Duke of Montrose, 27 June 1796, *ibid.*, **10**, 28–9.
114. MS. diary notes, 27 June 1796, *ibid.*, 42.
115. MS. diary notes, 17 June 1795, *ibid.*, **22**, 26.
116. Sir Joseph Banks to [—] Gibbs, 2 July [1796], *ibid.*, **10**, 32.
117. 3rd Duke of Montrose to Sir Joseph Banks, *ibid.*
118. 'Sketch of a Chronological Account of the Introduction of Merino Sheep into the United Kingdom', MS. note by Banks, *ibid.*, II, **1**, 60–1; see also note in *ibid.*, I, **19**, 46.
119. LPBS, I (1788) (preface), v.
120. LPBS, VI (1792) (introduction), ix.
121. *Ibid.*, xiii–xv.
122. Sir Joseph Banks to William Matthews, 14 August 1792, BM(SC), I, **17**, 4.
123. Near Avebury on the Marlborough Downs.
124. William Matthews to Sir Joseph Banks, 18 August 1792, BM(SC), I, **17**, 5.
125. Sir Joseph Banks to 1st Earl of Ailesbury, 18 July 1795, *ibid.*, **3**, 17–18.
126. William Matthews to 1st Earl of Ailesbury, 29 July 1795, *ibid.*, 19–20.
127. Lasteyrie, C.-P., *An Account of the Introduction of Merino Sheep into the Different States of Europe . . .*, translated by Benjamin Thompson (London, 1810), 101.

CHAPTER IX: THE PATRIOTS, 1792–1803

1. Rolleston, H., *Ann. Med. Hist.*, VII (1925), 237–311.
2. CBA, V, 433.
3. *Ibid.*, 434.
4. AM, I (December 1799), 370, 'Mr. Henry Jenner [*sic*], surgeon of Berkeley, visits Bristol at least once a week, for the purpose of inoculating for the *vaccine disease*; which, it is said, will effectually protect the human constitution from that dreadful disorder the *small-pox.*'
5. 'A Project for Extending the Breed of Fine Wooled Spanish Sheep, now in the possession of his Majesty, into all parts of Great Britain, where the Growth of Fine Cloathing Wools is found to be profitable.' [Sir Joseph Banks], *The Philosophical Magazine* (first series), VII (June–September 1800), 350–5.
The first draft for this paper appears to have been written about 10 April 1800 as 'A Project for Extending the breed of Spanish Sheep to such parts of the Island as may be most suitable to the Production of Fine Wool', BM(SC), II, **7**, 11–12.
The final draft, however, is probably the MS. in BM(SC), II, **5**, 43–6; the printed pamphlet is that in BM(SC), I, **14**, 53–6. It was printed also in the following:
    (i) AA, XXXV (1800), 285–93.
   (ii) *St. James Chronicle: British Evening Post*, Saturday, 25 October 1800, No. 6686.
  (iii) As an Appendix to *Observations on the Objections made to the Export of Wool from Great Britain to Ireland*, by Holroyd, John Baker, 1st Lord Sheffield (London, 1800).
   (iv) In the Appendix to *A Treatise on the Diseases and Management of Sheep . . .* , by Mackenzie, Sir George Steuart (Edinburgh, 1809).
    (v) As part of the text in *Histoire de l'Introduction des Moutons à Laine fine d'Espagne dans les divers États de l'Europe et au Cap de Bonne-Espérance*, by Lasteyrie, C.-P. (Paris, 1802). Cf. also the translation of this by Benjamin Thompson (London, 1810), pp. 122–31.
6. *Facts and Observations tending to shew the Practicability and Advantage, . . . of Producing in the British Isles Clothing Wool, equal to that of Spain . . .* , by Parry, Caleb Hillier (Bath, 1800).
7. *Ibid.*, 2.
8. 'A Report of the State of His Majesty's Flock of Fine Wooled Spanish Sheep during the Years 1800 and 1801; with some Account of the Progress that has been made towards the Introduction of that Valuable Breed into those Parts of the United Kingdom where Fine Clothing Wools are grown with Advantage. By The Right Hon. Sir Joseph Banks, Bart., P.R.S., &c. &c.', AM, IX (August 1803), 80–4.
9. CBA, V, 541.
10. 'An Essay on the Nature, Produce, Origin, and Extension of the Merino Breed of Sheep; to which is added, a History of a Cross of that Breed with Ryeland Ewes; describing their Qualities and Produce, and a successful Method of managing them', by Parry, Caleb Hillier, M.D., F.R.S., CBA, V (1806–7), 337–541.
11. Caleb Hillier Parry to Sir Joseph Banks, 26 April 1800, BM(SC), I, **6**, 25–6.
12. *Ibid.* Johann Frederick Blumenbach (1752–1840), the great comparative anatomist of Göttingen, was professor in the university for sixty years. From specimens provided by Banks he was the first to describe and classify the platypus as *Ornithorynchus paradoxus* (now *O. anatinus*). The cargo of specimens referred to by Charles Parry must have included what was probably the first specimen of this monotreme from within the area of County Cumberland, New South Wales.
13. Sir Joseph Banks to Caleb Hillier Parry, 19 May 1800, Kew BC, II, 237.
14. Caleb Hillier Parry to Benjamin Hobhouse, [— July 1800], BM(SC), I, **6**, 26–7.
15. *Ibid.*, 27.
16. John Wallace to Sir Joseph Banks, 28 June 1800, *ibid.*, 29–30.
17. Caleb Hillier Parry to Benjamin Hobhouse, [— July 1800], *ibid.*, 26–7.
18. Benjamin Hobhouse to Sir Joseph Banks, 7 July 1800, *ibid.*, 23.
19. Lord John Somerville to Sir Joseph Banks, 27 July 1800, *ibid.*, II, **5**, 116–17.
20. Details of the premiums are given in *Facts and Observations . . .* , by Parry, Caleb Hillier, p. 32; details of the wool and cloth, pp. 33–4.
21. Caleb Hillier Parry to Sir Joseph Banks, 10 September 1800, BM(SC), I, **5**, 36–7.
22. Caleb Hillier Parry to Sir Joseph Banks, 7 September 1800, *ibid.*, 37–8.
23. Sir Joseph Banks to Caleb Hillier Parry, 12 September [1800], *ibid.*, 38.
24. *Facts and Observations. . . .* Cf. this chapter, note 6.
25. Benjamin Hobhouse to Sir Joseph Banks, 10 September 1800, BM(SC), I, **1**, 24.
26. Sir Joseph Banks to Benjamin Hobhouse, 12 September [1800], *ibid.*, 25.
27. Sir Joseph Banks to Benjamin Hobhouse, 5 August 1801, *ibid.*, 25.
28. Sir Joseph Banks to Caleb Hillier Parry, 10 August 1802, *ibid.*, I, **14**, 21.
29. Caleb Hillier Parry to Sir Joseph Banks, 29 August 1802, *ibid.*, 30–1.
30. Thomas Peasey, the King's Cowman at Frogmore until about 1803.

31. Sir Joseph Banks to Caleb Hillier Parry, 3 September [1802], BM(SC), I, **14**, 31.

32. Benjamin Hobhouse to Sir Joseph Banks, 18 September 1802, *ibid.*, 1–3.

33. Caleb Hillier Parry to Sir Joseph Banks, 22 April 1804, *ibid.*, **22**, 61–2.

34. Cf. list of those advised of the King's public auction of August 1804, *ibid.*, II, **11**, 64.

35. Sir Joseph Banks to Caleb Hillier Parry, [— April 1804], *ibid.*, I, **22**, 63.

36. Correspondence: 'On the Improvement of British Wool', CBA, II, 459–73.

37. Cf. para. 3, pp. 1–2, *Facts and Observations* . . . , by Lord John Somerville (London, 1809) for a near-verbatim repetition of this statement.

38. *Lord Somerville's Address to the Board of Agriculture on the Subject of Sheep and Wool on the 14th of May, 1799,* 3–4.

39. Cf. Chapter IV, note 23: Sir Joseph Banks to Thomas March, 30 September 1788.

40. Lord John Somerville to the Bath and West of England Society, CBA, II, 461.

41. William Matthews to Lord John Somerville, 26 April 1799, *ibid.*, 460.

42. 33 Geo. III, c. 27.

43. 39 Geo. III, c. 98 (of 12 July 1799), BM(SC), II, **7**, 49–50, with Banks's MS. comments thereon.

44. Mitchison, Rosalind, 'The Old Board of Agriculture . . .', *Eng. Hist. Rev.* (January 1959), 57.

45. Parry, Caleb Hillier, *Facts and Observations* . . . (1800), 7 (my italics, H.B.C.).

45. Lord John Somerville to Sir Joseph Banks, 27 July 1800, BM(SC), II, **5**, 46–7.

47. Sir Joseph Banks to Lord John Somerville, 31 July 1800, *ibid.*, 48.

48. *Report of the Committee appointed by the Bath and West of England Society, to investigate the Claim of the Right Hon. Lord Somerville to a Premium 'for the greatest Number and most profitable Sort of Sheep'.—Vide Folio 45, Pr. 15,* Fitzhead, 2 June 1804. With Banks's MS. comments, BM(SC), I, **61**, 74–5.

49. Lord Somerville, *Facts and Observations* . . . (1809), 9–11.

50. 'A Report of the State of His Majesty's Flock of Fine Wooled Spanish Sheep during the Years 1800 and 1801; with some Account of the Progress that has been made towards the Introduction of that Valuable Breed into those Parts of the United Kingdom where Fine Clothing Wools are grown with Advantage. By the Right Hon. Sir Joseph Banks, Bart. P.R.S., &c. &c.', AM, IX (August 1803), 80–4.

51. 'Biographical Sketch of the Life of the Right Honourable, John, Lord Somerville, Ex-President of the Board of Agriculture, &c.', AM (second series), IX (July 1811), 5–12.

52. Lord John Somerville, *Facts and Observations* . . . (1809), 9–11.

53. *Ibid.*, 70.

54. *Ibid.*, 70 n.

55. AM (second series), II (March 1808), 225–33.

56. Lord John Somerville, *Facts and Observations* . . . (1809), 91–2.

57. Parry, Caleb Hillier, 'An Essay on the Nature, Produce, Origin, and Extension of the Merino Breed of Sheep . . . ', CBA, V (1806–7), 434.

58. George Tollet to Sir Joseph Banks, 6 August 1800, BM(SC), III, **3**, 38–9.

59. AA, XXXV (1800), 285–93.

60. Sir Joseph Banks to George Tollet, 7 August 1800, BM(SC), III, **3**, 39.

61. George Tollet to Sir Joseph Banks, 9 August 1800, *ibid.*, 40–1.

62. Sir Joseph Banks to George Tollet, 20 August 1801, *ibid.*, **4**, 23.

63. George Tollet to Sir Joseph Banks, 22 January 1802, *ibid.*, I, **14**, 15–16.

64. George Tollet to Sir Joseph Banks, 20 May 1802, *ibid.*, 16.

65. Sir Joseph Banks to George Tollet, 11 August 1802, *ibid.*, 17.

66. Sir Joseph Banks to George Tollet, 17 August [1803], *ibid.*, **11**, 52.

67. Not, apparently, to be confused with Young Snags also numbered 148.

68. 'Spanish Sheep', by George Tollet, Esq., of Swinnerton, Staffordshire, AA, XLII (1804), 55–71 [1 March 1804].

69. George Talbot of Guyting, Gloucestershire, made this offer. Cf. George Perrott to Sir Joseph Banks, 20 August 1803, BM(SC), I, **11**, 32.

70. John Darke of Bredon made this offer.

71. George Perrott of Evesham bought this animal, the full brother to the shearling ram for which George Talbot offered two hundred guineas. Cf. George Perrott to Sir Joseph Banks, 17 August 1803, BM(SC), I, **11**, 32–3.

72. George Tollet to Sir Joseph Banks, [— July 1803], *ibid.*, **8**, 41–2.

73. Sir Joseph Banks to George Tollet, 28 July 1803, *ibid.*, **11**, 50–1.

74. George Tollet to Sir Joseph Banks, 11 August 1803, *ibid.*, 44–5.

75. George Tollet to Sir Joseph Banks, 8 August 1804, *ibid.*, III, **11**, 54–5.

76. George Tollet to Sir Joseph Banks, 23 August 1804, *ibid.*, 52–3.

77. *A Report on the State of His Majesty's Flock of Fine Wooled Spanish Sheep For the Year ending Michaelmas 1803.* [By the Right Hon. Sir Joseph Banks, Bart., P.R.S., &c.], 17 August 1803,

with a postscript dated 10 July 1804, *ibid.*, 126–7. Printed also in the Appendix to *A Treatise on the Diseases and Management of Sheep* . . . , by Mackenzie, Sir George Steuart (Edinburgh, 1809), 138–41.

78. Sir Joseph Banks to Robert Fulke Greville, 4 August 1805, BM.A.MSS., 42072, 71–2. Cf. Chapter X.

79. AM XIII (July 1805), 57–9.

80. AM XIV (June 1806), 420–3.

81. Thomas Walton to Sir Joseph Banks, 23 October 1807, BM(SC), I, **9**, 29–30.

82. AM (second series), III (August 1808), 131–3.

83. AM (second series), IV (June 1809), 413–18.

84. AM (second series), VII (July 1810), 53–69.

85. George Tollet to Sir Joseph Banks, [31] August 1803, BM(SC), I, **11**, 52–3.

86. AA, XLII (1804), 58–71 n.

87. *Ibid.*

88. George Tollet to Sir Joseph Banks, 15 August 1802, BM(SC), I, **11**, 39–40.

89. George Tollet to Sir Joseph Banks, 1 February 1803, *ibid.*, 46–7.

90. Edward Sheppard to Sir John Sinclair, 31 December 1806, 'On the Subject of his Experiments regarding the Improvement of the fine-woolled Breed of Sheep in this Kingdom', CBA, VI, 65–74.

91. Lord Somerville, *Facts and Observations* . . . (London, 1809), 105.

92. John Darke to Sir Joseph Banks, 9 March 1802, BM(SC), I, **14**, 11.

93. Sir Joseph Banks to John Darke, 10 March [1802], *ibid.*, 12.

94. Edward Sheppard to Sir Joseph Banks, 28 May [1802], *ibid.*

95. Sir Joseph Banks to Edward Sheppard, [29 or 30 May 1802], *ibid.*, 13.

96. Edward Sheppard to Sir Joseph Banks, [— June 1802], *ibid.*, 10–11.

97. George Tollet to Sir Joseph Banks, [31] August 1803, *ibid.*, **11**, 52–3.

98. Sir Joseph Banks to Edward Sheppard, 11 August 1802, *ibid.*, **14**, 13–14.

99. Edward Sheppard to Sir Joseph Banks, 14 August 1802, *ibid.*, 14.

100. Edward Sheppard to Sir Joseph Banks, 22 January 1803, *ibid.*, **12**, 20–1.

101. Edward Sheppard to Sir Joseph Banks, 26 November 1803, *ibid.*, **13**, 1–2.

102. CBA, VI (1806), 74.

103. Edward Sheppard to Sir John Sinclair, 31 December 1806, *ibid.*, 65–74.

104. Daniel Lloyd to Sir Joseph Banks, 25 September 1801, BM(SC), I, **14**, 7.

105. Daniel Lloyd to Sir Joseph Banks, 10 October 1801, *ibid.*, 6–7.

106. Sir Joseph Banks to Daniel Lloyd [11 August 1802], *ibid.*, 8.

107. Sir Joseph Banks to Daniel Lloyd, 27 July [1803], *ibid.*, **12**, 14.

108. Daniel Lloyd to Sir Joseph Banks, 20 August 1802, *ibid.*, 15–16.

109. Daniel Lloyd to Sir Joseph Banks, 22 November 1803, *ibid.*, 18.

110. Daniel Lloyd to Sir Joseph Banks, 14 August 1805, *ibid.*, **22**, 12–13.

111. Daniel Lloyd to Sir Joseph Banks, [— — 1804], *ibid.*, II, **2**, 14.

112. Daniel Lloyd to Sir Joseph Banks, 14 August 1805, *ibid.*, I, **22**, 12–13.

113. MS. note, *ibid.*, III, **7**, 42.

114. John Maitland to Sir Joseph Banks, 21 June 1800, *ibid.*, **3**, 26–7.

115. John Maitland to Sir Joseph Banks, 13 May 1800, BM.A.MSS., 33980, 233–4.

116. Sir Joseph Banks to John Maitland, [— August 1802], BM(SC), I, **14**, 24.

117. Sir Joseph Banks to John Maitland, 16 August [1803], *ibid.*, **12**, 3.

118. John Fane to Sir Joseph Banks, 22 July 1800, *ibid.*, II, **3**, 29–30.

119. The actual horn number of this ram cannot be identified from any of Banks's lists. It was most probably one of those noted against the name of Major William Price.

120. Sir Joseph Banks to John Fane, 27 July 1800, BM(SC), II, **3**, 30–1.

121. Sir Christopher Willoughby to Sir Joseph Banks, 24 July 1806, *ibid.*, I, **7**, 17–18.

122. Reverend William Quartly to Sir Joseph Banks, 24 May 1800, *ibid.*, II, **3**, 24–6.

123. John White Parsons to Sir Joseph Banks, 7 July 1800, *ibid.*, 31–3.

124. Sir Joseph Banks to John White Parsons, 28 July [1800], *ibid.*, 33.

125. Reverend William Quartly to Sir Joseph Banks, 24 May 1800, *ibid.*, 24–6.

126. 1st Baron de Dunstanville to Sir Joseph Banks, 8 August 1800, *ibid.*, 41.

127. Sir Joseph Banks to 1st Baron de Dunstanville, 6 August [1801], *ibid.*, **4**, 23.

128. Wood and Cornish to Sir Joseph Banks, 14 August 1801, *ibid.*, 20.

129. Sir Joseph Banks to Wood and Cornish, 14 August 1801, *ibid.*, 21.

130. Sir Joseph Banks to Wood and Cornish, 20 August 1801, *ibid.*

131. Sir Joseph Banks to 1st Baron de Dunstanville, 20 August 1801, *ibid.*, 22.

132. 1st Baron de Dunstanville to Sir Joseph Banks, 16 October 1801, *ibid.*, I, **14**, 9.

133. 1st Baron de Dunstanville to Sir Joseph Banks, 5 September 1802, *ibid.*, 26.

134. 1st Baron de Dunstanville to Sir Joseph Banks, 13 August 1803, *ibid.*, II, **6**, 63.

135. MS. diary notes, *ibid.*, **5**, 55–7.
136. MS. diary notes, *ibid.*, I, **20**, 46.
137. Sir Joseph Banks to 2nd Duke of Northumberland, 20 August 1801, *ibid.*, II, **4**, 26.
138. 2nd Duke of Northumberland to Sir Joseph Banks, 23 August 1801, *ibid.*, I, **3**, 36–7.
139. The 'above extraordinary proposal' cited from an unnamed newspaper as a public notice in the name of Lord Somerville is given thus:
'. . . that his Lordship proposes, for the improvement of British wool and stock, to put under the care of the Secretary of the Bath Agricultural Society, during the ensuing season, from two to four Spanish rams, of the purest Merino breed, procured in Spain by his Lordship. The proportion of ewes to be 60 head only per ram, at one guinea each, with reasonable expences to the Secretary for keep and careful attention. The number of ewes to each subscriber not to exceed 20. The Ryeland, South-Down, and Leicester races, are suggested particularly as valuable crossings. Gentlemen intending to subscribe are requested to signify the same to Mr. Bradley [*sic*=Nehemiah Bartley], the Secretary, on or before the 12th of July next [1802]', AM, VI (June 1802), 433.
140. 'Remarks on the Duke of Bedford's Discontinuing his Premiums to the New Leicester and South-Down Breed of Sheep, and on Lord Somerville's and Dr. Parry's Encouragement of the Spanish Breed. By Practicus', *ibid.*, 433–5.
141. The King seems to have first made acquaintance with Sir George Onesiphorus Paul as early as 1788. During the summer of that year from 12 July to 16 August the Royal family resided at Cheltenham to try the effect of the waters on what were probably the premonitory signs and symptoms of the King's first serious insanity which developed later that year. During this month His Majesty made many neighbouring visits including one to the cloth manufactory of Sir George Paul. This is described in a letter from Samuel Lysons, F.R.S., to Sir Joseph Banks, 18 August 1788, DTC, VI, 65–7. Cf. also Dobson, Austin (ed.), *Diary and Letters of Madame D'Arblay*, IV, 1–101.
142. Cf. this chapter, note 38.
143. 'Dr. Parry in Answer to Practicus on the Breed of Sheep', AM, VII (July 1802), 7–14.

CHAPTER X: THE PAGODA, 1804–1810

1. 'A Report of the State of His Majesty's Flock of Fine Wooled Spanish Sheep For the Year ending Michaelmas 1803' (first draft), BM(SC), II, **11**, 23–5.
2. AM, IX (August 1803), 126–7.
3. Henry Lacocke to Sir Joseph Banks, 22 October 1803, BM(SC), I, **18**, 61–2.
4. Sir Joseph Banks to Sir Everard Home, 10 February 1804, Kew BC, II, 286: see also DTC, XIV, 227.
5. AM, X (March 1804), 216.
6. *Ibid.* (June 1804), 466–9.
7. *Ibid.*, XI (July 1804), 67–71; *London Chronicle*, 3–5 July 1804.
8. Sir Joseph Banks to Sir Henry Vane Tempest, 30 March 1804, BM(SC), I, **22**, 47. Cf. also 'Project for a shew and sale . . .', 18 April 1800, *ibid.*, II, **7**, 11–12.
9. 'A Report of the State of His Majesty's Flock of Fine Wooled Spanish Sheep For the Year ending Michaelmas 1803' (second draft), *ibid.*, II, **11**, 20–2.
10. *Ibid.* (printed version), 126–7.
11. Sir Joseph Banks to Richard Snart, 5 July [1804], *ibid.*, I, **19**, 15.
12. *Particular and Conditions of Sale of Some Rams and a few Ewes, from His Majesty's Pure Spanish Flock of Merino Sheep; . . . On Wednesday, August 15th, 1804, ibid.*, II, **11**, 35–6.
13. John Parkinson to Sir Joseph Banks, 17 July 1804, *ibid.*, I, **19**, 16.
14. John Parkinson to Sir Joseph Banks, 28 July 1804, *ibid.*
15. Richard Snart to Sir Joseph Banks, [21 July 1804], *ibid.*, II, **11**, 32–3.
16. Henry Lacocke to Sir Joseph Banks, 12 July 1804, *ibid.*, 19.
17. Sir Joseph Banks to Francis Freeling, 24 July 1804, *ibid.*, 60.
18. Sir Joseph Banks, MS. note, *ibid.*, 64.
19. Onslow, S. M., *Some Early Records of the Macarthurs of Camden* (Sydney, 1914), 89–94.
20. *Ibid.*, 76–8. See also MS. copy: '1804 Proposal for establishing a Company to encourage the increase of fine woolled Sheep in New South Wales' (London, 30 January 1804), BM(SC), I, **22**, 17–18; Banks's comments thereon, *ibid.*, 18.
21. Sir Stephen Cottrell to Edward Cooke, 14 July 1804, HRNSW, V, 398–400.
22. Henry Lacocke to Sir Joseph Banks, 12 July 1804, BM(SC), II, **11**, 19.
23. John Farnham to Sir Joseph Banks, 18 July 1804, *ibid.*, 63.
24. MS. correction to outer cover. Cf. this chapter, note 12; BM(SC), II, **11**, 37.
25. *Particular and Conditions of Sale . . .*, *ibid.*, 36.
26. Lawrence, John, *A General Treatise on Cattle . . .*' (London, 1805), 489.

27. See this chapter, note 25.
28. 'Sale of Part of His Majesty's Flock of Spanish Sheep', *The British Press*, No. 501, Friday, 17 August 1804; see also AM, XI (August 1804), 143–7; these are substantially similar accounts. They compare closely with the much-copied account in *The Morning Chronicle*, August 1804, for which see also Bischoff, J., *A Comprehensive History of the Woollen and Worsted Manufactures* . . . , I (1842), 358–64.
29. The Act 17 George III, c. 38.
30. MS. account, 'Amount of Sale of Merino Sheep August 15th 1804', BM(SC), II, **11**, 38.
An itemized statement showing the buyers and the prices paid for each lot prepared by John Farnham. The document is important for it shows clearly the exact number of rams and ewes bought by John Macarthur with the marginal notes in Banks's hand noting those which were bought on Macarthur's behalf by Hullett.
31. Lawrence, John, *A General Treatise on Cattle* . . . (London, 1805), 488.
32. 'The Establishment of a Flock of Sheep producing Wool of the Spanish Quality in the Vicinity of Botany Bay', AM, x (April 1804), 243–4.
33. Joshua Peart to Sir Joseph Banks, [1792, undated], BM.A.MSS., 33982, 246; MS. note, BM(SC), I, **14**, 47. A legal fee of four guineas was 'Paid for Council's opinion respecting the Legality of importing foreign sheep' in 1792.
34. Sir Joseph Banks to Governor Philip Gidley King, 29 August 1804, HRNSW, v, 457–60.
35. MS. memoranda, ML, Banks Papers, 4, A 78⁻³, 315, 317.
36. Governor Philip Gidley King to Sir Joseph Banks, 21 July 1805, HRNSW, v, 670–5.
37. Sir Joseph Banks to John Farnham, 17 August 1804, BM(SC), II, **11**, 63.
38. Sir John Riddell to Sir Joseph Banks, 10 August 1804, *ibid.*, 47–8.
39. Sir John Riddell to Sir Joseph Banks, 22 August 1804, *ibid.*, 45–6.
40. Richard Snart to Sir Joseph Banks, 18 August 1804, *ibid.*, 16.
41. Sir Joseph Banks to Richard Snart, 19 August 1804, *ibid.*, 17. In the same number of *The British Press* which reported the sale of the King's sheep—cf. this chapter, note 28—there is a news item on the same page to the following effect:
'CURIOUS PLANTS—A ship has recently arrived in the River from China, having on board a great number of Plants, most of them new to Europeans, which have been collected by a botanic gardener, which HIS MAJESTY, ever attentive to the interests of science, sent out some years ago to reside in China; they are expected in the course of a few days, at the Royal Gardens, at Kew, where SIR JOSEPH BANKS is to inspect them, previous to his leaving Spring Grove, for his summer residence in Lincolnshire.' The 'botanic gardener' who collected these plants was probably William Kerr.
42. John Farnham's 'Account of the Sale', BM(SC), II, **11**, 14 (cf. this chapter, note 30).
43. AM, XIII (August 1805), 129–35.
44. Lady Caroline Villiers was 'Car', later the first wife of the Marquess of Anglesey.
45. AM, XIII (August 1805), 132. It is to be noted that this report of the second sale of the King's Spanish sheep is the most expansive account written about any of the seven public sales.
46. *Particular and Conditions of Sale of some Rams & Ewes from His Majesty's Pure Spanish Flock* . . . *On Friday, August 16th, 1805*, BM(SC), I, **18**, 44–7. Two copies of the printed document each with buyers and prices paid marked against the individual lots with notes by Banks on those who bought for absentees.
47. Sir Joseph Banks to Richard Snart, 24 August 1805, DTC, XVI, 114–15.
48. Sir Joseph Banks to Robert Fulke Greville, 10 August 1805, BM.A.MSS., 42072, 78.
49. Sir Joseph Banks to Robert Fulke Greville, 17 August 1805, *ibid.*, 75–6.
50. Sir Joseph Banks to Robert Fulke Greville, 2 August 1805, *ibid.*, 67.
51. Sir Joseph Banks to Robert Fulke Greville, 4 August 1805, *ibid.*, 71–2.
52. Robert Fulke Greville to Sir Joseph Banks, 18 August 1805, DTC, XVI, 105–7 (copy); BM(SC), II, **11**, 129–30 (original).
53. Robert Fulke Greville to Sir Joseph Banks, 19 August 1805, DTC, XVI, 108–9 (copy); BM(SC), II, **11**, 129–30 (original).
54. Sir Joseph Banks to Robert Fulke Greville, 20 August 1805, BM.A.MSS 42072, 79–80; and BM.A.MSS., 33981, 218.
55. Sir Joseph Banks to Robert Fulke Greville, 20 August 1805, DTC, XVI, 110–11 (copy); BM.A.MSS., 42072, 81–2 (original).
56. Sir Joseph Banks to Robert Fulke Greville, 31 August 1805, DTC, XVI, 121–3 (copy); BM.A.MSS., 42072, 88–9 (original).
57. Sir Joseph Banks to Richard Snart, 24 August 1805, DTC, XVI, 114.
58. Robert Fulke Greville to Sir Joseph Banks, 25 August 1805, BM(SC), II, **11**, 131–2.
59. Sir Joseph Banks to Patrick Campbell, 8 February 1806, *ibid.*, I, **9**, 48–9.
60. George Evans to Sir Joseph Banks, 10 October 1805, *ibid.*, 37.
61. John Minet Fector to Sir Joseph Banks, 8 October 1805, *ibid.*, 42–4.

62. Sir Joseph Banks to Richard Snart, 18 October 1805, *ibid.*, 37; 1 November [1805], *ibid.*, 41; 2 December [1805], *ibid.*, **10**, 4; 6 January 1806, *ibid.*, 5.

63. Sir Joseph Banks to Robert Fulke Greville, 22 July 1806, DTC, XVI, 281–3.

64. Richard Snart to Sir Joseph Banks, 29 July 1806, *ibid.*, 288–9.

65. Sir Joseph Banks to Richard Snart, 1 August 1806, *ibid.*, 296–8.

66. Richard Snart to Sir Joseph Banks, 11 August 1806, BM(SC), I, 9, 52–3.

67. Sir Joseph Banks to Richard Snart, 16 August 1806, *ibid.*, 55–6.

68. *Particular and Conditions of Sale of some Rams & Ewes from His Majesty's Pure Spanish Flock of Merino Sheep; . . . On Tuesday, August 19th, 1806, ibid.,* **19**, 19–21.

69. AM (second series), 1 (August 1806), 135–6.

70. List of buyers and the prices paid at the sale of 1806, MS. sheet, BM(SC), I, **19**, 22.

71. 3rd Duke of Richmond to Sir Joseph Banks, 15 August 1806, *ibid.*, **7**, 4–5.

72. Sir Joseph Banks to Richard Snart, 20 August 1806, *ibid*, **9**, 57 and *ibid.*, **10**, 1.

73. Richard Snart to Sir Joseph Banks, 21 August 1806, *ibid.*, **10**, 2–3.

74. Richard Snart to Sir Joseph Banks, 26 August 1806, *ibid.*, **9**, 54.

75. Sir Joseph Banks to Richard Snart, [22 August 1806], *ibid.*, **10**, 2.

76. Sir Joseph Banks to Richard Snart, *ibid.*, 3.

77. Sir Joseph Banks to Richard Snart, [— November 1806], *ibid.*, **22**, 5.

78. Richard Snart to Sir Joseph Banks, 21 January 1807, *ibid.*, 6–7.

79. Richard Snart to Sir Joseph Banks, 12 March 1807, *ibid.*, 8.

80. Joseph Hall to Sir Joseph Banks, 26 May 1807, *ibid.*, **9**, 34.

81. John Dry to Doctor Sims, 29 May 1807, *ibid.*, 35.

82. Sir John Sebright to Sir Joseph Banks, 2 June 1807, *ibid.*, 35.

83. Daniel Smith was a resident of Windsor and his house stood next to the Royal Stables. Cf. Huish, Robert, *Memoirs of George the Third* (1821), 641.

84. Sir Joseph Banks to Richard Snart, 22 July [1807], BM(SC), I, **9**, 24.

85. Richard Snart to Sir Joseph Banks, 24 July 1807, *ibid.*, 27–8.

86. AM (second series), 1 (August 1807), 154–5.

87. Richard Snart to Sir Joseph Banks, 12 August 1807, BM(SC), I, **9**, 21–2.

88. Sir Joseph Banks to Richard Snart, 12 August [1807], *ibid.*, 22.

89. Richard Snart to Sir Joseph Banks, 19 August 1807, *ibid.*, 25–6.

90. Sir Joseph Banks to Richard Snart, [20 August 1807], *ibid.*, 26.

91. Sir Joseph Banks to Richard Snart, 8 December 1807, *ibid.*, 9–10.

92. Henry Lacocke to Sir Joseph Banks, 8 June 1808, *ibid.*, **8**, 8.

93. Richard Snart to Sir Joseph Banks, 14 August 1808, *ibid.*, 6–7.

94. Sir Joseph Banks to Richard Snart, 17 August 1808, *ibid.*, 7.

95. *Particular and Conditions of Sale, of several Rams and Ewes, selected from His Majesty's Pure Spanish Flock of Merino Sheep; . . . On Wednesday, August 17th, 1808* (with MS. list of buyers and the prices paid for each lot), *ibid.*, 9–10.

96. Sir Joseph Banks to Richard Snart, 22 December 1808, *ibid.*, 5.

97. Richard Snart to Sir Joseph Banks, 13 January 1809, *ibid.*

98. Richard Snart to Sir Joseph Banks, 14 February 1809, *ibid.*, II, **9**, 25–6.

99. Richard Snart to Sir Joseph Banks, 10 July 1809, *ibid.*, 10–12.

100. *Particular and Conditions of Sale, of several Rams and Ewes, both of the Paular and Negrete Breeds, selected from His Majesty's Pure Spanish Flock of Merino Sheep; . . . On Wednesday, July 26th, 1809* (with MS. list of buyers and the prices paid), *ibid.*, I, **8**, 33–6.

101. AM (second series), v (August 1809), 143.

102. Sir Joseph Banks to Richard Snart, 4 August 1809, BM(SC), III, **9**, 5.

103. AM (second series) VII (August 1810), 140–4.

104. *Ibid.* (second series) VI (May 1810), 346–8.

105. *Ibid.* (second series) VII (July 1810), 53–69.

106. Richard Snart to Sir Joseph Banks, 17 July 1811, BM(SC), II, **10**, 10–11.

107. The first symptoms of the King's final derangement were noted on 29 October 1810. The Regency was declared at Carlton House on 5 February 1811.

CHAPTER XI: THE SPANISH SHEPHERDS, 1808

1. MS. notes, 10 November 1808, BM(SC), I, **8**, 25.

2. Bourgoing, J.-F., *Tableau De l'Espagne Moderne* . . . (Paris, 1807), 83 n.

3. MS. notes, BM(SC), I, **8**, 25.

4. John Maitland to Sir Joseph Banks, 10 November 1808, *ibid.*, 18–19.

5. MS. notes, *ibid.*, 24.

6. Richard Snart to Sir Joseph Banks, 14 February 1809, *ibid.*, II, **9**, 25–6. Cf. 'Some Circumstances relative to Merino Sheep . . .', by Sir Joseph Banks, CBA, VI (1809), 269–86. The offices held by the four Ministers named were:
George Canning—Foreign Secretary;
Duke of Portland—Prime Minister;
Viscount Castlereagh—Secretary of State for War and the Colonies;
Lord Mulgrave—First Lord of the Admiralty.

7. MS. note by Richard Snart, BM(SC), I, **8**, 17.

8. 'Monthly Return of His Majesty's Spanish Flock at Kew', 1 November 1808 (from Richard Stanford), *ibid.*, 18.

9. MS. note by Banks, *ibid.*, 21.

10. Benjamin Thompson to Sir Joseph Banks, 31 October 1808, *ibid.*, 46–7.

11. Sir George Steuart Mackenzie to Sir Joseph Banks, 22 October 1808, *ibid.*, 37.

12. George Tollet to Sir Joseph Banks, 20 November 1808, *ibid.*, 47–8.

13. Nehemiah Bartley to Sir Joseph Banks, 15 December 1808, *ibid.*

14. John Fane to Sir Joseph Banks, 13 November 1808, *ibid.*, 38. In this letter Fane confirms that he had received two rams and two ewes from Captain Tower of the *Mary* who convoyed the ships from Gijon. Tower had apparently bought thirty sheep on his own account from among the surplus sheep brought down with the flock to make up losses before embarkation. (MS. notes by Banks, *ibid.*, 24.) According to Banks in a letter to Lord Spencer of 31 July 1809 (Althorp Papers (12)) the Duke of Bedford gave a hundred guineas for one of Tower's lot but 'These sheep were however in the opinion of the Spaniards the culls of the Principal Flock.'

15. 4th Earl of Macclesfield to Sir Joseph Banks, 2 November 1808, BM(SC), I, **17**, 30–1.

16. Banks's list of breeders who applied consisted of: Tollet, Fane, Coke, Allen, Bartley, Elliot, Everett, Foljambe, Macclesfield, Sheppard, and Thompson, *ibid.*, **8**, 49.

17. T. G. Elliot to Sir Joseph Banks, 22 December 1808, *ibid.*, 54.

18. Edward Sheppard to Sir Joseph Banks, 26 November 1808, *ibid.*, 54–5.

19. Sir Joseph Banks to Edward Sheppard, 28 November [1808], *ibid.*, 55.

20. Richard Snart to Sir Joseph Banks, 10 July 1809, *ibid.*, III, **9**, 10–12.

21. MS. notes by Banks, *ibid.*, I, **8**, 24–5.

22. MS. questionnaire by Banks, *ibid.*, 19.

23. This interview almost certainly occurred on 10 November 1808. On this occasion and for the following week until 17 November Mendoza y Rios translated all verbal and written communications between Banks and the Spaniards. Cf. Mendoza y Rios to Sir Joseph Banks, 14 and 17 November 1808, *ibid.*, 13.

24. All the preceding details of the Spanish shepherds, their life, the management of the travelling flocks, and the origins of the sheep sent to England, are derived from the MS. notes of Banks, *ibid.*, 22–5. They clearly answer all the questions posed in the questionnaire on f. 19 and are the essential basis of much of the text of *Some Circumstances relative to Merino sheep . . .* which Banks sent to Sir John Sinclair under cover of a letter dated 18 February 1809.

25. The Spanish shepherds to Sir Joseph Banks, 10 November 1808, BM(SC), I, **8**, 17 (original); *ibid.*, 16 (translation).

26. Cf. Richard Snart to Sir Joseph Banks, 14 February 1809, *ibid.*, II, **9**, 25–6.

27. AM (second series), III (November 1808), 348–9.

28. The Spanish shepherds to Sir Joseph Banks, 16 November 1808, BM(SC), I, **8**, 15 (original); *ibid.*, 14–15 (translation).

29. José Mendoza y Rios to Sir Joseph Banks, 17 November 1808, *ibid.*, 13.

30. Banks noted these figures at the foot of the Spanish original of the shepherds' memorial of 16 November. It may be noted here also that 1 real vellon=34 maravedis=25 centimes=2·63 pence sterling—approximately—at this period. Thus 1 franc=4 reals vellons.

31. The Spanish shepherds to Sir Joseph Banks, 18 November 1808, BM(SC), I, **8**, 16 (original); *ibid.*, 12 (translation).

32. Carmen, E. A., Heath, H. A., and Minto, J., *Special Report on the History and Present Condition of the Sheep Industry of the United States* (Washington, 1892), 184–9.

33. 'Particulars regarding the Merino Sheep, imported by Charles Downie, Esq. of Paisley in Scotland: in Answer to certain Queries transmitted by Sir John Sinclair, to the Spanish Shepherds who have the charge of them', CBA, VII (1811), 61–3.

34. De Cère, Peysère, 'Observations pour faciliter la connaissance des races de Moutons Espagnols importées en France, suivies d'un apperçu sur les troupeaux de Rambouillet et de la Malmaison', *Annales d'Agriculture*, XXXVIII (1809), 385 *et seq.* The document consulted here is a transcript in French made by Alexandre-Henri Tessier from the *Annales* and evidently sent to Banks, BM(SC), II, **9**, 37–43. Tessier also cites the same document in his *Instruction sur Les Bêtes à Laine . . .* (Paris, 1811), 24–6. The author, M. Peysère de Cère, was Director of one of the Imperial studs, established by Napoleon, under the general supervision of Tessier as Inspector-General of

the Government Flocks. This particular establishment was at Cère near Mont-de-Marsan in the department of Landes about sixty miles north of the Franco-Spanish border. Peysère de Cère was evidently one of those deputed in 1808 after the Spanish Insurrection of 2 May to secure sheep and wool for the French government. Although, as he says, 'l'extraction de 1808 ait eu lieu dans des circonstances difficiles', he was able to remove from the vicinity of Madrid and Segovia into France some six hundred animals of which, in the process, only six ewes and one ram died before they reached the neighbourhood of Paris. In this account he specifically claims to have secured a few sheep of the Negretti and Paular *cabanas* and states that these were established at Malmaison in the stud of the Empress Josephine, also one of the official flocks and under the direction of M. Bonplan. How many of these two *cabanas* were in fact obtained is not clear but it seems likely that the majority of the six hundred were of this stock. Malmaison seems to have been distinguished especially as the only stud which offered 'dans son ensemble le choix des deux cavagnes Leoneses les plus célèbres, celles du Paular et de Negrette'. But George III of England certainly had the lion's share of both.

CHAPTER XII: THE WICKED UNCLE, 1809

1. Sir Alexander Cochrane to the Hon. Basil Cochrane, 18 October 1808, NLS, MS. 2572, 172.
2. Sir Alexander Cochrane to the Hon. Andrew Cochrane-Johnstone, 25 October 1808, *ibid.*, 173.
3. Sir Alexander Cochrane to the Hon. Basil Cochrane, 2 November 1808, *ibid.*, 172.
4. Sir Alexander Cochrane to the Hon. Andrew Cochrane-Johnstone, 9 November 1808, *ibid.*, 174.
5. Sir Alexander Cochrane to the Hon. Basil Cochrane, 26 February 1809, *ibid.*, 174.
6. He returned to England in March and from thence went to Seville. Cf. a letter from Andrew Cochrane-Johnstone to an unknown, dated Seville, 26 April 1809, Wellington, 2nd Duke of, *Supplementary Despatches of . . . Arthur, Duke of Wellington*, VI (1860), 279.
7. Cf. Langnas, I. A., 'The Relations between Great Britain and the Spanish Colonies, 1808–1812', *Bull. Inst. Hist. Res.*, XVI (1939), 195: 'There were two ways by which [Great Britain] obtained Spanish-American silver: by trade in exchange for her goods, and through the activities of the agents of the Treasury which secured the licences necessary for the export of the silver from the colonies. These agents included A. F. Cochrane-Johnstone who managed to secure $3,000,000 (about £600,000) for the Treasury, but involved it in difficulties with the Supreme Junta by his irregular and extravagant transactions. Other agents obtained much less.'
8. The Hon. Andrew Cochrane-Johnstone to Sir John Sinclair, 3 May 1809, *Bathurst MSS., 1621–1811*, 1.
9. The Hon. Andrew Cochrane-Johnstone to Sir John Sinclair, 9 May 1809, BM(SC), II, 2, 15–16.
10. 'A Project for the Establishment of Merino Flocks in various parts of the Kingdom under the immediate superintendence and control of the committee of the Privy Council for Trade. April, 1809', *Bathurst MSS., 1621–1811*, 1.
11. WPR, XV, No. 25, Saturday, 24 June 1809, 990.
12. Sir John Sinclair to William Cobbett, 18 June 1809, BM(SC), I, 3, 1–2. See also BM.A.MSS., 33981, 298.
13. Sir John Sinclair to George Harrison, 30 May 1809, BM(SC), I, 2, 28–9.
14. George Harrison to the Secretary of the Transport Board, 13 June 1809, *ibid.*, 25–6.
15. William Cobbett to Sir John Sinclair, 20 June 1809, *Hist. Manuscript Comm., Bathurst MSS.* (1923), 95–6.
16. WPR, XV, No. 25, Saturday, 24 June 1809, 991.
17. 3rd Earl Bathurst to Sir Joseph Banks, 30 May 1809, DTC, XVII, 306.
18. 3rd Earl Bathurst to Sir Joseph Banks, [1] June 1809, *ibid.*, 307.
19. Viscount Castlereagh to Sir Arthur Wellesley, 3 June 1809, Wellington, 2nd Duke of, *Supplementary Despatches of . . . Arthur, Duke of Wellington*, VI (1860), 277.
20. Cameron, H. C., *Sir Joseph Banks . . .* (London, 1952), 206.
21. Sir Joseph Banks to 3rd Earl Bathurst, 10 June 1809, DTC, XVII, 308–10.
22. The Hon. Andrew Cochrane-Johnstone to Sir John Sinclair, 13 May 1809, *ibid.*, 305.
23. AM (second series), IV (June 1809), 418.
24. The preparations for the Walcheren expedition which set out in July 1809.
25. WPR, XV, No. 26, Saturday, 1 July 1809, 994.
26. Richard Snart to Sir Joseph Banks, 17 July 1809, BM(SC), II, 9, 9–10.
27. Richard Snart to Sir Joseph Banks, 10 July 1809, *ibid.*, 10–12.
28. Richard Snart to Sir Joseph Banks, 19 July 1809, *ibid.*, 6–7.
29. There is evidence elsewhere, e.g. in the Althorp Papers, that other sheep from various sources were probably received by Banks for the King in 1810 and that about three thousand more

for His Majesty remained in Spain at the end of that year. The search for these and other details of sheep importations from the Peninsula is a research project in itself which I have not as yet pursued.

30. The Hon. Andrew Cochrane-Johnstone to Captain Thomas Maling, 20 May 1809, NLS, Cochrane Papers, MS. 2316, 149.

31. Captain Thomas Maling to the Hon. Andrew Cochrane-Johnstone, 16 July 1809, *ibid.*, 155.

32. Captain Thomas Lord Cochrane to his father the 9th Earl of Dundonald, 5 September 1809, *ibid.*, 136–45.

33. Cf. Langnas, I. A., 'The Relations . . .' (1939), see this chapter, note 7.

34. The Hon. Andrew Cochrane-Johnstone to Patrick Wiseman, 18 January 1810, NLS, Accessions, 3224.

35. Carmen, Heath, and Minto, *Special Report* . . . (1892), 173.

36. The Hon. Andrew Cochrane-Johnstone to Messrs. John Murray and Sons, 13 December 1810, NLS, Accessions, 3224.

37. Messrs. John Murray and Sons to the Hon. Andrew Cochrane-Johnstone, 9 January 1811, *ibid.*

38. Messrs. John Murray and Sons to the Hon. Andrew Cochrane-Johnstone, 28 January 1811, *ibid.*

39. Messrs. John Murray and Sons to the Hon. Andrew Cochrane-Johnstone, 15 February 1811, *ibid.*

40. William Ogden to the Hon. Andrew Cochrane-Johnstone, 27 February 1811, *ibid.*

41. Andrew Smith to the Hon. Andrew Cochrane-Johnstone, 30 April 1811, *ibid.*

42. Sir Joseph Banks to 2nd Earl Spencer, 31 July 1809, Althorp Papers (12).

43. Sir Joseph Banks to 2nd Earl Spencer, 2 September 1809, *ibid.* (13).

44. Sir Joseph Banks to 2nd Earl Spencer, 10 June 1810, *ibid.* (14).

45. Sir Joseph Banks to 2nd Earl Spencer, 12 February 1811, *ibid.* (15).

46. Sir Joseph Banks to 2nd Earl Spencer, 13 February 1811, *ibid.* (16).

47. Carmen, Heath, and Minto, *Special Report* . . . (1892), 187–8.

48. The disaster of the Walcheren expedition extended from July to September 1809.

49. *Transactions, New York Agricultural Society*, II [1806], 66.

50. Livingston, Robert R., *An Essay on Sheep* (1811), Editor's Preface, v–vi.

51. *Ibid.*, i.

52. *Ibid.*, vi–viii.

CHAPTER XIII: THE TWILIGHT YEARS, 1810–1820

1. Tooke, Thomas, *Thoughts and Details on the High and Low Prices of the Last Thirty Years* (London, 1823), 55–6.

2. It is not easy to know which were the 'best' *cabanas* in Spain. In practice these always seem to have been those from which the sheep of an importation were drawn—regardless of which they were. In this foundation flock of Rambouillet the list is as follows: Alcolea, Escorial, Iranda, Negretti, Paular, Perales, Perella, Portago, Salazar, San Juan—in alphabetical order, to avoid any argument here on the niceties of precedence.

3. Cf. Chapter V, note 61.

4. There is some doubt about the actual numbers agreed. Some put the total as high as ten thousand.

5. Bernadin, Leon, *Mem. de la Soc. d'Agric. de France*, CXXXIII (1885).

6. Smith, Edward, *The Life of Sir Joseph Banks* . . . (London, 1911), 207 n.

7. 'A Project for Extending the Breed of Fine Wooled Spanish Sheep . . .', *The Philosophical Magazine* (first series), VII (June–September 1800), 350–5.

8. *Ibid.*

9. MS. draft, BM(SC), II, 7, 10–11.

10. MS. note, *ibid.*, 5, 46.

11. 'A Project for Extending the breed of Spanish Sheep to such parts of the Island as may be most suitable to the Production of Fine Wool', MS. draft, *ibid.*, 7, 11–12.

12. *Bathurst MSS.*, *1621–1811*, I, April 1809.

13. *Ibid.*

14. *Ibid.*

15. *Ibid.* It may be noted here that the number of sheep referred to in this extract approximate very closely to the total number of sheep on Richard Stanford's stock return for 3 April 1809. On this sheet may be seen Banks's pencilled figures from which he calculated the numbers cited in this document. Cf. BM(SC), II, 9, 27.

16. *First Report of the Merino Society* . . . (1811), 45–72. Translation from the *Moniteur* of 15 March 1811 by Benjamin Thompson, the Secretary of the new Society.

17. *Ibid.*, 67.

18. *Ibid.*, 72-5.

19. Cf. also *Instruction pour Les Bergers* . . . (fourth edition, 1810), ed. J.-B. Huzard.

20. Virgil, *Georgics*, lib. III, ver. 585

21. Charles Henry Hunt to Sir Joseph Banks, 7 November 1810, BM(SC), III, **10**, 21-2.

22. Printed circular, *ibid.*, 30.

23. Printed covering letter, signed jointly by Charles Henry Hunt and John Tharpe, 10 November 1810, *ibid.*, 29.

24. Printed circular letter signed by Charles Henry Hunt and John Tharpe, 7 February 1811, *ibid.*, 31.

25. MS. draft by Sir Joseph Banks [n.d.], *ibid.*, 31-2.

26. *Ibid.*

27. For example, French sheep of Rambouillet stock were imported by the Australian Agricultural Company where they joined the descendants of the King's sheep from Kew in the form of the Camden Park stock. The Australian Agricultural Company itself was in direct lineal descent from the original *Proposal for establishing a Company to encourage the increase of fine woolled Sheep in New South Wales* of 30 January 1804, prepared by John Macarthur, John Maitland, *et al.*

28. AM (second series), VIII (April 1811), 248-9.

29. *Ibid.*

30. *First Report of the Merino Society* . . . (1811), Preface, iv.

31. Benjamin Hobhouse to Sir Joseph Banks, 4 April 1811, BM(SC), III, **9**, 54-5.

32. John Hiley Addington to Benjamin Hobhouse, [— April 1811], *ibid.*, 55-6.

33. This may have been one source of the Escurial stock to which reference is often found among the Merinos which entered Britain about this period. Banks notes elsewhere that the distinctive marks were removed from the Escorial *cabana* sheep which were in the hands of Ynclan to conceal them from the French, *ibid.*, 53.

34. Don Manuel Ynclan to Sir Joseph Banks, 6 April 1811, *ibid.*, 52-3.

35. José Mendoza y Rios to Sir Joseph Banks, 7 April 1811, *ibid.*, 54.

36. Frederick Lennox Sandwell to Sir Joseph Banks, 27 April 1811, *ibid.*, **10**, 1. Cf. drawing of one of these sheep, *ibid.*, 6. There was a well-known coaching inn The Swan with Two Necks in Love Lane in the City and this may have been the one referred to here. There seems to be no 'Lad Lane' which can be identified.

37. Don Manuel Ynclan to Sir Joseph Banks, 27 April 1811, *ibid.*, **10**, 2-3.

38. Cf. this chapter, note 36.

39. Sir Joseph Banks to Frederick Lennox Sandwell, [27 April or later], 1811, BM(SC), II, **10**, 2.

40. Huish, Robert, *Memoirs of George the Third* (1821), 684-5. A full report by the Council appointed to assist Her Majesty in the administration of the Royal authority etc. for 6 July 1811 still contains an element of hope for recovery. That cited for 8 July 1812 by Dr. Matthew Baillie, however, is of a mind 'entirely lost in error' as the euphemism had it.

41. Richard Snart to Sir Joseph Banks, 15 October 1811, BM(SC), II, **10**, 6-7.

42. The Bill for the regulation of the Household and the administration of His Majesty's Personal and Real Estate was read a first time on 20 January 1812. Cf. Huish, Robert, *Memoirs of George the Third*, 687.

43. Commissioners of His Majesty's Real and Personal Estate to Sir Joseph Banks, 16 March 1812, BM(SC), II, **3**, 21-2.

44. MS. statement by Richard Snart, 14 March 1812, *ibid.*, 25.

45. Cf. this chapter, note 43.

46. Sir Joseph Banks to the Commissioners of His Majesty's Real and Personal Estate, BM(SC), II, **8**, 23-4.

47. Messrs. Martin and Oakley to Richard Snart, 3 September 1812, *ibid.*, 29-30.

48. William Taylor to Sir Joseph Banks, 9 September 1812, *ibid.*, 26-7.

49. Sir Joseph Banks to William Taylor, 17 September [1812], *ibid.*, 28-9.

50. Richard Stanford to Sir Joseph Banks, 4 January 1813, *ibid.*, 31.

51. Bucke, Thomas George, *Third Report of the Merino Society* . . . (1813), 11.

52. *Ibid.*

53. Sir Joseph Banks to Sir Everard Home, 27 August 1818, cited by Smith, Edward, *The Life of Sir Joseph Banks* . . . (London, 1911), 322.

54. William Taylor to Sir Joseph Banks, 23 September 1818, BM(SC), I, **19**, 5-6. Queen Charlotte predeceased the King, dying on 17 November 1818 after a long illness beginning in June that year.

55. 1st Lord Auckland to Sir Joseph Banks, 8 November 1791, DTC, VII, 271.

56. Francis Brothers to Sir Joseph Banks, 13 May 1820, BM(SC), II, **10**, 36-7.

57. Smith, Edward, *The Life of Sir Joseph Banks* . . . (London, 1911), 325.

CHAPTER XIV: THE LEGACY, 1788–1962

1. It is probable from contemporary and other estimates that there were probably no more than twenty-five to thirty thousand men engaged in shepherding the *transhumantes* flocks, both large and small together.

2. Lasteyrie, C.-P., *Traité sur Les Bêtes à Laine d'Espagne* ... (1799), said: 'I searched in vain during my sojourn in Spain for a work which would describe the breeding of wool-producing sheep in that country. I did not even find ten authors who discussed the subject of rural economy whereas I encountered entire Libraries replete with ascetic reveries. Herrera, the Olivier de Serres of the Spaniards, speaking of sheep merely copies what the Romans said. His silence on the subject of their migrations leads me to believe that these were not widely undertaken when he wrote.'

3. 'Account of the Sheep and Sheep walks of Spain in a letter from a gentleman in Spain to Mr. Peter Collinson F.R.S.' [signed W.B.= William Bowles], *The Annual Register . . . for the Year 1764, Natural History*, 77–89.

4. From a *Memoir* of Sir Humphry Davy by his brother Dr. John Davy; cited by Smith, Edward, *The Life of Sir Joseph Banks* . . . (London 1911), 300.

5. Cited by Smith, Edward, *ibid.*, 301.

6. 'A Biographical Sketch of the Life of Sir Joseph Banks Bart., President of the Royal Society . . .' [author anonymous], AM (second series), IX (December 1811), 341.

7. *Ibid.*, 340.

8. Robert Fulke Greville to Sir Joseph Banks, 11 March 1793, ML, Banks Papers, 18, A 81, 153.

9. For example, see the account of the inaugural fair at Hounslow in August 1805, drafted by Banks, BM(SC), I, **7**, 8–10. The atmosphere may be gleaned from one paragraph: '. . . Sir Jos: Banks Presided at dinner, many appropriate toasts were given, between the intervals of which the Band of the Brentford volunteers playd Patriotic & popular airs, much hilarity took place & some very excellent songs were sung. . . .' The toast list apparently prepared by Banks is also revealing:
'*The King*—The Great Shepherd of the Nation God Bless H.M.
'*The Queen* The P. of Wales & the Rest of the R.F.
'*The Fleece* & the Loom
'*The Gentlemen* buyers who have honord the Fair with their attendance
'Success to Hounslow W[ool] Fair
'our Friends at *Thetford* Lewis Bagshot Dorchester and at all other Established wool Fairs
'The Plough & the Soil
'*The wooden* walls of Old England Ribs of Oak & Copper Bottoms
'*The wall* within the wooden walls *the Army* arms of Iron & Bayonets of Steel
'our innermost wall of defence drawn round our King our Constitution & our Liberties—*The Volunteers of G.B.*
'Prosperity to Old England & Confusion to her Enemies', *ibid.*, 10–11.

10. Sir Christopher Willoughby to Sir Joseph Banks, 24 July 1806, *ibid.*, 17–18.

11. Thomas Young to Sir Joseph Banks, 10 September 1810, BM.A.MSS., 33982, 9–10; also 6 October 1810, *ibid.*, 7–8.

12. AM (second series), VI (June 1810), 418.

13. For example, Lord John Somerville in his *Facts and Observations* . . . (1809), 22, gives the following general figure for each sex:
'Ram=17 lb. per qtr. [=*c.* 68 pounds dead=*c.* 136 pounds live weight].
Ewe=11 lb. per qtr. [=*c.* 44 pounds dead=*c.* 88 pounds live weight].'
It is to be remembered also that Somerville was more concerned than most in selecting his stock for carcass qualities.

14. Among the first hundred and seventy rams sold from the Royal flock at least ten were specifically described as polled or with very small horns. There may well have been others not commented on. Among the thirty-four original Negretti ewes to reach Windsor on 19 November 1791 Banks identifies six as having horns. The rams are described on the other hand as having their horns 'broken off' very short. The Spanish method of roughly chiselling the horn off to a short stump might also have concealed from immediate notice one or more that were in fact naturally small-horned. See MS. note, BM(SC), I, **20**, 36–7. Cf. Chapter V, note 43.

15. AA, XX (1793), 526.

16. *Ibid.*, XIX (1793), 91.

17. *Ibid.*, 72.

18. Link, H. F., *Travels in Portugal and through France and Spain* . . . (London, 1801).

19. Somerville, Lord John, *Facts and Observations* . . . (1809), 16.

20. *Ibid.*, 18.

21. *Ibid.*, 18 n.

22. AA, XX (1793), 506.

23. MS. diary note by Banks, BM(SC), I, **17**, 9.

24. Lasteyrie, C.-P., *Traité sur Les Bêtes à Laine d'Espagne* ... (1799), 56. On the other hand, cf. Townsend, *A Journey through Spain in the Years 1786 and 1787* ... (1792), II, 64. '... The produce of wool is reckoned to be about five pounds from every ewe, and eight from the wethers; and to shear eight of the former, or five of the latter, is reckoned a good day's work. Some, indeed, allow twelve sheep to every shearer; but even this comes short of what we do in England, where a common hand will despatch sixty in a day, and a good workman has been known to finish half as many more....' However, the modern Merino presents the same difficulty to a modern English shearer.

25. Lasteyrie, C.-P., *Traité sur Les Bêtes à Laine d'Espagne* ... (1799), 82.

26. Sir Joseph Banks to Benjamin Thompson, 20 November 1809, Bodleian MS., Montagu. d. 6., 87–8.

27. Now Offerton, near Hope.

28. Cf. MS. notes by Banks, BM(SC), I, **10**, 6–7.

29. Cf. MS. diary notes, *ibid.*, **15**, 14–15.

30. AA. XIX (1793), 92.

31. MS. diary notes, 7 June 1792, BM(SC), I, **17**, 9.

32. AA, XX (1793), 506.

33. [Horne, Thomas Hartwell], *A Treatise on the Choice, Buying, and General Management of Livestock* ... (London, 1807).

34. Cf. the fleece weights from the flock of Viscount Castlereagh, June 1812:

'59 Paular and Escurial ewes
and ewe tegs: Average=6·4 lb.
Range =4·3–8·8 lb.
5 Paular and Escurial rams: Average=9·3 lb.
Range =7·0–12·0 lb.'

1st Viscount Castlereagh to Sir Joseph Banks, 20 June 1812, BM(SC), II, **8**, 38
Cf. also the fleece weights from the flock of George Tollet, June 1804:

'32 Negretti ewes [mainly from the Royal flock]
Average=6·0 lb.
16 Negretti rams do. do. do. do.
Average=8·2 lb.'

AA, XLIV (1806), 1.
In both these cases the weights are for the unwashed or greasy fleeces.

35. Bowden, P. J., *The Wool Trade in Tudor and Stuart England* (London, 1962), 46–8.

36. Ponting, K. G., *A History of the West of England Cloth Industry* (London, 1957), 91.

37. *Ibid.*, 92.

38. Herschel, William, 'Description of a Lamp Micrometer, and the Method of using it', *The Philosophical Transactions*, LXXII (1782), Part I, 163–72; 'A Paper to obviate some Doubts concerning the great Magnifying Powers used'. (Letter to Sir Joseph Banks, Bt., P.R.S.), *ibid.*, 173–8.

39. Cf. MS. diary notes, 'Review of Rams 1795', BM(SC), I, **10**, 6–7.

40. Cf. Chapter V, note 2.

41. *The Sydney Gazette*, 26 March 1803.

42. *Ibid.* John Macarthur to Governor Philip Gidley King, 30 September 1800, HRA, series I, II, 538.

43. William Augustus Fawkener to Sir Joseph Banks, 21 September 1803, BM.A.MSS., 32439, 140; DTC, XIV, 127.

44. Sir Joseph Banks to William Augustus Fawkener, 22 September 1803, BM.A.MSS., 32439, 141; original incomplete, ends at '... theoretical Speculation;' missing sheet beginning 'unsupported by any decisive evidence ...' completes original draft above and is now located in ML, Ref. Ab, 66–7; DTC, XIV, 128–30, copy complete; HRNSW, v, 224–5, incomplete transcript as in BM.A.MSS., 32439, 141 above.

The missing sheet from the British Museum document, which is an autograph draft by Banks, was found in the Mitchell Library, Sydney among a collection of a hundred and five letters and draft letters bought from Maggs in October 1946. The discovery of the displaced sheet was made after the present author (H.B.C.) had pointed to the discrepancies noted above in November 1961 suggesting the possible existence of a missing sheet. The final words are of vital importance in the interpretation of subsequent documents and events.

45. This quotation is the terminal part of the draft letter from Sir Joseph Banks to William Augustus Fawkener, 22 September 1803. It is taken from the copy, DTC, XIV, 128–30, with which the original draft checks, except for minor corrections. See this chapter, note 44.

46. Sir Joseph Banks to [John Maitland], 31 March 1804, ML, Banks Papers, 4, A 78⁻³, 319, footnote by Banks. The letter to which this is appended has been regarded as written to Macarthur. The context and circumstances however make it almost certain that John Maitland was addressed.

47. *The Memorial of Captain John Macarthur To the Right Honourable the Lords of the Committee of His Majesty's most Honourable Privy Council appointed for the Consideration of the Matters of Trade and Foreign Plantations*, 4 May 1804, HRNSW, v, 370–3; Onslow, S. M., *Some Early Records of the Macarthurs of Camden* (Sydney, 1914), 78–83.

48. Sir Stephen Cottrell to Edward Cooke, 14 July 1804, HRNSW, v, 398–400.

49. MS. record of sale of 1804, BM(SC), II, **11**, 38.

50. 1st Earl Camden to the Lords Commissioners of the Treasury, 5 October 1804, HRNSW, v, 476–7.

51. 1st Earl Camden to Governor Philip Gidley King, 31 October 1804, *ibid.*, 480–1.

52. AM, x (April 1804), 243–4.

53. *The Sydney Gazette*, 28 July 1805; HRA, series I, 1, 836.

54. Governor Philip Gidley King to 1st Earl Camden, 10 October 1805, HRNSW, v, 698–700.

55. Cf. this chapter, note 44.

56. These cattle about sixty in number when found in 1795 were descended from four cows, one bull and one bull calf, which strayed or were driven from the small settlement on 5 June 1788, the day after the somewhat unrestrained celebrations of the King's birthday, the first such occasion in Australia.

57. John Macarthur to Governor Philip Gidley King, 12 October 1805, HRNSW, v, 709–10.

58. Cf. *The Memorial of Captain John Macarthur . . .* , 4 May 1804, see this chapter, note 47.

59. Cf. this chapter, note 44.

60. James Meehan (1774–1826), a surveyor by training, was transported for an offence during the Irish rebellion of 1798. He was Assistant-Surveyor under Charles Grimes, the Deputy Surveyor-General.

61. Gregory Blaxland to Sir Joseph Banks, 15 September 1804, BM(SC), I, **21**, 73.

62. Sir Joseph Banks to Gregory Blaxland, 25 September 1804, *ibid.*, 74.

63. The way through the Blue Mountains was found by the party led by Gregory Blaxland in company with William Lawson and William Charles Wentworth in a journey from 11 to 28 May 1813. The complete crossing was finally made by George Evans at the end of November 1813.

64. Gregory Blaxland to Edward Cooke, 24 April 1805, HRNSW, v, 593.

65. MS. account by Daniel Smith the auctioneer for the sale of 1809, BM(SC), I, **8**, 33.

66. Robert Fulke Greville to Sir Joseph Banks, 27 October 1794, *ibid.*, II, **2**, 50–1.

67. John Mason Good to Reverend Samuel Marsden, [— 1809], ML, Marsden Papers, 1, A1992.

68. Charles Callis Western to Sir Joseph Banks, 20 April 1817. Printed record of the Annual Meeting of The Merino Society at The Freemason's Tavern on 8 May 1817, BM(SC), II, **10**, 64–5.

69. *A Letter from Lord Western on The Management of his Flock addressed to James Bischoff, Esq.* (London, 1842).

Index

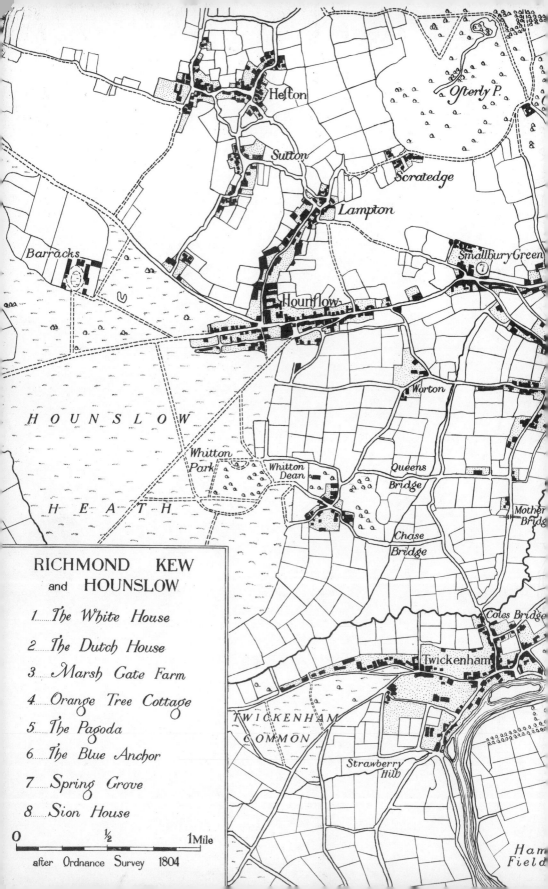

RICHMOND KEW
and HOUNSLOW

1 The White House

2 The Dutch House

3 Marsh Gate Farm

4 Orange Tree Cottage

5 The Pagoda

6 The Blue Anchor

7 Spring Grove

8 Sion House

0   ½   1 Mile

after Ordnance Survey 1804

Helton

Sutton

Scratedge

Lampton

Smallbury Green

Osterly P.

Barracks

Hounslow

Worton

H O U N S L O W

Whitton
Park

Whitton
Dean

Queens
Bridge

Mother
Bridge

H E A T H

Chase
Bridge

Coles Bridge

Twickenham

TWICKENHAM
COMMON

Strawberry
Hill

Ham
Field